PR...
STATE ... FOR
TECHNICAL EDUCATION
P9-ASC-201

**COMMITTEE FOR
TECHNICAL EDUCATION**

Kinematics and Dynamics

of Machinery

Kinematics and Dynamics of Machinery

ROBERT L. MAXWELL

Professor of Mechanical Engineering
University of Tennessee

PRENTICE-HALL, INC.

Englewood Cliffs, N. J., 1960

1903

10-63 Pub. 9-75

Library of Congress Catalog Card Number: 60-12246

Preface

This text was developed for use in the machine design courses taught in the Mechanical Engineering Department at the University of Tennessee. All mechanical engineering students are required to take nine quarter hours of machine design in the junior year and six quarter hours in the senior year. The junior courses cover kinematics and dynamics of machinery and the senior courses cover the selection of materials and the design of machine elements. This text is used throughout the junior year in conjunction with a separate text in mechanical vibrations. However, the text is self-contained and does not require a supplementary text.

The subject matter in the first eleven chapters is covered in the first quarter's work and the remaining chapters are covered in the next two quarters. The subject of mechanical vibrations is integrated in the latter two quarters. Cams and gearing are discussed at the end of the third quarter so that the principles of kinematics and dynamics can be used in the discussion of these machine elements.

An effort has been made to show that a kinematic analysis is not generally an end point but is a necessary start in a complete dynamic analysis of mechanisms. Too often the student is taught kinematics without a proper appreciation of the application of the acceleration analysis to the dynamic analysis of machinery.

The work on accelerations, Chapters 6, 7, and 8, is broader than that usually found in undergraduate texts.

Because of the advantages and increasing use of analytical methods of analysis in industry, the discussion in Chapter 10 is not limited to the slider crank mechanism but covers other mechanisms also. The advantages and disadvantages of this method of analysis are covered in detail.

Chapter 10 is used to compare the various methods of kinematic analysis and to show the student how the methods can be combined so as to reduce the time required for a complete analysis of a mechanism in all its phase positions. Also various means of presenting the results of a complete analysis are pointed out.

Chapters 12 and 13 are a review of the subject matter generally taught in undergraduate courses in dynamics, but on a more sophisticated level so as to bridge the gap between elementary and advanced dynamics.

The student must have a complete understanding of Newton's laws and the ideas of work and energy before he can be expected to deal intelligently with the dynamic analysis of machinery.

The author feels that the student does not appreciate the mathematics he is required to take unless he uses it. Therefore, mathematical expression has been used whenever it lends itself to a better understanding of the theory or application of the basic principles; however, the use of mathematics has been as an aid and not as an end point in itself.

Although an instructor is a necessity for a complete understanding of any undergraduate course in engineering, I feel that too many textbooks cover the material so briefly and with so little explanation that the student tends to depend on the instructor to read the text to him. Because of this, the student does not make full use of the text to gain a broader understanding of the subject matter. I have tried to approach the subject on this challenging level: To write a text that the student can read.

Robert L. Maxwell

Contents

Introduction

MECHANICS can be defined as the natural science relating to the motions of particles and bodies and the forces acting on particles and bodies. The study of mechanics is usually subdivided into three parts: statics, kinematics, and dynamics.

Statics deals with forces acting on bodies which are in equilibrium or at rest. The study of buildings, bridges and such structures is primarily concerned with the subject of statics. The mechanical engineer uses statics in the design of such elements as machine frames, hydraulic devices, crane hooks and cables, hangers and supports of various kinds, and all machine members under the action of forces which do not result in motion of the member. A thorough understanding of the subject of statics is necessary to the study of dynamics.

Kinematics is concerned with the motion of particles and bodies without regard to the cause of that motion. Forces are not considered in the study of kinematics. Kinematics could be considered as a special field of geometry. Displacement, velocity, and acceleration are the fundamental quantities that are used in the study of kinematics. Velocity and acceleration are derived from the basic quantities displacement and time. We could say that kinematics is the science we use in describing the motion of a particle or body. Layout of gear teeth and cam profiles, and the analysis of machine motions are examples of kinematics.

Dynamics is a study of the forces causing motion of a particle or body, or the study of forces acting on a body which is not at rest. Of necessity, a body under the action of dynamic forces is not in equilibrium. The use of principles of dynamics is required in the design of nearly all machines or machine members which have motion. The internal combustion engine, turbines of all types, and most moving elements of machinery require dynamic analyses so that the members can be so proportioned as to withstand the dynamic forces. Some moving elements have such slow motion that the dynamic forces are negligible, but most modern day equipment usually operates at such high speeds that a dynamic analysis is necessary.

Usually these subjects are studied separately, and that procedure will be followed here; but as the work progresses, we will bring subjects previously studied into the analysis as they are needed.

1

Chapter 1

Displacement, Velocity,
and Acceleration

1.1 Vectors

A vector quantity is any quantity which has magnitude, direction, and sense. Such a quantity can be represented by an arrow, as shown in Fig. 1.1,

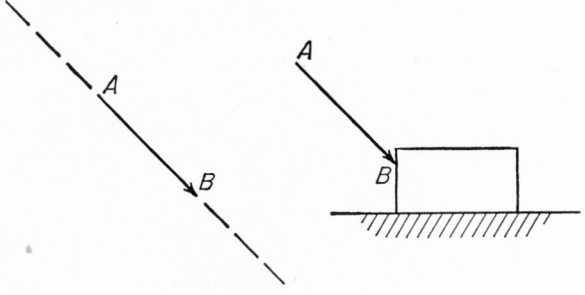

FIGURE 1.1

in which the length of the arrow represents the magnitude, the direction or line of action is given by the direction of the line, and the arrow head indicates the sense. The vector is one of the most important mathematical devices used in the study of applied and theoretical mechanics, and a complete understanding of vectors is especially necessary in applied mechanics of machines. They are the basis of most kinematic analyses as well as nearly all static and dynamic force analyses. Therefore, their importance cannot be overemphasized. Forces, displacements, velocities, and accelerations are all vector quantities. Quantities which have magnitude only are called scalar quantities; we shall also be interested in some of these quantities later. Examples of scalar quantities are horsepower, energy, mass, area, and volume. We should again emphasize the fact that magnitude alone does not completely describe a vector quantity. The direction and sense are also necessary. Giving only the magnitude is like telling someone how to get from Miami to New York by saying, "You go fifteen hundred miles." The traveler would have considerable difficulty unless you also gave him direction and sense.

The magnitude of a vector can be multiplied or divided by a scalar quantity. The result is also a vector, of new magnitude but with direction and sense unchanged.

Throughout this text, vectors will be labeled with capital letters with a bar over them, as $\overline{AB}$ in Fig. 1.1, and the sense will be understood to proceed from A to B. The end of vector $\overline{AB}$ labeled A is called the tail or origin of the vector, while the end labeled B is the terminus or the head of the vector. In Fig. 1.1 the vector $\overline{AB}$ represents the force acting on a machine member. The one to the right shows the vector, called a localized vector, located at the point of application of the force. The one at the left is in the same plane but is placed anywhere in the plane, and so is called a free vector.

1.2 Addition and Subtraction of Vectors

In treatises on vector mechanics it will be found that vectors can be handled as algebraic quantities, but at present we will only be interested in the two operations: addition and subtraction. To indicate addition and subtraction of vectors, the plus and minus signs will have arrow heads attached to them, as ↦ and →, to show we are dealing with vectors and not scalars. To add two vectors graphically, the origin of one vector is placed at

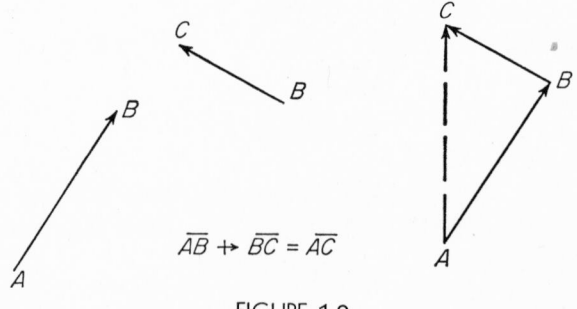

$$\overline{AB} \mathbin{+\!\!\!\rightarrow} \overline{BC} = \overline{AC}$$

FIGURE 1.2

the head of the other vector. This is shown in Fig. 1.2 where two vectors, $\overline{BC}$ and $\overline{AB}$, are shown added. The result of this addition is the vector $\overline{AC}$. We would write this as

$$\overline{AB} \mathbin{+\!\!\!\rightarrow} \overline{BC} = \overline{AC}$$

Any number of vectors can be added in the same way, always placing the tail of one vector at the head of the preceding vector (see Fig. 1.3).

The operation of subtraction is similar, but before this process is ex-

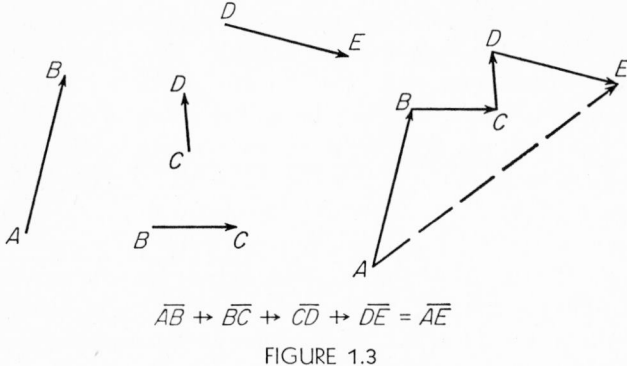

$$\overline{AB} \rightarrowtail \overline{BC} \rightarrowtail \overline{CD} \rightarrowtail \overline{DE} = \overline{AE}$$

FIGURE 1.3

plained we must define a negative vector. A negative vector is one in which the magnitude and direction, or line of action, are the same as a positive vector but the sense is opposite. Therefore, a negative vector is any positive vector the sense only of which has been reversed. To subtract one vector from another we reverse the sense or sign of the vector to be subtracted and

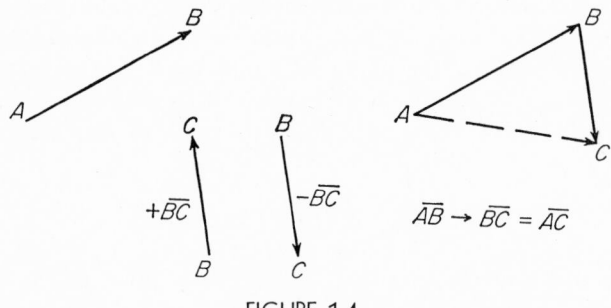

$$\overline{AB} \rightarrow \overline{BC} = \overline{AC}$$

FIGURE 1.4

then add the two. In other words, subtraction is the addition of a negative vector. This is shown graphically in Fig. 1.4, where the vector $\overline{BC}$ is subtracted from $\overline{AB}$.

1.3 Resolution of Vectors

Vectors can be resolved into component vectors of any lengths, directions, and senses so long as the sum of the component vectors reproduces the magnitude, direction and sense of the original vector. Considerable use will be made of the process of resolving a vector into components since it is often easier to work with component vectors. A special case of the resolution of vectors is the breaking up of the vectors into components perpendicular to a set of coordinate axes. This allows the addition of all components parallel to one of the axes by algebraically adding the magnitudes only, with proper algebraic signs. It should be pointed out that when a vector is resolved into two perpendicular components both components are smaller in magnitude than the original vector because the original vector is always the hypotenuse of a right triangle.

Figure 1.5 shows some examples of the resolution of vectors. In Fig. 1.5(a) vector $\overline{AC}$ is shown with its components $\overline{AB}$ and $\overline{BC}$. In this case

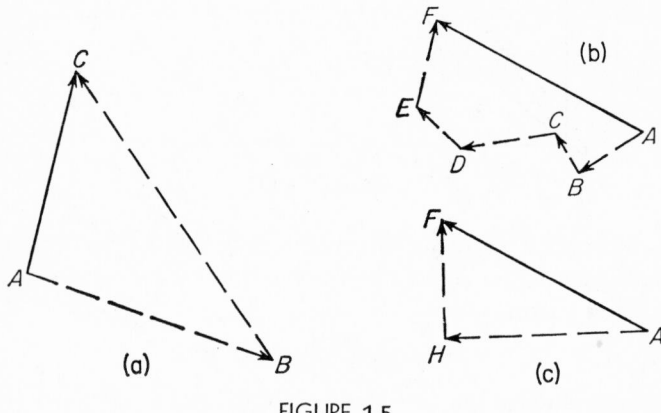

FIGURE 1.5

both components are larger in magnitude than the vector $\overline{AC}$. Figure 1.5(b) shows vector $\overline{AF}$ resolved into five components $\overline{AB}$, $\overline{BC}$, $\overline{CD}$, $\overline{DE}$, and $\overline{EF}$, and Fig. 1.5(c) shows the same vector $\overline{AF}$ resolved into perpendicular components $\overline{AH}$ and $\overline{HF}$.

1.4 Displacement

Displacement is a change in position of a point or body. The change in position of a body can always be determined by describing the change of position of two or more points on the body; therefore, we will deal with the motion of a point at present and discuss the motion of bodies later.

Considering points only, a displacement can always be described as a linear distance. Generally we will think of displacement as a function of time, or

$$s = f(t)$$

Some reference system, such as a set of coordinate axes, is needed to locate a point in space. In the plane determined by the coordinate axes x and y in

Fig. 1.6, assume a point moving along a path AB. The vector $\overline{OP}$ locates the point P at some given time as it moves along the path. A short time later point P has moved to point P' and is located by the vector $\overline{OP'}$. The

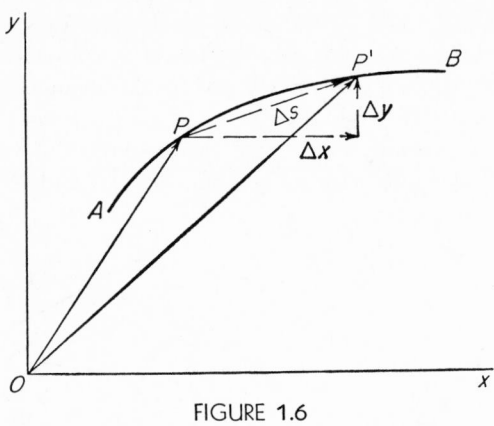

FIGURE 1.6

displacement of point P during this time is given by the vector $\overline{PP'}$ or Δs. The displacement vector Δs can be resolved into components Δx and Δy along the x and y axes, so that

$$\Delta s = \Delta x \mathbin{+\mkern-8mu+} \Delta y$$

In polar coordinates the position of points P and P' can be determined by the radius vectors of the points, of lengths r and $r \mathbin{+\mkern-8mu+} \Delta r$, and the angle they make with the x-axis as shown in Fig. 1.7. We can resolve the displace-

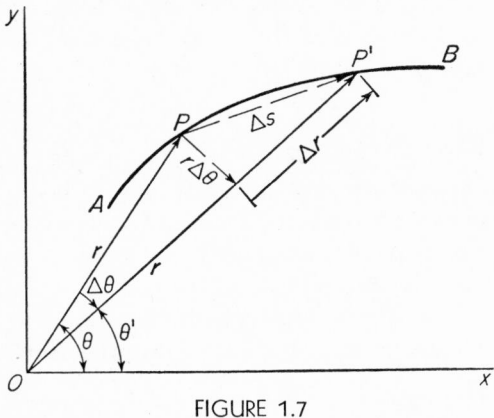

FIGURE 1.7

ment vector Δs into the normal components $r\Delta\theta$ and Δr, where $\Delta\theta$ (in radians) is the angle between the two radius vectors (which is equal to

$\theta - \theta'$) and Δr is the difference in magnitude between vectors $\overline{OP'}$ and $\overline{OP}$. This vector resolution is an approximation when $\Delta\theta$ is finite, but becomes exact as the angle $\Delta\theta$ approaches zero as a limit. In this case the vectors become differential quantities

$$ds = rd\theta \mathbin{\mapsto\hspace{-0.6em}\mapsto} dr \qquad (1.1)$$

If, in Eq. (1.1), the radius vector does not vary in length with time, we have the special case of a point moving in a circle about the origin, and the displacement becomes

$$ds = rd\theta \qquad (1.2)$$

We should point out at this time the difference between displacement and distance. Displacement is a vector quantity as already defined and represents the linear distance between two points; therefore, it has a direction and sense as $\overline{PP'}$ in Figs. 1.6 and 1.7. Distance is a scalar quantity having magnitude only. The distance the point moves in the two figures is the arc length $P - P'$, and we see that the distance moved depends on the path of motion between points P and P' while the displacement is independent of the path. Then Eqs. (1.1) and (1.2) are true for *displacement* only in the limit, and if we integrate these equations between limits, we get the distance the point moves but not the displacement.

Displacement is usually broken into two categories, linear displacement and angular displacement. Linear displacement, as its name implies, is a displacement along a straight line. Linear displacement is invariably used in dealing with moving points. In many cases we will find it to our advantage to deal with the displacements of lines, and for this purpose we will use angular displacement or linear displacement, or sometimes both. Angular displacement is a change in the angle that a line makes with some reference line, the reference line usually being one of the coordinate axes. In Fig. 1.7 the angle $\Delta\theta$ is the angular displacement of the radius vector. It should be noted that because of our definition we cannot speak of the angular displacement of a point. This will be emphasized later in the text. The units of linear displacement are the common units of distance. In machine analysis we will commonly use inches as our unit of linear displacement; however, other units which may be used are feet and miles. The units radians and degrees are the common units of angular displacements. Because of certain advantages, radians will be used in most instances in this text.

1.5 Velocity

A displacement-time curve is shown in Fig. 1.8 where the curve $A - B$ represents the position of a point at any given time. We will assume for the present that the point is moving along a straight line, so that the distance the point moves from t_1 to t_2 is the magnitude of the displacement. With the position or displacement as a function of time we are ready to consider the concept of velocity. Velocity will be defined as the rate of change of

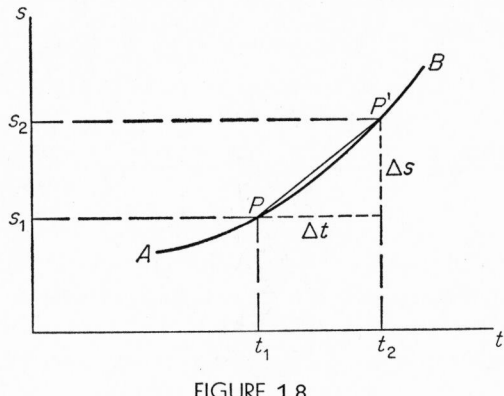

FIGURE 1.8

position with respect to time. Since velocity can vary with time we generally speak of the velocity at some particular time as the instantaneous velocity. The term rate immediately brings to mind the subject of differential calculus, and by the use of calculus velocity can be defined in a very concise and exact manner. Referring to Fig. 1.8, the average velocity of a point as it moves from point P to point P' is the displacement Δs, which represents the distance the point moves in time Δt, divided by the time Δt required for the motion, or

$$V_{\text{ave}} = \frac{\Delta s}{\Delta t} \qquad (1.3)$$

The instantaneous velocity, at the time t_1, is

$$V = \lim_{\Delta t \to 0} \frac{\Delta s}{\Delta t} = \frac{ds}{dt} \qquad (1.4)$$

As the increment of time, Δt, approaches zero, the line PP' tends to become tangent to the displacement-time curve at point P and we see that the slope of the displacement-time curve at any point is equal to the velocity of the point at that particular time. Since velocity is a displacement, which is a vector quantity, divided by a time, a scalar quantity, velocity is also a vector quantity. The direction of the velocity vector is along the straight line on which the point is moving and its sense is the same as the sense of displacement.

Consider a point moving along the curved path in Fig. 1.9. If we try to plot a displacement-time curve for this motion we immediately run into difficulty because we have two quantities, magnitude and direction, which are functions of time, and only one axis for displacement. We had no trouble as long as the point moved along a straight line, because the direc-

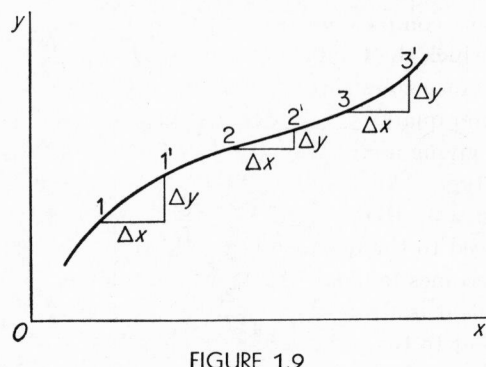

FIGURE 1.9

tion was constant with respect to time and there was no need to show the direction as a function of time. In order to eliminate the present difficulty, two methods of attack could be used: (1) we could plot the x and y components of the displacement individually as a function of time [Figs. 1.10(a) and 1.10(b)], or, (2) we could plot distance only as a function of time [Fig.

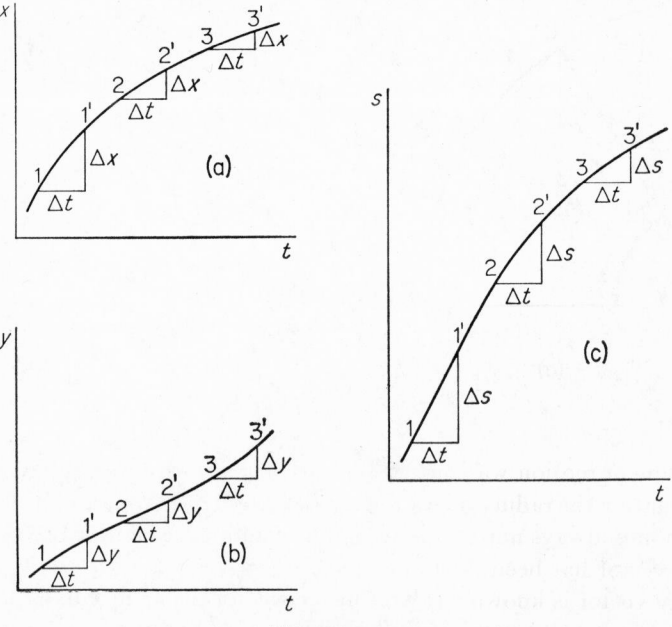

FIGURE 1.10

1.10(c)]. Either method would give us the necessary information to determine the velocity as a function of time. Taking method (1) first, the components of velocity in the x and y direction are given by the slopes of the curves in Figs. 1.10(a) and 1.10(b), respectively, for any given time. Then the sum of these components becomes the velocity at that time. For method (2), in which the total distance is plotted as a function of time, the slope of the distance-time curve will give us the *speed* at any time. Since distance is a scalar quantity, having magnitude but not direction, speed is a scalar quantity giving us the magnitude of the total velocity with no reference to its direction. The direction of the velocity must be determined from the curve in Fig. 1.9. Referring to Fig. 1.6 it can be seen that if the increments are reduced to the limit, so that we can write them as differentials, the vector ds becomes tangent to the path of motion. Therefore, direction of the displacement is always tangent to the path of motion, and the velocity is also tangent to the path at any given time.

We have now considered the general case of motion of a point where the point follows a curved path, and a particular case where the point moves along a straight line or rectilinearly. Another particular type of motion should be considered, that of a point moving in a circle around some given point. Assume a point moving in a circle about the origin as in Fig. 1.11(a).

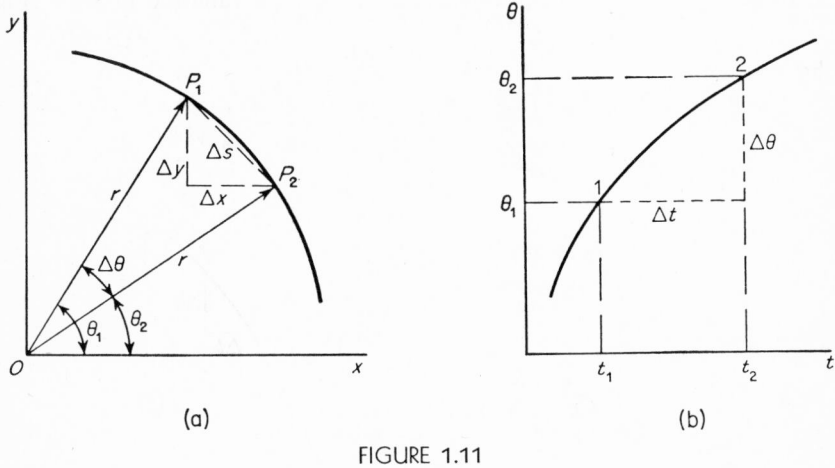

(a)   (b)

FIGURE 1.11

This type of motion was mentioned in the discussion of displacement. In this situation the radius vector remains constant in magnitude and the path of motion is always normal to the radius vector, so when the position of the radius vector has been determined at some given time the direction of the velocity vector is known. If we plot a curve of the angle θ as a function of time in Fig. 1.11(b), the *angular* velocity is given by the slope of the curve.

The Greek letter ω will be used to represent angular velocity. Then the equation for angular velocity is

$$\omega = \frac{d\theta}{dt} \tag{1.5}$$

and the relation of the linear velocity of the point and the angular velocity of the radius vector can be obtained from Eqs. (1.2) and (1.4)

$$V = \frac{ds}{dt} = r\frac{d\theta}{dt} = r\omega \tag{1.6}$$

where ω in this case is a function of time, and r is a constant.

If all motions fell into one or the other of these two special cases, rectilinear motion or circular motion, velocity analysis would be greatly simplified. Luckily a large majority of the motions of machine parts falls into one or the other of these categories, and when a case arises in which the motion is general and does not fit either case, we try to find points on the machine parts which do fit these cases to deal with.

Units of velocity are expressed as units of distance per unit time, as miles per hour, feet per second, feet per minute, inches per second, revolutions per minute, radians per second, and so on. In this text we will use the units inches per second for linear velocity, and radians per second for angular velocity.

1.6 Acceleration

From the displacement-time curve for linear motion we are now able to plot a curve of velocity as a function of time. Following the same reasoning as was used to define velocity, we can define another quantity as the rate of change of velocity with respect to time. This quantity is called acceleration. Expressed mathematically

$$a = \frac{dv}{dt} = \frac{d\left(\dfrac{ds}{dt}\right)}{dt} = \frac{d^2s}{dt^2} \tag{1.7}$$

The units of linear acceleration are inches per second squared, abbreviated in./sec². Acceleration, a vector quantity velocity divided by a scalar quantity time, is also a vector quantity, having direction and magnitude.

In a similar manner we can define angular acceleration as

$$\alpha = \frac{d\omega}{dt} = \frac{d\left(\dfrac{d\theta}{dt}\right)}{dt} = \frac{d^2\theta}{dt^2} \tag{1.8}$$

where the Greek letter α is angular acceleration in units of radians per second squared, abbreviated rad/sec². For the particular case of motion of a point at a fixed distance from some given point (i.e., a point moving in a circle about some given point), the acceleration is not as easy to handle as the velocity because the velocity vector can change in direction as well as in magnitude, and this complicates the problem. (We will defer consideration of this special case, going directly to the general case which covers all motion.)

For the case of general motion of a point along any path, the acceleration can be handled in the same manner as the velocity by dealing with components along the coordinate axes. Figure 1.12(a) shows curves of the

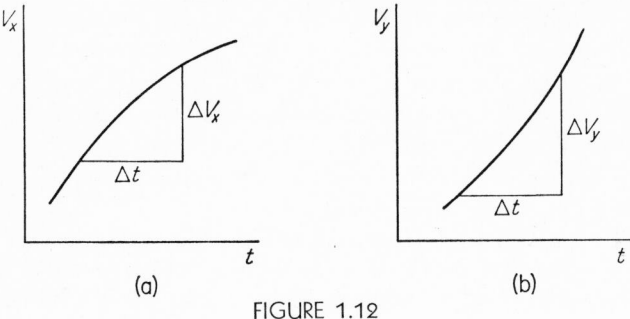

FIGURE 1.12

velocity in the x-direction as a function of time, and Fig. 1.12(b) the velocity in the y-direction as a function of time. The slopes of these curves give the acceleration in the x and y direction respectively at any given time, and the resultant or total acceleration is the vector sum of the x and y components.

The total acceleration can be resolved into other normal components which lend themselves to easier analysis. These components lie along the direction of motion and are perpendicular to the direction of motion. Since they will be found quite useful in acceleration analyses and are especially

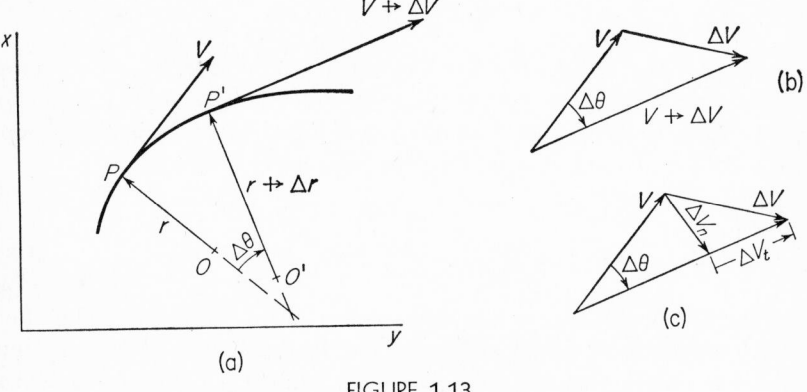

FIGURE 1.13

useful in visualizing the direction of the acceleration we will discuss these components in detail.

Consider a point moving along a path in Fig. 1.13(a). At some point P the point is moving with center of curvature at O and the velocity is given by the vector V tangent to the path at P. After a short time, Δt, the point is at P' and is moving with center of curvature at O' with velocity $V \nleftrightarrow \Delta V$ tangent to the path at P'. The difference in these velocities is ΔV, as shown in Fig. 1.13(b). The acceleration is given as

$$a = \lim_{\Delta t \to 0} \frac{\Delta V}{\Delta t} = \frac{dV}{dt} \qquad (1.9)$$

The change in velocity can be broken into components ΔV_n and ΔV_t as in Fig. 1.13(c). In the limit these components become dV_n and dV_t, and the angle $\Delta\theta$ becomes $d\theta$. The component dV_n is normal to the velocity vector or normal to the path of motion and is directed towards the center of rotation. The component dV_t is in the direction of the velocity vector, or tangential to the path of motion. Therefore, we will call these components the normal and tangential components, respectively. The component dV_n is the result of a change in the direction of the velocity vector, and the component dV_t is the result of a change in the magnitude of the velocity vector. The components of acceleration are

$$a_n = \frac{dV_n}{dt} \qquad (1.10)$$

and
$$a_t = \frac{dV_t}{dt} \qquad (1.11)$$

If we look more closely at these components we will find that they can be given in terms of the linear velocity V, the radius r, and the angular acceleration α. By definition the average normal acceleration is equal to the vector ΔV_n divided by the time Δt required for the point to move from point P to P'; from Fig. 1.13(c) we see that ΔV_n is approximately equal to $V\Delta\theta$. Then the average normal acceleration over the time Δt is

$$a_n \text{ (ave)} = \frac{\Delta V_n}{\Delta t} \cong \frac{V\Delta\theta}{\Delta t} \qquad (1.12)$$

As Δt approaches zero as a limit, $V\Delta\theta$ approaches ΔV_n and the instantaneous acceleration is

$$a_n = \lim_{\Delta t \to 0} V \frac{\Delta\theta}{\Delta t} = V \frac{d\theta}{dt} \qquad (1.13)$$

and the direction of this vector becomes perpendicular to the velocity vector in the limit. Since $d\theta/dt$ is the angular velocity ω, and $V = r\omega$, we can write the normal acceleration as

$$a_n = V\omega = \omega^2 r = \frac{V^2}{r} \qquad (1.14)$$

Later we will find that each of the three expressions for normal acceleration, as given in Eq. (1.14), are useful on certain occasions. For instance, when one drives a car through a curve at a reasonably high speed it is natural to enter the curve as far on the outside as is safe, move closer to the inside of the curve at the middle, then move back to the outside as one comes out of the curve. The last expression of Eq. (1.14) expresses normal acceleration as inversely proportional to the instantaneous radius of curvature. It is therefore descriptive of the normal manner of driving a car through a curve: use of the largest radius possible yields the smallest normal acceleration (which is the acceleration causing a tendency to skid). From experience we also know that the greater the vehicle's speed the harder it is to round a corner without skidding. This phenomenon is described by the same expression, where we see that the acceleration is proportional to the square of the speed. If we are observant, we will find that many of the things that we do naturally are done in conformity with laws of mechanics of which we make good use without being conscious of it.

From Fig. 1.13(c) we see also that the average tangential acceleration over the time increment Δt is the difference in the magnitude of the linear velocity of the particle at point P and P'. Writing the velocity at point P as $r\omega$ and the velocity at P' as $(r + \Delta r)(\omega + \Delta\omega)$ (remembering that the magnitude of the radius vector as well as the angular velocity is changing)

$$a_t \text{ (ave)} = \frac{(r + \Delta r)(\omega + \Delta\omega) - r\omega}{\Delta t}$$

and the instantaneous acceleration is

$$a_t = \lim_{\Delta t \to 0} \frac{(r + \Delta r)(\omega + \Delta\omega) - r\omega}{\Delta t}$$

or, dropping infinitesimals of higher order,

$$a_t = r\frac{d\omega}{dt} + \omega\frac{dr}{dt} = r\alpha + \omega\frac{dr}{dt} \tag{1.15}$$

Again referring to Eq. (1.14) it will be noted that the normal acceleration is independent of the change in angular velocity and also independent of the change in radius of curvature. It is a function only of the instantaneous angular velocity and the instantaneous radius of curvature. Looking at Eq. (1.15) we find that the tangential acceleration is a function of the change in angular velocity and the change in radius with respect to time. Since these last two terms determine the change in magnitude of the velocity of the vector, it is seen that the normal acceleration is dependent only on the change in direction of the velocity vector and the tangential acceleration is dependent only on the change in magnitude of the velocity vector. We shall consider this general case further in a later chapter.

Now considering the case in which the radius vector is of constant magnitude and the point P is moving about some fixed point O as in Fig. 1.14, we find that the normal acceleration is the same as in the general case,

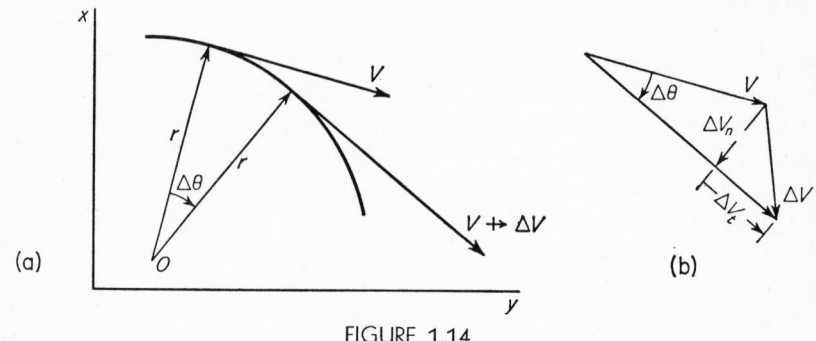

FIGURE 1.14

but that the tangential acceleration now contains only the term which is a function of the angular acceleration, since the radius of curvature is constant with time. This is quite a simple matter compared to the general case, and we will find it advantageous to deal with points that have this type of motion, whenever possible. In the analysis of the acceleration of machine parts we will deal almost exclusively with points that have either linear motion or rotation with a constant radius of curvature. In many cases we will go to considerable trouble in order to avoid working with points which follow a general path of motion.

If we further limit motion to that in which the radius vector not only remains of constant magnitude but also has a constant angular velocity, it is obvious that there will be no tangential acceleration. The linear velocity of the point will then remain constant in magnitude, and the only acceleration will be that caused by a change in direction of the velocity vector, or a normal acceleration.

1.7 Relative Motion

In the discussion of displacement mention was made of the fact that we had to have a reference system in order to locate a point in space; such a reference system was also used in the discussion of velocity and acceleration. It was tacitly assumed that this reference system was fixed in space, although from a practical viewpoint such a reference system has little use for our purposes. We could very well define a coordinate system fixed in space but since we, being on the Earth's surface, are not standing still in space the system would appear to us to be in motion. Motion referred to such a fixed coordinate system is called absolute motion, or more specifically, absolute displacement, absolute velocity, and absolute acceleration.

We will find a reference system based on the Earth's surface to be of much more practical value in our work, and we will say that motion with reference to a coordinate system fixed on the Earth's surface is motion *relative* to the Earth's surface, meaning that if the Earth were standing still in space the motion would be absolute. In many cases a machine's frame is fixed to the Earth's surface, and we will use the term absolute motion to mean motion in such a machine relative to the Earth.

The concept of relative motion is not limited to motion relative to the Earth exclusively, however. We could just as well have a coordinate system which is moving relative to the Earth and deal with motion relative to this moving coordinate system. In this case we would deal with the motion as if the system were standing still with respect to the Earth and then treat the motion of the coordinate system relative to the Earth as a separate motion unrelated to the motion relative to the coordinate system. An example of this case would be a car moving along the Earth's surface in which the frame of the car could be the reference system. The motion of the engine components and gearing would be taken relative to a coordinate system fixed to the frame. This idea of relative motion is one of the most important concepts of which we will make use, and it should be thoroughly understood. It is not even necessary to define a coordinate system in all cases; we can speak of motion relative to some point, such point being either fixed relative to the Earth or moving.

Using velocity as representative of the vector quantities of motion, and remembering that displacement and acceleration can be handled in exactly the same manner, we will define the relative velocity of one point with respect to another as the difference between the absolute velocities of the two points, remembering that by absolute we mean relative to the Earth's surface. Specifically, if $\vec{V}_A$ is the absolute velocity of point A and $\vec{V}_B$ is the absolute velocity of point B, as shown in Fig. 1.15(a), the relative velocity of B with respect to A is equal to the absolute velocity of B minus the absolute velocity of A, which is shown in Fig. 1.15(b). In the same manner the relative velocity of A with respect to B is equal to the absolute velocity of A minus the absolute velocity of B, as shown in Fig. 1.15(c). In Fig. 1.15(d) it is seen that the relative velocity of point B with respect to A has the same magnitude and direction as does the relative velocity of A with respect to B, but with opposite sense, or sign.

In order to better visualize the concept of relative velocity we could say that the relative velocity of a point A with respect to a point B is the velocity that point A would seem to have to an observer if he were moving with point B, and if point B were taken as the origin of a coordinate system, every point of which was moving exactly as point B. Then the relative velocity of point A with respect to point B would be the motion of A with respect to the coordinate system. As an example, consider two cars moving

along a highway side by side, one traveling at 50 mph and the other traveling at 40 mph. To a passenger riding in the car moving 40 mph the other
car would seem to be moving forward at a speed of 10 mph (if he saw

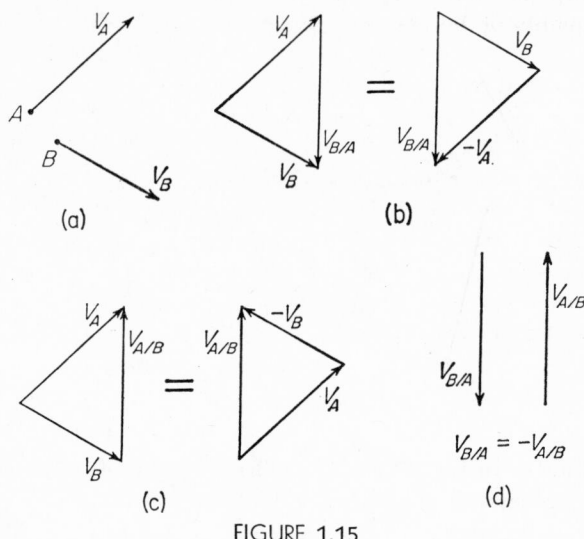

FIGURE 1.15

nothing but the other car) and to a passenger in the car moving 50 mph the
other car would seem to be moving backward at a speed of 10 mph.

   The notation used in Fig. 1.15 will be used throughout the text, and will
be found useful in writing vector equations. The absolute velocity of a
point or body will be indicated by a single subscript which will designate the
point or body, as $\overline{V}_A$. Relative velocity of a point or body with respect to
another will be indicated by two subscripts with a bar between them, as
$\overline{V}_{B/A}$, which will indicate the velocity of B with respect to A. Now, in
mathematical notation, we can define the relative velocity of point B to
point A in a much shorter way as

$$\overline{V}_{B/A} = \overline{V}_B \rightarrow \overline{V}_A \tag{1.16}$$

   Referring again to Fig. 1.15 it will be observed that the absolute velocity
of A is equal to the absolute velocity of B plus the relative velocity of A with
respect to B, Fig. 1.15(c), or

$$\overline{V}_A = \overline{V}_B \nrightarrow \overline{V}_{A/B} \tag{1.17}$$

and from Fig. 1.15(b)

$$\overline{V}_B = \overline{V}_A \nrightarrow \overline{V}_{B/A} \tag{1.18}$$

and also $\overline{V}_{A/B} = -\overline{V}_{B/A}$

as mentioned previously. Equations (1.17) and (1.18) will be the basis of most of our work in velocity and acceleration analysis (using acceleration vectors instead of velocity vectors in the latter) to be covered later.

The concept developed in Eqs. (1.17) and (1.18) can be extended to any number of points or bodies; similar equations could be written for any

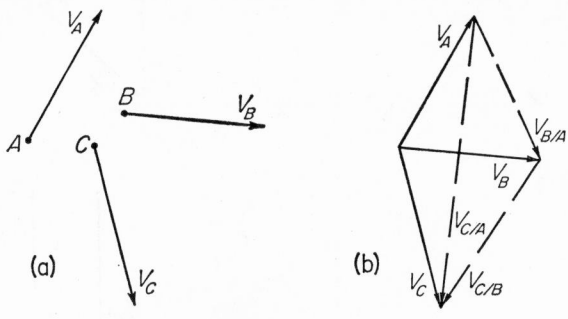

FIGURE 1.16

number of points. In Fig. 1.16(a) the absolute velocities of the three points A, B, and C are shown. From Fig. 1.16(b) we find that

$$\vec{V}_C = \vec{V}_B + \vec{V}_{C/B} = \vec{V}_A + \vec{V}_{B/A} + \vec{V}_{C/B} \qquad (1.19)$$

and
$$\vec{V}_{C/A} = \vec{V}_{B/A} + \vec{V}_{C/B} \qquad (1.20)$$

It is helpful, when the equations contain many terms, to make use of the notation to determine the result by canceling all subscripts which appear above and below the bar indicating relative velocity. For example

$$\vec{V}_{A/B} + \vec{V}_{B/C} + \vec{V}_{C/D} + \vec{V}_{D/E} = \vec{V}_{A/E} \qquad (1.21)$$

1.8 Simple Harmonic Motion

Certain types of motion that occur very frequently in nature and are quite important in the study of engineering lend themselves to algebraic analysis, but we will find a large majority of motions in machines are not so easily handled. We should bear in mind that when an algebraic analysis can be made conveniently the analytical method of attack should be used. Generally, much more information will be available from it, with less work and greater accuracy, if an analytical analysis can be carried out.

One such natural motion is called simple harmonic motion. The vibration of a weight suspended from a spring is an example of such motion, as are the oscillations of a playground swing. Simple harmonic motion can be defined for rectilinear motion as the motion of a point about a fixed point such that the acceleration is always proportional to the distance from the fixed point and directed toward that point. Mathematically it can be defined as

$$a = -kx \tag{1.22}$$

where a = acceleration of the point
k = a proportionality constant
x = distance from the fixed point at any time.

The negative sign means that the acceleration is always directed oppo-site to the direction of the displacement relative to the fixed point. Such a motion is shown in Fig. 1.17(a). Simple harmonic motion can be represent-

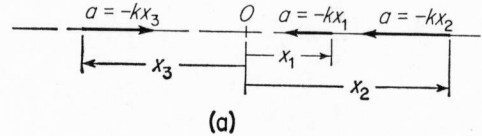

(a)

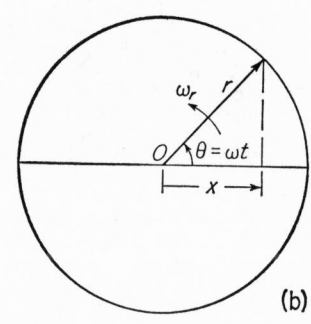

(b)

FIGURE 1.17

ed as the projection of the end of a vector, as the vector rotates about a fixed point with a constant angular velocity, on a diameter of the circle described by the end of the vector. Consider a vector of magnitude r, as shown in Fig. 1.17(b), rotating about the point O with an angular velocity ω. If time is considered zero when the vector is horizontal and pointing to the right, the angle θ which the vector makes with the horizontal axis or diameter is equal to ωt. If the displacement is considered positive when to the right of the center of the circle and negative when to the left, the pro-jection of the vector on the diameter is given as

$$x = r \cos \theta = r \cos \omega t \tag{1.23}$$

This equation holds for any time t corresponding to any angle θ from zero through a full revolution or any number of revolutions of the vector. The velocity of the projection of the end of the vector is

$$v = \frac{dx}{dt} = -r \sin\theta \frac{d\theta}{dt} = -r\omega \sin\omega t \qquad (1.24)$$

and the acceleration

$$a = \frac{d^2x}{dt^2} = -r \cos\theta \left(\frac{d\theta}{dt}\right)^2 = -r\omega^2 \cos\omega t \qquad (1.25)$$

From Eqs. (1.23) and (1.25) we see that

$$a = -\omega^2 x \qquad (1.26)$$

which corresponds to the definition of simple harmonic motion as given by Eq. (1.22) where ω^2 is the proportionality constant.

The vector could have been projected onto any diameter and the same equations would hold, providing the time was considered zero at the proper position. The position of the vector relative to the diameter when time is considered zero will not affect the motion except to change the starting position of the projection. For example, consider Fig. 1.18(a) where the

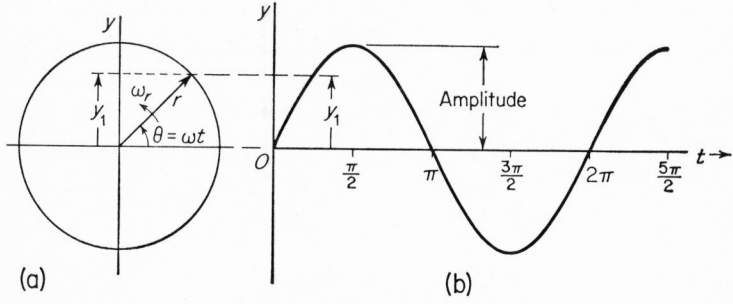

FIGURE 1.18

projection is on the vertical diameter and the time is zero when the vector is horizontal and pointing to the right. The equations of motion are

$$y = r \sin\omega t$$

$$v = r\omega \cos\omega t$$

$$a = -r\omega^2 \sin\omega t$$

A curve of this motion as a function of time is shown in Fig. 1.18(b), and we recognize this curve as a sine wave. The maximum displacement from the center is called the amplitude of the motion. A complete revolution of the vector is termed a cycle, and the time required for one cycle is called the period, T. The frequency, f, of the motion is the number of cycles completed per unit time, and the angular velocity is sometimes called the circular frequency. The relations between these terms are

$$f = \frac{1}{T} = \frac{\omega}{2\pi} \tag{1.27}$$

These terms will be used in discussing most motions that are periodic or repeat themselves after a certain time such as rotating members.

We have defined simple harmonic motion and discussed it only in terms of rectilinear motion. Simple harmonic motion is not restricted to this type of motion. An equation similar to Eq. (1.22) can be written to define simple harmonic motion in terms of angular motion as

$$\alpha = -k\theta$$

where θ is the angular displacement from some reference line. For, say, playground swings, θ would be the angle between the ropes or chains at any position and a vertical line. The angular motion can also be represented by a rotating vector by letting the magnitude of the vector be θ_0. It should be pointed out that the angular velocity of the rotating vector, ω, is not a function of the amplitude θ_0 in this case.

1.9 Constant Acceleration

Another frequently occurring motion is motion of a point which has a constant or uniform acceleration. Any freely falling body has this motion if the effect of air resistance is negligible. Since the acceleration is constant we see from Eq. (1.9) that the slope of the velocity-time curve is constant and the acceleration is given by the equation

$$a = \frac{v - v_0}{t} \tag{1.28}$$

where t is any time increment required for the velocity to go from v_0 to v, or the velocity at any time t, measured from the time the velocity is v_0, is

$$v = v_0 + at \tag{1.29}$$

The displacement can be obtained from Eq. (1.4)

$$s = \int_0^t v\,dt$$

$$= \int_0^t (v_0 + at)\,dt$$

$$= v_0 t + \tfrac{1}{2}at^2 \tag{1.30}$$

For the special case where the initial velocity is zero, the equations, as a function of time, become

$$v = at \tag{1.31}$$

$$s = \tfrac{1}{2}at^2 \tag{1.32}$$

1.10 *Graphical Differentiation*

Consider the curve in Fig. 1.19(a), which is a displacement-time curve for the piston of an internal combustion engine through a complete cycle of operation. We have previously found that the slope of this curve at any

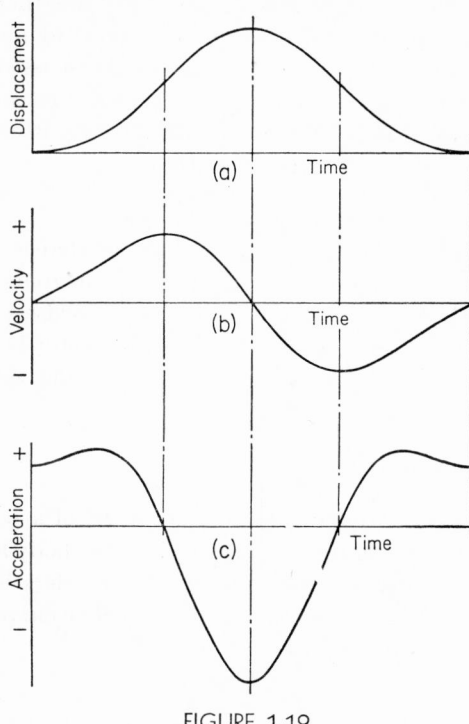

FIGURE 1.19

point is the velocity of the piston at that time. Then in order to get a velocity-time curve for the piston, all we need do is lay out a velocity-time coordinate system, plot points for the velocity at close intervals of time and draw a smooth curve through these points. The magnitude of the velocity at any time is equal to the slope of the displacement-time curve at the corresponding time. Such a curve is shown in Fig. 1.19(b). In a similar manner, since the slope of the velocity curve at any time is the acceleration at that time, we could use the velocity-time curve to plot a curve of acceleration as a function of time, as shown in Fig. 1.19(c). This is, then, a method of differentiating a curve graphically.

The only difficulty with such a procedure is the accurate determination of the slope of the curves. Various means have been devised to determine the slope of a curve but none of these methods yields greater accuracy than close approximation to the true slope. It is particularly difficult to determine the slope of a curve accurately at points where the radius of curvature is changing rapidly. The error introduced into the graphical differentiation of a curve is a smoothing of the true curve where peaks and valleys are diminished in magnitude. This error is compounded when a second graphical differentiation is made, such as plotting an acceleration-time curve from a displacement-time curve. Therefore, when a velocity-time curve, and especially an acceleration-time curve, is obtained by the process of graphical differentiation of a displacement-curve, the resulting curves should be taken only as approximations of the true curves. Despite these drawbacks, however, graphical differentiation is often a useful tool. If the displacement-time curves to be differentiated are smooth with gradual changes in curvature, graphical differentiation gives fairly accurate velocity and acceleration curves. Also, it gives a convenient means of approximating the velocity and acceleration curves rapidly. In many cases graphical differentiation will show critical points for which more accurate determination should be made, obviating the necessity of determining all the points of the curve with great accuracy. Since velocity and acceleration curves obtained by graphical differentiation are at best approximations, we are not usually justified in determining the slopes by some elaborate method. The following procedure gives a satisfactory curve to any degree of accuracy necessary for most engineering work.

Figure 1.20(a) shows a portion of a time displacement curve and a time increment Δt_1, during which time the displacement is Δs_1. The ratio $\Delta s_1 / \Delta t_1$

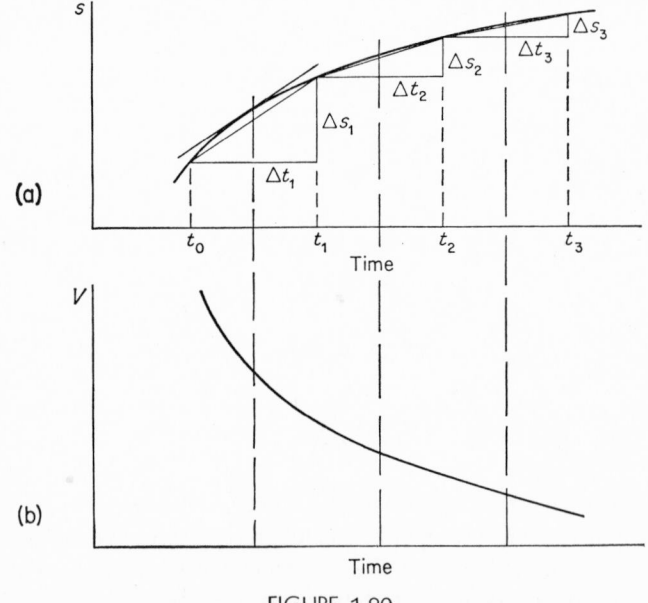

FIGURE 1.20

is equal to the slope of the line joining the points of the displacement curve at t_0 and t_1. This slope is very nearly equal to the slope of the displacement-time curve at the time midway between the times t_0 and t_1. This slope, $\Delta s_1/\Delta t_1$, is approximately equal to the velocity at a point midway between the times t_0 and t_1. This approximation becomes closer to the true velocity as the increment, Δt, becomes smaller. This same argument holds for the other time increments Δt_2 and Δt_3. Then if we set up velocity-time axes below the displacement-time axes, with zero time directly below the zero time for the upper axes, and use the same time scale as shown in Fig. 1.20(b), we can plot the velocity-time curve. This is done by laying off to

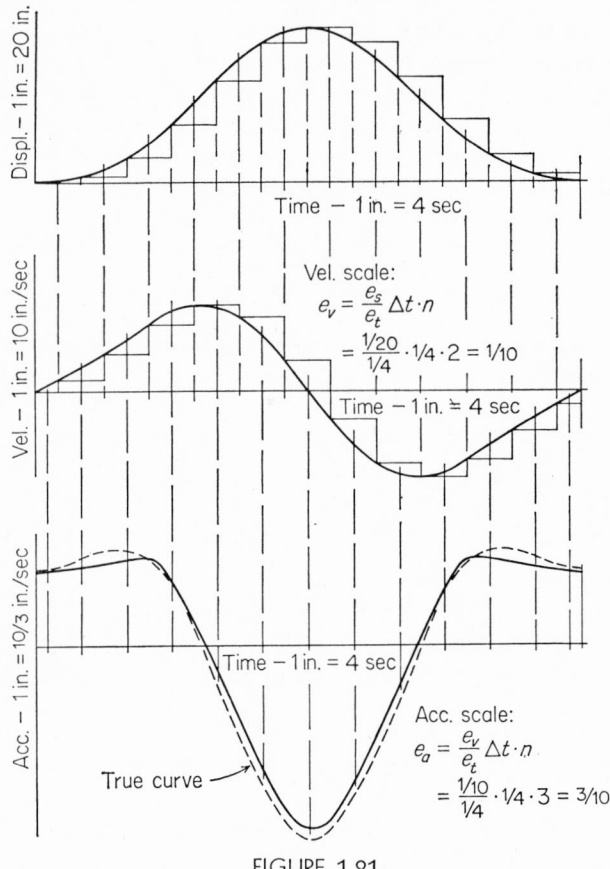

FIGURE 1.21

some scale the velocity (using the ratio $\Delta s/\Delta t$ as the velocity) on the corresponding time at the mid-point of the time increments and drawing a smooth curve through these points. The acceleration-time curve can be obtained from the velocity curve in exactly the same manner.

Velocity and acceleration curves obtained in this manner are shown in Fig. 1.21, where the displacement-time curve represents the motion of the piston in a steam engine. In plotting these curves, the displacement-time curve was broken up into a number of equal time increments and the mid-points of these increments were projected down to the time axis of the velocity-time curve. Since all the time increments are equal, the denominator of all the velocity approximations, $\Delta s/\Delta t$, is the same and the displacement increment represents the approximate velocity at the midpoint of the time increment to some scale, the scale being the same for all time increments. Therefore, we can lay off this Δs distance, or a multiple of it, on the corresponding time ordinate for each increment on the velocity axes and thereby greatly speed up the laying out of the curve, since we do not have to figure each slope independently. The Δs distances were doubled in Fig. 1.21 so as to give a better velocity curve, with the velocity scale increased. The scale is determined in the following manner.

Let the displacement scale be e_s. In Fig. 1.21 the displacement is plotted with one inch on the axis equal to twenty inches actual displacement; therefore, the scale is one-twentieth. The time scale is one-fourth. Let the time scale be e_t. The velocity scale is then

$$e_v = \frac{e_s}{e_t} \Delta tn \tag{1.33}$$

where e_v = velocity scale
  e_s = displacement scale
  e_t = time scale
  Δt = actual distance on time axis of time increment
  n = factor by which actual length of Δs was increased in transferring to velocity axis.

For Fig. 1.21 the time increments are $\frac{1}{4}$ inch actual distance, so the velocity scale is

$$e_v = \frac{\frac{1}{20} \times \frac{1}{4}}{\frac{1}{4}} \times 2 = \frac{1}{10}$$

or one inch equals ten inches per second.

The acceleration-time curve was plotted in the same way, using the increments already laid out on the velocity curve. This gives us one increment at the beginning and one at the end of the curve which are each one-half the rest of the increments. In laying these two ordinates out on the acceleration-time axes, the length of each must be multiplied by a factor twice the factor used for the other ordinates so that all the ordinates will be to the same scale. The equation for the acceleration scale is given in the figure and is found in the same way as is the velocity scale. The velocity ordinates were tripled in laying out the acceleration curve.

In cases where the radius of curvature is changing rapidly, the increments should be made smaller than the regular time increments, in each case making the increments either $\frac{1}{2}$, $\frac{1}{4}$, $\frac{1}{8}$, etc., of the regular time increments and multiplying the ordinate by a factor of 2, 4, 8, etc., to keep a common scale.

A means of checking the accuracy of a graphical differentiation will be discussed later when we deal with graphical integration. (The curve obtained by graphical differentiation can be graphically integrated, the integration curve compared with the original curve, and inaccuracies can be picked out.)

PROBLEMS

1.1 (a) Plot the position or displacement of the slider "*e*" in Fig. P5.1 as a function of the angular position of the crank, link "*a*." Let the displacement of the slider be the ordinate, and let three inches on the diagram represent one inch actual displacement. Let one-half inch on the abscissae represent a 15° displacement of the crank. Plot points for every 15° of the crank through a full cycle, letting the crank rotate clockwise, and draw a smooth curve through these points.

(b) If the crank is rotating at a constant angular velocity of 3600 rpm clockwise each 15° increment of the crank displacement represents a fixed time increment. Determine the time scale to which the abscissae is drawn.

(c) Having a displacement-time curve from parts (a) and (b) construct the velocity-time curve for the slider by graphical differentiation. Triple the Δs ordinates.

(d) Construct the acceleration-time curve for the slider by graphical differentiation. Triple the ΔV ordinates.

1.2 Plot the displacement-time curve for the slider "*e*" in Fig. P4.12 to convenient scales for $\omega_a = 250$ rpm clockwise and construct the velocity-time and acceleration-time curves by graphical differentiation.

1.3 Plot the displacement-time curve for the slider "*e*" in Fig. P4.11 to a convenient scale for $\omega_a = 30$ rpm clockwise and construct the velocity-time and acceleration-time curves by graphical differentiation.

1.4 Plot the displacement-time curve for slider "*e*" in Fig. P4.13 to a convenient scale for $\omega_a = 150$ rpm counterclockwise and construct the velocity-time and acceleration-time curves by graphical differentiation.

1.5 Plot the angular position of link "*c*" in Fig. P10.1 as a function of time for $\omega_a = 45$ rpm counterclockwise and construct the angular velocity-time and angular acceleration-time curve for link "*c*" by graphical differentiation.

1.6 Plot the angular displacement-time curve for link "*b*" in Fig. 7.6(a) for $\omega_a = 250$ rpm clockwise and construct the angular velocity-time and angular acceleration-time curve by graphical differentiation. Let distance O–P be $2\frac{1}{4}$ in. and plot the curves from the instant that the pin first comes into contact with a slot until it breaks contact with the same slot, corresponding to 90° of motion of link "*b*."

Chapter **2**

Linkages and Constraint

2.1 Plane Motion

A large majority of machines are so constructed that any point on any member of the machine is always a given distance from some reference plane and remains at this same distance during any motion of the machine relative to the frame. Such motion is called plane motion, since all points on the machine move in planes parallel with the reference plane. The internal combustion engine is an example of motion of this type where all the pistons with their connecting rods and cranks move in plane motion. Plane motion is convenient for analysis since the machine components can be represented by projecting them onto the reference plane and analyzing the motion in that plane.

Plane motion can be divided into two types of motion, rotation and translation. A body has plane rotation when every point on the body remains at a constant distance from an axis perpendicular to the plane of motion. Translation is motion in which any line on a body remains parallel to its original position during the motion. A wheel turning on its axis is an example of plane rotation, and the seats on a ferris wheel at a carnival represent translation, since the seats always remain parallel. If the seats rotated about the axis of the wheel, they would remain fixed relative to the frame and would be upside down at some position of the wheel.

Translation can be subdivided into two classes, rectilinear translation and curvilinear translation. In rectilinear translation all points on the body move in straight lines, and in curvilinear translation points on the body move along curved lines. The piston in a reciprocating engine is an example of rectilinear translation and the seats of the ferris wheel are examples of curvilinear translation. The motion of any body, which is moving with plane motion, can be shown to consist of either rotation or translation or a combination of the two. Figure 2.1 shows a body at (*a*) which has moved later to position (b). This is a general displacement. The body can be moved from position (a) to position (b) by rectilinear translation along the

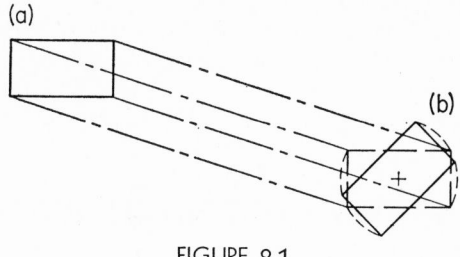

FIGURE 2.1

dashed lines to the dotted position at (b) and then brought to position (b) by rotation. Figure 2.2 shows the same body with the same displacement,

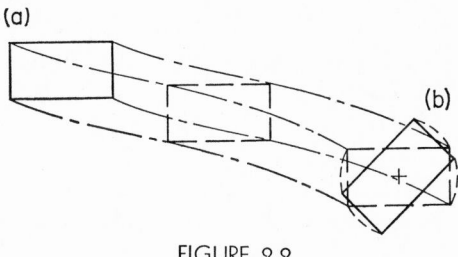

FIGURE 2.2

but in this case the body moved to the dotted position with curvilinear translation followed by a rotation.

2.2 Helical and Spherical Motion

Two other classes of motion which are common in machinery are helical motion and spherical motion. Helical motion is motion in which a body rotates about an axis and at the same time moves in translation along that

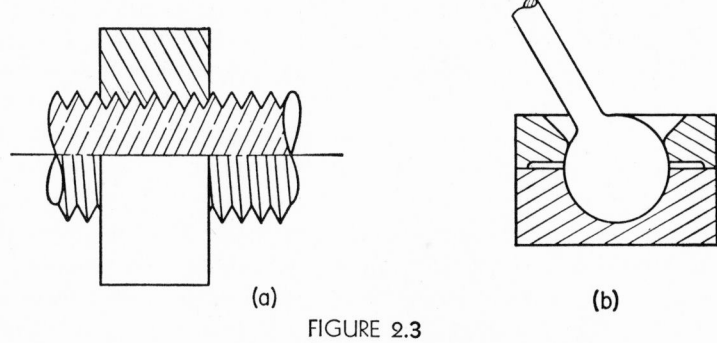

FIGURE 2.3

axis. A nut on a bolt is an example of this class of motion, as shown in Fig. 2.3(a). Spherical motion is motion of a body in which all points of the body move on the surfaces of concentric spheres, as represented by the ball and socket joint shown in Fig. 2.3(b). These motions are three dimensional motion since points do not remain in planes.

2.3 Motion of a Body

With a little thought it can be seen that the position of a body in space is determined by the location of three points on the body which are non-collinear. Since any two of these points determine a line on the body, we can say that the position of a body in space can also be determined by a line and a point not on that line. As a corollary to this we can say that the *motion* of three non-collinear points on a body determine the motion of the body in space.

When a body has plane motion, the motion of two points on the body determines the motion of the body so long as these two points do not lie on a line perpendicular to the plane of motion, and, if the body is moving in translation, the motion of one point will determine the motion of the body. When we are analyzing the motion of machine members later, we will use these ideas to pick points that are easy to analyze in order to determine the motion of each single member.

2.4 Kinematic Components of Mechanisms

A mechanism is a combination of bodies, made of resistant materials, that have constrained relative motion. Resistant materials are those that resist deformation under the action of forces. Most machine members are made of metal or other material that tends to hold shape when acted on by forces. Although we know that all materials deform to some extent when acted on by forces, when this deformation is small we call such materials resistant. We can then say that a resistant material is a material that deforms to such a small extent that this deformation is negligible in relation to the displacements of the body made from the material, and the deformation will not affect the motion of the body. A body made from such a resistant material is called a rigid body. For our purposes two points on a rigid body remain the same distance apart at all times regardless of the forces that act on the body. When the deformation is not negligible, the rigid body has failed (from a kinematic viewpoint). The design of members so that they do not deform appreciably under the loads imposed on them is taken up in the study of machine design. Constrained motion means that the motion of the members is controlled and the members are made to move in a desired manner. A mechanism must be so constrained or controlled that if one member is moved in a certain manner, the other members must always move in a certain prescribed manner. Complete constraint of a combination of rigid bodies would mean that no relative motion is possible between the bodies. We will study later how the members of a machine are constrained relative to each other.

We should point out the difference between a machine and a mechanism. A mechanism (a kinematic term) is independent of any forces that may be acting on it. A machine is made up of one or more mechanisms which transmit forces and energy in order to do work. A mechanism could be termed a motion modifier and in a mechanism we are concerned only with the change of one type of motion to another, such as the change of rotation of the crankshaft of an engine to the translation of the piston.

The individual members or bodies that go together to form a mechanism are called links, or more specifically, kinematic links. When the links are joined together, the composite is called a kinematic chain. The joining of links is termed pairing. Various types of pairs or joints will be discussed later.

Mechanisms can be classified as simple mechanisms and compound mechanisms. A simple mechanism is a mechanism which is made up or composed of three or four links. All other mechanisms, or those composed of more than four links, are compound mechanisms. Compound mechanisms are usually made up of combinations of simple mechanisms. This will be amplified later in the chapter.

2.5 Pairing

A body or link free to move in space can translate along any one of the three coordinate axes and can rotate about any one of these axes. Each of these motions is termed a degree of freedom of motion. A link in space, then, has six degrees of freedom. One or more of these freedoms of motion can be removed by certain types of constraint. A link in plane motion has only three degrees of freedom: translation along the coordinate axes defining the plane, and a rotation about an axis normal to the plane of motion. A link moving in plane translation has only two degrees of freedom: translation along the coordinate axes. Since we will be concerned primarily with plane motion, we will be dealing with links having only three degrees of freedom and, unless otherwise stated, we will be dealing with plane motion for the rest of the text.

Consider a group of four rigid bodies moving in plane motion, as shown in Fig. 2.4, which are free to move independently. Since each body has three degrees of freedom, the bodies as a whole have twelve degrees of freedom. In order to combine these bodies so as to make a mechanism they must be connected in such a manner that the degrees of freedom are removed to such an extent that only one degree of freedom remains for the whole group. This constraint is accomplished by pairing or connecting the links, and fixing one of the links to serve as a frame.

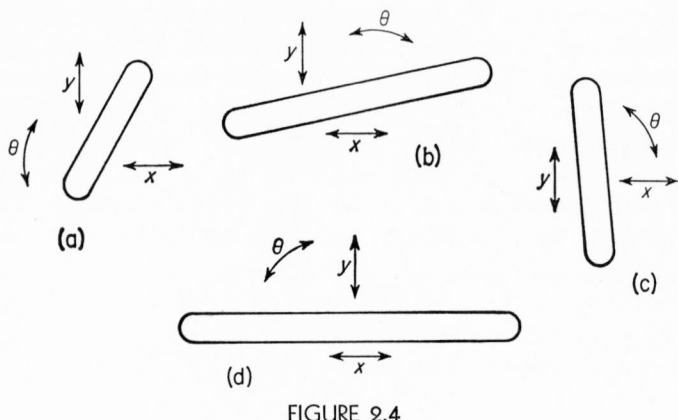

FIGURE 2.4

When two links are paired, the part of the joint attached to each link is called an element of the pair. A shaft and bearing is an example of such a pair. The journal or shaft is one element of the pair, and the bearing in which the shaft rotates is the other element of the pair. Such a pair is referred to as a pin joint, turning pair, or rotating pair. Pairs are divided into two categories; higher pairs and lower pairs. Higher pairs are those in which the elements are in contact along a line or have point contact, and lower pairs are those which have surface contact between the elements. The pin joint mentioned above has surface contact around the shaft and is, therefore, a lower pair.

If a body is paired to a fixed body by means of a pin joint, as shown in Fig. 2.5(a), the only motion which the body can have is rotation about the

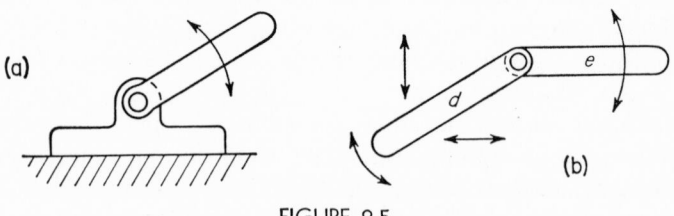

FIGURE 2.5

pin joint. Therefore, the pin joint removes two degrees of freedom. A turning pair between any two links will always remove two degrees of freedom, even if one of the links is not fixed. Figure 2.5(b) shows two links, connected by a pin joint, neither of which is fixed. Either of these links is free to translate in two directions and rotate in one direction, but the other link is only free to rotate relative to the first link. In the example, link "*d*" is assumed to have complete freedom of motion while link "*e*" can only rotate relative to link "*d*"; therefore, link "*e*" must translate in the same manner as link "*d*," but can rotate independently, giving four degrees of freedom for the system. The two links, were they free to move independently, would have six degrees of freedom. If a third link were pinned to link "*d*" at the same point that link "*e*" is pinned to "*d*," the third link would have only one degree of freedom relative to link "*d*" and the system composed of the three links would have only five degrees of freedom. This type of pair will be called a double pair, meaning that one link is paired to two other links by a single joint.

The four links in Fig. 2.4 can be made into a chain or mechanism by the use of rotating pairs as shown in Fig. 2.6. Here link "*d*" is made a fixed link to serve as a frame and pin joints are used to join the members. This particular mechanism is so common that it has been given the name quadric crank. The number of degrees of freedom for the system can be determined by remembering that a fixed link has no degree of freedom and each pin

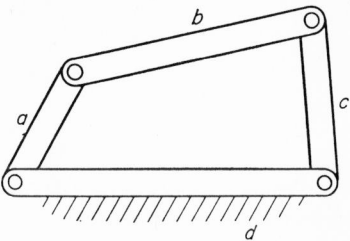

FIGURE 2.6

joint removes two degrees of freedom. Therefore, of the twelve degrees of freedom possible if there is no constraint, only one degree of freedom is left after constraining the links by fixing one link and putting in four pin joints. For this simple mechanism it is easy to see that the system satisfies the definition of a mechanism. Examining the system, we note that if any link such as link "*a*" moves, then the motion of the other links must follow in a certain prescribed manner. We will find later another manner in which to determine whether a system of links is so constrained that it satisfies the definition of a mechanism. For more complicated systems it will be difficult to tell by observation alone whether the constraint is complete or not.

We will now consider the other types of pairs. Another lower pair is the lower sliding pair as shown in Fig. 2.7(a). Here one body moves in translation relative to another body and the bodies have surface contact. It can be seen from the figure that the only relative motion between the two bodies is rectilinear translation so long as the bodies stay in contact; therefore, a lower sliding pair removes two degrees of freedom: rotation and one translation. Figure 2.7(b) shows a higher sliding pair. In this case there is line contact between the two bodies and they have not only relative translation as shown, but also relative rotation about the line of contact. A higher sliding pair, then, removes only one degree of freedom, a translation.

The other type of pair which we will discuss is a rolling pair, shown in Fig. 2.7(c). Since the two bodies are in contact along a line, this is a case of higher pairing. Before discussing the degrees of freedom removed by such a

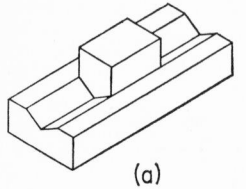
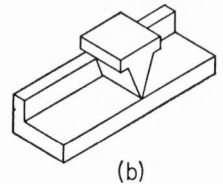
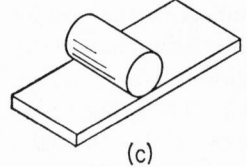

(a)   (b)   (c)

FIGURE 2.7

pair we must define the phrase "rolling contact." When two bodies are in rolling contact, there is no relative velocity between the bodies at the point or line of contact. By this definition we remove the possibility of sliding at the point of contact and the only motion possible is relative rotation about the point of contact; therefore, a rolling pair removes two degrees of freedom. As a means of further clarifying the meaning of rolling contact, consider the rear wheels of an automobile. If force is suddenly applied to the rear wheels of an automobile while it is standing still, the wheels will slip on the road and very little motion will be imparted to the car, while if the force is applied gradually, there is no slipping of the wheels and the car starts moving smoothly. In the first case there is relative motion between the wheels and the road while in the second case there is no relative motion. The second case is an example of pure rolling contact while the first case is an example of a combination of rolling and sliding contact. According to our definition the second case is the only one of rolling contact. The first case is a case of a higher sliding pair.

Pairs can also be classified as self-closed pairs and force-closed pairs. A self-closed pair is one in which the constraint of the links is imposed by the elements of the pair. A force-closed pair is one in which the constraint is not completed by rigid elements alone but depends on some force, such as a spring or the weight of the link holding the links together, to complete the constraint. A journal bearing in which the bearing completely surrounds the journal is an example of a self-closed pair while if a half-bearing were used a force would be needed to keep the journal in the bearing; this would be a force-closed pair. A half-bearing is used in many pieces of heavy equipment where the weight of the members keeps the journal in the bearings; for example, the wheels and axles of railway cars usually rest in half-bearings. The ways of a planer is also an example of a force-closed pair.

Another example of a force-closed pair is shown by the cam and follower arrangement shown in Fig. 2.8. There are three pairs in this mechanism, two self-closed and one force-closed. The self-closed pairs are the turning pair connecting the cam to the frame or fixed link and the lower sliding pair connecting the cam follower and the frame. The pair connecting the cam and the follower is a force-closed, higher sliding, pair. The compression spring furnishes the force to close the pair, holding the follower against the cam.

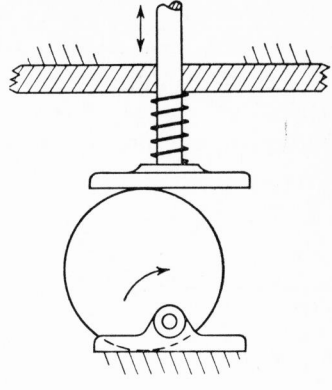

FIGURE 2.8

In three dimensional motion the principal pairs are the spherical pair such as the ball and the socket shown in Fig. 2.3(b) and the helical pair as shown in Fig. 2.3(a). Both of these pairs are self-closed.

There is another means of distinguishing between higher and lower pairs which will prove useful in some cases. This can best be explained by means of examples. Consider the two links connected by a turning pair shown in Figs. 2.9(a) and 2.9(b). These figures represent the same two links, with

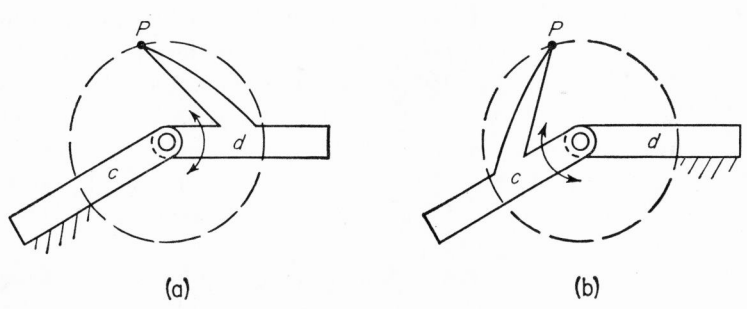

(a)   (b)

FIGURE 2.9

link "c" fixed in Fig. 2.9(a) and link "d" fixed in Fig. 2.9(b). In Fig. 2.9(a), if point P is connected to link "d" the point will describe a circle about the pin joint when link "d" is rotated relative to link "c." In Fig. 2.9(b) if the same point P is connected to link "c," it will describe the same circular path if link "c" is rotated relative to link "d." Therefore, the point P will have the same absolute motion regardless of which link is fixed so long as it is a part of the moving link. This condition will always exist if two links are

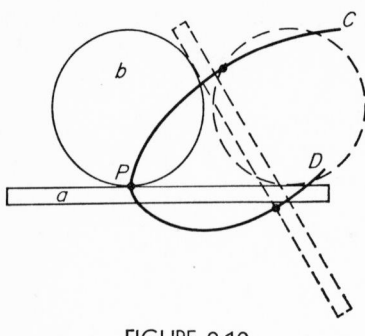

FIGURE 2.10

joined with lower pairing. To show that this will not happen with higher pairing, consider Fig. 2.10 which shows a wheel and straight bar in rolling contact at point P. If the bar is held fixed and the wheel rolled on the bar, point P, considered as a point on the wheel, will describe a curve $P–C$, which we know as a cycloid. If the wheel is held fixed and the bar rolled on the wheel point P, considered as a point on the bar, will describe a curve $P–D$, which we recognize as an involute.

2.6 Kinematic Drawings

We have seen that motion of a body in plane motion is determined by the motion of two points on the body; or, since two points determine a line on the body, the motion of the body is determined by the motion of the line. With this in mind, it is easy to see that in order to analyze the motion of a mechanism, the drawing of the complete mechanism is not necessary. The links may be represented by lines in the mechanism. These lines are usually drawn to connect the elements of the various pairs of the mechanism. Such a representation is called a kinematic drawing. For example, the quadric crank mechanism shown in Fig. 2.6 can be represented for kinematic purposes as a line drawing as shown in Fig. 2.11 (Fig. 2.6, redrawn for the

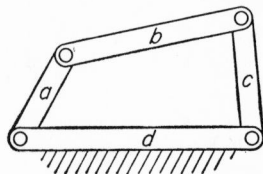
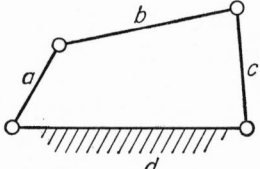

FIGURE 2.11

comparison). The turning pairs are represented by a circle at the points where the links are joined. The ground lines drawn from link "d" indicates that link "d" is the fixed link or the frame of the mechanism. This manner of representing mechanisms greatly simplifies kinematic analyses of them.

Another common mechanism is the slider crank mechanism which is shown kinematically in Fig. 2.12. In this mechanism link "a" is pinned to the fixed link "d" and link "b," while link "c" is pinned to link "b" and slides with rectilinear translation relative to the fixed link "d." The slider is shown as a body since the relative translation between it and link "*d*" cannot be shown by using a line. It should be noted that link "*d*" is not shown as a continuous link. This is not necessary since it is a fixed link and serves

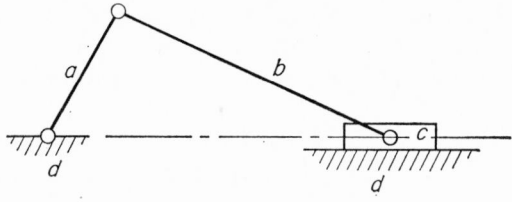

FIGURE 2.12

as the frame of the mechanism. Any time a link is paired with the fixed link it is only necessary to use a line with ground lines attached to indicate the fixed body. Also, link "*c*" is not shown as completely constrained to move in translation as there is nothing to indicate that it cannot leave the fixed body. This is standard practice and in such cases it is assumed that the two links will always remain in contact through the complete cycle of motion. For this mechanism link "*a*" is called the crank, link "*b*" the connecting rod, and link "*c*" the slider. We recognize this as the mechanism of the internal combustion engine where the slider corresponds to the piston.

It should be pointed out that since kinematic drawings do not show the links, but only a line or lines representing the links, the drawings do not limit the extent of the links. Kinematically, the links extend indefinitely in all directions without limit, and a point anywhere on the plane of the drawing can be designated as a point on any of the links of the mechanism.

Other examples of kinematic drawings are shown in Figs. 2.13 and 2.14. Figure 2.13 represents a crank-shaper quick-return mechanism, so called

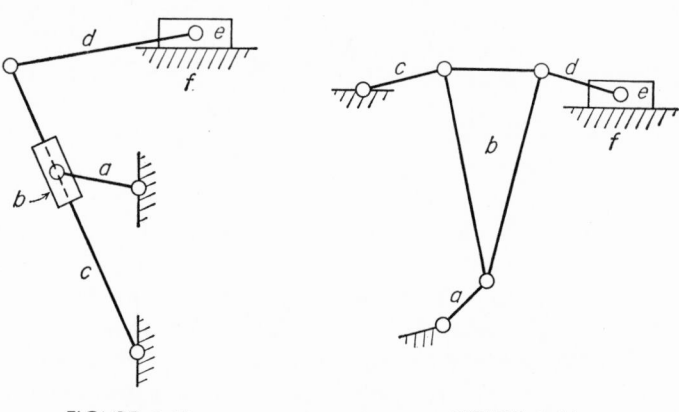

FIGURE 2.13   FIGURE 2.14

because the slider, link "*e*," requires less time to move from one extreme position to the other, moving in one direction, than is required in the other direction, assuming the crank, link "*a*," is rotating with a constant velocity. In this mechanism link "*b*" is pinned to link "*a*" and slides relative to link "*c*" with rectilinear translation. Link "*c*" is pinned to link "*d*" and the fixed link "*f*." Figure 2.14 shows a rock crusher mechanism. A very large force can be given to the slider "*e*" with but a small torque on link "*a*" with such a mechanism. (This will be explained in detail in the chapter on static forces.) Link "*b*" in this mechanism is represented by three lines since it contains the elements of three pairs and cannot be represented by a single line.

In the kinematic drawings to be used here, all links will be designated by lower case letters starting with "*a*" and going down the alphabet as far as needed. Usually "*a*" will be used to designate the crank of a mechanism, which in most cases is the link which has a constant angular velocity and is generally the driving link or driver. Points of the links will be designated by capital letters.

In concluding this section of kinematic drawings, we should remember that a kinematic drawing has one purpose and that purpose is to represent a mechanism, with a minimum of drafting, but with enough detail so that the motion of each link is completely defined. Therefore, when a single line is not sufficient, enough detail should be added so that the motion of a link is completely defined.

2.7 *Constrained Systems*

In Articles 2.4 and 2.5 the idea of constraint was developed in relation to the combining of links to form a mechanism. A more concise definition of a mechanism can be written as follows: a mechanism is a combination of rigid bodies so constrained by the pairing of links that the combination has only one degree of freedom. This definition can be used to determine if a complex grouping of links are so constrained that they form a mechanism. In the discussion of the quadric crank mechanism, it was shown that the pairing removed all but one degree of freedom which makes it a mechanism according to the above definition.

As another example, consider the slider crank mechanism shown in Fig. 2.12. This mechanism contains four links giving a total of twelve possible degrees of freedom. Fixing one link removes three degrees of freedom, the three pin joints remove two degrees of freedom each, and the lower sliding pair between links "*c*" and "*d*" removes two, making a total of eleven degrees of freedom removed and leaving only one degree of freedom. Therefore, the slider crank is a mechanism. In Fig. 2.14 there are six links giving eighteen possible degrees of freedom. Seventeen of these are removed by the fixing of one link, the six turning pairs, and the lower sliding pair.

Let us now look at some combinations of links that do not form mechanisms. Figure 2.15 shows a combination of five links which have fifteen

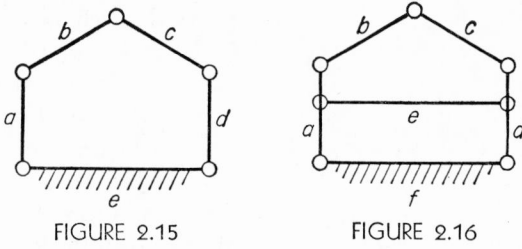

FIGURE 2.15   FIGURE 2.16

possible degrees of freedom. The five turning pairs and the fixing of one of the links, "*e*," removes only thirteen degrees of freedom and, therefore, the combination, having two degrees of freedom, is not a mechanism. This result is obvious by noting that if link "*d*" is also fixed, the remaining unfixed links then form a quadric crank mechanism with the fixed link, and can move independent of link "*d*." Therefore, the motion of one of the links does not determine the motion of the other links in the system. By adding a link, as shown in Fig. 2.16, the combination becomes a mechanism: we now have six links with eighteen possible degrees of freedom, of which seventeen are removed by the seven pin joints and the fixing of one of the links. It should be pointed out that the two single links, link "*a*" and link "*d*," could be mistaken for two links each. In order to show these as single links, the lines representing the links are continued through the circles representing the turning pairs between them and link "*e*," whereas, in the cases in which the links terminate at the turning pairs, the lines representing the links stop at the circles.

Figure 2.17 shows three links joined by three turning pairs. In this case

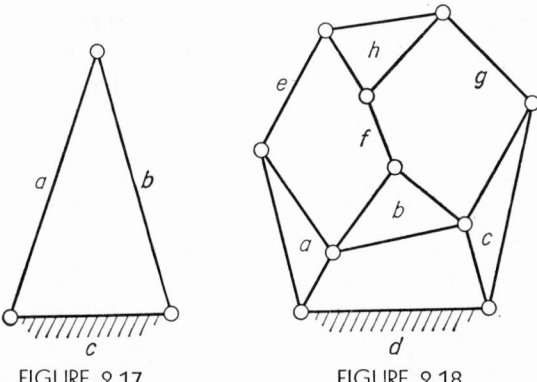

FIGURE 2.17   FIGURE 2.18

the three turning pairs and the fixing of one of the links removes all nine of the possible degrees of freedom and the combination has no degree of freedom and cannot move. Such a combination must be considered as a rigid body or a single link when combined with other links, and is called a structure.

The mechanism shown in Fig. 2.18 contains eight links. If one made only a cursory inspection of the combination, he might think it contained many more than eight links, but remembering that three links connected by three pin joints form one link, it is seen that there are only eight links. It is rather difficult to tell, just by observation, whether this combination satisfies the definition of a mechanism, but by analyzing the mechanism according to the definition given in this Article it is fairly easy to see that it is a mechanism. Of the twenty-four possible degrees of freedom, twenty are removed by the ten pin joints and three more are removed by fixing link "*d*," making a total of twenty-three degrees of freedom which are removed and leaving one degree of freedom. Therefore, the combination does satisfy our definition of a mechanism.

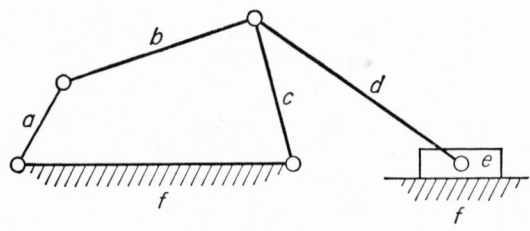

FIGURE 2.19

As another example, consider Fig. 2.19 which contains six links. There are eighteen possible degrees of freedom. Analyzing the combination as we have done previously, the fixed link removes three degrees, the five turning pairs remove ten and the lower sliding pair removes two, making a total of fifteen degrees of freedom removed. This leaves three degrees of freedom and, therefore, we might say that it is not a mechanism. This is a false conclusion, however, because we overlooked a constraint. The turning pair connecting links "*b*," "*c*," and "*d*" is a double turning pair and should be counted as two turning pairs. Note that this pin joint constrains link "*b*" and link "*d*" to rotation relative to link "*c*" and, therefore, serves to remove two degrees of freedom from each of the links "*b*" and "*d*." Counting this joint as two turning pairs, the combination has only one degree of freedom and is a mechanism. In the same manner, if a turning pair were to connect four links at the same point, it would be a triple pair and would be counted as three turning pairs.

While this method is quite useful and convenient in analyzing a mechanism for the proper number of constraints, there are some pitfalls for which one should be prepared. Quite often a mechanism will have more constraints than are necessary to the removal of all but one degree of freedom, but they will nevertheless be applied in such a manner that the mechanism still has the required single degree of freedom. Such constraints are called redundant constraints. An example of such redundant constraints is the planer carriage and bed shown in Fig. 2.20(a). The over-constraint here is

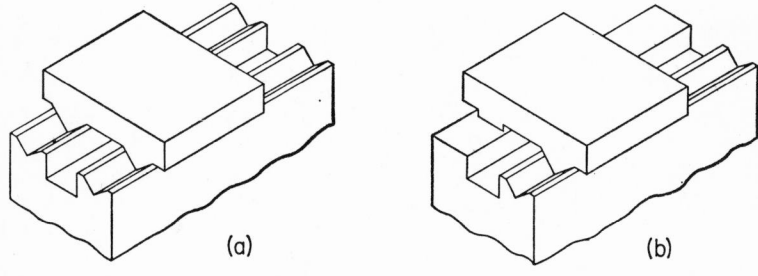

FIGURE 2.20

obvious without analyzing the mechanism. In Fig. 2.20(a), the carriage is constrained to move with rectilinear translation lengthwise along the bed. Figure 2.20(b) shows a similar planer carriage and bed in which the carriage is also constrained to translation lengthwise along the bed, but in this case only one V-groove is used to prevent motion transverse to the bed. Therefore, two V-grooves in Fig. 2.20(a) are not necessary for complete constraint — one groove is a redundant constraint which does not remove any constraint that is not removed by the other groove. However, if the grooves were not parallel, the carriage could not move in a longitudinal direction and all degrees of freedom would be removed. It should be noted that the extra groove adds unnecessarily to the manufacturing cost, because the grooves must be held to a close parallelism and the distance between the grooves and the corresponding V's on the carriage must be held to close tolerance.

Another example of redundant constraints is found in the two rolling wheels shown in Fig. 2.21(a). In this example, all the possible degrees of freedom are removed by the fixing of one link, the two turning pairs, and one rolling pair, which removes the nine possible degrees of freedom. Motion is possible only because the two links "a" and "b" are circular. If the links "a" and "b" were not both circular, the mechanism would not have any degree of freedom. Such a case is shown in Fig. 2.21(b), where a similar combination of links is shown with one of the links not circular. The latter case can be made into a mechanism only if one of the constraints is so made as to remove only one degree of freedom, as shown in Fig. 2.21(c) where the

pair between link "*a*" and the fixed link "*c*" is made a higher sliding pair
which does remove only one degree of freedom. In such a case as is shown in

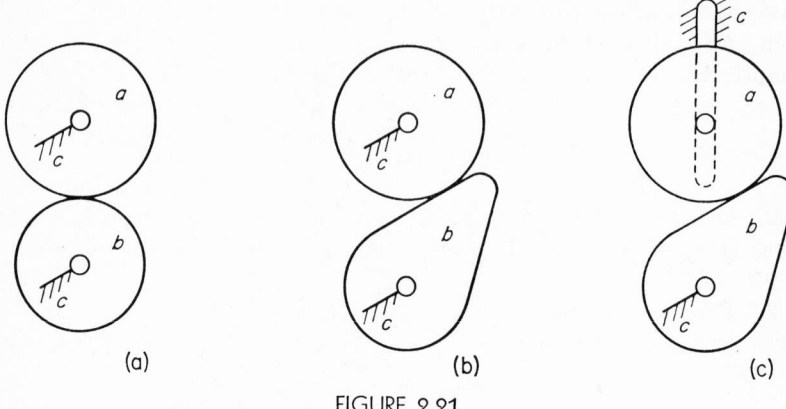

FIGURE 2.21

Fig. 2.21(a) an analysis can be made only if the turning pair is considered to
remove only one degree of freedom.

An analysis of the gear train represented in Fig. 2.22 will clarify the
handling of gear trains. (Gears are usually represented as rolling wheels.
In the analysis of gear trains later in the text, the rolling pairs will be consid-

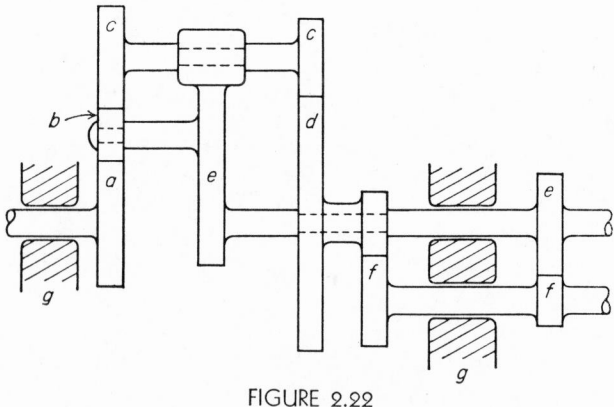

FIGURE 2.22

ered to remove only one degree of freedom. We will find later that gears
actually are not rolling pairs but higher sliding pairs except when they are
in contact at one particular point.) The mechanism is shown in a view
normal to the plane of motion so that the details of the mechanism can be
better presented. There are seven links giving a possible twenty-one
degrees of freedom. Three degrees of freedom are removed by fixing one of

the links. There are six turning pairs which remove twelve more degrees of freedom, and five rolling pairs which, if considered to remove one degree of freedom each, will give a total of twenty degrees of freedom removed leaving a single degree of freedom. We conclude that the system is a mechanism. An analysis of the relative motions of this mechanism will be made in Chapter 22.

PROBLEMS

2.1 Determine all possible three link mechanisms having only turning pairs, higher sliding pairs, and lower sliding pairs in any combination, and sketch examples of each.

2.2 Determine all possible four link mechanisms having only turning pairs, higher sliding pairs, and lower sliding pairs in any combination, and sketch examples of each.

Chapter 3

Instant Centers

3.1 *Introduction*

A body in space motion can be shown to rotate, relative to another body, about some axis which is fixed or has no motion, relative to the two bodies, at any instant of time. This axis may be changing position with time, relative to the two bodies. Such an axis is called the instantaneous axis of rotation for the two bodies. These axes are very important in our analysis of velocities of a mechanism, as will be shown in succeeding articles.

In plane motion these instantaneous axes of rotation are always normal to the plane of motion and intersect the planes of motion at coincident points. Such points are called instantaneous centers of rotation, or for brevity, instant centers.

3.2 *Relative Velocity of Two Points on a Rigid Body*

Before the idea of instant centers is developed, we need to consider the relative velocity of two points on a rigid body. The velocity of a point on a body relative to any other point on the body must be in a direction perpendicular to a line joining the two points. This idea is extremely important in all velocity analyses and will be used in developing the concept of instant center. We will prove this statement concerning relative velocities by showing that the relative velocity of two points on a rigid body can have no component along the line joining the two points.

Figure 3.1 shows a rigid body containing the two points, P and R. Assume that the velocity of P with respect to R is as shown in Fig. 3.1(a). The velocity vector can be broken into two perpendicular components, one along the line joining the points and one perpendicular to that line. The component along the line indicates that the point P is approaching point R and a short time later will be closer to point R. But this is impossible, because we found in the second chapter that two points on a rigid body remain at a fixed distance from each other. Therefore, the velocity of P with respect to R cannot have a component towards R. Figure 3.1(b) shows

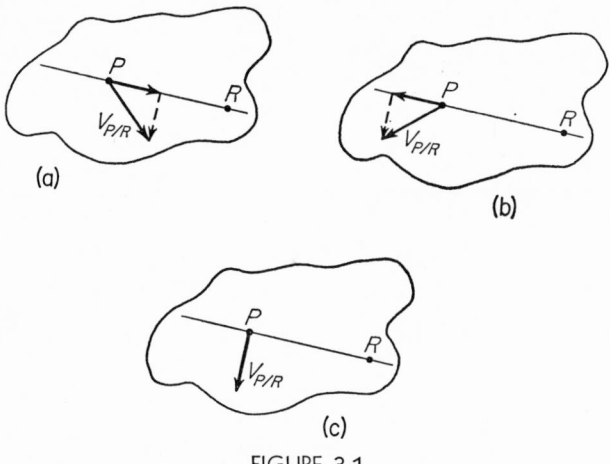

(a)

(b)

(c)

FIGURE 3.1

the velocity of P with respect to R with a component away from R. In this case the distance between the two points would have to be increasing, so again the definition of a rigid body is not satisfied, and there cannot be a component away from point R. Then, since the point P cannot have a velocity component relative to point R along the line joining P and R, the relative velocity of P with respect to R must be perpendicular to the line joining the two points, as shown in Fig. 3.1(c). In the same manner we can show that the velocity of point R with respect to point P must be perpendicular to the line joining the two points, and the same must be true for any two points on the body.

3.3 The Concept of Instant Centers

Consider the two bodies, "a" and "b," shown in Fig. 3.2, where body "b" is moving with plane motion relative to body "a," which is fixed. The illustration shows the two bodies at their relative positions at some instant of time. Two points P and R on body "b" have velocities relative to the fixed body, the direction of which is shown by the vectors (unbounded as to magnitude) shown in the figure as V_P and V_R. If a line m–n is drawn on body "b" so as to pass through point P and be perpendicular to V_P, we know from the preceding paragraph that all points on the line m–n must have a velocity relative to P, perpendicular to the line m–n. Then, since the absolute velocity of point P is perpendicular to line m–n, the absolute velocity of all points along the line must be normal to that line. In the same manner we can show that the absolute velocity of all points on line s–r, which is also on body "b" and perpendicular to V_R, are perpendicular to the line s–r. The point where lines m–n and s–r intersect is in the peculiar position of having to have an absolute velocity in two directions, one normal

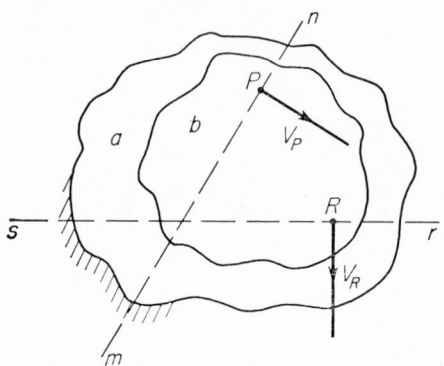

FIGURE 3.2

to each of the two intersecting lines. Obviously the point cannot have a velocity relative to the fixed body in two directions, and in order to satisfy the conditions stated above it must have zero absolute velocity. Then, having no velocity relative to the fixed body "a," it is the point on body "a" about which body "b" is rotating at the instant considered. This point is then the instantaneous center of rotation of body "b" relative to body "a." Inversely, it is the instant center of body "a" relative to body "b."

If body "a," in Fig. 3.2, is not fixed, the same analysis can be made concerning bodies "a" and "b" and the instant center of the two bodies will still be located in the same manner. In this case the instant center would not be fixed in space but would be a point at which the two bodies have no relative motion.

The definition of an instant center can then be stated as follows: when two bodies have plane relative motion, the instant center common to the two bodies is the point in the plane of motion about which each body rotates relative to the other body at the instant considered; or, the instant center is the point at which two bodies have no relative velocity at the instant considered. This definition should be thoroughly understood because it will be referred to quite often in succeeding chapters.

Another example of the location of an instant center is shown in Fig. 3.3. Here the instant center lies outside the boundaries of the bodies as outlined in the figure, but when we recall that kinematically the bodies extend indefinitely in all directions in the plane of motion, the instant center is still a point on both the bodies and both parts of the definition apply in all cases.

At times one part of the definition will be more convenient for our purposes than the other part, and we will use whichever best serves our purpose, remembering that both parts actually define the same thing.

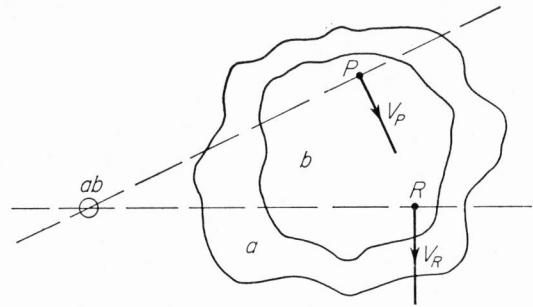

FIGURE 3.3

An instant center will be labeled with the two lower case letters of the bodies for which it is a common center, and the point will be circled as shown by instant center "*ab*" in Fig. 3.3. For all mechanisms there will be an instant center common to each link in combination with any other link of the mechanism, and the total number of instant centers for every mechanism is given by the equation

$$\text{number instant centers} = \frac{n(n-1)}{2} \qquad (3.1)$$

where n is the number of links in the mechanism.

3.4 Location of Instant Centers for Simple Mechanisms

We are now ready to determine the location of instant centers for a mechanism. First we will take the common, simple, mechanisms and find all the instant centers by use of the definition, and then develop a theorem which will simplify the finding of instant centers for more complex mechanisms.

A quadric crank mechanism is shown in Fig. 3.4(a), and all the instant centers are listed in the center of the figure. We immediately see that the pin joints between the various links satisfy the definition of an instant center as the point about which one body rotates with respect to another body, and therefore they are the instant centers for the links which they connect. The four instant centers "*ab*," "*bc*," "*cd*," and "*ad*" are located in this manner and labeled as shown in Fig. 3.4(a). A box is drawn about the instant centers in the list that have been located, and we see that there are two instant centers, "*ac*" and "*bd*," yet to be determined. We will locate the instant center *"ac"* first. If we consider instant center *"bc,"* we know that it is a point on link *"b"* and also a point on link *"c."* Its velocity

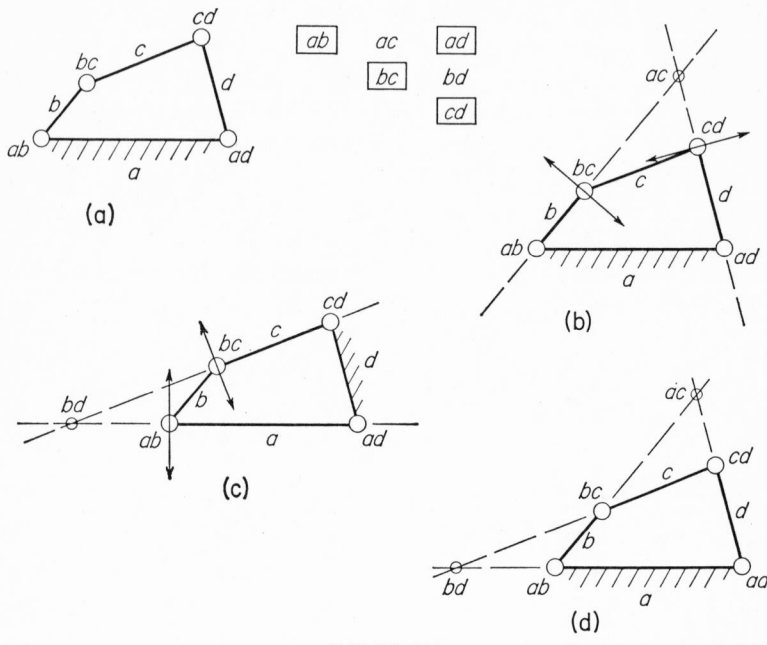

FIGURE 3.4

relative to the fixed body must be normal to the line joining it and the instant center *"ab"* common to link *"b"* and the fixed link *"a,"* as shown by the vectors in Fig. 3.4(b). In the same manner the velocity of instant center *"cd"* must be normal to the line joining *"cd"* and *"ad"* as shown. Knowing the direction of the velocity of two points on link *"c"* with respect to link *"a,"* we draw lines normal to these two velocities (dashed lines in the figure), the lines lying on link *"c."* The point at which these two lines meet must be the point about which the link *"c"* rotates with respect to link *"a,"* and this point is the instant center *"ac."*

In order to locate *"bd"* in the same manner, link *"d"* will be made the fixed link instead of link *"a."* This is called an inversion of the original mechanism. An inversion of a mechanism will not alter the relative motion of the links with respect to each other, but will change the absolute motion of the links, since a different link is fixed. Also, the positions of the instant centers will not be altered since the instant centers are determined by the relative motion of the links for any given phase position of the mechanism. Going now through an analysis similar to that we used to find instant center *"ac,"* we can find instant center *"bd,"* as shown in Fig. 3.4(c). Figure

3.4(d) shows the mechanism with all the instant centers located for the instant of time at which the mechanism is in the position shown.

Referring again to Fig. 3.4(d), it will be noted that the instant centers "ab," "bc," "cd," and "ad," which are located at the pin joints, are always located at the same point on the various links regardless of the phase position of the mechanism. Such instant centers are called permanent instant centers. The instant centers "ab" and "ad" are always at the same position in the plane of motion and are called fixed instant centers. The other two instant centers "ac" and "bd" change positions on their respective links and also change positions in space with time, as the phase position changes, and could be called transient instant centers.

As another example of a simple mechanism consider the slider crank

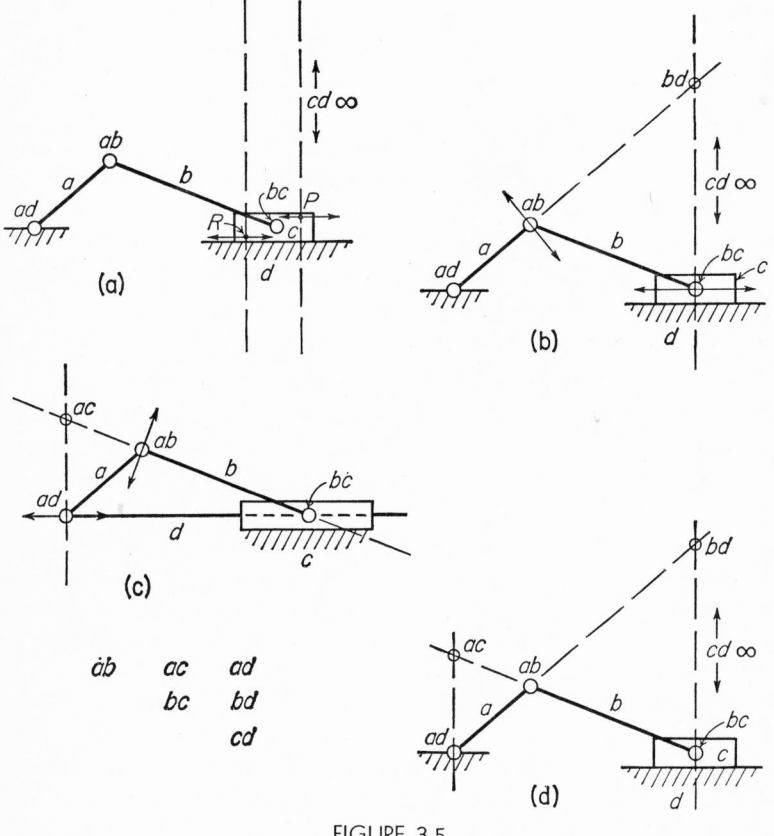

FIGURE 3.5

mechanism shown in Fig. 3.5(a). The three pin joints determine the permanent instant centers "ad," "ab," and "bc." The instant center "cd" can be found in the following manner: since the link "c" moves with rectilinear translation relative to the fixed link "d," any two points on link "c" have a velocity relative to the fixed body in the same direction as shown by the velocity of points P and R in the figure. If lines normal to their direction of velocity are drawn through each point, we find that the instant center will lie at the point where these two lines intersect. Since these two lines are parallel, they never intersect; or, since infinity can be defined as the point where two parallel lines intersect, the lines intersect at infinity, and the instant center "cd" lies at infinity on either line. At first thought it might seem that an instant center lying at infinity along a line is at an indefinite position, but its position is just as definitely located as one which we can show as a point on the plane of motion, since an instant center at infinity indicates that the two links common to it have translation relative to each other. We therefore know the relative motion of the two links. It is also a point through which we can draw a line from any given point by drawing the line parallel to a line on which the instant center lies. Such an instant center is indicated by putting the letters of the instant center along a line on which it lies and drawing arrows along the line from the letters with an infinity sign beside the letters as shown in the figure. Instant center "bd" can be found by noting the velocity of the two instant centers "ab" and "bc" on link "b," as shown in Fig. 3.5(b), and drawing lines perpendicular to these velocities. The point at which these lines meet will be instant center "bd." Note that instant center "cd" lies at infinity along the vertical line passing through the instant centers "bc" and "bd."

In order to find the instant center "ac," an inversion of the mechanism will again be used as shown in Fig. 3.5(c), with link "c" as the fixed link. Link "d," in the inversion, has been indicated as a rod sliding through link "c," giving rectilinear translation between links "c" and "d." The velocities of the instant centers "ab" and "ad" relative to link "c" will then determine the instant center "ac." Fig. 3.5(d) shows the mechanism with all the instant centers located.

3.5 Special Cases of Instant Centers

In the example discussed in Article 3.4 we found that a pin joint between two links was always the instant center common to the links connected by the pin joint. This is always true since a turning pair satisfies the definition of an instant center. Therefore, for any mechanism, the instant centers common to the links which are paired with a turning pair can be immediately located at the pin joints.

Also we found in the preceding Article that for a link having rectilinear translation relative to another link the instant center common to the two links was at infinity along a line perpendicular to the direction of relative motion between the two links. Then for all cases in which two links have relative motion of rectilinear translation, the instant centers common to the two links can be located with no preliminary construction.

There is another special case in which the instant center common to two links can be found directly by use of the definition. This is the case of rolling contact. From the definition of rolling contact as given in Chapter 2, the two bodies in rolling contact have no relative motion at the point of contact, and this coincides with the definition of an instant center. Therefore, the point of contact is the instant center common to two links in rolling contact.

Another special case which should be considered is the case of two bodies in higher sliding contact. In this case we will not be able to locate the instant center directly, but will be able to determine a line on which the instant center lies, and in a later Article we will find means of determining another line on which the instant center lies and these two lines will be sufficient to determine the instant center.

Consider the two links "a" and "b" in Fig. 3.6, which are in sliding

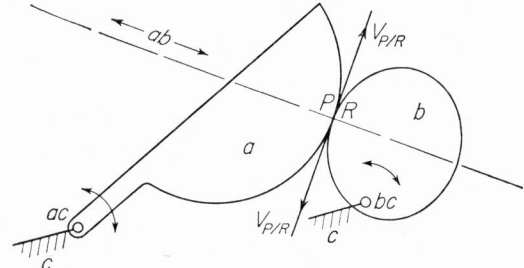

FIGURE 3.6

contact. The points in contact are point P on link "a" and R on link "b." The relative velocity of P with respect to R must be along the common tangent at the point of contact for the following reasons. If P had a component of velocity, relative to R, normal to the tangent line and with a sense towards R, an instant later it would have pushed into link "b." Since link "b" is a rigid body, this is impossible. If point P had a component of velocity normal to the tangent line and with a sense away from R, the two links would be separating, and this would be opposed to the definition of a kinematic mechanism. Therefore the relative velocity between the two points must be along the common tangent, as shown in the figure. Then, since we know the velocity of a point on link "a" relative to a point on link "b," the instant center "ab" will lie somewhere on the line normal to the velocity and be passing through the point P or the contact point. We indicate that the instant center lies along the line by placing the letters "ab" adjacent to the line and directing arrows from the letters along the line as shown in the figure.

3.6 Kennedy's Theorem

The determination of instant centers for complex mechanisms by the methods used for simple mechanisms would be a long and tedious process, impossible in many instances. We will now develop a theorem that greatly simplifies the location of instant centers and makes it possible to find centers which would be very difficult to locate otherwise. This theorem is known as Kennedy's theorem, which can be stated as follows: if three bodies are moving with relative plane motion, the three instant centers for the three bodies lie on a straight line. As a proof of this theorem, we will show that the three instant centers cannot lie anywhere except on a straight line.

Figure 3.7 shows the three bodies "*a*," "*b*," and "*c*" which have plane relative motion. The instant centers "*ab*" and "*ac*" are located in the figure

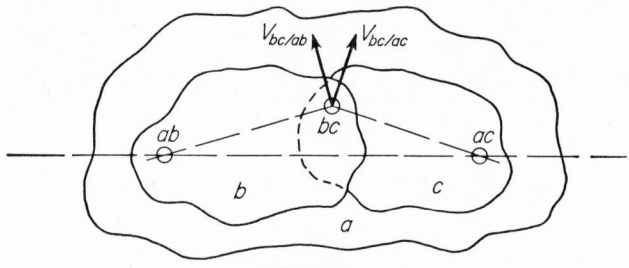

FIGURE 3.7

and we will assume that the third center "*bc*" lies at some point not on the line joining the other two. If "*bc*" is considered a point on link "*b*," it will have a velocity, relative to link "*a*," normal to the line joining the instant centers "*ab*" and "*bc*" since "*ab*" is the point about which every other point on link "*b*" rotates relative to link "*a*." Then if "*bc*" is a point on link "*c*" it will have a velocity normal to the line joining "*ac*" to "*bc*." This indicates that the point on "*b*" has a velocity in a direction different than that of the corresponding point on "*c*," and the two points have a relative velocity. If this be true, the point indicated as "*bc*" in the figure could not be the instant center "*bc*" because the definition states that an instant center is the point at which two bodies have no relative motion. The only points on the two links which can have no relative motion must then lie on the line joining "*ab*" and "*ac*," which proves the theorem. (We have not established where the instant center is located along the line, but we do know that it must lie on the line.)

Kennedy's theorem, along with the special cases discussed in the preceding Article, gives us sufficient information to locate all the instant centers for most plane mechanisms. In the case of links having higher sliding contact the use of Kennedy's theorem will provide us with another line which will determine the instant center.

3.7 Location of Instant Centers by Kennedy's Theorem

The use of Kennedy's theorem in the location of instant centers for complex mechanisms will be explained by the use of examples. As a first example we will use the shaper quick-return mechanism shown in Fig. 3.8

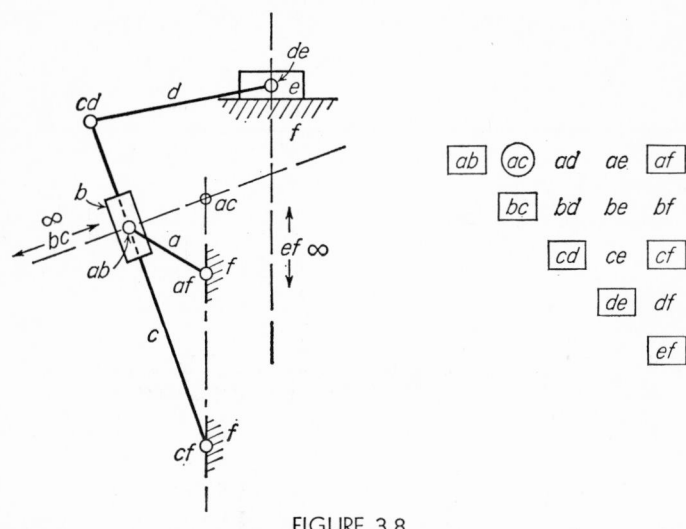

FIGURE 3.8

First we locate all the instant centers that can be found by means of the special cases. All the instant centers have been listed to the right of the drawing and those instant centers which can be found by the special cases have been located on the drawing and boxes drawn about the corresponding ones on the list. Then, remembering that two intersecting lines locate a point, we will find two lines on which an instant center, which we wish to locate, lies. Suppose we try to locate instant center "ac." From Kennedy's theorem we know it lies on the line joining the following pairs of instant centers: "ab" and "bc"; "ad" and "cd"; "ae" and "ce"; and "af" and "cf." From the list of instant centers we find that only two of the pairs have been located and are available for use; "ab"–"bc" and "af"–"cf". Drawing lines through these points we locate the center "ac" at the intersection of the lines, as shown in the figure, and then circle that instant center in the list, indicating it has been located and can be used in locating other instant centers. It should be noted that if we had picked some of the instant centers we would not have sufficient centers to locate it, center "ae" for example. We could continue in this manner and find all the remaining instant centers, since each center we locate makes another one available for use in finding other centers. However, such a process is tedious and requires considerable time. We will develop a system which can be used to simplify the selection of instant centers which can be found, by using those which we have already located, and also a tabulation method that will immediately show us which instant centers we need in order to determine the lines on which other centers lie.

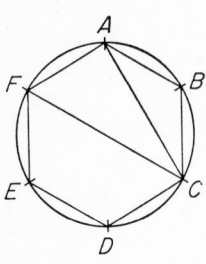

FIGURE 3.9

An excellent system for this purpose is a diagram called the circle diagram. A circle is drawn and points are evenly spaced around the periphery of the circle, one for each link of the mechanism, and each point labeled with capital letters to correspond to the links, as shown in Fig. 3.9. The diagram in the figure corresponds to the quick-return mechanism in Fig. 3.8. Now when an instant center is found a line is drawn between the letters corresponding to that instant center. For the mechanism in Fig. 3.8 we have found eight of the instant centers and we draw the lines AB, AC, BC, CD, DE, EF, CF, and AF on the circle as shown. All these instant centers except "ac" were found by special cases. If we inspect the circle diagram we notice that the line AC, corresponding to instant center "ac," completes two triangles on the diagram, triangles ABC and AFC. Considering triangle ABC, we see that the three legs of the triangle are AB, BC, and AC, corresponding to the instant centers. From Kennedy's theorem we know that center "ac" lies on the line joining "ab" and "bc" and we see that when we complete a triangle on the diagram, with a line, the other two legs of the triangle determine a line on which the instant center, corresponding to the line, lies. In the same manner line AC completes the triangle AFC and instant center "ac" lies on the line joining the instant centers "af" and "cf" corresponding to the other two legs of the triangle. By checking other lines on the diagram we will find that those that complete a triangle also locate legs of the triangle (or instant centers) which determine the instant centers corresponding to the line picked. Then we see that when we can draw a line completing two triangles, the instant center corresponding to that line can be located on the mechanism. In the figure, then, we can complete two triangles with lines BF, DF, and EC, indicating that we can find those centers. It is usually advisable to draw the line dashed until the instant center has been found and then make it a solid line, since we will find that in some instances the two lines corresponding to the legs of the completed triangles are collinear and therefore not sufficient to determine the instant center; or one of the centers may lie off the paper. In cases of the latter type other instant centers must be found before the one desired can be located.

Figure 3.10 shows the shaper quick-return mechanism with all the instant centers, except "ae," and the circle diagram corresponding to the figure. On the circle diagram the line AE has been drawn with dashed lines and we see that it completes not only the two triangles necessary for the location of the corresponding instant center but the four triangles AFE,

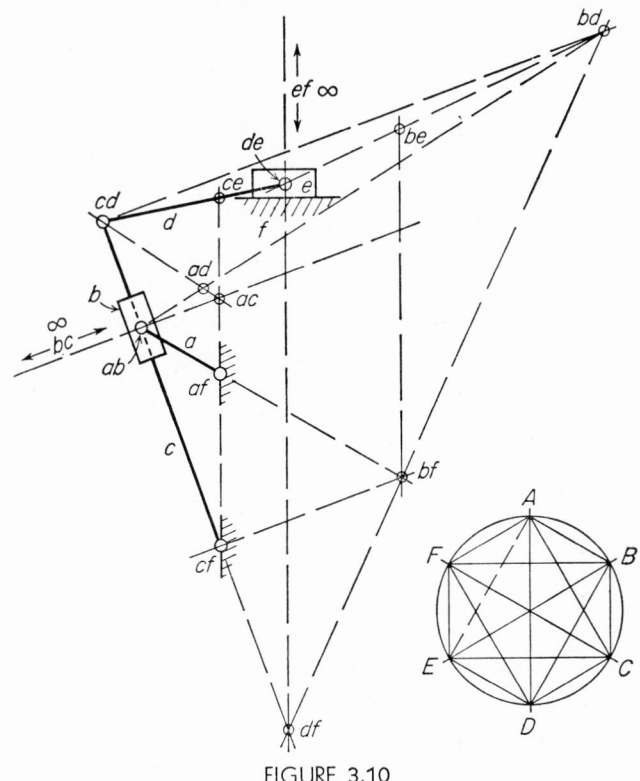

FIGURE 3.10

ABE, ACE, and ADE. This means that there are four lines on which the instant center "ae" lies, and they must all intersect at the same point at which the instant center is located. We can use these lines to check the accuracy of the instant center locations, because if they do not all pass through the instant center "ae," there is an error in the location of some of the instant centers. It should be noted that the lines determined by the two triangles AFE and ACE are collinear and do not determine the location of the instant center.

As another example of the location of instant centers we will use the mechanism shown in Fig. 3.11 which contains two higher sliding pairs and a rolling pair. All the instant centers which can be found by use of the special cases have been located and the lines indicating they have been located have been drawn on the circle diagram. Special attention should be paid to the instant center "cd" at the point of rolling contact between links "c" and "d." The two sliding pairs are between links "b" and "c" and links "*a*" and "*b*." For these two cases we draw lines through the points of contact, normal to the common tangent, and indicate that the instant centers lie on these lines; however we do not know where on these lines the instant

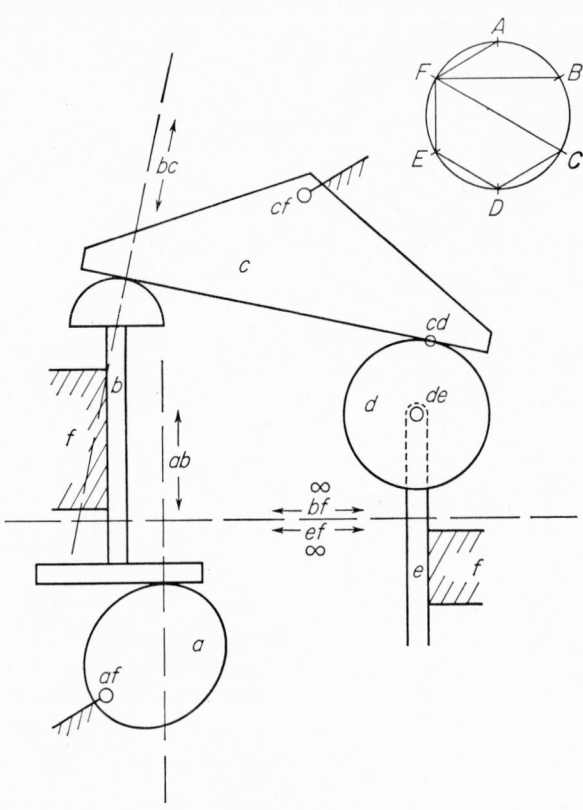

FIGURE 3.11

centers lie. Therefore we cannot draw lines on the circle diagram indicating they have been found. Considering instant center "*bc*" first, we see that if the line *BC* is drawn on the circle diagram it will complete only one triangle, *BFC*, indicating that the center lies on the line joining instant centers "*bf*" and "*cf*." But this line joining "*bf*" and "*cf*," together with the line on which we know "*bc*" lies from the case of sliding contact, is sufficient to determine the location of the center. In the same manner we see that the line *AB* will complete a triangle, giving us another line on which instant center "*ab*" lies. With this line we can locate the center "*ab*." The student should try to complete the location of all the instant centers for the mechanism and circle diagram as shown in Fig. 3.11 without taking advantage of the two lines found by the special cases of sliding contact. It will be found that only the instant centers "*df*" and "*ce*" can be located under such conditions.

The student should now sketch the mechanism in Fig. 3.11 on a sheet of paper and locate all the instant centers. Fig. 3.12 shows the mechanism with all the instant centers located. The instant centers "*be*" and "*ad*" lie

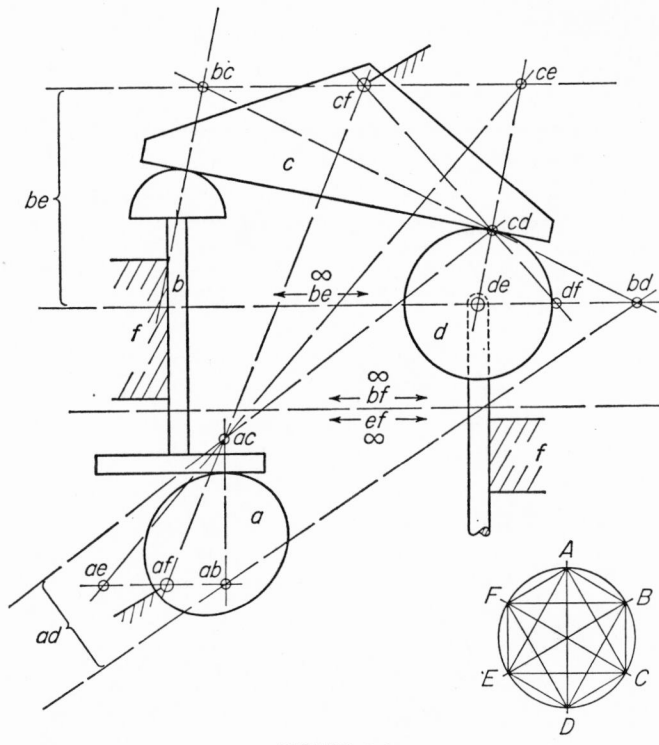

FIGURE 3.12

off of the paper at the left and are indicated as being at the intersection of the two lines by a brace between the two lines, the labels "*be*" and "*ad*" placed at the center of the braces. On further examination we see that the lines determining the location of center "*be*" both contain the instant center "*ef*" which lies at infinity. Therefore they must be parallel and we can say that instant center "*be*" lies along either line at infinity. We should not assume that if an instant center lies at the intersection of two lines which *look* as if they are parallel it follows that the center is at infinity. We must be able to prove that the lines are parallel before we consider that the instant center lies at infinity.

The above methods can be used to locate most of the instant centers for any mechanism. In a few special cases other methods must be used. Such methods will be pointed out in a later chapter.

3.8 Centrodes

If the location of instant centers for a mechanism were an end point in itself, we would have gained an important concept of motion—the idea that any body in plane motion can be considered to be rotating relative to any other body about some point on both bodies, at which point the bodies have no relative motion. We would also have discovered the fascinating pastime of locating instant centers. However these are not sufficient reasons for devoting a chapter to this process. In this section we will find a use for instant centers in developing rolling surfaces for two links in a mechanism, and in the next chapter we will use instant centers in the determination of velocities in mechanisms. We will also find the idea of instant centers useful in the study of other subjects to be taken up later.

If we plot the locus of one of the movable, permanent, instant centers of a quadric crank mechanism on a fixed body (the paper on which the mechanism is drawn), the path which the instant center follows as the phase position changes is called a centrode. The centrodes of the moving permanent instant centers will be circles with centers at the fixed instant centers, as shown in Fig. 3.13. These particular centrodes have no importance except

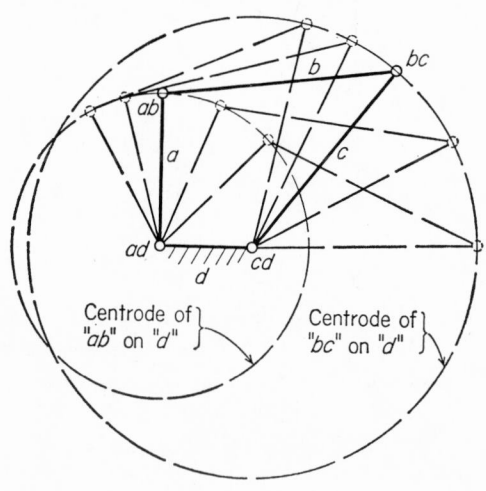

FIGURE 3.13

as a means of defining the term centrode. But the centrodes for the non-permanent instant centers can serve a useful purpose. Consider the centrode of instant center "bd" on link "d" for the same mechanism shown in Fig. 3.14. The locus of the same instant center "bd" on link "b" can be

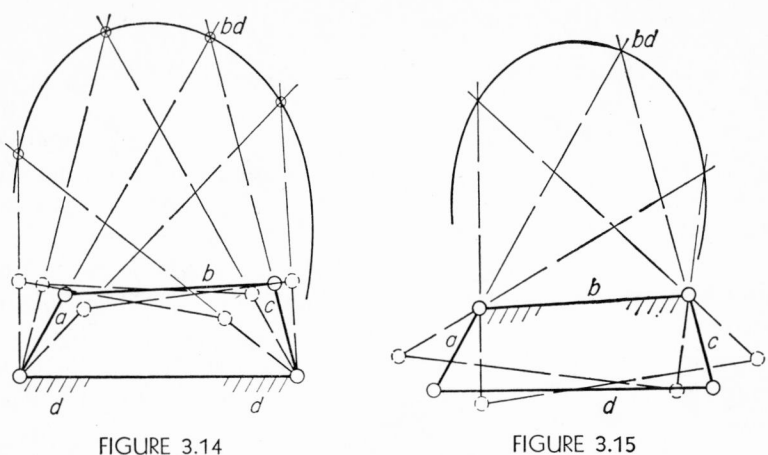

FIGURE 3.14   FIGURE 3.15

drawn by inverting the mechanism and fixing link "*b*" as shown in Fig. 3.15. By attaching the centrode of "*bd*" on "*b*" to the link "*b*" so that it shows as a part of the link, we can show both centrodes on the same drawing, as in Fig. 3.16. Then, since by definition of the instant center the two bodies are

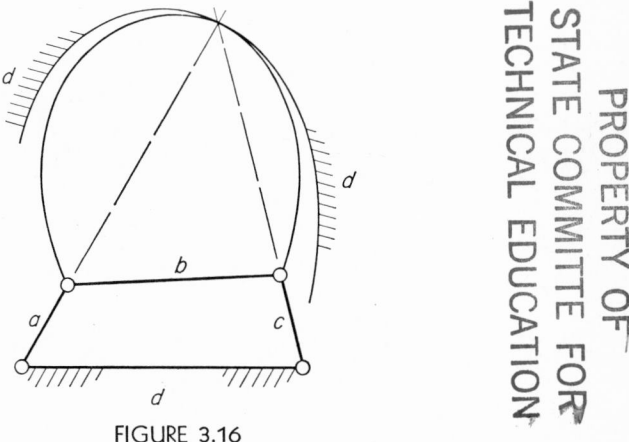

FIGURE 3.16

in rolling contact at all points along the centrodes, we can have the same relative motion of the two links by eliminating the links "*a*" and "*c*" and having the links contoured along the centrode, with one rolling relative to the other along the centrodes. We can assure pure rolling by putting gear teeth along the two contours of the centrode. In this way we can get the same relative motion by using an entirely different mechanism. In some cases this will prove an advantage over the pin jointed mechanism. Particularly will this be useful in the layout of disc cams so as to give rolling

contact rather than sliding contact. Figures 3.17(a) and 3.17(b) show a
comparison of two equivalent disc cams having the same relative motion,
one with sliding contact and the other with rolling contact achieved by the

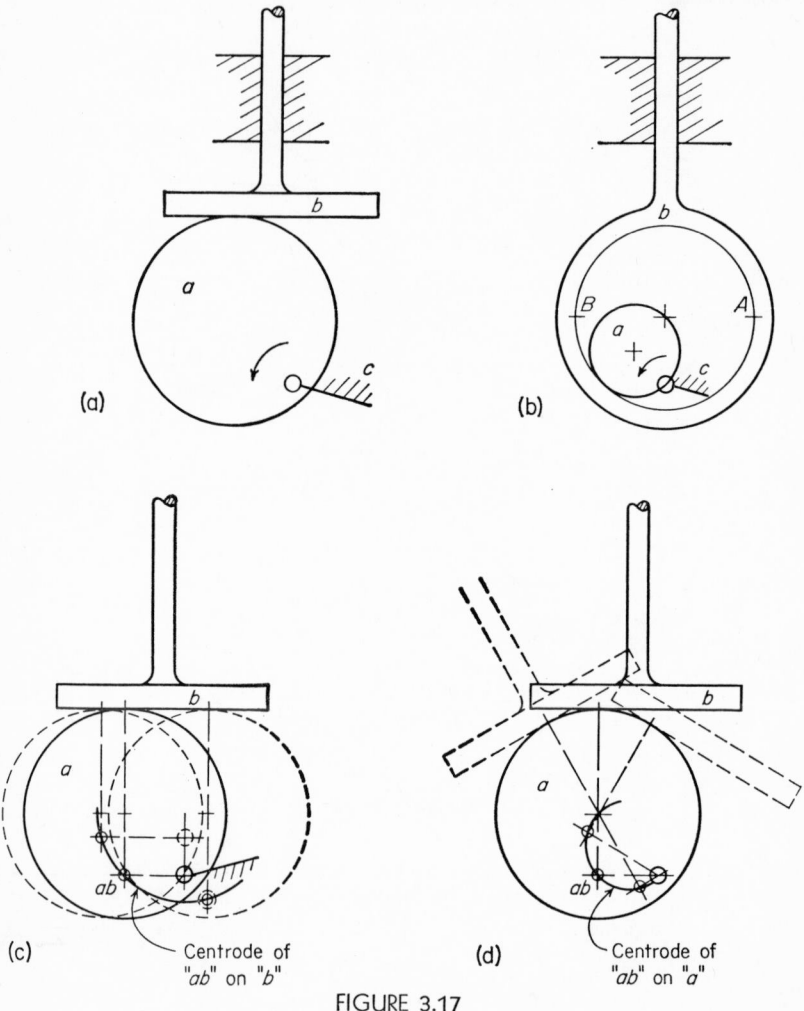

FIGURE 3.17

use of centrodes. It should be noted that the equivalent cam and follower
in Fig. 3.17(b) would not be practical for a complete cycle of the driving
link "a" since slippage will occur at points A and B if any force is exerted on
link "b." However, the mechanism would be satisfactory for small oscillations of link "a" so long as the points A and B are not approached. Figures
3.17(c) and 3.17(d) show the construction of the centrodes for mechanism
(a) from which mechanism (b) is made.

PROBLEMS

3.1 Locate all instant centers of velocity for the mechanism in Fig. P3.1.

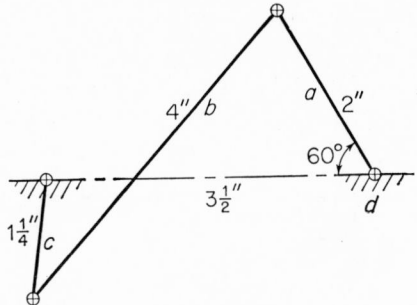

FIGURE P3.1

3.2 Locate all instant centers for the mechanism in Fig. P3.2.

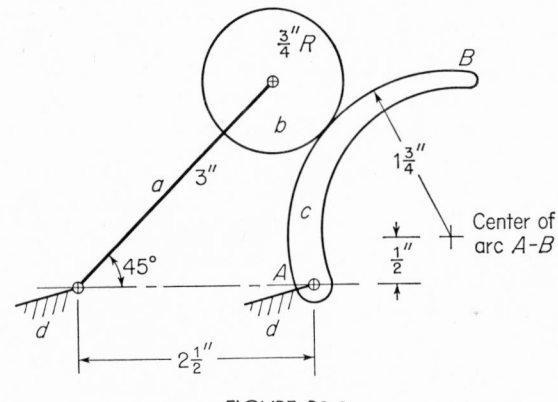

FIGURE P3.2

3.3 Locate all instant centers for the mechanisms in Fig. P4.1, P4.2, P4.3, P4.4, P4.5, P4.6, P4.7, P4.8, P4.9, P4.10, P4.11, P4.12, P4.13, and P4.14.

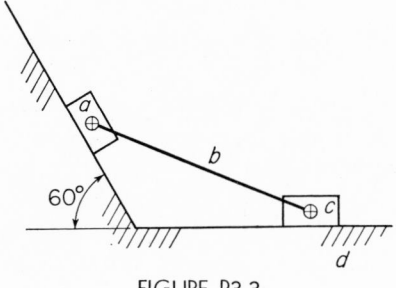

FIGURE P3.3

3.4 Plot the centrode of instant center "bd" on link "d" for the slider crank mechanism in Fig. 3.5, letting link "a" be $1\frac{1}{4}$ in. long and link "b" $2\frac{1}{2}$ in. long. Plot only for 90° of motion of link "a," 45° to either side of that phase position in which "a" is horizontal towards the slider.

3.5 Plot the centrode of instant center "bd" on link "b" for the same mechanism as in Problem 3.4 and for the same motion of link "a."

3.6 Draw a two link mechanism that will have the same relative motion with rolling contact as the relative motion of link "b" to link "d" in Fig. P3.3 by use of centrodes.

Chapter 4

Velocity Analysis by Use of Instant Centers

4.1 Velocity of Points on a Rigid Body in Rotation

Consider the rigid body "a" shown in Fig. 4.1, rotating relative to the fixed body "b" about point O, with angular velocity ω_a. Point O then is the

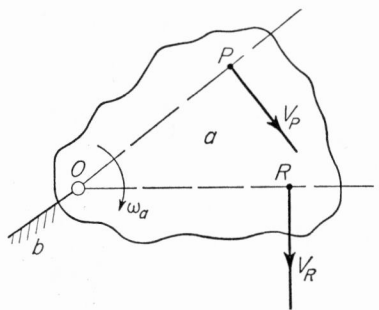

FIGURE 4.1

instant center "ab." The points P and R on body "a" have velocities relative to the fixed body in a direction normal to the lines joining the respective points with the instant center "ab," as shown in the figure. The magnitudes of these velocities can be determined by the relations developed in Chapter 1. Since the points are on a rigid body, the radius vector from the center of rotation to any point is fixed in magnitude, and the velocity for any point is given by the equation

$$V = \omega_a r \tag{4.1}$$

where r is the radius to any point from the center of rotation. From this

relation the absolute velocity of any point on a body or link can be determined if the angular velocity of the body relative to the fixed body is known,
together with the location of the instant center with respect to the fixed
body; or, if the velocity of any point and the location of the instant center is
known, the angular velocity of the body can be determined, and thereby the
velocity of any other point on the body can be found.

The velocity of points on a rigid body can be found graphically if the
instant center common with the fixed body is known and the velocity of any
point is known. Fig. 4.2 shows a rigid body with point P, the velocity of

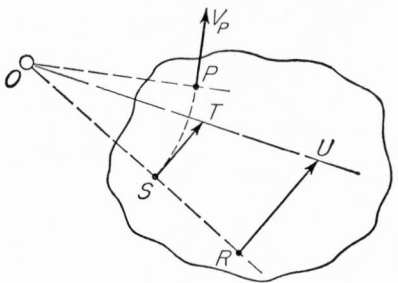

FIGURE 4.2

which is known, and point R, the velocity of which is to be found. Point O
is the instant center with respect to the fixed body. Point R must have a
velocity perpendicular to the line joining it with the instant center (since it
is rotating about the instant center). Any point on the line O–R will have a
velocity in the same direction and of a magnitude proportional to its distance from the instant center O. All points on the body which are the same
distance from the instant center will have the same velocity magnitude as
shown by Eq. (4.1). Then if we rotate the velocity vector of point P about
the instant center O until the tail of the vector lies at S on the line O–R, the
velocity vector in this position will give us the velocity of point S. If now a
line is drawn through the instant center O and the end of the velocity
vector, point T, as shown in the figure, and a vector is drawn perpendicular
to O–R from point R to the line O–T extended, meeting the line at U, this
vector will represent the velocity of point R. We can show that the vector
$\overline{RU}$ has the correct magnitude by noting that the two triangles TOS and
UOR are similar, and therefore the ratio of the magnitude of the vector $\overline{RU}$
to the magnitude of the vector $\overline{ST}$ is equal to the ratio of the distance O–R
to the distance O–S, which are respectively the distances of points R and S
from the center of rotation. Therefore the ratio of the velocities of the two
points as shown by the vectors are proportional to their distance from the
center of rotation as is required by Eq. (4.1).

4.2 *Direct Method of Velocity Determination*

We will now use this graphical method to determine the velocity of points in a mechanism. Again we will start with a simple mechanism in order to establish the method and then progress to more complicated ones. Consider the quadric crank mechanism in Fig. 4.3 with the crank or driving

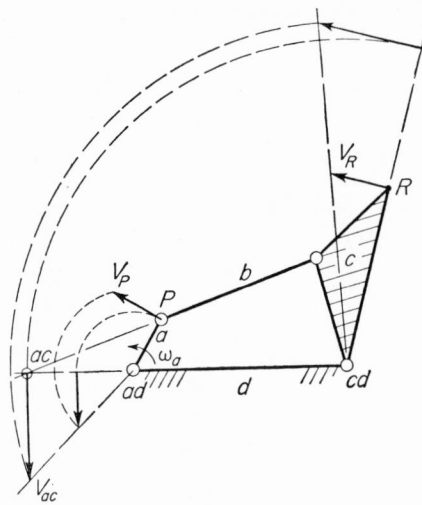

FIGURE 4.3

member, link "a," turning with angular velocity ω. The velocity of point R on link "c" is to be determined. With the angular velocity of link "a" known, the linear velocity of any point on link "a" can be determined by use of Eq. (4.1). The velocity of point P, which is the instant center common to links "a" and "b," can be calculated and a vector representing the velocity is drawn to some given scale on the figure from point P, as shown. The direction of this velocity vector, V_P, is normal to the line joining point P and the instant center common to link "a" and the fixed link "d." If we can find the velocity of any point on link "c," the velocity of any other point on link "c" can be determined as explained in the previous Article. Since the instant center "ac" is a point on link "c" which has the same absolute velocity as a coincident point on link "a," if we find the velocity of "ac" we have the velocity of a point on link "c." The vector V_P is rotated about instant center "ad" until the tail of the vector lies on the line joining centers "ad" and "ac." Then drawing a line through "ad" and the head of the vector in its rotated position, we determine the velocity of "ac" by triangulation, as explained previously. Now, having the velocity of a point on link "c," we can find the velocity of point R by the same method, this time rotating the vector V_{ac}.

As another example we will use the quick-return mechanism shown in Fig. 4.4. We have given the angular velocity of the crank "a" and wish to

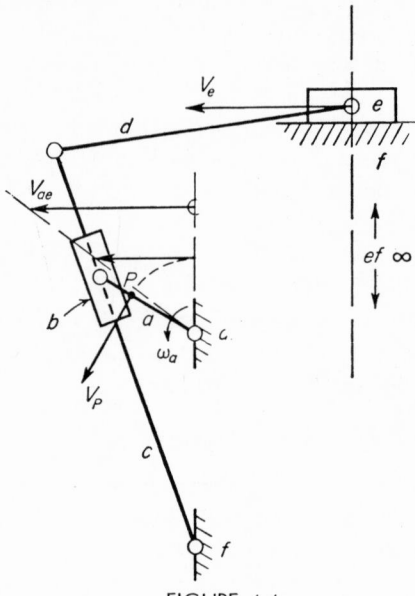

FIGURE 4.4

find the velocity of the slider "e." In the interest of clarity only the instant centers needed for the determination of the slider velocity are shown on the figure. These centers are "af," "ae," and "ef." The center "af" gives us the point about which the link "a" is rotating with respect to the fixed body. With the angular velocity of link "a" known we can determine both in magnitude and direction the velocity of any point on link "a." Instant center "ae" is the point at which both links "a" and "e" have the same velocity and center "ef" gives us the point about which link "e" is rotating with respect to the fixed link.

By calculation we determine the velocity of any point on link "a," say point P, and draw the velocity vector representing the velocity of P to some scale at point P. Rotating this vector until the tail lies on the line joining "af" and "ae" we find we can draw a vector representing the velocity of center "ae" by triangulation, as shown in Fig. 4.2 Since the instant center "ef" lies at infinity, all points on link "e" have the same velocity and therefore the velocity of center "ae" is the velocity of the slider. A vector V_e, of the same magnitude and direction as V_{ae} can be drawn from the slider, as shown in the figure.

An enterprising person might now ask why we didn't calculate the velocity of the instant center "ae" instead of point P since the calculation requires the same amount of effort but the graphical work is eliminated. If the velocity of the slider were all that we wished to determine this would

indeed be the logical way of handling the problem, but here we are presenting the general method of determining the velocity of a point on a link if the
velocity of a point on another link is known. Also we usually will be interested in the velocity of other points on various links and in this case only one
calculation need be made; the other velocities can be determined   graphically.

The direct method is generally the most straightforward and simplest
method of determining velocities by the use of instant centers, if the instant
centers are readily available.   However it should be pointed out that the
particular instant centers needed in order to use this method are sometimes
difficult to find and in some cases will lie off the paper on which the construction is being made.   In the mechanism shown in Fig. 4.4 the instant
center "*ae*" is one of the last ones we can find (see Fig. 3.10) and a method
not requiring that particular center might be simpler.   Such a method will
be taken up in the following Articles.

4.3 Transfer Method of Velocity Determination

In the transfer method of determining velocities we will proceed from
the link on which the velocity of a point is known to the next adjoining link
in the chain, and progress thus from link to adjacent link until we get to
that link which contains the point whose velocity we wish to determine.
Consider the mechanism shown in Fig 4.5.   The velocity of point P on link

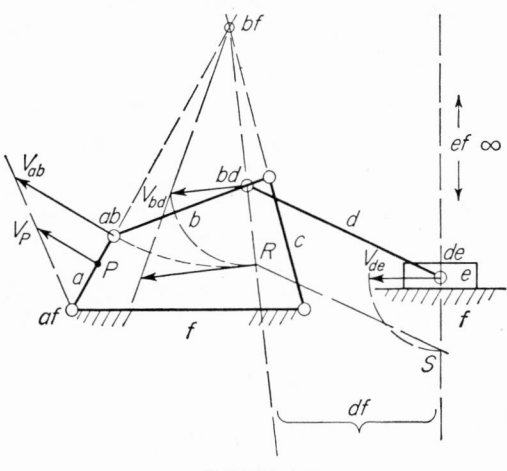

FIGURE 4.5

"a" is known and we wish to determine the velocity of the slider "e." We
will proceed from link "a" to link "b" then to link "d" and finally to a point
on link "e."

Having the velocity of a point on link "a" we find the velocity of a point
on link "b." The velocity of instant center "ab," being a point on both links

"*a*" and "*b*" where they have no relative velocity, can be found by triangulation as shown and now we have the velocity of a point on link "*b*." Next we find the velocity of a point on link "*d*," and the velocity of instant center "*bd*" can now be found by rotating the vector V_{ab} about the center "*bf*." Then the velocity of "*bd*" can be found by triangulation. Now, having the velocity of one point on link "*d*," we can find the velocity of any other point on link "*d*" by rotation of the velocity vector V_{bd} about the common instant center between link "*d*" and the fixed link "*f*," or center "*df*." Since we wish to find the velocity of a point on link "*e*," we will find the velocity of instant center "*de*" by rotation of V_{bd} and triangulation. The velocity of "*de*" is the velocity of a point on link "*e*," and since link "*e*" moves with rectilinear translation (the instant center common with the fixed body being at infinity), all points on the link move with the same velocity and we have found the velocity of the slider.

This process has not been completed in Fig. 4.5 because the instant center "*df*" is not available as a center of rotation. Therefore we use another graphical means of obtaining the velocity of the center "*de*." The vector V_{bd} is rotated about the center "*bd*" until it lies on the line joining "*bd*" to "*df*," the head of the vector being at R and pointing towards "*df*." From the end of the vector a line is drawn parallel to the line joining "*bd*" and "*de*" until it intersects the line joining "*de*" and "*df*" at point S. The distance between "*de*" and point S represents the magnitude of the velocity of instant center "*de*." By rotating a vector from "*de*" to S clockwise about "*de*" until it is normal to the line joining "*de*" and "*df*," the vector represents the velocity of instant center "*de*."

This last construction needs some further explanation to show that the vector so found does represent the velocity of "*de*." The points "*bd*," "*de*," and "*df*" form a triangle and the points R, S and "*df*" form a similar triangle (all corresponding sides parallel). The magnitudes of the velocities of any two points on a body have been shown to be proportional to their distances from the instant center common to the body and the fixed body, or

$$\frac{V_{bd}}{V_{de}} = \frac{\overline{bd\text{-}df}}{\overline{de\text{-}df}}$$

From the similar triangles we can see that

$$\frac{\overline{bd\text{-}R}}{\overline{de\text{-}S}} = \frac{\overline{bd\text{-}df}}{\overline{de\text{-}df}}$$

and therefore

$$\frac{V_{bd}}{V_{de}} = \frac{\overline{bd\text{-}R}}{\overline{de\text{-}S}}$$

so that if the distance $\overline{bd\text{-}R}$ represents the magnitude of the velocity of "*bd*" the distance $\overline{de\text{-}S}$ represents the magnitude of the velocity of "*de*." This gives us a means of using an instant center even if it does not fall on the paper on which our work is being done.

4.4 The Resolution or Component Method of Velocity Determination

We will consider one other method of velocity determination by the use of instant centers which is quite useful and convenient in many cases. This method will be called the resolution, or component, method. We will make use of the concept of the relative velocity of two points on a rigid body as discussed in Article 3.2. It was shown there that the velocity of one point relative to another point on the same rigid body must be perpendicular to the line joining the two points. As a corollary to that statement we can say that two points on a rigid body must have the same absolute velocity in a direction along the line joining the two points. This gives us a means of determining the velocity of a point on a body if we know the direction of the velocity relative to the fixed body and the velocity of any other point on the body.

Figure 4.6 shows the general case of a rigid body or link in motion containing two points P and R. Point O is the instant center common to the

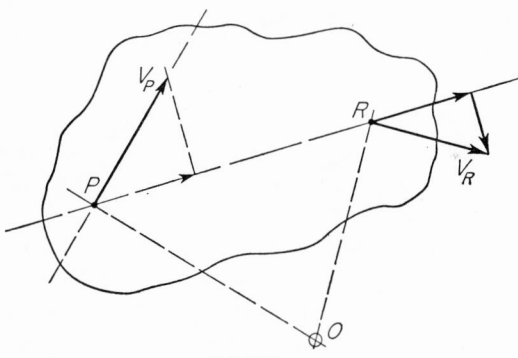

FIGURE 4.6

body and the fixed link. The velocity of R is given as shown in the figure. This vector will be broken into perpendicular components, one along the line joining P and R and one normal to that line. If we knew the velocity of point P, we could also break it up into perpendicular components, one along the line between P and R and the other normal to that line. If we did this, the component of P along the line would have to be of the same magnitude and direction as the component of R in the direction of the line. If P and R did not have the same component of velocity along this line the distance between the two points would be either increasing or decreasing, and this is impossible in a rigid body. Then if we draw a vector from P along the line in the same sense and of the same magnitude as the component of V_R along this line, we have one normal component of the velocity of P. The absolute velocity of P must be normal to the line from P to O and since we now have one perpendicular component of this velocity, if we draw a normal to the line P–R at the head of the component of V_P, this normal line will represent the other perpendicular component of the velocity of P and the point where it intersects the normal to the line O–P will determine the velocity of P with respect to the fixed link.

The resolution method will be used to determine the velocity of point P on link "c" in Fig. 4.7. The velocity of the instant center "ab" is known.

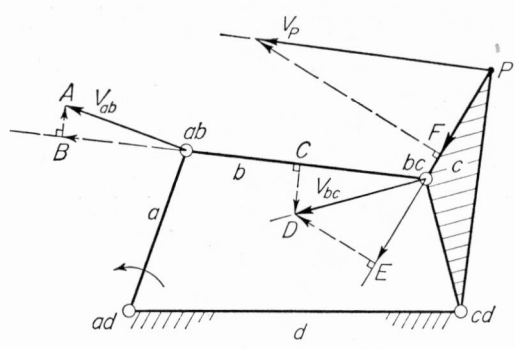

FIGURE 4.7

Since P is a point on link "c," we need to find the velocity of some point on link "c" and with this we can determine the velocity of P. Knowing the velocity of a point on link "b" we will be able to find the velocity of instant center "bc" and then the velocity of P. To find the velocity of "bc," the velocity of "ab" is resolved into two normal components, one along the line joining "ab" and "bc" (extended) and one normal to this line. These components are "ab"–B along the line and B–A normal to the line. The components of the velocity of "bc" along the line will be "bc"–C, equal in magnitude, and of the same sense, to vector "ab"–B. The absolute velocity of "bc" must be normal to line "bc"–"cd" and a line through C perpendicular to line "ab"–"bc" will intersect this normal at D. The vector "bc"–D will then be the velocity of "bc" and C–D is the component normal to line "ab"–"bc". The velocity of point P can now be found since it lies on the same link, link "c," that center "bc" is on. The component of V_{bc} along the line P–"bc" is determined as "bc"–E and the component of V_P along the same line is laid off as P–F. A normal to the line is drawn through F and the point where it intersects the line in the direction of V_P will determine the vector V_P.

Two points should be emphasized as a means of checking the construction and thereby reducing the possibility of error. One is that the component vectors are *always* smaller in magnitude than the absolute vector, and the other is that one component is always along the line joining the two points on the body and the other component is always perpendicular to that line.

Another example will show the advantage of the component method and lead to an interesting sidelight which will prove helpful. In Fig. 4.8, showing a quick-return mechanism, the angular velocity of the crank, link "a,"

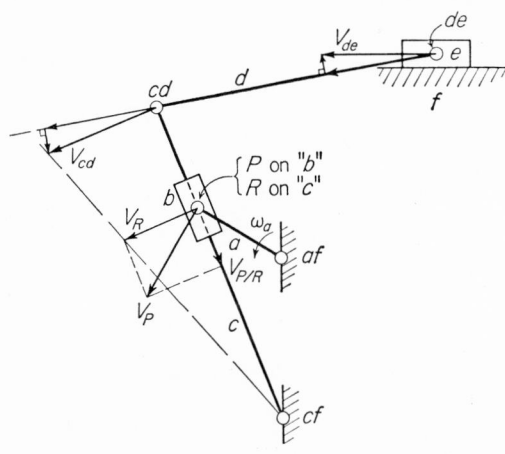

FIGURE 4.8

is given and the velocity of the instant center "ab" or point P can be calculated and laid out as shown. The velocity of the slide, link "e," is to be determined. This instant center, "ab," is labeled P on link "b" and a coincident point on link "c" is labeled R. Since the motion between links "b" and "c" is rectilinear translation, the velocity of P with respect to R must be in the direction of sliding, as shown in the figure. The absolute velocity of R must be perpendicular to the line R–"cf." Using the equation for the addition of vectors

$$V_P = V_R \mathbin{+\!\!\!\!+} V_{P/R}$$

these two vectors, V_P and V_R, can be constructed as shown. The velocity of the instant center "cd" will be found next, but it cannot be found by the component method because the velocity of R has no component along the line joining R and "cd." Therefore, the velocity of "cd" is found by triangulation. The velocity of the instant center "de" is then found by the component method as shown in the figure.

The component method can also be used to determine the velocity of points on links whose instant center with respect to the fixed body is not readily available. Fig. 4.9 shows a link with the velocities of the two points S and T known, and we wish to determine the velocity of point U. This

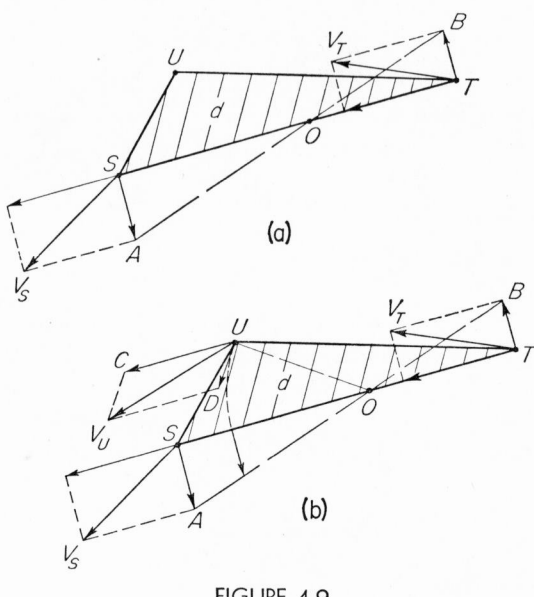

FIGURE 4.9

could be link "d" of Fig. 4.8. The velocities of points T and S are broken into their normal components along, and normal to, the line joining the two points, and the localized vectors are drawn as shown in Fig. 4.9(a). If we now draw a line connecting the heads of the component vectors which are normal to the line S–T, this line will cross line S–T at point O. Every point on line S–T will have a velocity component along that line of the same magnitude as the component of S or T, along the line, and a component normal to that line equal to the distance from the point to the line A–B. Then point O has no component normal to line S–T, and its total velocity will be along the line S–T. In Chapter 2 it was shown that the motion of any body consisted of a rotation and a translation, either of which could be zero. Therefore, we can consider the motion of the link in Fig. 4.9 to be a rotation about the point O and a translation in the direction of the line S–T and of the magnitude of all points along that line. The velocity of point U is then composed of a translation and a rotation about point O. The total velocity of U is then the vector sum of the translation vector $\overline{U\text{–}C}$ and the rotation vector $\overline{U\text{–}D}$, as shown in Fig. 4.9(b).

4.5 Angular Velocities of Links

Various methods have been presented for the determination of velocities of any given point on a body. We will now turn our attention to the determination of the angular velocities of the links in the mechanism. Quite often the angular velocities of the links are as important as the velocities of the various points.

If the velocity of any point on a link has been determined and the instant center of the link with respect to the fixed body has been located, the angular velocity of the link can be easily determined by direct calculation from Eq. (4.1) which can be rearranged as:

$$\omega = \frac{V}{r} \tag{4.2}$$

where ω is the absolute angular velocity of the link in radians per second, V is the velocity of any given point, and r is the distance from that point to the instant center common to the link and the fixed body. This follows from the definition of instant centers and the discussion of the angular velocity and linear velocity in Chapter 1.

A graphical method of determining the angular velocities of links can also be used, which does not depend on the location of the instant center common to the fixed link. Consider the three links "a," "b," and "c" in Fig. 4.10 with their common instant centers as shown. Link "c" is fixed and

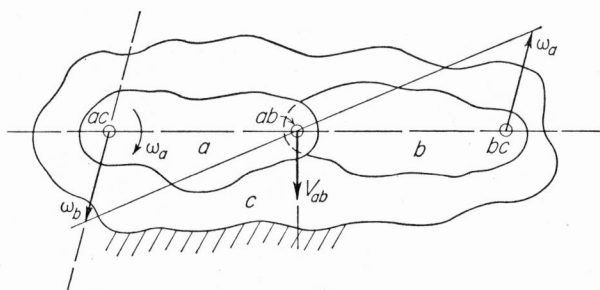

FIGURE 4.10

the angular velocity of link "a," ω_a, with respect to the fixed link is known. We will determine the angular velocity of link "b" graphically. The absolute velocity of center "ab" can be calculated from the equation

$$\omega_a = \frac{V_{ab}}{ab-ac} \tag{4.3}$$

We can also write a similar relation for link "b"

$$\omega_b = \frac{V_{ab}}{ab-bc} \tag{4.4}$$

Dividing Eq. (4.4) by Eq. (4.3)

$$\frac{\omega_b}{\omega_a} = \frac{\overline{ab-ac}}{\overline{ab-bc}} \qquad (4.5)$$

We see that the ratio of the angular velocities of the links is the inverse ratio of the distances from the common instant center to the respective centers common to the fixed link.

Referring again to Eq. (4.5), if we let the distance $\overline{ab-bc}$ represent to some scale the magnitude of ω_a, then the distance $\overline{ab-ac}$ will represent the magnitude of ω_b to the same scale. This has the disadvantage that the scale is fixed by the distances between instant centers and we cannot use a convenient scale of our choice.

To overcome this difficulty we will let these two distances be corresponding legs of two similar triangles and lay out the other leg of the triangles to represent the angular velocities to a chosen scale. This is most conveniently done as follows.

Through center "bc" draw a vector in some convenient direction representing, to the chosen scale, ω_a. Draw a line through center "ac" parallel to vector ω_a. Then through the end of vector ω_a draw a line passing through center "ab" until it intersects the line through "ac." The line from "ac" to the intersection will then represent ω_b to the given scale.

The magnitude of the angular velocity of link "b" has now been determined and next we need to find the direction. In the figure ω_a was given as clockwise and therefore center "ab" must have a velocity downward as shown. Considering it a point on link "b" we see that link "b" must be turning counter-clockwise. If we direct the vectors through the instant centers (as shown in the figure) the sense of the vectors indicate the direc-

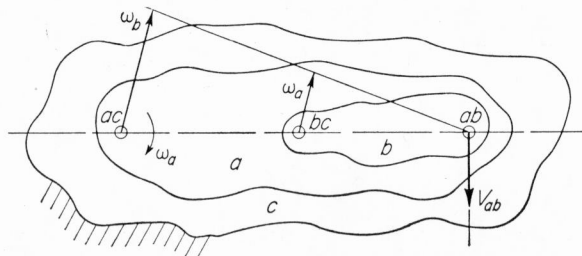

FIGURE 4.11

tions. If the sense of the vectors are in the same direction, the angular velocities are in the same direction; if the sense of the vectors are opposite, then the direction of the angular velocities are opposite. In the figure the sense of the vectors are opposite and therefore ω_b must be opposite in direction to ω_a or counter-clockwise. Fig. 4.11 shows a case where the angular velocities of the links are in the same direction.

4.6 Comparison of the Previous Methods

In the velocity analysis of a mechanism, any of the above methods gives a satisfactory result and ordinarily the most convenient method should be used in an analysis. In many cases a combination of the methods will give quicker results and thereby prove more satisfactory. It was noticed in the analysis of the various methods that some required fewer instant centers than others and would in many cases prove quicker. The direct method is probably the most accurate, assuming the same scale is used in the laying out of the mechanism. It should be noted that the larger the scale the more accurate the results should be if we do not go beyond the limits of our instruments.

In all engineering work it is imperative that the work be checked for errors and in velocity analysis one of the best checks is to determine the velocities by two different methods. The possibility of repeating the same error is greatly reduced by using two methods which are different.

PROBLEMS

4.1 In the mechanism shown in Fig. P4.1 point P has a velocity in direction shown of 40 in./sec. Letting V_P be represented by a vector 2.4 in. long, determine the vector V_R by direct method.

4.2 In Fig. P4.1, if $\omega_a = 100$ rpm clockwise, determine ω_b and ω_c.

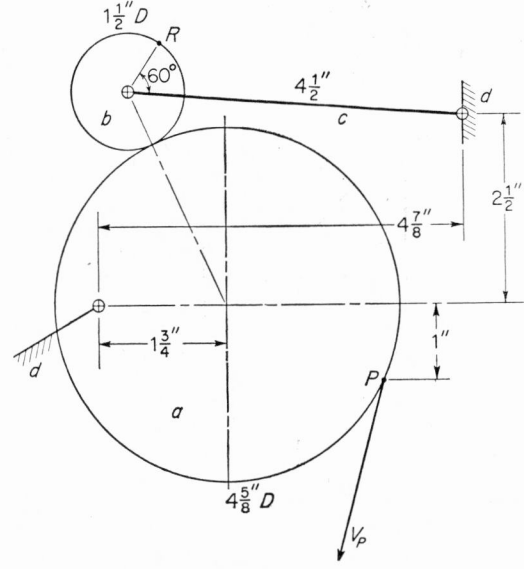

FIGURE P4.1

4.3 In Fig. P4.2, $V_P = 25$ in./sec. Determine V_R, ω_a, ω_b, and ω_c.

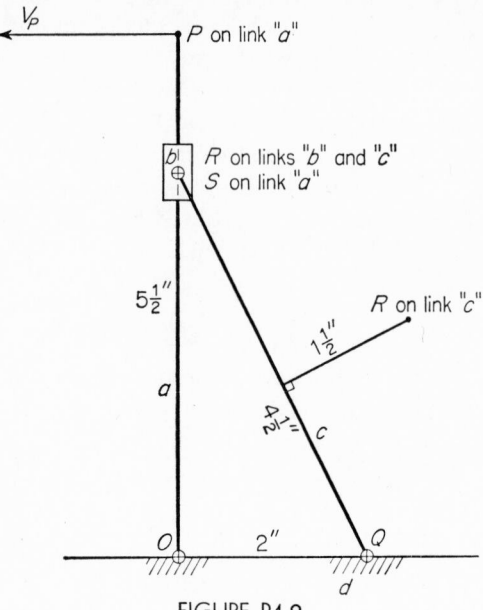

FIGURE P4.2

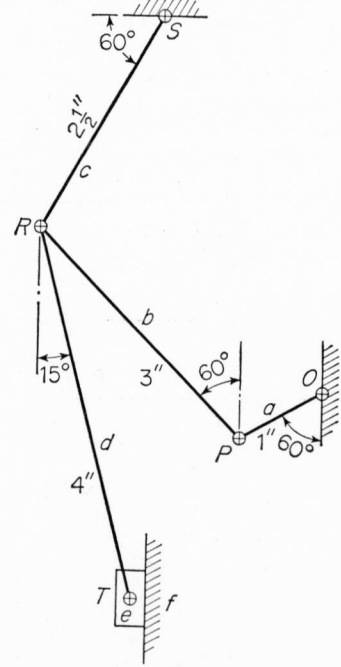

FIGURE P4.3

4.4 In Fig. P4.3, if $\omega_a = 100$ rpm counterclockwise determine the velocity of slider "e" by the transfer method, using a velocity scale for the vectors of 1 in. = 5 in./sec.

4.5 Repeat Prob. 4.4 using the component method.

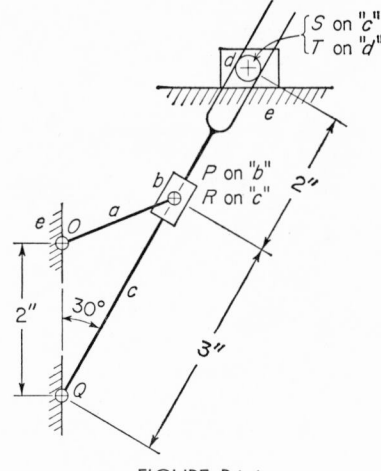

FIGURE P4.4

4.6 In Fig. P4.4, if the velocity of slider "d" is 100 in./sec to the right, determine the angular velocity of link "a" in direction and magnitude.

4.7 In Fig. P4.4, if $\omega_a = 100$ rpm counterclockwise determine the velocity of slider "d" using a velocity scale for the vectors of 1 in. = 10 in./sec.

4.8 In Fig. P4.5 determine the velocities of point P and slider "d" if $\omega_a = 50$ rpm clockwise.

4.9 Determine ω_b and ω_c for Prob. 4.8 by the graphical method and check the results by calculation using the velocity of a point on the links and the appropriate radius.

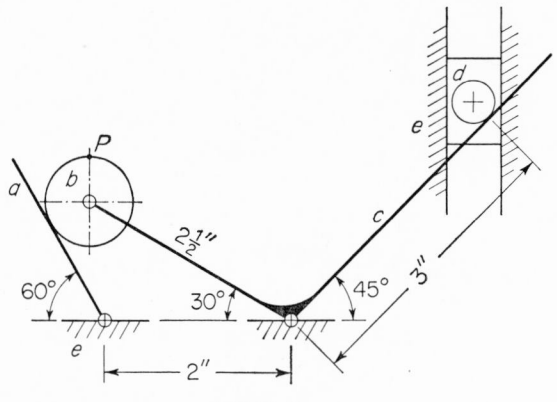

FIGURE P4.5

4.10 Determine the velocity of slider "d" in Fig. P4.6 if $\omega_a = 100$ rpm counter-clockwise.

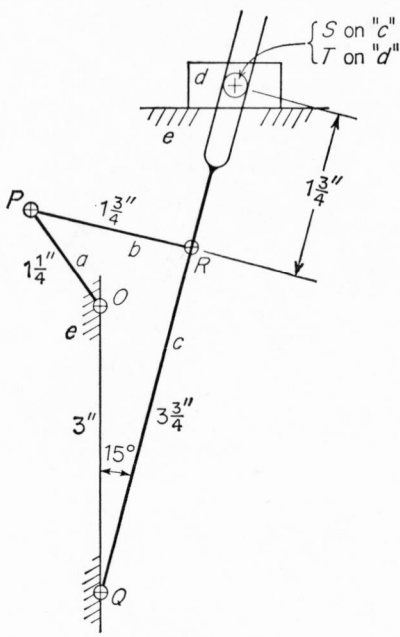

FIGURE P4.6

4.11 In Fig. P4.7, $V_s = 200$ in./sec. If V_s is a vector 2 in. long, determine the vector V_p and the angular velocity of link "c."

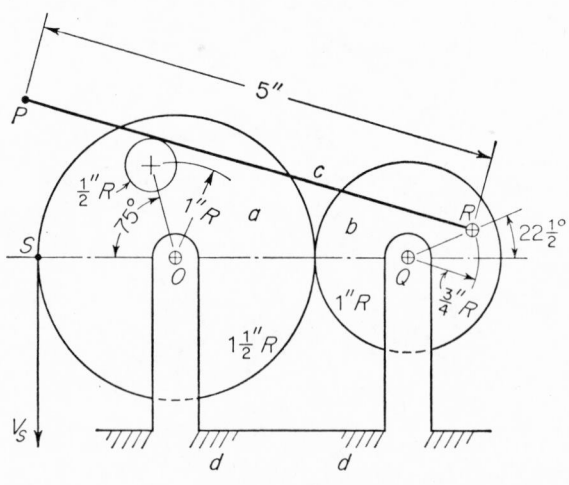

FIGURE P4.7

4.12 In Fig. P4.8, $\omega_a = 50$ rpm clockwise. Determine the velocities of points R and S and slider "c" by any instant center method and check the results by a different instant center method. Also determine the angular velocity of link "b."

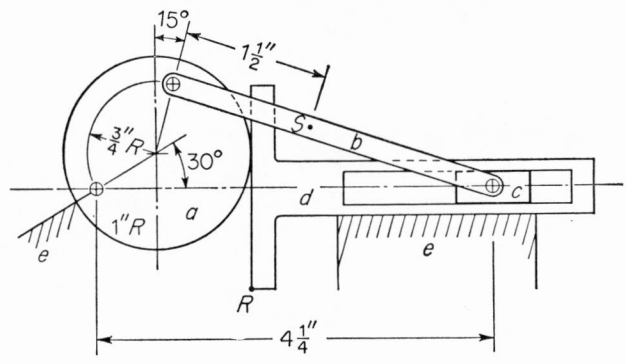

FIGURE P4.8

4.13 In Fig. P4.9, $\omega_a = 300$ rpm clockwise. Determine the velocities of point T and slider "d," and angular velocities of links "b" and "c."

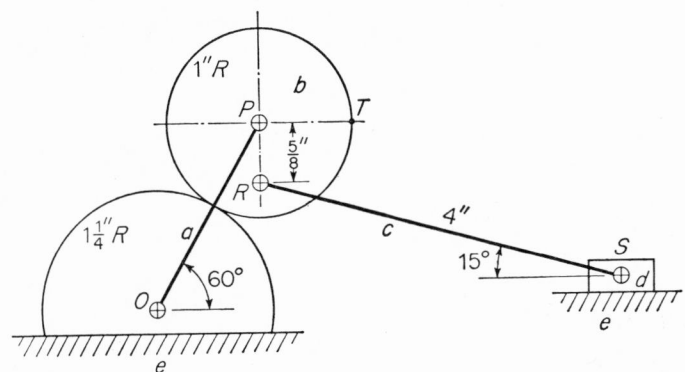

FIGURE P4.9

4.14 In Fig. P4.10 let the velocity of point P be represented by a vector upwards and to the right, 1 in. long. If $V_P = 100$ in./sec determine the vectors V_R, V_S, and V_T.

4.15 For Prob. 4.14 if $V_P = 100$ in./sec determine ω_b, ω_c and ω_e.

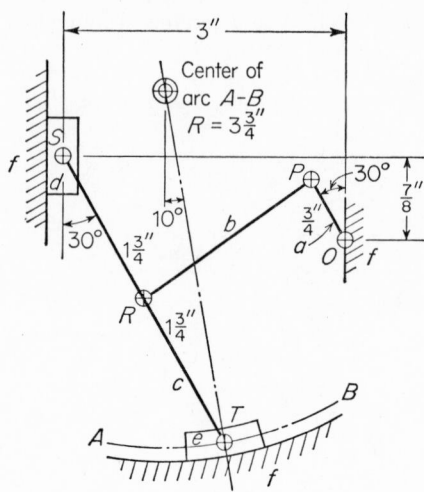

FIGURE P4.10

4.16 Draw the mechanism in Fig. P4.11 to some suitable scale and determine the velocities of points P, Q, R, and S, if $\omega_a = 30$ rpm clockwise.

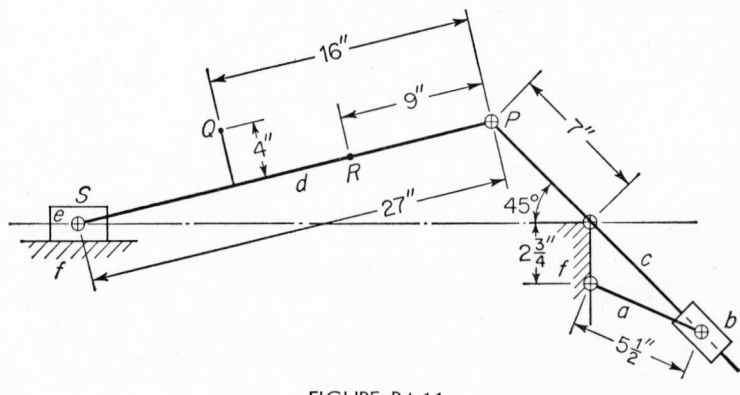

FIGURE P4.11

4.17 Determine the angular velocities of all the links for Prob. 4.16 graphically and check results analytically.

4.18 In Fig. P4.12, $\omega_a = 250$ rpm clockwise. Determine the velocities of points P, R, T, U, and S.

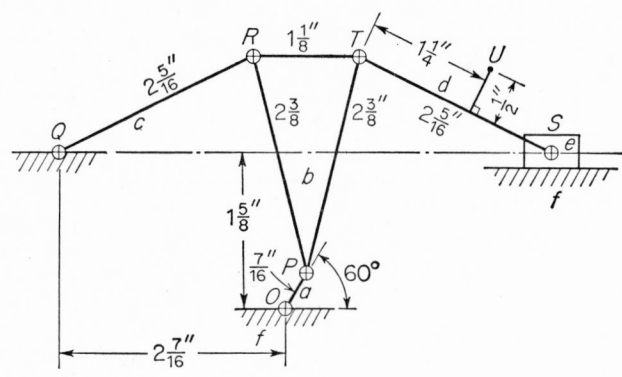

FIGURE P4.12

4.19 For Prob. 4.18 determine the angular velocities of all links.

4.20 In Fig. P4.13, $\omega_a = 150$ rpm counterclockwise. Determine the velocities of points P and S and slider "e" and ω_d.

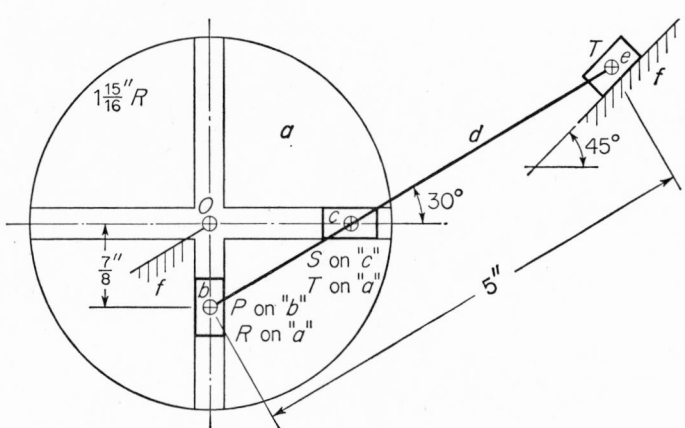

FIGURE P4.13

4.21 In Fig. P4.14, ω_a = 100 rpm clockwise. Determine the velocities of points P, R, and S.

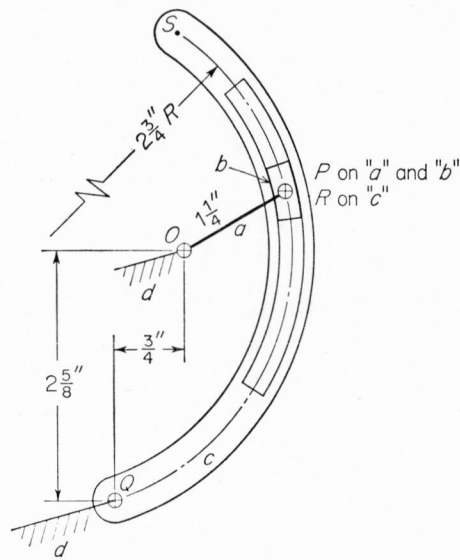

FIGURE P4.14

4.22 Determine the angular velocities of links "b" and "c" in Prob. 4.21.

Chapter 5

Velocity Image or Vector
Diagram Method

5.1 Introduction

We are now ready to discuss a completely different method of velocity analysis which does not make direct use of the concept of instant centers. We should bear in mind however that the idea of instant centers will be in the background in all velocity analyses, and an understanding of instant centers will be necessary in the following discussion even though we do not specifically use them in our analysis. The present discussion will be almost wholly based on the idea of relative motion and the use of velocity vectors. We give the name velocity image or vector diagram to this method. The analysis will be made up of a diagram composed of vectors and this is the reason for the latter name. The basis of the first name will have to wait until the method of analysis has been explained at which time the name will become obvious.

5.2 Vector Diagrams

We found in Chapter 4 that the absolute motion of a body constrained to plane motion is defined by, and the motion of any point on a body is determined by, (1) the absolute velocity of any point of the body and (2) the direction of the absolute velocity of any other point on the body. This is sufficient information to determine the instant center of the body with respect to the fixed body, and therefore the velocity of any point on the body can then be determined by triangulation. We will now attempt to show that the velocity of any point on a body or link can be found with respect to any point on another body, without resorting to the use of instant centers, with this same information.

We shall make use of two basic principles, which have been discussed previously, as a basis of the velocity image method:

1. The direction of the relative velocity of any point on a given body with respect to any other point on the same body is perpendicular to the line joining the two points. This was proved in the preceding chapter where it was shown that for any two points on a rigid body to have a relative velocity along the line joining the two points, the points would have to be approaching each other or be moving farther apart; this would mean the link or body did not satisfy the definition of a rigid body.

2. The absolute velocity of a point is equal to the vector sum of the absolute velocity of a second point and the relative velocity of the first point with respect to the second point, or in vector notation:

$$V_{A/C} = V_{B/C} \mathbin{+\mkern-8mu+} V_{A/B}$$

where $V_{A/C}$ is the velocity of a point A with respect to another point C, $V_{B/C}$ is the velocity of a second point B with respect to the same point C, and $V_{A/B}$ is the relative velocity of point A with respect to point B. This relationship was discussed in Chapter 1 when we developed the vector notation.

Using these two principles we will draw the velocity vector diagram for link "a" shown in Fig. 5.1(a). Points P, Q, and R are on link "a" which has

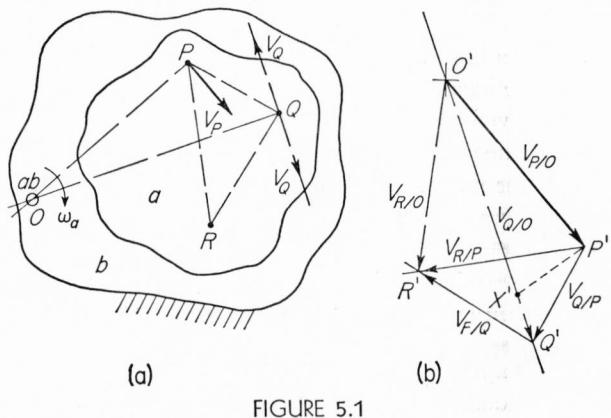

(a)   (b)

FIGURE 5.1

plane motion relative to fixed link "b." We have given the absolute velocity of point P in direction and magnitude, and the direction but not the magnitude of the absolute velocity of point Q. We wish to determine the absolute velocities of points Q and R. In Fig. 5.1(b) we draw a vector O'–P', to some given scale, representing the absolute velocity of point P. Through point O' we also draw a line in the same direction as the velocity of point Q. If we knew the magnitude and sense of this velocity we could draw the complete velocity vector. Let us assume that this vector is $O'-X'$. Then the vector from P' to X' is the relative velocity of point Q with respect to point P. But from the first principle stated on page 84, this vector must be perpendicular to the line joining point P and point Q, and, since we assumed point X', the line $P'-X'$ is probably not perpendicular to the line $P-Q$ and does not represent the relative velocity of Q with respect to P. However we can find the true vector by drawing from point P' a line perpendicular to the line through points P and Q. The intersection of this line with the line $O'-X'$ extended must locate a point Q' such that $O'-Q'$ is a vector representing the absolute velocity of point Q and the vector $P'-Q'$ represents the relative velocity of Q with respect to P, and the second principle is satisfied, that is

$$V_{Q/O} = V_{P/O} \mathbin{+\mkern-8mu+} V_{Q/P}$$

where O' is the point of zero velocity.

We will now find the velocity of point R. The direction of the velocity of point R with respect to point P is perpendicular to the line joining P and R, so through P' we draw a line perpendicular to the line $P-R$. Similarly a line through Q' perpendicular to the line $Q-R$ is drawn so that the line is in the direction of the relative velocity of R with respect to Q. These two lines intersect at point R' and the line $P'-R'$ is a vector representing the relative velocity of point R with respect to point P. The line $Q'-R'$ is also a vector representing the relative velocity of R with respect to Q. Now a line from O' to R' must be a vector representing the absolute velocity of point R, from the condition

$$V_{R/O} = V_{P/O} \mathbin{+\mkern-8mu+} V_{R/P}$$

or
$$V_{R/O} = V_{Q/O} \mathbin{+\mkern-8mu+} V_{R/Q}$$

The velocity of R with respect to the fixed body has then been found without reference to the instant center. Note that all absolute velocities are measured from point O' which represents all points with zero velocity, or all points on the fixed body. The instant center "ab" was not needed for the determination of the velocities; however, since it is a point on the fixed body, it has no velocity and is represented by point O' on the velocity diagram, and was labeled O on the figure.

Referring again to Fig. 5.1, we see that triangle $P'Q'R'$ is similar to triangle PQR (corresponding sides perpendicular) and that triangle $P'Q'R'$ is rotated 90° relative to triangle PQR in the direction of rotation of link "a." Then triangle $P'Q'R'$ can be considered an image of triangle PQR rotated 90° in the direction of rotation of body "a," from whence we get the name "*velocity image.*"

The angular velocity of link "a" can also be found without the use of the instant center "ab." The magnitude of the angular velocity of link "a" is found by dividing the relative velocity of any two points on link "a" by the distance between the two points. In Fig. 5.1 the angular velocity of link "a" is given by the following equation

$$\omega_a = \frac{V_{P/Q}}{(P\text{-}Q)}$$

This can be proven by the use of the instant center "ab" or point O as follows. The velocity of P with respect to the fixed body is given by the equation

$$V_{P/O} = \omega_a(\overline{O\text{-}P}) \tag{5.1}$$

where $\overline{O\text{-}P}$ is the distance from the instant center to point P. Also

$$V_{Q/O} = \omega_a(\overline{O\text{-}Q}) \tag{5.2}$$

then, by subtracting Eq. (5.2) from Eq. (5.1)

$$V_{P/O} \rightarrow V_{Q/O} = \omega_a(\overline{O\text{-}P}) \rightarrow \omega_a(\overline{O\text{-}Q}) \tag{5.3}$$

or $\qquad V_{P/O} \rightarrow V_{Q/O} = \omega_a[(O\text{-}P) \rightarrow (O\text{-}Q)] \tag{5.4}$

but $\qquad V_{P/O} \rightarrow V_{Q/O} = V_{P/O} \leftrightarrow V_{O/Q} = V_{P/Q} \tag{5.5}$

and $\qquad (\overline{O\text{-}P}) \rightarrow (\overline{O\text{-}Q}) = (\overline{O\text{-}P}) \leftrightarrow (\overline{Q\text{-}O}) = (\overline{P\text{-}Q}) \tag{5.6}$

Therefore, by substitution of Eqs. (5.5) and (5.6) in Eq. (5.4)

$$V_{P/Q} = \omega_a(\overline{P\text{-}Q}) \tag{5.7}$$

or $\qquad \omega_a = \dfrac{V_{P/Q}}{(P\text{-}Q)} \tag{5.8}$

which we started out to prove.

This same reasoning could be used for any other two points on body "a," such as P and R. Using these two points, the angular velocity of body "a" is given by the equation

$$\omega_a = \frac{V_{P/R}}{(P\text{-}R)}$$

The equations above are sufficient for the determination of the magnitude of the angular velocity and also can be used to determine the direction of the angular velocity.

5.3 The Velocity Image Method

The ideas developed in the preceding Article will now be used to determine velocity in mechanisms. First we will consider the quadric crank

mechanism as shown in Fig. 5.2. A pole position, O', will be selected first
to represent the image of all points which have no velocity. Q' will be at the
same point as O' since point Q has no velocity. Note that the points on the

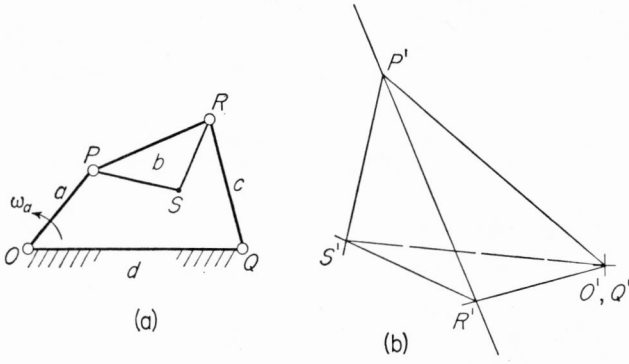

(a)

(b)

FIGURE 5.2

mechanism are labeled with capital letters and we will use the capital letters
with a prime to denote the velocity image of the point. Knowing the
angular velocity of link "a," we can calculate the velocity of point P on link
"a," and we can draw the line O'–P' in the direction of the velocity of point
P, representing the velocity of P to some given scale. The primed letters
indicate the sense of the vectors. For example, the line from O' to P',
directed towards P', gives the sense of the vector $V_{P/O}$. Also the same line
from P' to O', directed towards O', gives the sense of the vector $V_{O/P}$. The
arrowheads may thus be omitted from the vectors since they are unnecessary.

In order to find the image of point R, we note that it is on the same body
as point P (link "b"). Therefore the velocity of R relative to P must be in a
direction perpendicular to the line joining P and R, and we draw a line
through P' perpendicular to line P–R. Since we do not know the magnitude
of the velocity of R with respect to P, or the sense of the vector, we extend
the line to both sides of P'. Knowing also that point R is a point on link "c,"
the absolute velocity of P must be in a direction perpendicular to line Q–R.
Then through Q', or O', a line is drawn normal to Q–R representing the
velocity of R relative to Q. The intersection of this line and the line through
P' is the velocity image of point R, or R', and the line P'–R' represents the
relative velocity of R with respect to P; also Q'–R' represents the relative
velocity of R with respect to Q, or the absolute velocity of R.

To find the image of point S, or S', a line perpendicular to the line P–S
is drawn through P' and a line perpendicular to line R–S is drawn through
R'. The intersection of these two lines is the image of S, or S'. P'–S' is the

relative velocity of S with respect to P and $R'-S'$ is the relative velocity of S with respect to R. The absolute velocity of point S is represented by the line from O' to S'. Note that triangle $P'R'S'$ is similar to the triangle PRS, and is the velocity image of link "b."

Next we will determine the velocities for the slider crank mechanism. Figure 5.3 shows the mechanism and the velocity image. A pole point, O', is

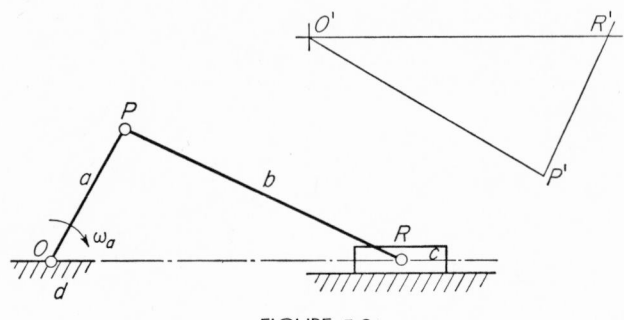

FIGURE 5.3

selected, representing the image of the points which are fixed, and the line $O'-P'$ is drawn to some scale representing the velocity of P with respect to O which we can calculate. The velocity of R relative to P is in a direction normal to the line $P-R$; therefore, through P' a line is drawn perpendicular to $P-R$. The velocity of R relative to the fixed body is horizontal since it is on a body "c" which moves with rectilinear translation in a horizontal direction. Then through O' we draw a horizontal line, and the intersection of this line with the line through P' locates the point R' which is the image of point R.

Now we will consider a more complicated mechanism, as shown in Fig. 5.4, which is called the Whitworth quick-return mechanism. We will find that we need to use two coincident points in the analysis, a point P on link "a" and a point R on link "c." Since point P is the instant center "ab," it is also a point on link "b." In all cases where we have two bodies in sliding contact and in which one has rotation two coincident points, one on each body, will be needed for the velocity analysis. The reason for this will be seen as we analyze the mechanism in Fig. 5.4. As before the pole point O' will be selected for the image of all fixed points and it is also Q'. The velocity of point P can be calculated and the vector $O'-P'$ is drawn to some scale to represent the absolute velocity of point P. From the previous examples we know that in order to locate the image of a point we need to know the direction of the velocity of the point with respect to two points whose image has been located. For example we could not now locate the image of point T because we only know the location of the image of points O', Q', and P' and we know the direction of T with respect to the fixed body only, therefore all we know about T' is that it lies on the horizontal line through O'. The only point whose image we can now locate is some point the direction of which is

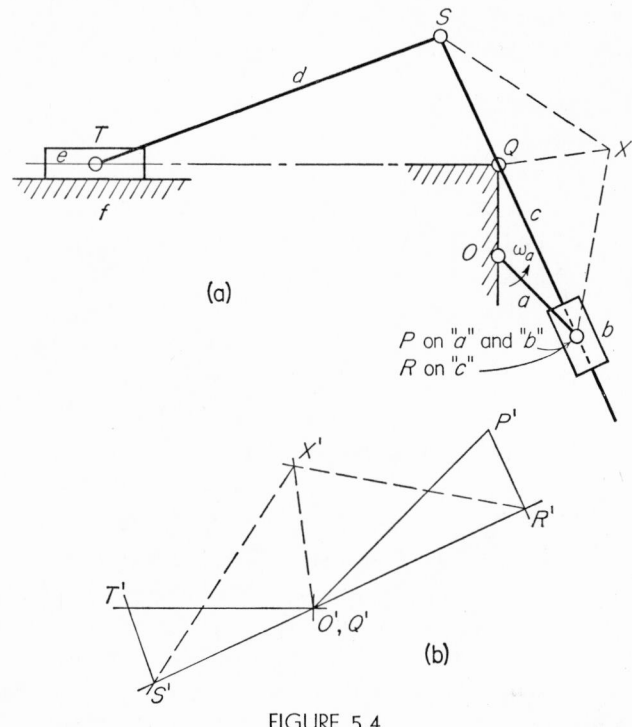

FIGURE 5.4

known relative to the fixed body and relative to point P. Point R is the only point which satisfies these conditions. Since link "b" is sliding, relative to link "c," with rectilinear translation, the velocity of R with respect to P is in the direction of translation, or along the line representing link "c." Then through P' we draw a line in that direction. Link "c" is connected to the fixed body by a pin joint at Q, therefore R must have an absolute velocity normal to the line Q–R, so we draw a line through Q' in this direction and the intersection of this line with the line through P' locates R', the image of point R.

We still do not know the direction of the velocity of point T with respect to any point except the fixed body, so T' cannot be located. But we know the direction of the velocity of point S with respect to Q and also with respect to the point R (R and S both are on the same link). However since the velocity of S with respect to Q is in the same direction as the velocity of S with respect to R and also in the same direction as the velocity of R with respect to Q, this only tells us that S', the image of S, lies on the line through Q' and R' and does not give us two intersecting lines which would locate S'.

We have two methods by which we can still locate S' from the information we have available. If we recall that the image of the points on a link of the mechanism form similar geometric figures to the points on the link, and that the distances between any two points on the image are proportional to the distances between the same points on the link, we can locate S' on line Q'–R' (extended) by proportional relationships, as follows

$$\frac{Q'-S'}{Q-S} = \frac{Q'-R'}{Q-R}$$

Then by this method we can calculate the distance Q'–S'.

A neater graphical method requires the use of an auxiliary point. We pick any point on link "c" which does not lie on the line S–R, say point X in the figure. Now since X lies on link "c" we know the direction of its velocity relative to the two points Q and R which are also on link "c," we can locate the image of X as the intersection of the line through R' normal to R–X and the line through Q' normal to the line Q–X. Now since X lies on the same link as point S we know the direction of the velocity of S with respect to X. We can draw a line through X' normal to X–S. The intersection of it with the line through Q' and R' locates S'.

Now knowing the location of the image of S and noting it also lies on the same link as point T, we know the direction of the velocity of T with respect to two points whose images have been located and T' can be located as shown in the figure.

5.4 Discussion of the Method

From the foregoing Articles we found that in order to locate the image of a point on the velocity image we must know the direction of the velocity of the point with respect to two other points whose image has been found on the diagram. These two points can be on the same link as the body in question or on any other link — just so we know the direction of the relative velocity. Through the images of these points we can draw lines the intersection of which locates the image of the point in question. This, then, is the general method of attack in the velocity image method. Generally we can complete the velocity image of most mechanisms by using the above method, starting with the image of a point on the driving link which can be determined by calculation. An exception to this will be discussed in the next Article.

The velocity image method of velocity determination has many advantages over the instant center methods. It is usually quicker and, once it has been mastered, it is a much easier method to work with. Possibly the main advantage of the velocity image method is that once the image has been completed we have a complete vector diagram of the relative velocities of all points with respect to all other points. It also lends itself to the next step in our kinematic analysis which is the determination of the acceleration of the various points of the mechanism. Because of these advantages we will use the velocity image as a means of determining the velocities in the remainder of the text.

One might now ask why we spent so much time on the other methods if the velocity image method is so much better than the other methods. The answer is that our knowledge of velocities would be incomplete if we did not know the instant center methods. Too, the information gained in learning the instant center methods makes the velocity image method much easier to understand and use. Also it gives us an excellent means of checking the results obtained from the velocity image, and it is useful if we wish to obtain the velocity of only a single point.

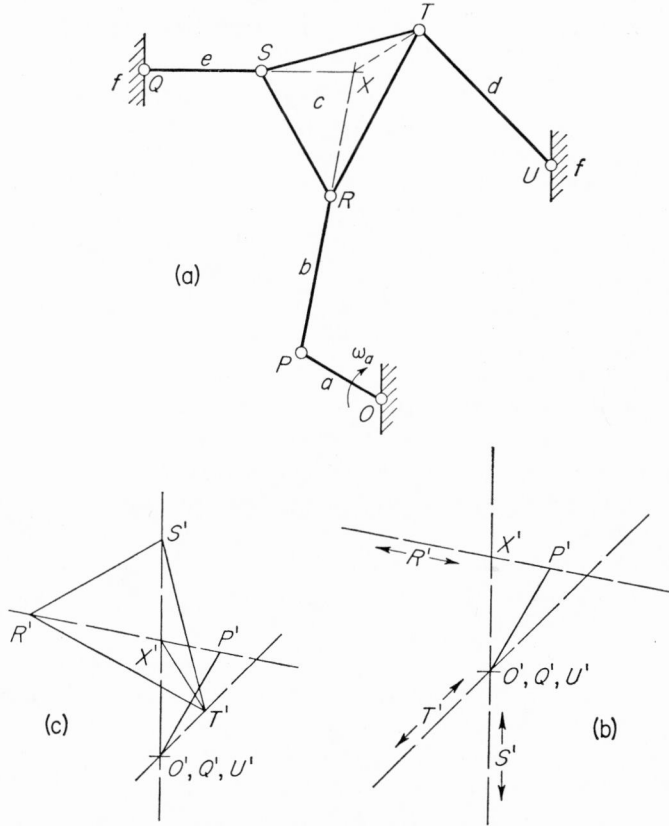

FIGURE 5.5

5.5 Floating Link Mechanisms

There are a few mechanisms the velocity images of which cannot be completed by use of the foregoing methods without the use of some additional construction. Such a mechanism is shown in Fig. 5.5(a). If we start the velocity image of the mechanism we can locate P' by calculating the velocity of point P and laying off the vector $O'–P'$ to some scale. Then R' will lie on a line through P' perpendicular to line $P–R$. But we do not know the direction of the velocity of point R with respect to any other point whose image we have found. Therefore R' cannot be located. In searching for a point whose image we can find we see that we know the direction of the velocity of points S and T with respect to the fixed body. Therefore we can draw lines through the image of the fixed points on which S' and T' lie, but again we cannot find the direction of their velocity with respect to any other point whose image has been located, and we find ourselves at a point where we cannot proceed with the velocity image without further information. Such a mechanism will be called a floating link mechanism. We will now develop a method for handling such mechanisms.

Consider the point X, on link "c," determined by the intersection of lines $Q–S$ and $P–R$, extended. This point has a velocity with respect to point R perpendicular to line $X–R$, and a velocity with respect to S perpendicular to line $X–S$ (all points being on link "c"). But the velocity of S with respect to Q has the same direction as the velocity of X with respect to S. Using the vector relation

$$V_{X/Q} = V_{S/Q} \nrightarrow V_{X/S}$$

we see that since $V_{S/Q}$ and $V_{X/S}$ are in the same direction the velocity of X with respect to Q must be in the same direction. Then point X has the same direction of velocity with respect to the fixed body as point S, and X' must lie on the same line through Q' that S' lies on. Using the same argument we see that X' lies on the same line through P' that R' lies on, and the intersection of these two lines then determines X' as shown in the Fig. 5.5(b). Now we have located the image of a point on link "c," and this gives us a reference point for use in determining the image of other points on link "c." It will not help us in determining the image of points R and S, however, since they lie on the same line that we used to locate X'. But we can use it to determine the image of point T. T' lies on a line through X' normal to line $X–T$, and the intersection of this line with the line through U', previously found, locates T' as shown in Fig. 5.5(c) where we have redrawn the velocity image for clarity. Having determined T' we can now use it to locate R' and S' as shown.

There are two other points which can be located on link "c" in a similar manner and which also give us a point whose image can be located and thereby give us sufficient information to complete the image of the mechanism. We will locate these two points in Fig. 5.6 where we have redrawn the same mechanism. First, consider the point Y determined by the intersection of lines $U–T$ and $P–R$ extended. Remembering that this is a point

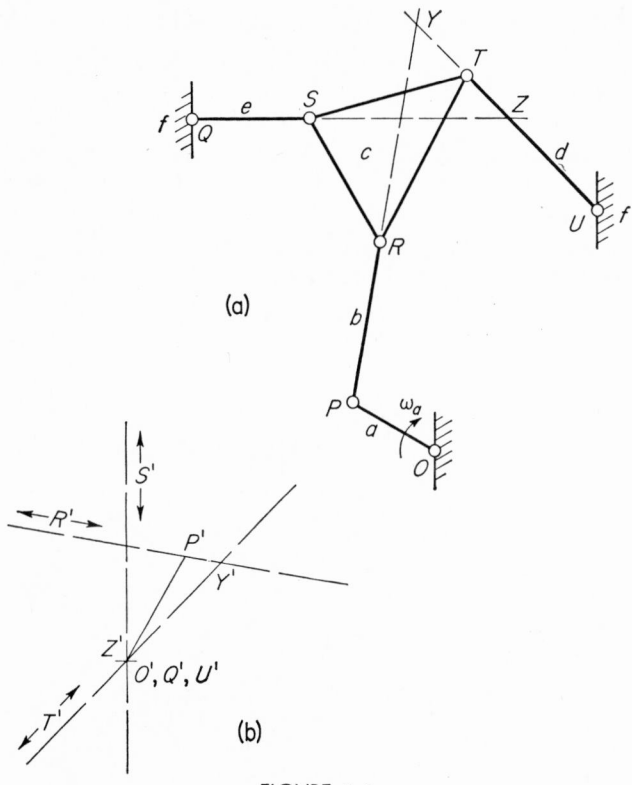

FIGURE 5.6

on link "c," we see that it has a velocity relative to T in the same direction as the velocity of T with respect to the fixed body, therefore it must lie on the same line through U' that T' lies on. Also its direction of velocity with respect to R is the same as the direction of the velocity of R with respect to P, and it must lie on the same line through P' that R' is on. The intersection of these lines is then Y', and we have located the image of a point on link "c." Then we can find a line through Y' on which S' lies and thereby locate S' from which we can proceed to locate T' and S'. Now taking point Z determined by the intersection of line $Q–S$ extended and line $U–T$ we see by the same reasoning that its image lies on the same lines as T' and S' through the image of the fixed point and we see that the only point that satisfies this condition is the image of the fixed points O', Q', and U'. Therefore Z' lies at that point and point Z has zero absolute velocity. Using this point we can determine the position of R' and then complete the image of the mechanism. Since Z is a point on link "c" which has zero absolute velocity, by definition it is the instant center "cf." Quite often one of the points used in the floating link mechanisms is an instant center with respect to the fixed body and we will use this method in a later example to determine the instant centers of the mechanism.

Another example of a floating link mechanism is shown in Fig. 5.7. Here again when we start to locate the image of a point on link "c" we find

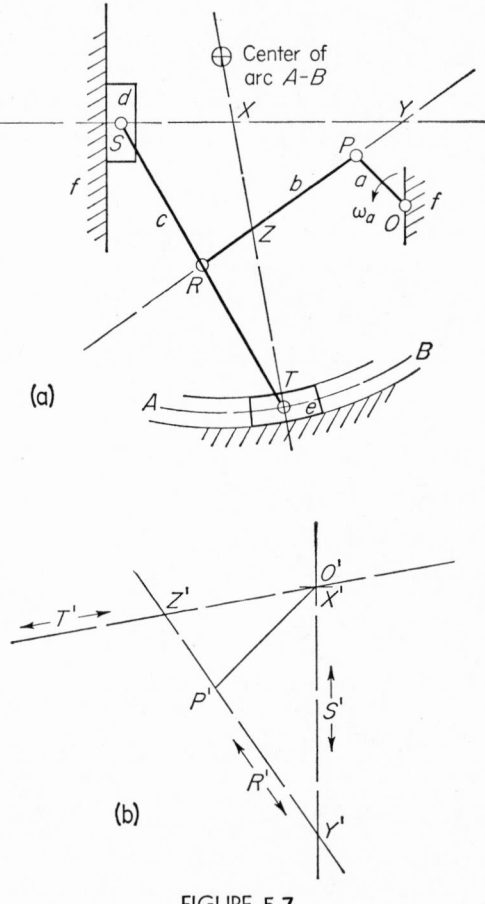

FIGURE 5.7

that only one line is available for the determination of the images of the points R, S, and T on the link. In order to complete the image we must find some point on link "c" whose image we can locate. As in the previous case there are three such points available. One is the point on link "c" which has the same direction of velocity with respect to point S that S has with respect to the fixed link, and the same direction with respect to T that T has with respect to the fixed link. This point we will label X. Another point, which will be labeled Y, is the point which has velocities in the same direction relative to S that S has with respect to the fixed body and relative to R that R has with respect to P. The third point, labeled Z, has velocities relative to points T and R in the same direction as the velocities of T relative to the fixed link and R with respect to P. These points will be found at the intersection of the lines passing through the points S and T normal to the direction of their velocity and the line through R normal to the direction of its velocity relative to point P, as shown in Fig. 5.7. The images of these points will then be at the intersections of the lines on which R', S' and T' lie. Then using the image of point X we can locate the image of point R, with Y' we can locate the image of point T, and with Z' we can locate S'. The images of points R, S, and T are not located in the figure because the student should now be able to locate them. It should be remembered that only one of the auxiliary points is needed in order to complete the velocity image, because once we have located any one of the three points R', S', and T' the other two can be located without using another auxiliary point.

Two more examples of floating link mechanism are shown in Figs. 5.8 and 5.9. The three auxiliary points needed for completion of the velocity

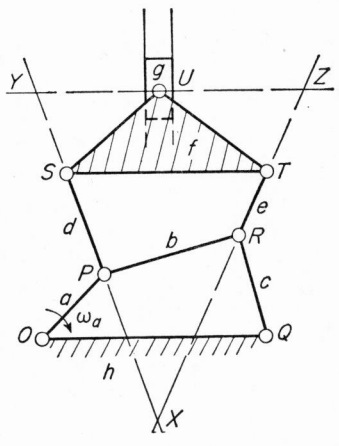

FIGURE 5.8

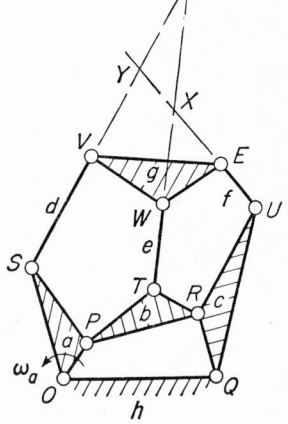

FIGURE 5.9

image are shown in each figure as points X, Y, and Z. The floating link in Fig. 5.8 is link "f," and link "g" is the floating link in Fig. 5.9. If the

student will draw a velocity image for the mechanism in Fig. 5.8, he will see
that none of the auxiliary points fall at the point on the image which indicates zero velocity. Therefore none of the points are the instant center
common to the floating link and the fixed body, as has been the case with
the previous examples. However, if the instant centers for the mechanism
are located it will be found that point X is the instant center *"bf."*

The mechanism in Fig. 5.9 is an interesting mechanism which we will
discuss in detail. If we start locating the instant centers for the mechanism
we will find that all the instant centers cannot be located by any means
discussed in Chapter 3. After locating the centers corresponding to all the
pin joints it will be seen that only two more centers can be located by use of
the circle diagram. These two are centers *"ac"* and *"bh."* Figure 5.10 shows
the mechanism, with these instant centers located, and the corresponding

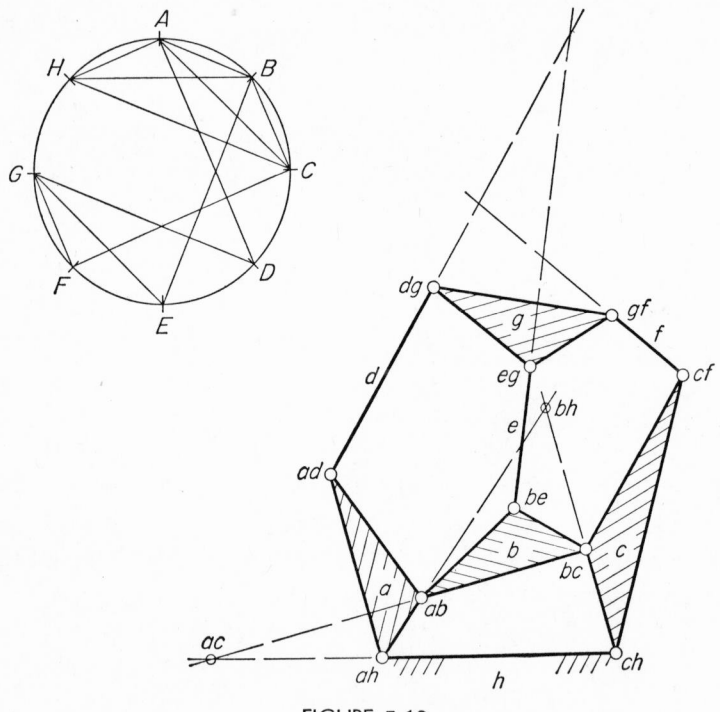

FIGURE 5.10

circle diagram. It will be seen that no other centers can be found by the
circle diagram because we cannot complete two triangles with any other
line. We can, however, complete the location of the instant centers by using
the velocity image of the mechanism. Remembering that the pole point of
the velocity image always is an image of all points which have no velocity,

then by definition it is the image of all instant centers common to any link and the fixed link. Then for the mechanism, O' will be the image of all instant centers common with link "h." With the completed velocity image we also have the images of at least two other points on each link and the point corresponding to the image of the instant center common with the fixed link can be located on the *mechanism* by reversing the procedure for finding the velocity image of a point. This will then give us enough information to complete the location of the instant centers. In this case only one or two of these instant centers will need be located from the velocity image in order to complete the location of the instant centers.

PROBLEMS

For the problems below construct the velocity polygon for the figures indicated locating the image of all labeled points. Use any convenient scale for the velocity vectors.

5.1 Fig. P4.2, with $V_P = 25$ in./sec. Determine ω_c.

5.2 Fig. P5.1, with $\omega_a = 3600$ rpm clockwise. Determine ω_b, ω_c, and ω_d.

5.3 Fig. P4.14, with $\omega_a = 100$ rpm clockwise. Determine ω_b and ω_c.

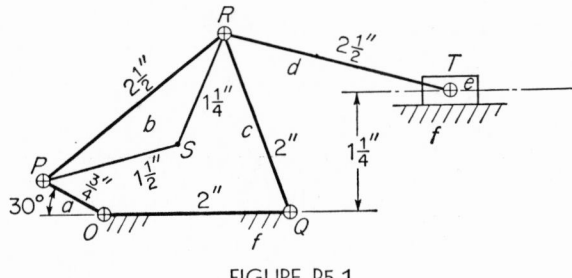

FIGURE P5.1

5.4 Fig. P5.2, with $\omega_a = 500$ rpm counterclockwise. Determine ω_b and ω_c.

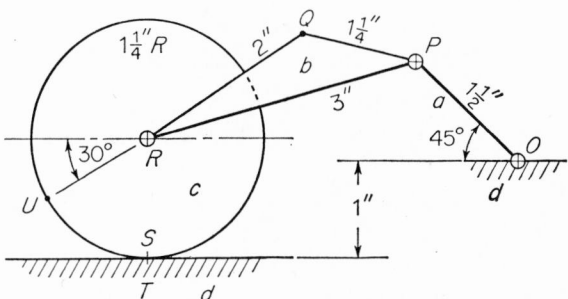

FIGURE P5.2

5.5   Fig. P5.3, with $\omega_a = 1000$ rpm counterclockwise. Determine ω_c.

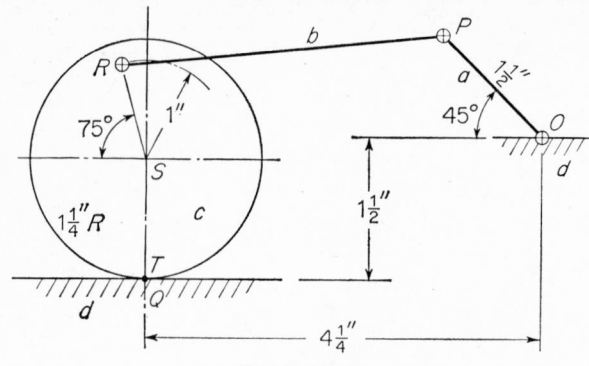

FIGURE P5.3

5.6   Fig. P5.4, with $\omega_a = 1800$ rpm counterclockwise. Determine ω_b and ω_c.

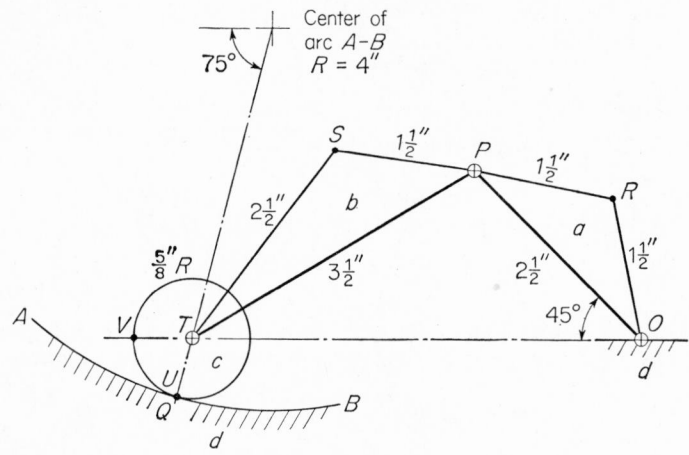

FIGURE P5.4

5.7   Fig. P5.5, with $\omega_a = 200$ rpm counterclockwise. Determine ω_c.

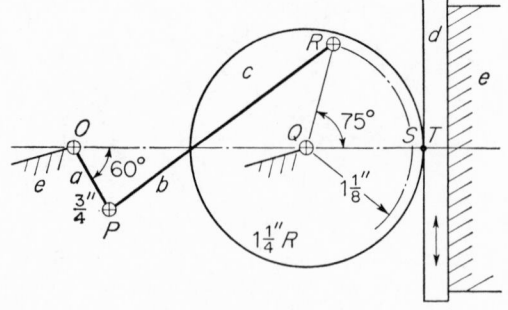

FIGURE P5.5

5.8   Fig. P5.6, with $\omega_a = 500$ rpm clockwise. Determine ω_c and ω_d.

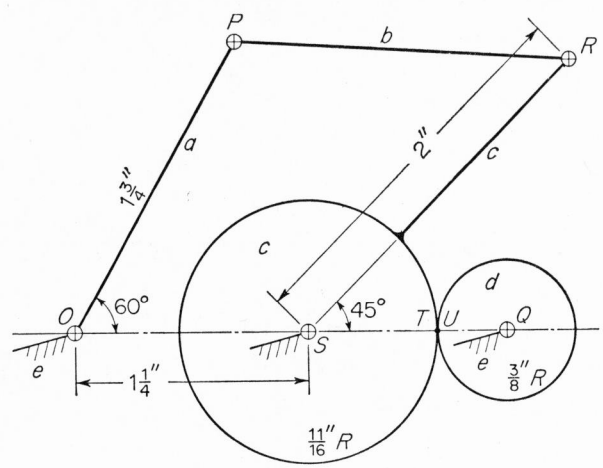

FIGURE P5.6

5.9   Fig. P 5.7, with $\omega_a = 1000$ rpm clockwise. Determine ω_b, ω_c, and ω_d

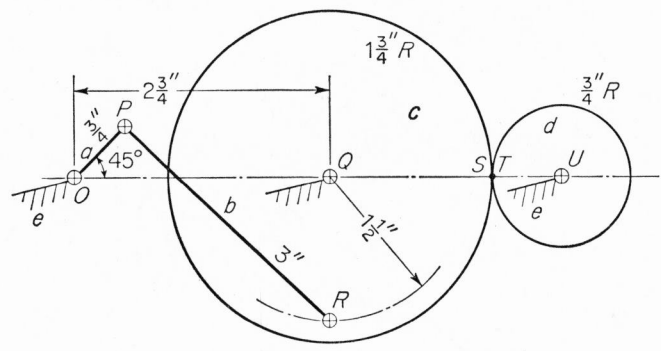

FIGURE P5.7

5.10 Fig. P4.6, with $\omega_a = 100$ rpm counterclockwise. Determine ω_b and ω_c.
5.11 Fig. P4.4, with $V_T = 200$ in./sec to right. Determine ω_a and ω_c.

5.12 Fig. P5.8, with $\omega_a = 800$ rpm clockwise. Determine ω_c.

5.13 Fig. P4.9, with $\omega_a = 300$ rpm clockwise. Determine ω_b and ω_c.

5.14 Fig. P4.12, with $\omega_a = 250$ rpm clockwise. Determine ω_b, ω_c, and ω_d.

5.15 Fig. P4.11, with $\omega_a = 30$ rpm clockwise. Determine ω_c and ω_d.

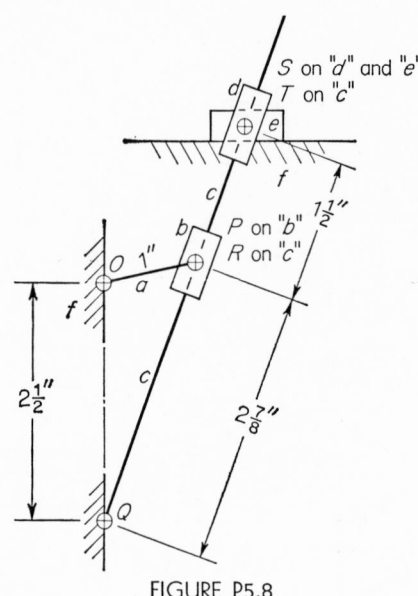

FIGURE P5.8

5.16 Fig. P5.9, with $\omega_a = 1800$ rpm clockwise. Determine angular velocity of all links.

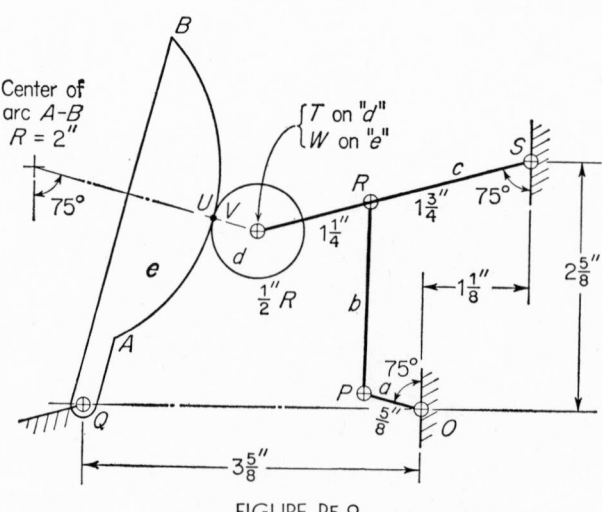

FIGURE P5.9

5.17 Fig. P5.10, with $\omega_a = 60$ rpm clockwise. Determine ω_d and ω_e.

5.18 Fig. P4.10, with $V_P = 100$ in./sec upwards to right. Determine ω_b and ω_c.

5.19 Fig. P4.13, with $\omega_a = 150$ rpm counterclockwise. Determine ω_d.

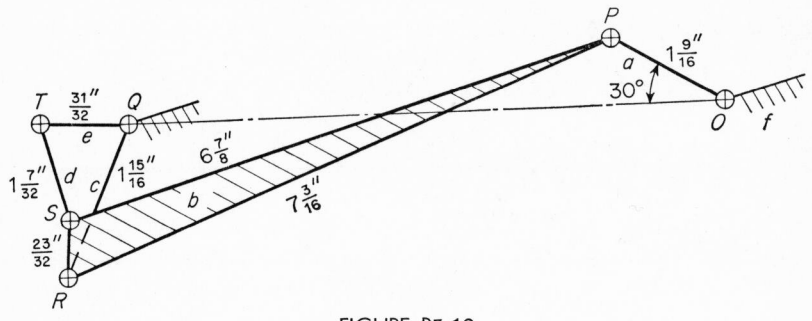

FIGURE P5.10

Chapter 6

Acceleration Image

6.1 Introduction

In determining the acceleration of points of a mechanism we will use a vector diagram method similar to the method used in the previous chapter for determining velocities and the diagram will be called the acceleration image. This vector diagram will be based on relative accelerations, which can be defined as a difference in absolute accelerations. It will be found, however, that the acceleration image is considerably more complicated than the velocity image. There are two methods of laying out the acceleration image, one a completely graphical method and the other requiring a calculation for each point. In the completely graphical method the scale of the vectors is fixed and cannot be selected at our convenience; therefore, the second method will be the one emphasized in this chapter, although the graphical method will be described.

In Chapter 1 we derived the equations for the normal and tangential accelerations and our acceleration image will be based on these two components of the total relative acceleration. This chapter will be concerned only with the mechanisms in which the radius vectors have a constant magnitude and we will consider cases in which the magnitude of the radius vector is a function of time in succeeding chapters. The relations between linear and angular displacement, velocity and acceleration are tabulated below for ready reference

	Linear	*Angular*
Displacement:	s	$\theta = \dfrac{s}{r}$
	ds	$d\theta = \dfrac{ds}{r}$
Velocity:	$V = \dfrac{ds}{dt}$	$\omega = \dfrac{d\theta}{dt} = \dfrac{1}{r}\dfrac{ds}{dt} = \dfrac{V}{r}$
Acceleration:	$a = \dfrac{dV}{dt} = \dfrac{d^2s}{dt^2}$	$\alpha = \dfrac{d\omega}{dt} = \dfrac{d^2\theta}{dt^2}$
		$= \dfrac{1}{r}\dfrac{dV}{dt} = \dfrac{1}{r}\dfrac{d^2s}{dt^2}$
		$= \dfrac{a_t}{r}$

The equations for normal and tangential acceleration which are the basis of our acceleration analysis are repeated below:

$$a^n = \omega^2 r = \frac{V^2}{r} \tag{6.1}$$

$$a^t = \alpha r \tag{6.2}$$

Note that we have used the superscripts "t" and "n" to denote tangential and normal acceleration so that the subscripts can be used to denote the points to which we are referencing the acceleration.

Before we start developing the idea of the acceleration image we need to develop the equations of plane motion for the general case. This will give us a much better idea of accelerations and serve as a firm base on which to develop the acceleration image. We will also develop the notion of a moving coordinate system which we will use not only in acceleration analyses but will find necessary later in the development of dynamic analyses.

Consider the body shown in Fig. 6.1 moving in plane motion relative to a fixed coordinate system with axes x and y and origin O. On the body another coordinate system is drawn with axes ϵ and η and origin Q. This latter coordinate system is in the plane of motion and is fixed to the body. A point P is moving relative to the body along a line $A-B$ which is also in the plane of motion so that the point P always remains in the plane of

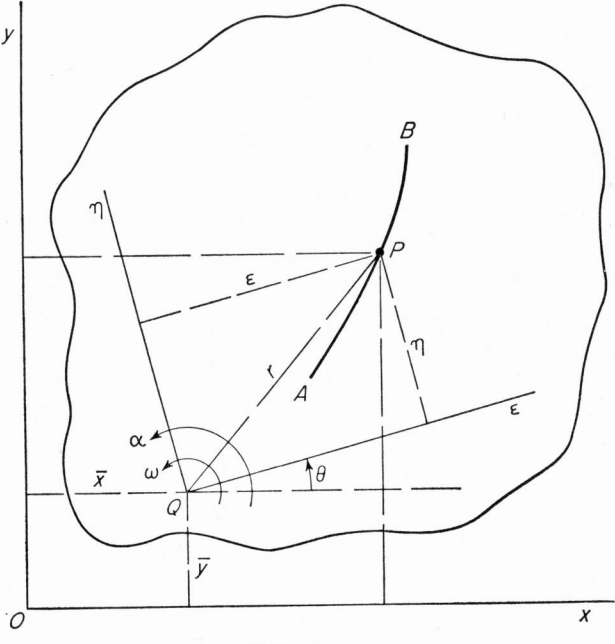

FIGURE 6.1

motion. We will develop the equations of motion of the point P relative to the fixed axes, x and y. This system could be thought of as an airplane moving relative to the Earth's surface in a plane normal to the Earth's surface. The ϵ-η system then would be a coordinate system attached to the frame of the airplane with the curve A–B fixed relative to the airplane's frame, with point P moving along this curve and the x-y system would represent the plane of motion normal to the Earth's surface.

At some instant of time the ϵ axis is at an angle θ relative to the x axis, the origin Q is at a position, relative to the x-y system, given by the coordinates $\bar{x}$ and $\bar{y}$, and the point P is at a position relative to the ϵ-η system given by the coordinates ϵ and η. Then the position of the point P, relative to the absolute x-y axis, is given by the equation

$$x = \bar{x} + \epsilon \cos \theta - \eta \sin \theta \tag{6.3}$$

$$y = \bar{y} + \epsilon \sin \theta + \eta \cos \theta \tag{6.4}$$

The components of the absolute velocity of P in the x and y directions are found by taking the derivatives of x and y with respect to time, remembering that $\bar{x}$, $\bar{y}$, θ, ϵ, and η are all functions of time, or

$$V_P^x = \frac{dx}{dt}$$

$$= \frac{d\bar{x}}{dt} + \frac{d\epsilon}{dt} \cos \theta - \epsilon \sin \theta \frac{d\theta}{dt} - \frac{d\eta}{dt} \sin \theta - \eta \cos \theta \frac{d\theta}{dt} \tag{6.5}$$

$$V_P^y = \frac{dy}{dt}$$

$$= \frac{d\bar{y}}{dt} + \frac{d\epsilon}{dt} \sin \theta + \epsilon \cos \theta \frac{d\theta}{dt} + \frac{d\eta}{dt} \cos \theta - \eta \sin \theta \frac{d\theta}{dt} \tag{6.6}$$

The vector sum of the velocity components is the total velocity of P with respect to the fixed axis, or letting $d\theta/dt = \omega$

$$V_{P/O} = \frac{dx}{dt} \nrightarrow \frac{dy}{dt}$$

$$= \left(\frac{d\bar{x}}{dt} \nrightarrow \frac{d\bar{y}}{dt} \right) \nrightarrow \left(\frac{d\epsilon}{dt} \nrightarrow \frac{d\eta}{dt} \right) \cos \theta \nrightarrow \left(\frac{d\epsilon}{dt} \nrightarrow \frac{d\eta}{dt} \right) \sin \theta$$

$$\nrightarrow \omega(\epsilon \nrightarrow \eta) \cos \theta \nrightarrow \omega(\epsilon \nrightarrow \eta) \sin \theta \tag{6.7}$$

The various components of the velocity are shown in Fig. 6.2 and, since we are now dealing with vector quantities, all signs are made positive. The direction of the vector components along the x-y axes are given by the sign in Eqs. (6.5) and (6.6).

From Fig. 6.2 we see that the components $d\epsilon/dt$ and $d\eta/dt$ are components of the velocity of P relative to the curve A–B (being the only com-

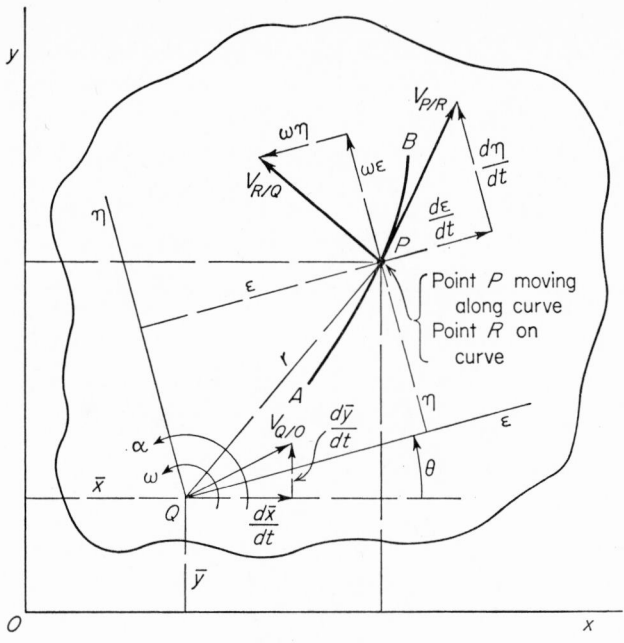

FIGURE 6.2

ponents that contain a change in position relative to the ϵ-η axes) and the components $\omega\epsilon$ and $\omega\eta$ are components of the velocity of a point fixed to A–B and coincident with P whose only velocity is that caused by a change in the angular position of the ϵ-η axes. The coincident point fixed relative to the ϵ-η axes will be called point R. Then from Eq. (6.7), noting that $\epsilon \nrightarrow \eta = r$

$$V_{P/O} = V_{Q/O} \nrightarrow V_{P/R} \nrightarrow \omega r$$
$$= V_{Q/O} \nrightarrow V_{P/R} \nrightarrow V_{R/Q} \tag{6.8}$$

which is a vector equation such as was developed in Chapter 1.

The components of the absolute acceleration of P are found by taking the second derivative of x and y with respect to time or the derivative of V_P^x and V_P^y, as given by Eqs. (6.5) and (6.6), with respect to time, or

$$a_P^x = \frac{d^2x}{dt^2} = \frac{dV_P^x}{dt}$$

$$= \frac{d^2\bar{x}}{dt^2} + \frac{d^2\epsilon}{dt^2}\cos\theta - \frac{d\epsilon}{dt}\sin\theta\,\frac{d\theta}{dt} - \frac{d\epsilon}{dt}\sin\theta\,\frac{d\theta}{dt}$$

$$- \epsilon\cos\theta\left(\frac{d\theta}{dt}\right)^2 - \epsilon\sin\theta\,\frac{d^2\theta}{dt^2} - \frac{d^2\eta}{dt^2}\sin\theta$$

$$- \frac{d\eta}{dt}\cos\theta\,\frac{d\theta}{dt} - \frac{d\eta}{dt}\cos\theta\,\frac{d\theta}{dt} + \eta\sin\theta\left(\frac{d\theta}{dt}\right)^2$$

$$- \eta \cos \theta \frac{d^2\theta}{dt^2} \tag{6.9}$$

$$a_P^y = \frac{d^2y}{dt^2} = \frac{dV_P^y}{dt}$$

$$= \frac{d^2\bar{y}}{dt^2} + \frac{d^2\epsilon}{dt^2} \sin\theta + \frac{d\epsilon}{dt}\cos\theta\frac{d\theta}{dt} + \frac{d\epsilon}{dt}\cos\theta\frac{d\theta}{dt}$$

$$- \epsilon \sin\theta \left(\frac{d\theta}{dt}\right)^2 + \epsilon\cos\theta\frac{d^2\theta}{dt^2} + \frac{d^2\eta}{dt^2}\cos\theta$$

$$- \frac{d\eta}{dt}\sin\theta\frac{d\theta}{dt} - \frac{d\eta}{dt}\sin\theta\frac{d\theta}{dt} - \eta\cos\theta\left(\frac{d\theta}{dt}\right)^2$$

$$- \eta \sin\theta\frac{d^2\theta}{dt^2} \tag{6.10}$$

The total acceleration of P with respect to the fixed axis is given by the vector sum of the acceleration components, or

$$a_{P/O} = \left[\frac{d^2\bar{x}}{dt^2} \leftrightarrow \frac{d^2\bar{y}}{dt^2}\right]$$

$$\leftrightarrow \left[\left(\frac{d^2\epsilon}{dt^2} \leftrightarrow \frac{d^2\eta}{dt^2}\right)\cos\theta \leftrightarrow \left(\frac{d^2\epsilon}{dt^2} \leftrightarrow \frac{d^2\eta}{dt^2}\right)\sin\theta\right]$$

$$\leftrightarrow \left[\left(2\frac{d\epsilon}{dt}\frac{d\theta}{dt} \leftrightarrow 2\frac{d\eta}{dt}\frac{d\theta}{dt}\right)\cos\theta \leftrightarrow \left(2\frac{d\epsilon}{dt}\frac{d\theta}{dt} \leftrightarrow 2\frac{d\eta}{dt}\frac{d\theta}{dt}\right)\sin\theta\right]$$

$$\leftrightarrow \left[\left(\epsilon\frac{d^2\theta}{dt^2} \leftrightarrow \eta\frac{d^2\theta}{dt^2}\right)\cos\theta \leftrightarrow \left(\epsilon\frac{d^2\theta}{dt^2} \leftrightarrow \eta\frac{d^2\theta}{dt^2}\right)\sin\theta\right]$$

$$\leftrightarrow \left[\left\{\epsilon\left(\frac{d\theta}{dt}\right)^2 \leftrightarrow \eta\left(\frac{d\theta}{dt}\right)^2\right\}\cos\theta \leftrightarrow \left\{\epsilon\left(\frac{d\theta}{dt}\right)^2 \leftrightarrow \eta\left(\frac{d\theta}{dt}\right)^2\right\}\sin\theta\right] \tag{6.11}$$

Note we have made all signs positive since we are dealing with vectors. We can simplify this equation by using the following symbols:

$$\frac{d\epsilon}{dt} = V_P^\epsilon = \text{velocity of } P \text{ relative to the } \epsilon\text{-}\eta \text{ axes in the } \epsilon \text{ direction}$$

$$\frac{d\eta}{dt} = V_P^\eta = \text{velocity of } P \text{ relative to the } \epsilon\text{-}\eta \text{ axes in the } \eta \text{ direction}$$

$$\frac{d\theta}{dt} = \omega = \text{angular velocity of the body relative to the } x\text{-}y \text{ axes}$$

$$\frac{d^2\theta}{dt^2} = \alpha = \text{angular acceleration of the body relative to the } x\text{-}y \text{ axes}$$

$$\frac{d^2\bar{x}}{dt^2} = a_{Q/O}^x = \text{acceleration of } Q \text{ relative to the } x\text{-}y \text{ axes in the } x \text{ direction}$$

$$\frac{d^2\bar{y}}{dt^2} = a^y_{Q/O} = \text{acceleration of } Q \text{ relative to the } x\text{-}y \text{ axes in the } y \text{ direction}$$

$$\frac{d^2\epsilon}{dt^2} = a^\epsilon_P \quad = \text{acceleration of } P \text{ relative to the } \epsilon\text{-}\eta \text{ axes in } \epsilon \text{ direction}$$

$$\frac{d^2\eta}{dt^2} = a^\eta_P \quad = \text{acceleration of } P \text{ relative to the } \epsilon\text{-}\eta \text{ axes in } \eta \text{ direction}$$

Then substituting and rearranging in Eq. (6.11)

$$a_{P/O} = [a^x_{Q/O} \mathbin{+\mkern-8mu+} a^y_{Q/O}]$$
$$\mathbin{+\mkern-8mu+} [(a^\epsilon_P \mathbin{+\mkern-8mu+} a^\eta_P) \cos\theta \mathbin{+\mkern-8mu+} (a^\epsilon_P \mathbin{+\mkern-8mu+} a^\eta_P) \sin\theta]$$
$$\mathbin{+\mkern-8mu+} [2(V^\epsilon_P \mathbin{+\mkern-8mu+} V^\eta_P)\,\omega\cos\theta \mathbin{+\mkern-8mu+} 2(V^\epsilon_P \mathbin{+\mkern-8mu+} V^\eta_P)\,\omega\sin\theta]$$
$$\mathbin{+\mkern-8mu+} [(\epsilon \mathbin{+\mkern-8mu+} \eta)\alpha\cos\theta \mathbin{+\mkern-8mu+} (\epsilon \mathbin{+\mkern-8mu+} \eta)\,\alpha\sin\theta]$$
$$\mathbin{+\mkern-8mu+} [(\epsilon \mathbin{+\mkern-8mu+} \eta)\omega^2\cos\theta \mathbin{+\mkern-8mu+} (\epsilon \mathbin{+\mkern-8mu+} \eta)\omega^2\sin\theta] \qquad (6.12)$$

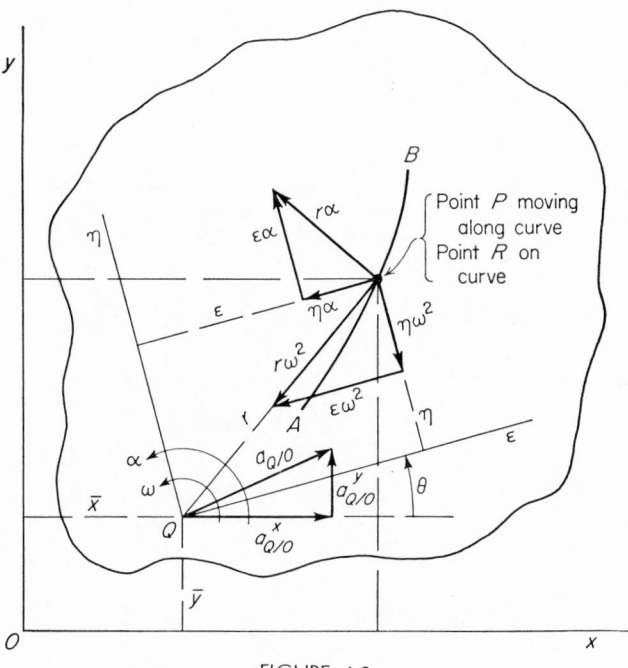

FIGURE 6.3

Note that in adding these components we have grouped certain components and enclosed them in brackets. We did this so that we can consider each bracketed quantity as a separate component and discuss each individually.

Figure 6.3 shows the vectors corresponding to the components in the first, fourth, and fifth brackets. The first bracket gives the components of the acceleration of the moving origin Q relative to the fixed axes. The fourth bracket contains all terms which are dependent on the angular acceleration of the body and noting that the quantity $(\epsilon \leftrightarrow \eta)$ is the vector "r," we conclude that this is a component "$r\alpha$" which can be considered as the tangential component of the acceleration of a point R on line A–B, coincident with point P, relative to Q. The fifth bracket we recognize as a vector $r\omega^2$ which is the normal component of R relative to Q.

Now considering the second bracket, since it is the acceleration of P relative to the ϵ-η axes, it can be considered as the acceleration of P relative to R (R having no motion relative to the ϵ-η axes). Then it is the acceleration that P would have relative to the moving body if the body were fixed in space and P were moving along the curve A–B. Under these conditions P will have a normal acceleration equal to the square of the velocity along the curve divided by the radius of curvature at the point P; and a tangential acceleration equal to the change in magnitude of the velocity along the curve. If the path of P along the body were a straight line the normal acceleration would be zero. The vector of these two components is shown in Fig. 6.4. This acceleration will be discussed in detail in the following chapters.

The third bracket is a component which we have not encountered in any manner previously. The vector represented by the terms in parentheses,

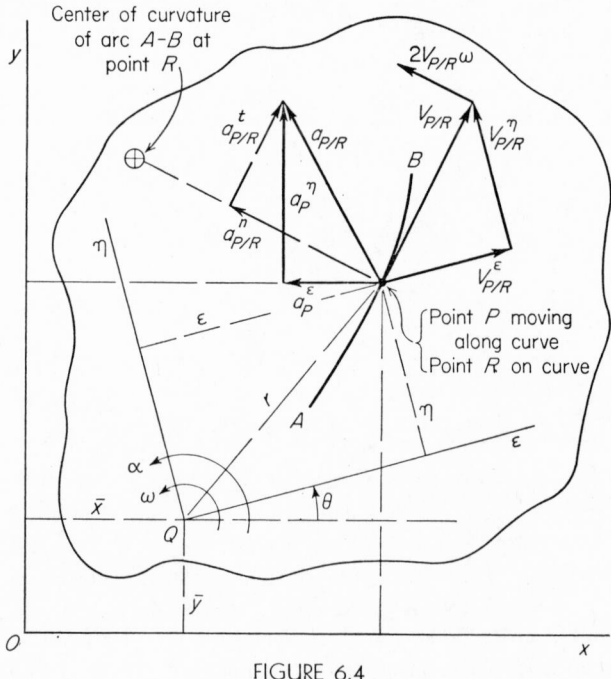

FIGURE 6.4

$(V_P^e \mathbin{+\mkern-8mu+} V_P^n)$, is the velocity of P relative to R and the bracket, then, is a component whose magnitude is $2V_{P/R}\omega$. Referring back to Fig. 6.2, we see that the velocity $V_{P/R}$ is tangential to the curve $A–B$ and the vector $2V_{P/R}\omega$ can be thought of at present as representing the change in the velocity vector $V_{P/R}$ caused by its rotation with an angular velocity ω. This vector is shown in Fig. 6.4. Since it is an acceleration which results from a change in direction of the velocity with respect to time, it is a normal acceleration and its direction is normal to the velocity vector, its sense being in the direction of the angular velocity ω. This particular component of acceleration has been given the name Coriolis' component of acceleration, named after the man who established the law defining this acceleration component. Since this component only occurs when a point is moving relative to a path which has rotation, it is sometimes called the compound supplementary component of acceleration. We will use the simpler term Coriolis' component of acceleration. This component is rather complicated and will be covered in detail in the next chapter.

Now we can simplify Eq. (6.12) by writing it in the following manner

$$a_{P/O} = a_{Q/O} \mathbin{+\mkern-8mu+} a_{R/Q} \mathbin{+\mkern-8mu+} a_{P/R} \qquad (6.13)$$

where $a_{Q/O}$ = acceleration of the origin on the moving body relative to the fixed origin

$\quad\quad a_{R/Q}$ = acceleration of point R, attached to the moving body, relative to Q

$\quad\quad\quad\ = r\omega^2 \mathbin{+\mkern-8mu+} r\alpha$

$\quad\quad a_{P/R}$ = acceleration of point P, moving along the curve, relative to point R

$\quad\quad\quad\ = a_{P/R}^n \mathbin{+\mkern-8mu+} a_{P/R}^t \mathbin{+\mkern-8mu+} 2V_{P/R}\omega$

where $(a_{P/R}^n \mathbin{+\mkern-8mu+} a_{P/R}^t)$ is the acceleration P would have relative to R if the body were fixed in space and P were moving along line $A–B$. Then we see that the equation for vector addition is satisfied.

6.2 The Acceleration Image

The acceleration image will be developed first for simple mechanisms which contain only pin jointed pairs and links which have rectilinear translation relative to the fixed body. The general case of mechanisms which contain higher sliding and rolling pairs is quite complicated and will be taken up after we have gained a thorough understanding of the acceleration analysis of the simpler mechanisms.

Consider the link shown in Fig. 6.5(a) which is constrained to a rotation relative to the fixed body by a pin joint at point O. The link has an angular

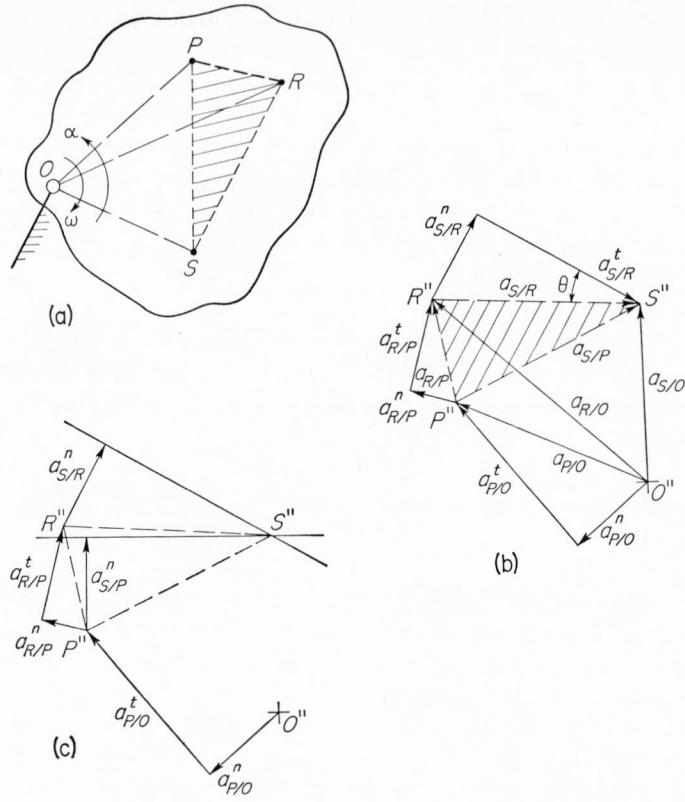

FIGURE 6.5

velocity ω and an angular acceleration α both of which are known. We will determine the acceleration of the points P, R, and S, on the link, relative to the fixed body. As with the velocity image we will first locate a pole point which will represent the acceleration of all points on the mechanism which have no acceleration. This point will be designated O'', see Fig. 6.5(b), the double prime used to designate points on the acceleration image in the same manner that the single prime was used to designate points on the velocity image.

The acceleration of P relative to O will be determined by calculating the normal and tangential components and adding the vectors representing these components. The magnitude of the normal component can be obtained from Eq. (6.1)

$$a^n_{P/O} = \omega^2(\overline{O\text{–}P})$$

and is directed from P towards O. Then we draw a vector from O'', in direction from P towards O, to represent this acceleration to some scale as shown in Fig. 6.5(b). The magnitude of the tangential acceleration is obtained from Eq. (6.2)

$$a_{P/O}^t = \alpha(\overline{O\text{-}P})$$

and its direction is perpendicular to the normal acceleration vector and directed as shown in the figure since the tangential acceleration is counter clockwise. The sum of these two vectors is the total acceleration of P relative to O as given by the vector equation

$$a_{P/O} = a_{P/O}^n \mathbin{+\!\!\!\!+} a_{P/O}^t$$

Now we have located P'', the acceleration image of point P. The acceleration images of points R and S could be located in the same manner but instead we will use the relative acceleration equations since the use of these equations will be necessary for links whose angular acceleration we do not know.

The relative acceleration equation for point R is

$$a_{R/O} = a_{P/O} \mathbin{+\!\!\!\!+} a_{R/P}$$

The vector $a_{P/O}$ we found when we located P'' so we need to determine the vector $a_{R/P}$. This acceleration will also be resolved into its normal and tangential components since we can calculate the components from Eqs. (6.1) and (6.2) where the radius "r" is the distance between points P and R. The discerning student might well question the use of these equations for this case since they were derived in Chapter 2 on the basis of a point moving at a fixed radius from some point on the fixed body, and here we are attempting to use them for two points on a body, neither of which is fixed, relative to the fixed body. In order to show these equations do hold for any two points on a rigid body we refer back to the development of the equations of motion for the general case which was covered in Article 6.1. If we consider the points R and Q, both of which are on the moving body, we see from Eq. (6.13) that the acceleration of R relative to Q is composed of a normal and tangential component as given by Eqs. (6.1) and (6.2) where r is the distance between the two points, and ω and α are the angular velocity and angular acceleration of the moving body which has no fixed point relative to the fixed body. Then we can locate R'' as shown in Fig. 6.5(b).

In this same manner we can locate S'' by taking the normal and tangential acceleration components of S relative to R. We should note that the direction of the normal component of acceleration is always directed from the point in question towards the point to which we are referring it.

Note that the triangle formed by the three image points, P'', R'', and S'', form an image of the triangle formed by the three points, P, R, and S, on the link. However, this acceleration image of the triangle formed by the three points does not have its sides normal to the corresponding sides of the triangle on the link, as was the case in the velocity image. The tangential component of acceleration for any two points is normal to the line joining the points, and the line joining the two image points is the vector sum of the tangential and normal components of acceleration and the relative acceleration between two points forms the hypotenuse of a right triangle with the tangential and normal components forming the other two sides. If we consider the line R–S in the figure, we see that the image of the line R''–S'', is rotated relative to line R–S by an angle of 90° plus an angle θ in the direction of the angular acceleration. The angle θ is defined by its tangent as

$$\tan \theta = \frac{a_{S/R}^n}{a_{S/R}^t} = \frac{\omega^2 r}{\alpha r}$$

or
$$\tan \theta = \frac{\omega^2}{\alpha}$$

and we see that the angle of rotation of the acceleration image of a line is dependent on the relative magnitude of the angular velocity and acceleration of the link which contains the line and would be different for various links; however the angle is the same for all lines on the same link.

After we have located the image of points P and R in Fig. 6.5(a) we can locate the image of point S in a manner which does not require the knowledge of the angular acceleration of the link. This method of locating S'' is very important since it is the method which will be used in drawing the acceleration image for all mechanisms. Figure 6.5(c) shows this method of determining S''. We locate P'' and R'' in the same manner as before. Now assuming that we know only the angular velocity of the link we can calculate the normal acceleration of point S relative to point P. We draw a vector to represent this as shown in the figure. If the link has an angular acceleration, then the tangential component $a_{S/P}^t$ will be normal to the normal acceleration vector. Then through the end of the normal vector we draw a line perpendicular to it and we know that S'' must lie on this line at some point. In the same manner we draw a vector representing the normal acceleration of S relative to R and we know that S'' must lie on the line passing through the head of that vector and normal to it. We know two lines on which S'' must lie, and the intersection of these two lines must be the point S''. The intersection of these two lines at S'' determines the tangential component of the acceleration of S relative to points P and R. If we did not know the angular acceleration of the link, these tangential components could be a means of determining that angular acceleration. This will be the method used in finding the angular acceleration of links in mechanisms as we shall see later.

We are now ready to draw the acceleration image for a complete mechanism. Figure 6.6.(a) shows a quadric crank mechanism with driving link

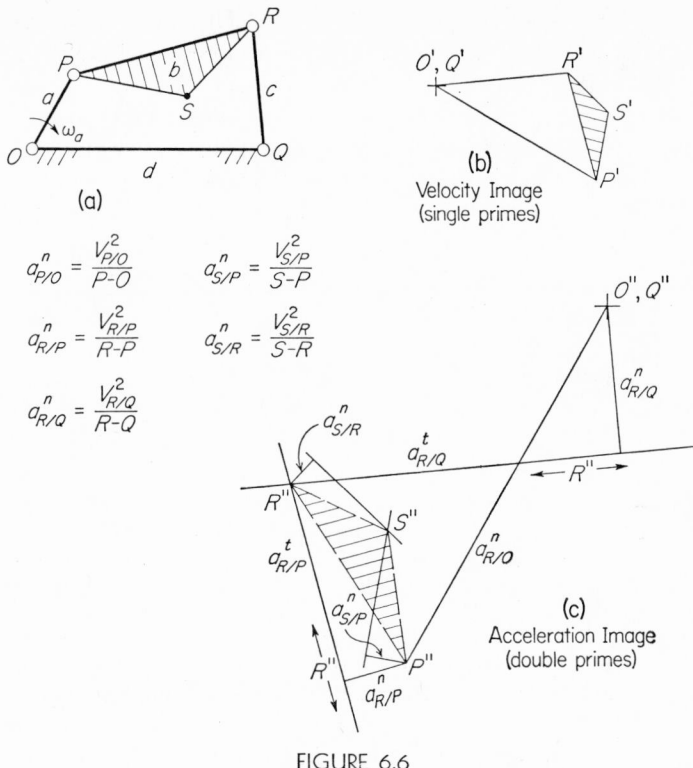

$$a^n_{P/O} = \frac{V^2_{P/O}}{P-O} \qquad a^n_{S/P} = \frac{V^2_{S/P}}{S-P}$$

$$a^n_{R/P} = \frac{V^2_{R/P}}{R-P} \qquad a^n_{S/R} = \frac{V^2_{S/R}}{S-R}$$

$$a^n_{R/Q} = \frac{V^2_{R/Q}}{R-Q}$$

FIGURE 6.6

"a" turning at a constant angular velocity, ω_a. Since the normal accelerations, which must be calculated, are determined by the relative velocities of the various points, we must first draw a velocity image for the mechanism so that the relative velocities are readily available. The velocity image is shown in Fig. 6.6(b). The acceleration image is started by locating the pole O'' representing all points which have no acceleration, and therefore it represents all points on the fixed link "d." Points O on link "a" and Q on link "c" always remain at the same position relative to the fixed link and therefore they have no acceleration. Then O'' will also be Q''. Since link "a," the driving link, has no angular acceleration (turning as it does with constant angular velocity) the only acceleration any point on that link will have relative to any other point will be a normal acceleration, and knowing the angular velocity of the link we can calculate the normal acceleration. It will be found more convenient to use the relative linear velocity between two points in calculating the normal acceleration since the linear velocity can be obtained directly from the velocity image. The image of point P, on link "a," can then be found by calculating the normal acceleration of P relative to O and drawing a vector to some given scale from O'', in direction from P towards O (points on the mechanism). This is shown in Fig. 6 6(c). The calculations for the normal accelerations are also tabulated on the figure.

Considering now link "b" we find that it is not so easy to handle as was link "a." We do not know whether it has an angular acceleration or not and therefore must assume that it does. Since it is connected to link "a" with a pin joint at P, we realize that because of the pin joint the point on link "b" at the pin joint must have the same motion as the coincident point on link "a." Therefore P'' must also be an image of a point on link "b," and we can determine the normal acceleration of any point on link "b" relative to P and draw a vector representing it on the image from P''. Taking point R we calculate the normal acceleration, $a_{R/P}^n$, as shown on the figure and draw a vector to represent it from P'', the direction being from R towards P on the mechanism. If link "b" has an angular acceleration then point R will have also a tangential component of acceleration relative to P and it will be perpendicular to the normal component. Then through the head of the vector representing the normal acceleration we draw a perpendicular line and R'' must lie on that line. Point R is at the pin joint connecting links "b" and "c," therefore it must have the same acceleration as the coincident point on link "c"and we can calculate the normal acceleration of R relative to Q whose image we have. Then through Q'' we draw the vector representing $a_{R/Q}^n$ as calculated on the figure, in direction from R towards Q, and through the head of that vector we pass a line in the direction of the tangential acceleration and R'' must lie somewhere on that line. The intersection of the two lines in the direction of the tangential accelerations of R is the image R''.

Having now the image of two points on link "b," the image of any other point on that link can be found by referencing it to those two points. The image of S or S'' can be found by drawing the normal accelerations of S relative to P and R and finding the intersection of the lines in the direction of the tangential accelerations through the heads of these vectors, as shown on the figure.

As in the case of the velocity image we did not place arrowheads on the vectors because they are not necessary. The sense of the acceleration is determined by the position of the primed points. For example, the normal acceleration of R relative to Q is always from R towards Q, on the figure, or leading away from Q'' on the image; and the normal acceleration of Q relative to R is always from Q towards R on the mechanism or in opposite direction to $a_{R/Q}^n$. The tangential acceleration is always perpendicular in direction to the normal acceleration and the sense must be determined from the acceleration image. The sense of $a_{R/Q}^t$ is from the end of the normal acceleration vector, $a_{R/Q}^n$, towards R''. From the fact that the relative accelerations of two points are always equal in magnitude and opposite in sense, we see that the sense of $a_{R/Q}^t$ is opposite to the sense of $a_{Q/R}^t$.

The total acceleration of a point relative to any other point is represented in magnitude by the distance between the images of the two points, and the direction of this total acceleration is along the line joining the image points. The sense is towards the image of the point whose relative acceleration we wish to find and away from the image of the point to which we are referring it. The absolute acceleration of a point, or the total acceleration relative to the fixed body, is always the vector from the image of the fixed point to the image of the point in question.

The sense of the angular accelerations of a link is determined from the sense of the relative tangential accelerations of any two points on the link. Taking link "b" in the previous example and using points P and R we find that the tangential acceleration of R relative to P is up and towards the left from the acceleration image and since this is a relative acceleration, if we consider P fixed in the drawing of the mechanism, then R is being accelerated upward relative to P and link "b" has an angular acceleration in a counter clockwise sense. Using points S and R we see from the image that

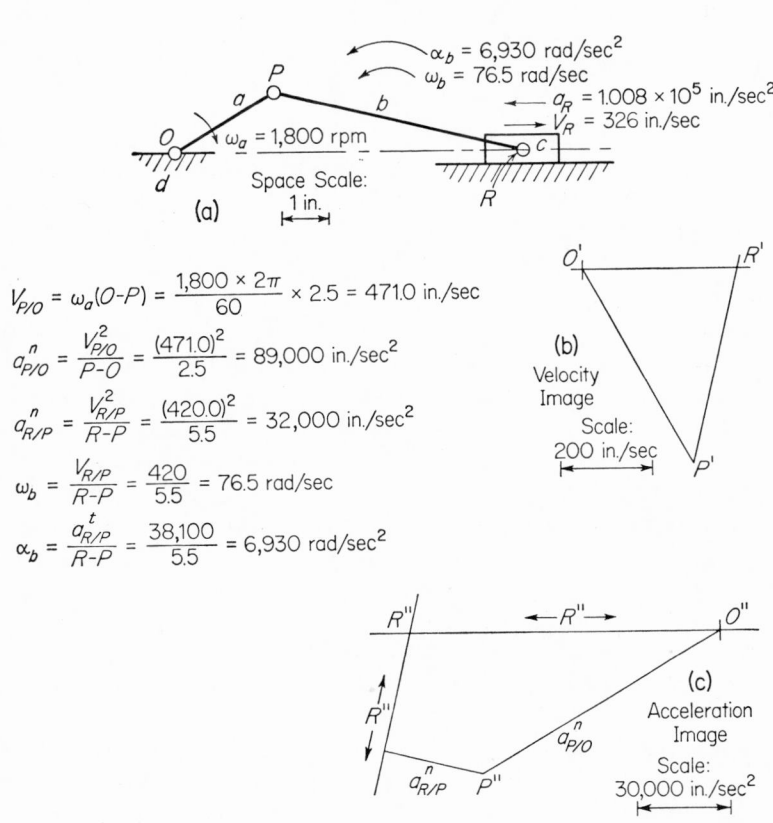

$$V_{P/O} = \omega_a(O\text{-}P) = \frac{1,800 \times 2\pi}{60} \times 2.5 = 471.0 \text{ in./sec}$$

$$a_{P/O}^n = \frac{V_{P/O}^2}{P\text{-}O} = \frac{(471.0)^2}{2.5} = 89,000 \text{ in./sec}^2$$

$$a_{R/P}^n = \frac{V_{R/P}^2}{R\text{-}P} = \frac{(420.0)^2}{5.5} = 32,000 \text{ in./sec}^2$$

$$\omega_b = \frac{V_{R/P}}{R\text{-}P} = \frac{420}{5.5} = 76.5 \text{ rad/sec}$$

$$\alpha_b = \frac{a_{R/P}^t}{R\text{-}P} = \frac{38,100}{5.5} = 6,930 \text{ rad/sec}^2$$

FIGURE 6.7

S has a downward tangential acceleration relative to R, and if S (on the mechanism drawing) is accelerating down relative to R, then as before, link "b" has a counter clockwise angular acceleration.

As another example we will take the slider crank mechanism as shown in Fig. 6.7(a). This mechanism has a link moving with rectilinear translation relative to the fixed body. The velocity image is shown in Fig. 6.7(b). Figure 6.7(c) shows the acceleration image. The image of all points on the fixed body is at O'' and the image of point P has been found as in the previous example. In order to locate the image of the point R we reference it to point P, which is on the same link (link "b") and the fixed body. As before we calculate the normal acceleration, $a_{R/P}^{n}$, and draw a line perpendicular to

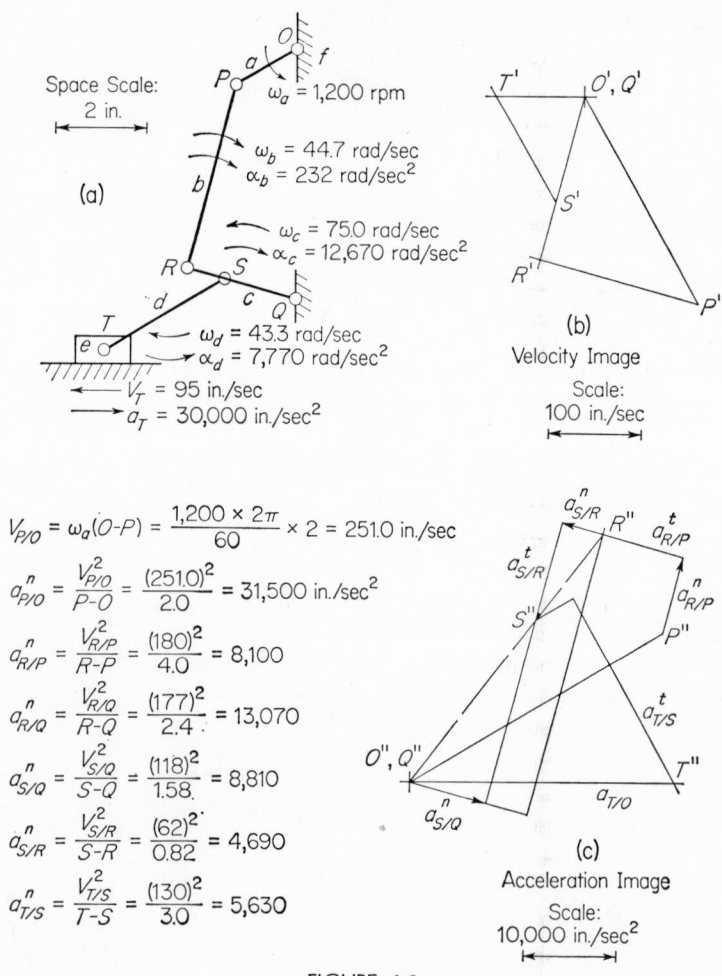

Space Scale:
2 in.

(a)

$\omega_a = 1{,}200$ rpm

$\omega_b = 44.7$ rad/sec
$\alpha_b = 232$ rad/sec^2

$\omega_c = 75.0$ rad/sec
$\alpha_c = 12{,}670$ rad/sec^2

$\omega_d = 43.3$ rad/sec
$\alpha_d = 7{,}770$ rad/sec^2

$V_T = 95$ in./sec
$a_T = 30{,}000$ in./sec^2

(b)
Velocity Image
Scale:
100 in./sec

$$V_{P/O} = \omega_a(O\text{-}P) = \frac{1{,}200 \times 2\pi}{60} \times 2 = 251.0 \text{ in./sec}$$

$$a_{P/O}^{n} = \frac{V_{P/O}^{2}}{P\text{-}O} = \frac{(251.0)^2}{2.0} = 31{,}500 \text{ in./sec}^2$$

$$a_{R/P}^{n} = \frac{V_{R/P}^{2}}{R\text{-}P} = \frac{(180)^2}{4.0} = 8{,}100$$

$$a_{R/Q}^{n} = \frac{V_{R/Q}^{2}}{R\text{-}Q} = \frac{(177)^2}{2.4} = 13{,}070$$

$$a_{S/Q}^{n} = \frac{V_{S/Q}^{2}}{S\text{-}Q} = \frac{(118)^2}{1.58} = 8{,}810$$

$$a_{S/R}^{n} = \frac{V_{S/R}^{2}}{S\text{-}R} = \frac{(62)^2}{0.82} = 4{,}690$$

$$a_{T/S}^{n} = \frac{V_{T/S}^{2}}{T\text{-}S} = \frac{(130)^2}{3.0} = 5{,}630$$

(c)
Acceleration Image
Scale:
10,000 in./sec^2

FIGURE 6.8

it through its head and R'' must lie on this line. Since point R always moves in a horizontal direction relative to the fixed body, the total acceleration of R must be in a horizontal direction and through O'' we draw a horizontal line on which R'' must lie. The intersection of this line and the line through the head of the vector $a_{R/P}^n$ then is the image of point R, or R''. In this example the scales of the various drawings are given on the figure and all necessary calculations are carried out. Also it will be noted that on the drawing of the mechanism arrows have been drawn to indicate the direction of the angular velocity and angular acceleration of link "b" and the linear velocity and linear acceleration of link "c." It will be found later that these arrows will be quite helpful for use in the dynamic analysis of the links of a mechanism. Therefore, we should form the habit of always placing them on the drawing.

A more complicated example of a mechanism having only links connected by pin joints or links moving with rectilinear translation relative to the fixed body is shown in Fig. 6.8. The links "a," "b," "c," and "f" compose a quadric crank mechanism which we have already analyzed. Link "c," combined with links "d," "e," and "f" make up a slider crank mechanism similar to the previous example except that in this case we will find that all links have angular acceleration. The acceleration analysis proceeds from P'' to R'', as shown. Having the acceleration image of two points on link "c," we can find the image of point S on link "c." Since S lies on the line joining R and Q, the image of S must lie on the line R''–Q''. Then we calculate the normal acceleration of S relative to either R or Q and draw a line to represent the tangential acceleration. This line will intersect the line R''–Q'' at S''. In the figure both normal accelerations and both tangentials are shown, but only one need be used to determine S''. From S'' we proceed to find T'' as in the previous example.

6.3 *Instant Centers of Acceleration*

In the discussion of velocities of mechanisms we used the concept of instant centers of velocity, and we defined the instant center of velocity of two bodies as the point on one body which had no velocity relative to a coincident point on the other body. We can also define an instant center of acceleration of two bodies as the point on one body which has no acceleration relative to a coincident point on the other body. This analogous concept is not as useful in relation to accelerations but will still be found of considerable value in acceleration analyses, as will be seen.

One important point should be made immediately. There is no relation between the instant centers of velocity and the instant centers of acceleration, and although they *may* be at the same location in the mechanism, they are separate and distinct concepts. The instant center of velocity should

never be used in acceleration analyses. Only the instant center of acceleration, as defined above, should be used in the analysis of accelerations.

To show that the instant center of velocity is not necessarily an instant
center of acceleration we refer to Fig. 6.9(a) which shows a quadric crank
mechanism with the instant center of velocity for links "b" and "d" at point

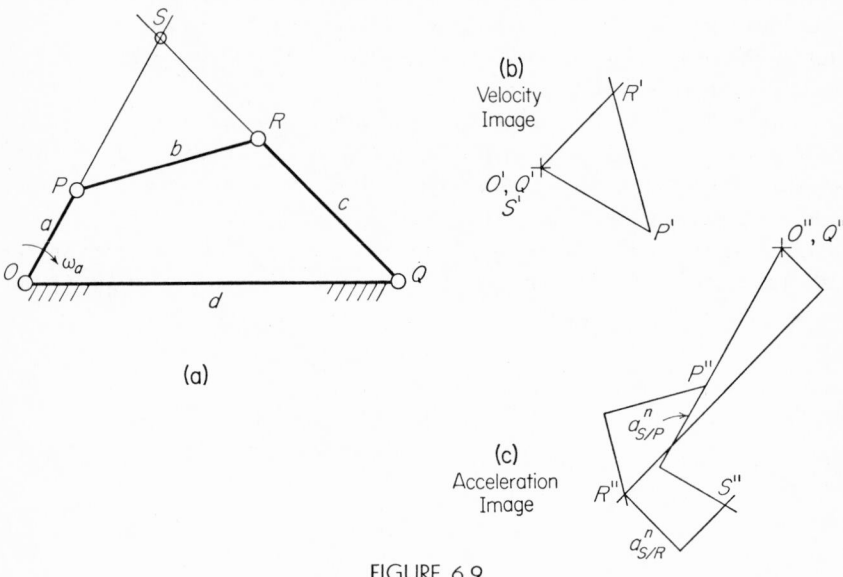

FIGURE 6.9

S. The velocity image for the mechanism is drawn in Fig. 6.9(b), and we
see that the velocity image of S on link "b" is at the same point as O', since
it is an instant center of velocity, and therefore has no velocity relative to
the fixed link. However, when we look at the acceleration image of point S,
Fig. 6.9(c) we see that point S'' does not lie at the same point as O''; therefore, point S has an acceleration relative to the fixed link "d" and cannot be
an instant center of acceleration for links "b" and "d."

Kennedy's theorem gave us a simple means of determining the instant
centers of velocity. A straightforward method such as this is not available
for the location of instant centers of acceleration.

In the preceding work on acceleration images we found that the pin
joint connecting two links was a point on both links at which there was no
relative acceleration between the links. Then, by definition, the pin joint
connecting two links is the instant center of acceleration common to the two
links. We also found in the previous discussion that a link moving with
rectilinear translation relative to the fixed link had an acceleration only in
the direction of the motion. This acceleration is caused only by a change in
magnitude of the velocity vector, since the direction of the velocity vector

remains constant, and therefore the acceleration is a tangential acceleration. All points on the link have the same acceleration relative to the fixed link, and we could think of the instant center of acceleration as being at infinity along a line normal to the velocity and acceleration vector.

We make use of these instant centers in drawing the acceleration image and therefore they are important to our analysis, but since any other instant centers of acceleration are not easily found (and in many cases almost impossible to locate), this is the main extent to which we will make use of instant centers of acceleration.

The instant centers of acceleration of the various links common to the fixed link will prove of value to us in some instances. These we can locate by means of the acceleration image. Figure 6.10 shows a slider crank mechanism and its acceleration image. Remembering that point O'' on the image diagram is the image of the point on each link which has no acceleration relative to the fixed link, then by definition it is the image of the instant

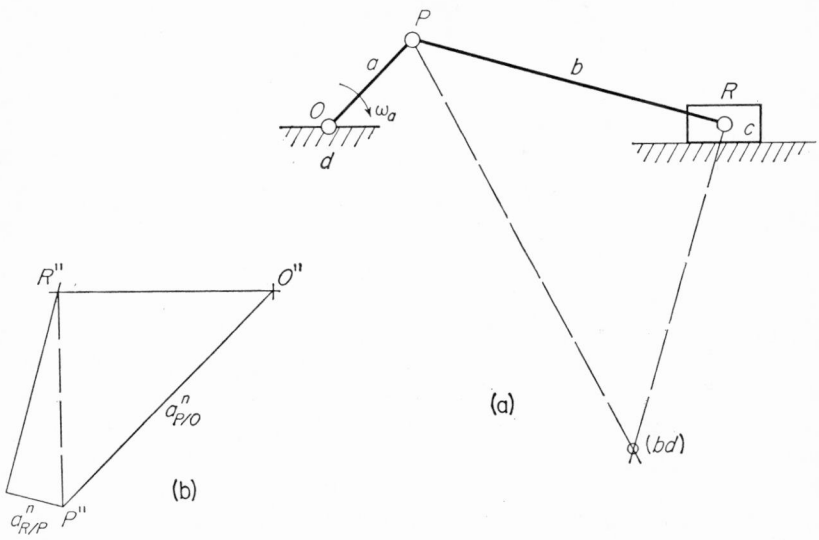

FIGURE 6.10

center of all links common to the fixed link. Taking it as the image of the instant center of acceleration common to link "b" and link "d," we can find the instant center on the mechanism by locating the point on link "b" whose acceleration image it represents. This can best be accomplished by remembering that the triangle $O''P''R''$ and the triangle formed by the points P, R, and the instant center (bd), are similar. Then by drawing a triangle on the mechanism similar to triangle $O''P''R''$ with line P–R corresponding to link P''–R'' on the image triangle the intersection of the other two legs is the instant center of acceleration "bd," as shown in the figure.

Instant centers of acceleration will be discussed further when we take up acceleration images for mechanisms having rolling and higher sliding pairs in a later chapter.

6.4 Floating Link Mechanisms

In the construction of acceleration images for mechanisms containing a floating link (as described in the chapter on velocity images), we find that again we cannot complete the acceleration image directly and must make use of the auxiliary points which we used in the velocity image. Consider the mechanism shown in Fig. 6.11, the same mechanism shown in Figs. 5.5 and 5.6. Since the velocity image was constructed in those figures we will only construct the acceleration image in Fig. 6.11. The acceleration image is started at O'' in Fig. 6.11(b), and the image of P, or P'', is located. We

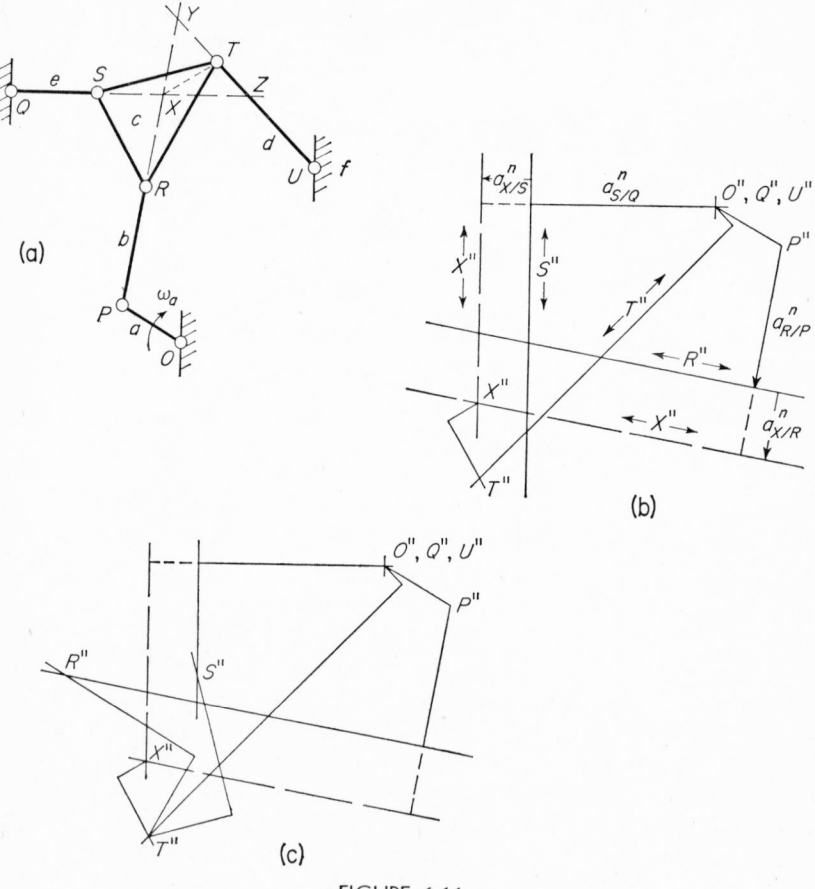

FIGURE 6.11

can calculate the normal acceleration of R relative to P and draw the vector representing it from P''. Then R'' will lie on the line passing through the end of that vector and normal to it. Now we find that we have no other point from which we can reference R so as to get another line on which R'' lies. The same condition exists for the other two points, S and T, on link "c" which is the floating link. A line can be found on which the images of these points lie by referencing them to the fixed link. But we cannot find any other line on which the images lie, and therefore cannot locate the image of the points. This is the same condition that existed in the case of the velocity image and we again must resort to the use of auxiliary points in order to locate the images of points on link "c." We will consider the auxiliary point X first. Since it is on the link "c" we can calculate the normal acceleration of X relative to R. Its direction is the same as the normal acceleration of R relative to P. The tangential acceleration of X relative to

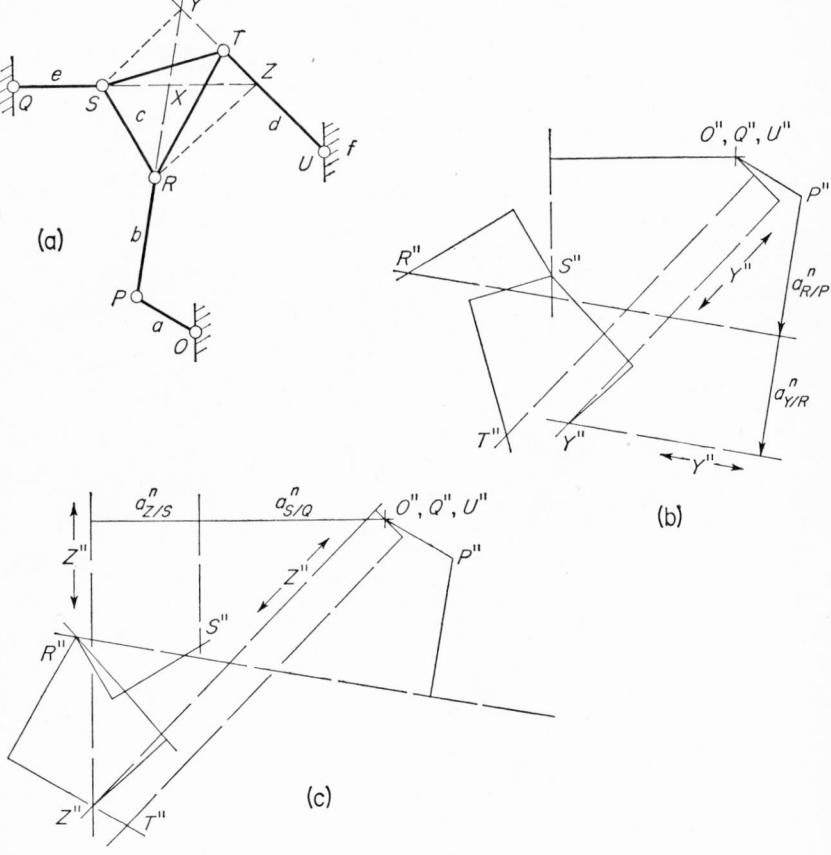

FIGURE 6.12

R will be perpendicular to the normal vector. From the figure we see that the line containing X'' is parallel to the line containing R''. The construction of the normal vector and the line in the direction of the tangential vector are constructed with dashed lines to avoid confusion. Note that we do not need R'' in order to lay out the line on which X'' lies because the line is parallel to the line on which R'' lies; the normal acceleration vector is the distance between these lines, and can be drawn at any point along them. It should be pointed out that we cannot calculate the normal acceleration of X relative to P because they are on different links. In the same manner we can find another line on which X'' lies by noting that the direction of the normal acceleration of X relative to S is the same as the direction of the normal acceleration of S relative to Q. Then X'' must lie on a line parallel to the line which contains S'' and at a distance from that line equal to the normal acceleration of X relative to S. Thus we have two lines on which X'' must lie and the intersection of these two lines locates X''. Now we have a point on link "c" whose image we know. We can reference T to that point and locate T''. Using T'' as a reference point, we can locate R'' and S'', thereby completing the acceleration image. The completed image is shown in Fig. 6.11(c).

The other two auxiliary points, Y and Z, could have been used instead of point X. If we had used Y the image of point S could have been found, and by the use of Z the image of point R could have been found. The constructions of the images using these points are shown in Fig. 6.12(b) and 6.12(c).

The construction of the acceleration image for another floating link mechanism will be discussed in a later chapter after we have covered the material on acceleration of mechanisms having links paired with higher sliding and rolling pairs in conjunction with pinned joints.

6.5 Graphical Determination of Normal Acceleration

At the beginning of this chapter we mentioned a method of constructing the acceleration image by graphical methods only, where the normal accelerations are not calculated for each point. This method will be taken up now. Consider the link represented by line $O–P$ in Fig. 6.13. The velocity of P relative to O is represented by the vector $P–S$ drawn normal to the line $O–P$. The link is drawn to a space scale of 1 in. $= e_s$ in., and the velocity vector is drawn to a velocity scale of 1 in. $= e_v$ in./sec. The actual length of the line $O–P$ on the mechanism is given by the relation

$$s_{P/O} = e_s(O–P) \qquad\qquad (a)$$

and the actual velocity of P relative to O is

$$V_{P/O} = e_v(P–S) \qquad\qquad (b)$$

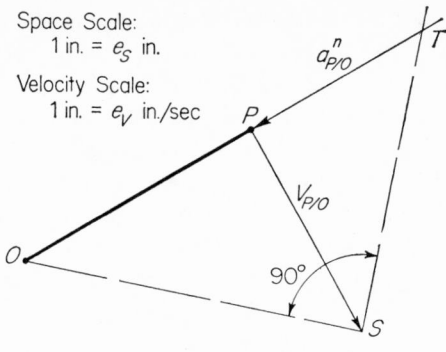

Space Scale:
  1 in. = e_S in.

Velocity Scale:
  1 in. = e_V in./sec

FIGURE 6.13

where e_s and e_v are the scales as defined above and the distances $O-P$ and $P-S$ are the true lengths of the lines on the figure. A line is drawn between the points O and S. From point S a line is drawn normal to line $O-S$ until it intersects the line $O-P$ extended at point T. This construction forms two triangles, OPS and SPT which are similar, and we can write the relation

$$\frac{O-P}{P-S} = \frac{P-S}{P-T}$$

or

$$P-T = \frac{(P-S)^2}{O-P}$$

and using equations (a) and (b)

$$P-T = \frac{V_{P/O}^2 \left(\dfrac{1}{e_v}\right)^2}{s_{P/O}\left(\dfrac{1}{e_s}\right)}$$

$$= \frac{V_{P/O}^2 \, e_s}{s_{P/O} \, e_v^2}$$

Then

$$(P-T)\frac{e_v^2}{e_s} = \frac{V_{P/O}^2}{s_{P/O}} = a_{P/O}^n$$

and we see that the factor e_v^2/e_s is the scale to which the line $P-T$ is drawn to represent the acceleration, $a_{P/O}^n$. The line $P-T$ represents the normal acceleration of P relative to O to a scale of 1 in. $= e_v^2/e_s$ in./sec². This gives us the magnitude of the normal acceleration only; the direction is from P towards O as shown on the figure. It should be noted that we are free to choose arbitrarily any two of the three scale factors, and the third is then determined by the two selected. Since the space scale and the velocity scale have been selected before we can draw the velocity image, it is usually more convenient to choose these scales and this leaves us with a predetermined acceleration scale.

An example of a quadric crank mechanism whose acceleration image is drawn by this complete graphical method is shown in Fig. 6.14. There are two disadvantages in drawing acceleration images in this manner; (1) finding the normal acceleration graphically tends to clutter up the kinematic drawing of the mechanism, and (2) we are not free to choose a con-

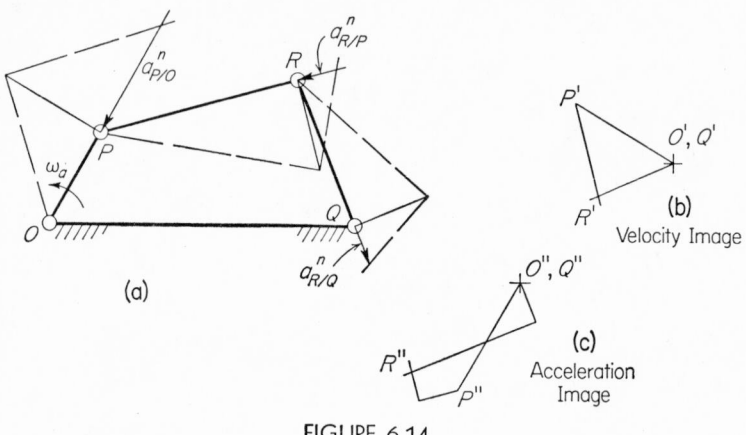

FIGURE 6.14

venient scale for the acceleration image. Offsetting these disadvantages is the time saved in not having to calculate each normal acceleration. If speed of calculation is of primary importance, the completely graphical method will usually require less time, particularly if we only wish to determine the acceleration of a few points of the mechanism.

PROBLEMS

For the problems below construct the acceleration polygon for the figures indicated, locating the acceleration image of all labeled points. Excepting Prob. 6.3 calculate the normal accelerations and select any appropriate scale for the acceleration vectors.

6.1 Fig. P4.3, with $\omega_a = 100$ rpm counter clockwise. Determine the angular velocity and angular accelerations of all links if ω_a is constant.

6.2 Fig. P5.1, with ω_a constant at 3600 rpm clockwise. Determine ω_d and α_d.

6.3 Repeat Prob. 6.2 except determine the normal accelerations graphically.

6.4 Locate the instant center of acceleration of link "b" with respect to the fixed link for Fig. P5.1.

6.5 Fig. P4.12, with ω_a constant at 250 rpm clockwise. Determine the angular velocity and angular acceleration of all links.

6.6 Fig. P4.12, with $\omega_a = 250$ rpm clockwise and $\alpha_a = 100$ rad/sec². Determine the angular velocity and angular acceleration of all links.

6.7 Fig. P5.10, with ω_a constant at 60 rpm clockwise. Determine the angular velocity and angular acceleration of all links.

6.8 Fig. P4.10, with ω_a constant at 1272 rpm clockwise. Determine the angular velocity and angular acceleration of all links.

6.9 Fig. P4.10, with velocity of slider "*d*" zero and acceleration of slider "*d*" 100 in./sec² upward. Determine the angular velocity and angular acceleration of all links.

Chapter 7

The Coriolis Component of
Acceleration

7.1 Introduction

In the preceding chapter we confined our discussion of acceleration images to mechanisms which contained only pin jointed pairs and links moving with rectilinear translation relative to the fixed link. We will now expand our discussion so as to include those mechanisms in which the Coriolis component of acceleration occurs. An example of such a mechanism is the quick-return mechanisms shown in Figs. 4.4 and 5.4. The Coriolis component occurs in both these cases in the relative acceleration of a point on link "*b*" relative to a point on link "*c*," where link "*b*" moves with rectilinear translation relative to link "*c*" at the same time that link "*c*" has rotational motion relative to the fixed link. However we should note that the Coriolis acceleration is not limited to such cases, as we shall see in the present chapter.

The Coriolis component of acceleration was discussed briefly in the preceding chapter when we discussed the general case of plane motion. In the present chapter the concept of the Coriolis component will be developed in detail. In the preceding chapter the concept of Coriolis' component was developed in a rigorous manner, but, as often happens in a mathematically rigorous analysis, the full physical significance is lost in the mathematical manipulations. In order to show more clearly just what the Coriolis component is and to better understand use of it in acceleration analyses, we will develop the idea for two particular cases. It should be remembered from the previous discussion, however, that any time we have a point moving relative to a path which has rotation there will be a Coriolis component of acceleration of the point relative to a coincident point on the rotating path, and the magnitude of the component will be $2V\omega$, where V is the velocity of the point relative to the path and ω is the angular velocity of the path.

7.2 *Particular Cases*

The first case which we will take up is the case of a link sliding with rectilinear translation relative to another link which has rotation. Figure 7.1(a) represents such a mechanism where link "a" is rotating relative to the fixed link "c" with angular velocity ω_a, and link "b" is sliding along link "a" with linear velocity V_L. Since we must deal with points we could think of this as a rotating wire with a bead sliding along it. For the present we will

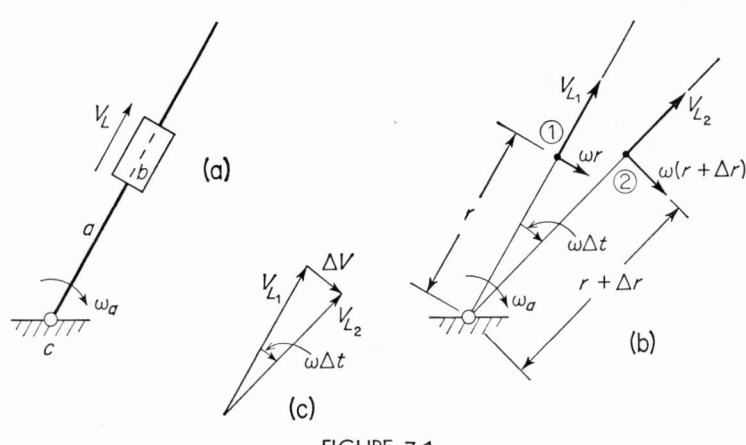

FIGURE 7.1

consider ω_a and V_L to be constant with respect to time. Figure 7.1(b) shows the position of the rod and bead at some instant of time with the bead at point (1), and also the position of rod and bead at a small instant of time, Δt, later with the bead at point (2). At point (1) the bead has a velocity V_L along the rod and a velocity normal to the rod of magnitude ωr, where r is the distance from the center of rotation to the bead at that instant. After the increment of time Δt, the rod will have rotated through an angle $\omega \Delta t$ and the bead will be at point (2) at a radius from the center of rotation of $r + \Delta r$ where Δr is equal to $V_L \Delta t$. The velocity of the bead at this time will be V_L along the rod and $\omega(r + \Delta r)$ normal to the rod. The change in the velocity of the bead, relative to a coincident point on the rod, will be the difference between the relative velocities at point (1) and point (2). This change is composed of two parts, one a change in direction of the vector V_L and the other a change in magnitude of the vector ωr. There is also a change in direction of the vector ωr but the coincident point on the rod has the same change in direction and there is no *relative* change caused by this change in direction. Considering first the change in the vector V_L, we see from Fig. 7.1(c) that the velocity vector at point (2) makes an angle relative to the vector at point (1) of $\omega \Delta t$, and the change in velocity, ΔV, is

$$\Delta V = V_L \omega \Delta t$$

By definition, the acceleration is given by the relation:

$$a = \frac{dV}{dt} = \lim_{\Delta t \to 0} \frac{\Delta V}{\Delta t} = \lim_{\Delta t \to 0} \frac{V_L \omega \Delta t}{\Delta t}$$

$$= V_L \omega$$

Its direction is normal to the vector V_L towards the right, as seen from the figure. Now considering the change in magnitude of the vector ωr, the change in velocity is

$$\Delta V = \omega(r + \Delta r) - \omega r = \omega \Delta r$$

and the acceleration is

$$a = \lim_{\Delta t \to 0} \frac{\Delta V}{\Delta t} = \lim_{\Delta t \to 0} \frac{\omega \Delta r}{\Delta t}$$

$$= \omega \frac{dr}{dt}$$

Noting that the quantity dr/dt is the change in radius with respect to time which is specifically V_L, the acceleration becomes

$$a = V_L \omega$$

It should be remembered that this and the previous component caused by a change in V_L are accelerations of the bead relative to a coincident point on the wire and not the total acceleration of the bead. The direction of this second component is also a normal to the vector V_L and towards the right. The Coriolis component of acceleration then is the sum of these two components and is equal to $2V_L \omega$, or

$$a^c = 2V_L \omega \tag{7.1}$$

and the direction of the component is normal to V_L and to the right. The absolute acceleration of the bead is the vector sum of the absolute acceleration of the coincident point on the rod and the relative acceleration satisfying the equation

$$a = \omega^2 r \leftrightarrow 2V_L \omega$$

In the above case, and in the case discussed in Chapter 6, the direction of the Coriolis component was normal to the sliding velocity vector. Noting that the acceleration component is caused by a change in the direction of that velocity vector and a change in the magnitude of the velocity component normal to the sliding velocity, we see that the direction will always be perpendicular to the vector representing the sliding velocity. We will now develop a simple rule for determining the direction and sense of the Coriolis component which will apply in all cases.

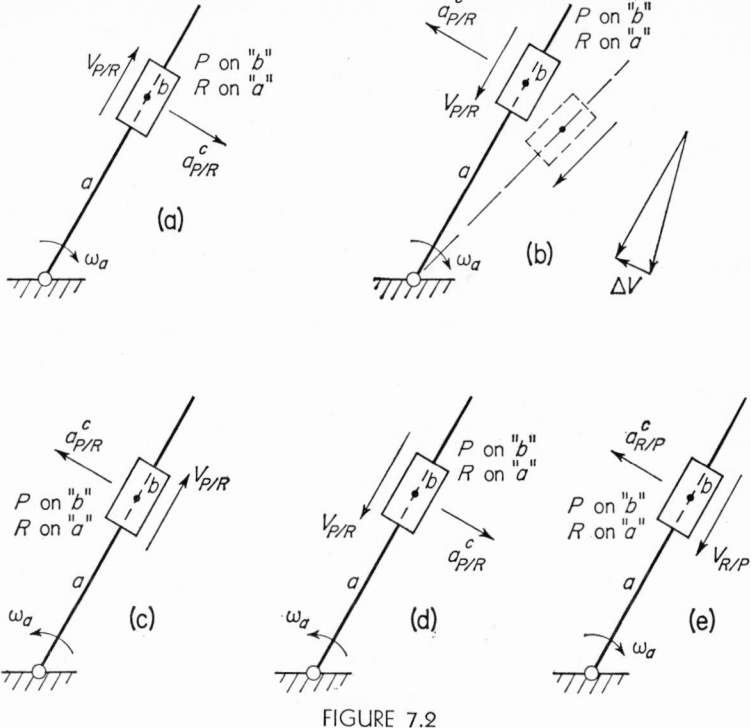

FIGURE 7.2

In Fig. 7.2(a) we have redrawn the mechanism discussed above, and we wish to determine the direction and sense of the Coriolis component of acceleration of point P on the slider, relative to the coincident point R, on the rotating rod. The direction and sense of the acceleration vector is shown on the figure and we see that if we rotate the relative velocity vector, $V_{P/R}$, ninety degrees in the direction of rotation of link "a," then this rotated vector will have the direction and sense of the Coriolis component. Fig. 7.2(b) shows the same mechanism with the same angular velocity, ω_a, but with the sliding velocity $V_{P/R}$ of opposite sense. The position of the slider and rod after a short increment of time is indicated by dashed lines and the change in the sliding vector is shown on the figure, which indicates that the Coriolis component is directed as shown. Here again, if we rotate the vector $V_{P/R}$ ninety degrees in the direction of ω_a, the resulting vector will indicate the direction and sense of the Coriolis component. The other two possibilities of motion for the slider with the rod having counter clockwise rotation are shown in Figs. 7.2(c) and 7.2(d). It is left to the student to show that the above rule holds for these two cases.

In all cases discussed so far we have dealt with the acceleration of a point on the slider relative to a coincident point on the rod, or relative to a coinci-

dent point on the path of the slider. In many cases the absolute acceleration of a point on the slider will be known and we will wish to determine the
relative acceleration of a coincident point on the path. For example the
mechanism shown in Fig. 7.2(e) is the same as that shown in Fig. 7.2(a) with
the same relative motion of slider and rod. But in this case we have given
the relative velocity $V_{R/P}$ and wish to find $a_{R/P}^c$. Obviously it is equal in
magnitude and has the same direction as $a_{P/R}^c$ but with opposite sense. But
we will note that the above rule holds if we use the velocity vector $V_{R/P}$ and
rotate it ninety degrees in the direction of ω_a.

Figure 7.3(a) shows the same type of mechanism as discussed above, but
in this case link "a" has an angular acceleration and the slider has an
acceleration along the rod as indicated on the figure. The acceleration

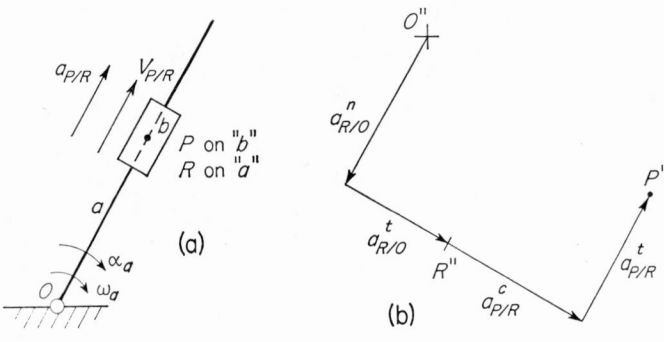

(a)

(b)

FIGURE 7.3

image for the mechanism is shown in Fig. 7.3(b). The normal and tangential accelerations for point R, on the rod, are laid out to determine the image
of R. The Coriolis acceleration of P relative to R is calculated and drawn
normal to the rod as shown. The vector representing the acceleration of P
relative to R along the rod is added to the Coriolis vector in order to determine P'' the image of point P. It should be pointed out that since the path
of P on link "a" is a straight line, there is no normal acceleration of P
relative to R caused by curvature of the path. The component of acceleration of P relative to R along the rod is labeled as a tangential acceleration,
or $a_{P/R}^t$ since it is directed along the path of R on link "a" and in most cases
must be determined by the intersection of two lines. The Coriolis acceleration can always be calculated since it is a function of the velocities of the
mechanism and we deal with it in the same manner that we handle a normal
acceleration. This will be amplified when we consider, later in the chapter,
some examples of mechanisms in which Coriolis' acceleration occurs.

As another example in which the Coriolis component of acceleration
occurs, let us consider the mechanism shown in Fig. 7.4. This mechanism is
composed of a circular table, link "a," constrained to rotate relative to the

fixed link about the center, point O, with
a concentric groove cut in it at a radius r
from the center. Link "b" is a slider
moving in the groove relative to the table.
Consider the point P on the slider, and the
coincident point R on the table. The
table is rotating with an angular velocity
ω_a and point P on the slider has velocity
$V_{P/R}$ relative to the table. The point P
remains at a constant radius r from the
center of rotation, O. The velocity of P
relative to the fixed link is

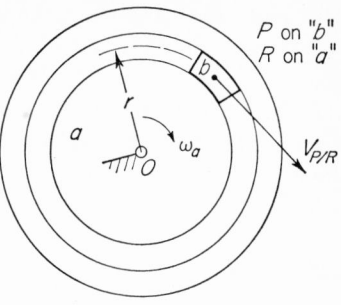

FIGURE 7.4

$$V_{P/O} = V_{R/O} \overset{+}{\rightarrow} V_{P/R}$$

but

$$V_{R/O} = \omega_a r$$

and then

$$V_{P/O} = \omega_a r \overset{+}{\rightarrow} V_{P/R}$$

Since P is moving in a circular path of radius r about O, its total acceleration is directed from P towards O and is of magnitude

$$a_{P/O} = \frac{V_{P/O}^2}{r} = \frac{(\omega_a r \overset{+}{\rightarrow} V_{P/R})^2}{r}$$

$$= \omega_a^2 r \overset{+}{\rightarrow} 2V_{P/R}\omega_a \overset{+}{\rightarrow} \frac{V_{P/R}^2}{r}$$

$$= a_{R/O} \overset{+}{\rightarrow} a_{P/R}$$

where:

$$a_{R/O} = \omega_a^2 r$$

$$a_{P/R} = 2V_{P/R}\omega_a \overset{+}{\rightarrow} \frac{V_{P/R}^2}{r}$$

In this example, where the slider is moving along a curved path, we find
that the Coriolis acceleration is still present since we again have a point
moving relative to a path which has an angular velocity, even though the
sliding velocity is in the same direction as the velocity of the coincident
point on the table. The total acceleration of point P is directed toward the
center of rotation O and is equal to the sum of the Coriolis acceleration, the
normal of P relative to R as if R were fixed and the slider were moving in a
curved path relative to the table, and the total acceleration of R. The rule
for the direction and sense of the Coriolis component still holds. If we give
an angular acceleration to the table and also a linear acceleration of P
relative to R, we will have a tangential acceleration of R relative to O and
also a tangential acceleration of P relative to R in the same direction.

If we hold ω_a and $V_{P/R}$ both constant and let $V_{P/R}$ be equal in magnitude
but opposite in sense to $\omega_a r$, then we have a particular case in which the
slider, link "b," is standing still in space. The slider now has no acceleration

relative to the fixed link and the Coriolis acceleration of P relative to R must be equal in magnitude to the sum of the normal acceleration of R and the normal acceleration of P relative to R but of opposite sense. Thus the three accelerations cancel, leaving the absolute acceleration of P zero.

7.3 Analysis of Mechanisms Which Have a Coriolis Acceleration

The quick-return mechanism shown in Fig. 7.5(a) contains a slider, link "b," which slides on link "c," and link "c" has an angular velocity. Therefore we must make use of the Coriolis acceleration in the acceleration analysis of the mechanism. We have given the angular velocity of link "a" which is constant. The velocity image is shown in Fig. 7.5(b). In the construction of the acceleration image, Fig. 7.5(c), we locate point P'' and proceed to R'', the image of point R on link "c." The normal acceleration of R relative to Q is drawn, and the perpendicular line corresponding to the

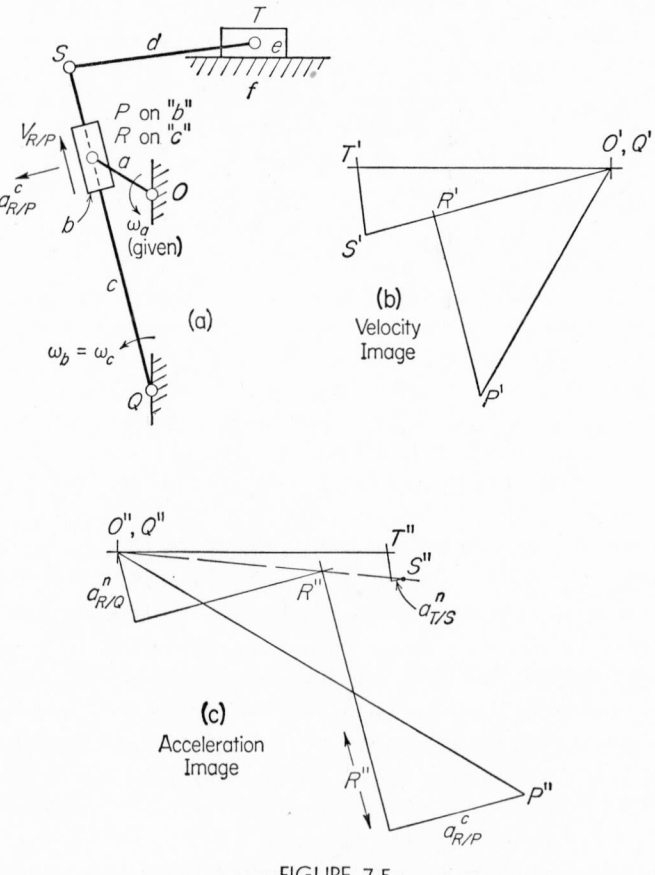

FIGURE 7.5

tangential acceleration is laid out. Now we need another line on which point R'' lies in order to locate the point R''. We can get this line from the acceleration of R relative to P, which contains a Coriolis component normal to the velocity vector $V_{R/P}$. From the velocity image we determine the direction and sense of this velocity and the angular direction of link "b." These we indicate on the mechanism drawing. We then indicate the direction and sense of the Coriolis component as shown. The magnitude of this component can be calculated by use of Eq. (7.1), obtaining the magnitudes of $V_{R/P}$ and ω_b from the velocity image. Now, knowing one component of the acceleration of R relative to P, we can draw in the vector representing it, from P'', as shown, in the same manner that we draw in a normal acceleration. Since there is no normal acceleration of R relative to P caused by curvature of the path, this gives us the total component of acceleration normal to the relative velocity of the points. The only other component of acceleration must be in the direction of the velocity, and it is a tangential acceleration. We now have another line on which R'' must lie, and the intersection of this line with the other line on which R'' must lie locates R''. Having R'' we can complete the acceleration image as shown in the figure. Note that we handle the Coriolis component and the component perpendicular to it as normal and tangential components respectively.

Another mechanism which can be analyzed by use of the Coriolis acceleration is shown in Fig. 7.6(a). This is a Geneva stop mechanism used for intermittent motion, in which link "a" rotates with uniform angular velocity and link "b" is forced to rotate one quarter revolution by the pin on link "a" for each complete cycle of link "a." Then link "b" is held fixed until the pin again makes contact with a successive slot causing another quarter turn.

The velocity image for the mechanism is shown in Fig. 7.6(b) and the acceleration image is shown in Fig. 7.6(c). Since link "a" has no angular acceleration, we can readily find P'' by calculating its normal acceleration relative to O. Also, we can calculate $a_{R/Q}^n$ and draw the line normal to it in the direction of $a_{R/Q}^t$ and then R'' must lie on this normal line. Now we must reference R'' to P'' in order to get another line on which R'' will lie. This presents a difficulty in that the path of R on link "a" is not known. We could develop the path, which would be a curved path, and then determine the Coriolis and normal accelerations of R relative to P. But this becomes rather complicated, as we will find in the next chapter.

A much simpler method is possible if we note that the path of P on link "b" is a straight line which we know. Then the total acceleration of P relative to R is composed only of a Coriolis component and a tangential component, and there is no normal component caused by curvature of the path. Let us now compare this component, $a_{P/R}^c$, with the component of the total acceleration, $a_{R/P}$, which has the same direction as $a_{P/R}^c$.

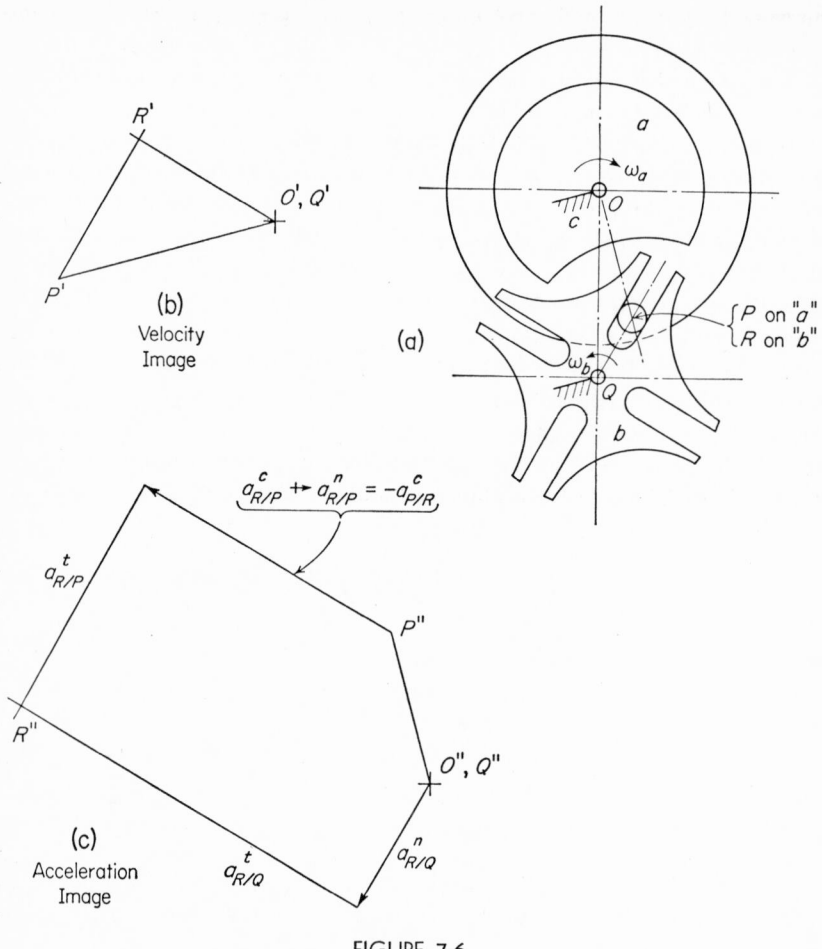

FIGURE 7.6

The Coriolis component of P relative to R is normal to the velocity, $V_{P/R}$, and in this paragraph we will only consider relative components of acceleration in this direction. The Coriolis component of R relative to P is also in this direction; and, since the velocity of a point is always tangent to the path of the point, the normal acceleration of R relative to P (caused by curvature of the path) is also in this direction. Then from the relative acceleration equation

$$a_{R/P} \text{ (normal to } V_{R/P}) = -a_{P/R} \text{ (normal to } V_{R/P})$$

or

$$a_{R/P}^c + a_{R/P}^n = -a_{P/R}^c$$

Then we see that the component of $a_{R/P}$ normal to the velocity, $V_{R/P}$, has the same magnitude and direction as $a_{P/R}^c$ but opposite sense. This component can then be calculated and laid off as shown in the figure.

The image of R can then be determined by drawing a line in the direction of $a_{R/P}^t$ as shown.

In both cases considered the path of the point with motion relative to the rotating body has been a straight line and there has been no normal acceleration of the point relative to the path other than the Coriolis component. In many cases no point can be found which has a straight-line path on the rotating body; therefore we will consider one other mechanism in which the path is not a straight line. Fig. 7.7(a) shows such a mechanism where the slider, link "b," moves along the curved path $A–B$ relative to the rotating member, link "c." The radius of curvature of arc $A–B$ is r and the center of the arc on link "c" is as shown. Figures 7.7(b) and 7.7(c) show the velocity and acceleration images respectively. In the acceleration analysis, point P'' is found and then the image of point R, or R'', is referenced to P'' and Q''. There is a Coriolis component of R relative to P normal to the

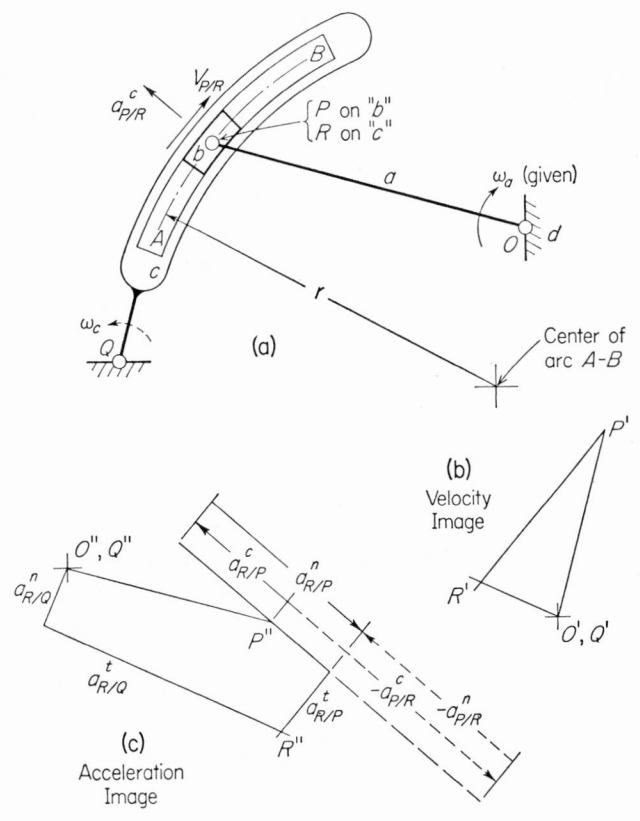

(a)

(b) Velocity Image

(c) Acceleration Image

FIGURE 7.7

velocity $V_{R/P}$, and in this case there is also another component in the same direction caused by the curvature of the path. Note that the path of R on link "b" is a circular arc with radius r. Then the magnitude of the Coriolis component, $a_{R/P}^c$, is

$$a_{R/P}^c = 2V_{R/P}\omega_b$$

But the angular velocity of link "b" is not the same as that of link "c" since link "b" has an angular velocity relative to link "c" as it slides along the slot. The magnitude of this relative angular velocity is given by the equation

$$\omega_{b/c} = \frac{V_{P/R}}{r}$$

and its direction is clockwise. The absolute angular velocity of link "b" can then be determined from the equation

$$\omega_b = \omega_c \mathbin{+\!\!\!\!+} \omega_{b/c}$$

where ω_c can be seen from the figure to be counterclockwise. In the mechanism as shown, $\omega_{b/c}$ is greater in magnitude than ω_c so that ω_b is clockwise, and the Coriolis acceleration will then be directed up and to the left. The other component normal to the velocity $V_{R/P}$ we will designate $a_{R/P}^n$ and its magnitude is determined by the equation

$$a_{R/P}^n = \frac{V_{R/P}^2}{r}$$

where r is the radius of curvature of the path of R on link "b," and it is directed towards the center of curvature, which is opposite the sense of the Coriolis acceleration. The total component of acceleration normal to the relative velocity is the vector sum of these two components and the other component is a tangential in the direction of sliding. This tangential component together with the tangential component relative to Q will locate R'', the image of point R.

A shorter method of finding the total component of acceleration normal to the sliding velocity is that used in the previous example making use of the relation

$$(a_{R/P}^c \mathbin{+\!\!\!\!+} a_{R/P}^n) = -(a_{P/R}^c \mathbin{+\!\!\!\!+} a_{P/R}^n)$$

In this case ω_b does not have to be determined. This method is shown in dashed lines in the acceleration image.

7.4 Discussion of Coriolis Acceleration

The analysis of a mechanism in which the Coriolis acceleration must be used should not give us any difficulty so long as we recognize that a Coriolis component is present. We should always bear in mind that, although we deal with the Coriolis component as if it were a normal component of acceleration, it is not a true normal component in the sense we have previously defined a normal component. The Coriolis component is a relative component of acceleration of a point moving along a path attached to a body which has an angular velocity, and the normal acceleration, as previously defined, is the relative acceleration of two points on the same body, or the acceleration of a point moving along a curved path relative to a fixed body.

We should emphasize that by selecting the link which contains the simplest path the acceleration image can be greatly simplified as shown in the example in Fig. 7.6, where one path was curved and unknown and the path used was a straight path. Also in the last example the path on one of the links made a simpler analysis than the path on the other link. Therefore we should carefully examine a mechanism which contains a Coriolis acceleration in order to select which method of attack will give us the simplest analysis.

We will find later in our discussion of dynamic forces that the Coriolis component of acceleration will explain some peculiar phenomena which would be puzzling otherwise. We will also find that it gives us a simple method of analyzing such devices as the fluid coupling or fluid drive as used in automobile transmissions.

PROBLEMS

For the problems below construct the acceleration polygon for the figures indicated, locating the acceleration image of all labeled points. Select any appropriate scale for the acceleration vectors.

7.1 Fig. P4.2, with $V_P = 25$ in./sec and $a_P = 0$.

7.2 Fig. P4.6, with ω_a constant at 100 rpm counter clockwise. Determine the angular velocity and angular acceleration of all links.

7.3 Fig. P4.11, with ω_a constant at 30 rpm clockwise. Determine the angular velocity and angular acceleration of all links.

7.4 Fig. P4.4, with $V_T = 200$ in./sec to right and $a_T = 100$ in./sec^2 to the left. Determine the angular velocity and angular acceleration of all links.

7.5 Fig. P4.4, with ω_a constant at 500 rpm clockwise.

7.6 Fig. P5.8, with $\omega_a = 800$ rpm and $\alpha_a = 50$ rad/sec^2. Determine the angular velocity and angular acceleration of all links.

7.7 Fig. P4.13, with ω_a constant at 150 rpm counter clockwise. Determine the angular velocity and angular acceleration of link "d."

7.8 Fig. P4.14, with ω_a constant at 100 rpm clockwise. Determine the angular velocity and angular acceleration of links "b" and "c."

7.9 Fig. P4.14, with ω_c constant at 100 rpm clockwise. Determine the angular velocity and angular acceleration of links "a" and "b."

Chapter **8**

Acceleration Analysis for Sliding and Rolling Contact

8.1 Introduction

We have covered, in the two preceding chapters, the acceleration analysis of mechanisms which contain links paired with pin joints, those having links which move with rectilinear translation relative to the fixed link and the special case in which a Coriolis component of acceleration is present. In the present chapter we will consider the special cases of mechanisms which contain rolling pairs and higher sliding pairs. We will find that a general rule can be developed for the case of rolling contact, but in the case of higher sliding pairs, a simple method cannot be developed which will apply to all cases.

8.2 Rolling Contact

In the discussion of the relative acceleration of points on links which are joined by rolling pairs we will start with simple cases which can be analyzed almost intuitively and progress to more complicated systems. Consider a circular disc "a," of radius "r," rolling along a fixed flat surface "b" with uniform angular velocity ω and with no slipping, as shown in Fig. 8.1(a). Point O is the center of the disc and P is the point on the disc in contact with the flat surface at point Q. Points S, T, and U are points on the circumference of the disc, the accelerations of which we shall try to determine.

The path of the center of the disc, point O, will be the dashed line shown in the figure at a distance r from the flat surface, and parallel to it. The magnitude of the velocity of O will be constant, equal to ωr, and its direction will aways be the same. Therefore the center of the disc will have no acceleration relative to the flat surface. Now, knowing the acceleration of

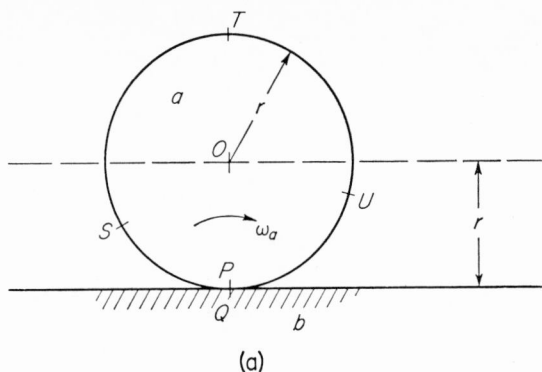

(a)

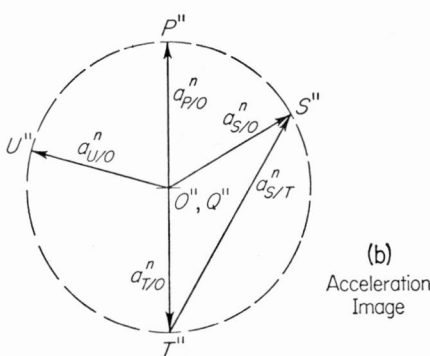

(b)

Acceleration
Image

FIGURE 8.1

one point on the disc (zero in this case), we can find the acceleration of any
other point on the disc with reference to the center since the disc has a
uniform angular velocity. The only acceleration of any point on the disc
relative to any other point on the disc will be a normal acceleration. The
acceleration of point P relative to O is equal to $\omega^2 r$ and directed from P
towards O. The acceleration image of the disc is shown in Fig. 8.1(b). The
dashed circle on the acceleration image is the image of the circumference of
the disc. In this particular case it will be noted that the center of the disc
is the instant center of acceleration relative to the fixed body.

Now we consider the disc rolling along a circular convex surface of radius
R, and center of curvature K, as shown in Fig. 8.2(a), with uniform angular
velocity. In this case, the path of the center of the disc will be a circle of
radius $(R + r)$ and the linear velocity of the center relative to the fixed
surface will be ωr. The center, O, will now have a normal acceleration,
relative to the surface, of magnitude

$$\frac{V_{O/Q}^2}{(R+r)} = \frac{(\omega r)^2}{(R+r)}$$

directed from O towards Q, the point of contact on the surface, as shown in the acceleration image in Fig. 8.2(b). The acceleration of point P, the point of contact on the disc, relative to O will be equal to $\omega^2 r$ and will be directed from P towards O which is in the same direction but of opposite sense to $a_{O/Q}^n$. The other points on the circumference will have the same magnitude of acceleration relative to O. The instant center of acceleration will always lie somewhere on the line O–P.

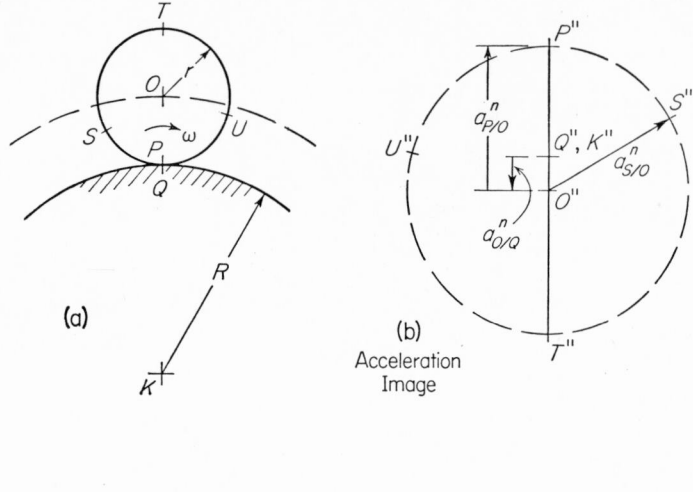

(a)

(b)
Acceleration
Image

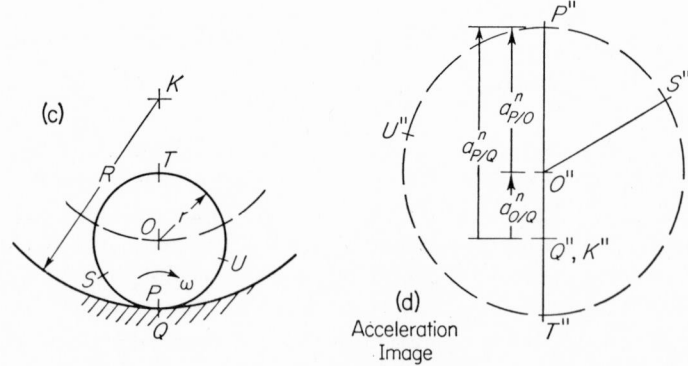

(c)

(d)
Acceleration
Image

FIGURE 8.2

If the disc rolls along a circular concave surface as shown in Fig. 8.2(c), the acceleration image will be as shown in Fig. 8.2(d) in which $a_{O/K}^n$ and $a_{P/O}^n$ are in the same sense. In this case the acceleration of O relative to Q is given by the relation

$$a_{O/Q}^n = \frac{(\omega r)^2}{(R - r)}$$

The instant center of acceleration in this case will lie somewhere on the line passing through the contact point P and the center O and be between O and K.

In the three cases considered so far we have always found the acceleration of the center of the disc first, then found the acceleration of any point on the disc relative to the center. Thus we could use vector addition in determining the image of any point on the rolling disc. This same method will be used in all cases of rolling contact, as will be seen in the following examples in which the disc has an angular acceleration at the same time that it has an angular velocity.

Consider the case of the disc rolling along a flat surface as in the previous example but in this case the disc has an angular acceleration as well as an angular velocity, as in Fig. 8.3(a). The center has an acceleration relative to the fixed surface in a direction parallel to the surface. The magnitude of this acceleration will be $r\alpha$ as shown in the acceleration image in Fig. 8.3(b). This is the same acceleration as the tangential acceleration of O relative to P, P being the point on the disc in contact with the surface. From the relative acceleration equation for the three points O, P, and Q in the horizontal direction

$$a_{O/Q}^h = a_{O/P}^h \rightarrowtail a_{P/Q}^h$$

where
$$a_{O/P}^h = a_{O/P}^t = r\alpha$$

we see that the horizontal acceleration of P relative to Q must be zero. This fact is evident if we look at the path of point P on the fixed body as the point P comes in contact with the fixed surface. This path is shown in Fig. 8.3(c), and we recognize it as a cycloid. The path is normal to the flat surface at the point of contact and the only motion of P relative to Q is in a direction normal to the surface. Therefore the only acceleration P can have relative to Q must be normal to the surface at that instant and the relative acceleration in a horizontal direction is zero.

A rigorous proof that the horizontal acceleration of P relative to Q is zero can be obtained by writing the equation for the path of P on the fixed body, and taking derivatives with respect to time to get the acceleration. The path for a complete revolution of the disc is shown in Fig. 8.3(c). Taking the origin of an x-y coordinate system at point Q where the point P is in contact with the surface we can write equations for the x and y displacements as a function of the angle θ, the angle of rotation of the disc, letting θ be zero at the instant when P is at the origin. These equations are

$$x = r\theta - r \sin \theta = r(\theta - \sin \theta)$$
$$y = r(1 - \cos \theta)$$

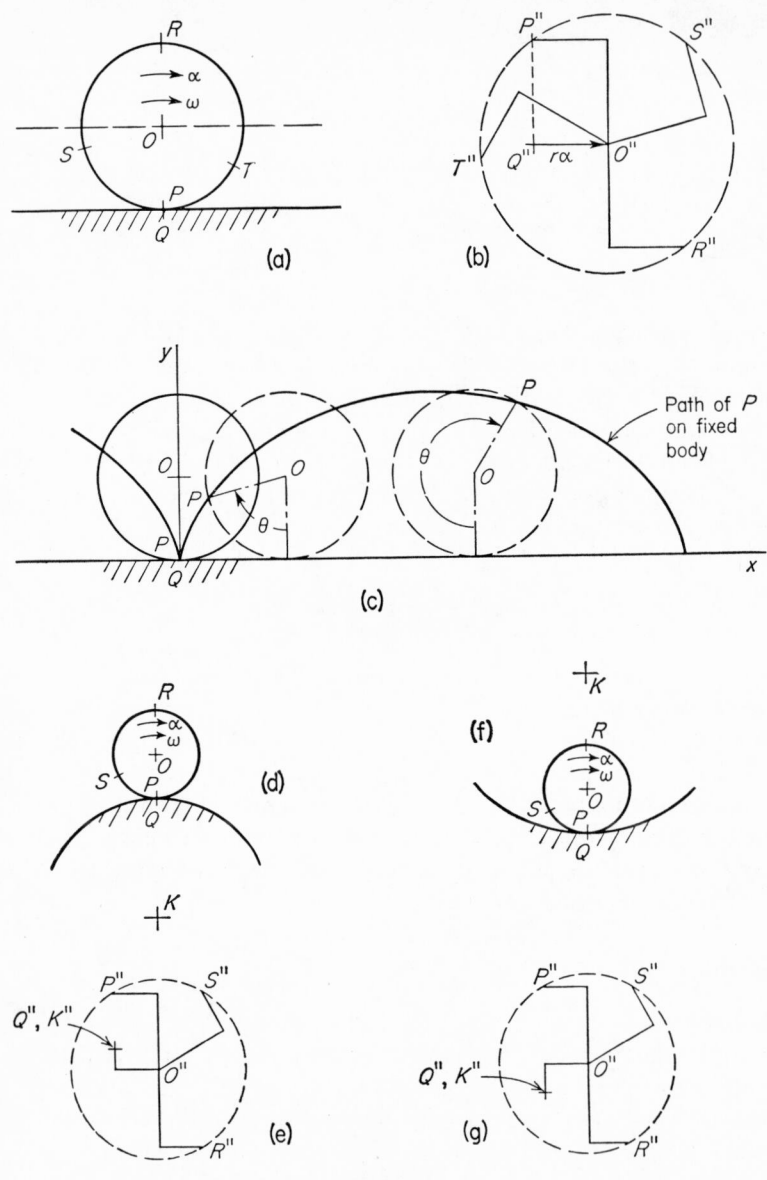

FIGURE 8.3

The velocity and acceleration in the x and y direction are given by the first and second derivatives of these equations with respect to time, or

$$\dot{x} = r\left(\frac{d\theta}{dt} - \cos\theta \frac{d\theta}{dt}\right) = r\omega(1 - \cos\theta)$$

$$\dot{y} = r \sin \theta \frac{d\theta}{dt} = r\omega \sin \theta$$

and
$$\ddot{x} = r\alpha(1 - \cos \theta) + r\omega \sin \theta \frac{d\theta}{dt}$$

$$= r\alpha(1 - \cos \theta) + r\omega^2 \sin \theta$$

$$\ddot{y} = r\alpha \sin \theta + r\omega \cos \theta \frac{d\theta}{dt}$$

$$= r\alpha \sin \theta + r\omega^2 \cos \theta$$

From these equations we see that the acceleration in the x direction (the horizontal direction) is zero for θ equal to zero or 360° where P is in contact with the fixed surface. Also we should note that the total acceleration of P can be readily obtained for any angle θ so long as the angular acceleration and angular velocity are known at that instant. This is one of the advantages of an analytical solution. Analytical solutions will be discussed in more detail in a later chapter.

The acceleration of P relative to the fixed point Q then satisfies the equation

$$a_{P/Q} = (a_{P/O}^n \mathbin{+\!\!\!+} a_{P/O}^t) \mathbin{+\!\!\!+} a_{O/Q}^t$$

where $a_{P/O}^t$ is equal to $a_{O/Q}^t$ but in opposite sense and the image of P can be located by referencing it to O''. Point P will have a normal and tangential acceleration relative to O as shown in the image diagram, Fig. 8.3(b), and we see that the acceleration of P relative to Q is normal to the surface. The images of the other points on the disc are as shown in the figure.

In the same manner we can draw the acceleration image of the disc rolling along a convex surface, Figs. 8.3(d) and 8.3(e), or a concave surface, Figs. 8.3(f) and 8.3(g).

8.3 Rolling Contact Along a Rotating Surface

In cases where there is rolling contact along a surface which has rotation, the same method as that in the preceding section is applicable but since now the path of the center of the disc has rotation there will be a Coriolis acceleration of the center of the disc relative to a corresponding point on the path. All other components will be the same as in the previous discussion.

Consider the mechanism shown in Fig. 8.4(a), which is a circular arc cam and roller follower. If the cam, link "a," is rotating with constant angular velocity as shown, the velocity image for the mechanism will be as shown in Fig. 8.4(b). Since points P and R are in rolling contact, their velocity image will be at the same point. In drawing the acceleration image for the mechanism we can locate the image of points P and S directly since they have only a normal acceleration relative to the fixed link. The next point whose image

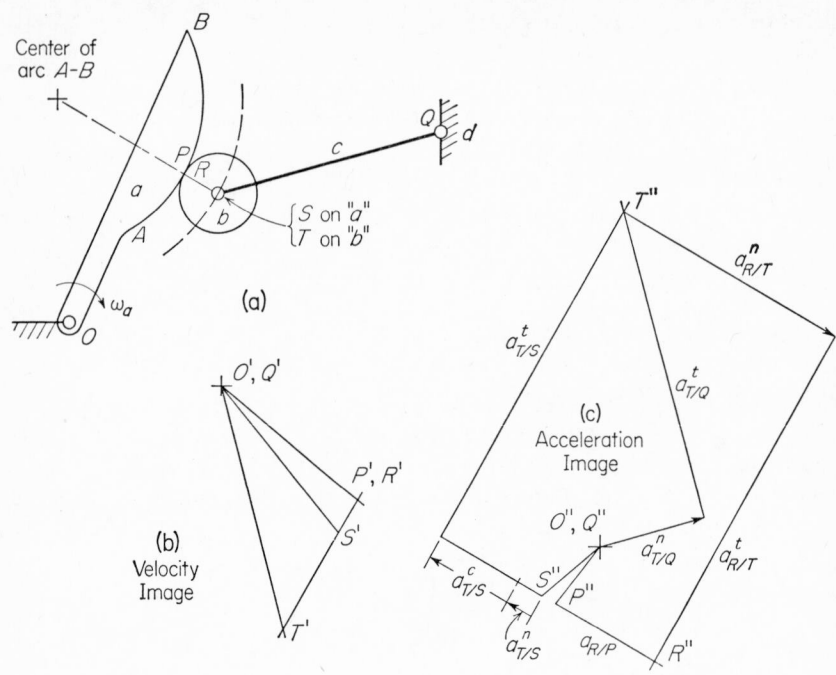

FIGURE 8.4

we will locate is point T, the center of the roller. Since its path on link "a" is curved and the path rotates with link "a," it will have two components of acceleration normal to the path, relative to the coincident point S, and one component tangential to the path. One normal component is that which it would have if T moved along the path while the path had no rotation. The other is the Coriolis component caused by rotation of the path. The student should review Eq. (6.10) and the discussion of the second and third brackets, which cover these two components. The first of these components, which we will designate the normal acceleration of T relative to S, is given by the equation

$$a^n_{T/S} = \frac{V^2_{T/S}}{r}$$

where r is the radius of curvature of the path at point S, and the Coriolis component is dependent only on the velocity of T relative to S and the angular velocity of link "a." Therefore both these components can be calculated and drawn as shown in the acceleration image, Fig. 8.4(c). We can now draw a line in the direction of the tangential acceleration. By referencing T to point Q, we can locate T'' as shown. Having T'' we can calculate the normal acceleration of R relative to T and draw a line in the direction of the tangential acceleration on which R'' must lie. From the preceding discussion we found that the acceleration of R relative to P must be normal to the arc A-B. Although this was shown for the case in which the path was fixed, we can see that it also holds if the path has rotation as in the present case. Then we can draw from P'' a line in the direction of the acceleration of R relative to P and the intersection of this line with the line representing the tangential acceleration of R relative to T locates the point R'', the acceleration image of point R.

Now if we take the same cam mechanism, but with link "c" having a constant angular velocity, we can consider the case in which the path of the center of the roller has an angular acceleration as well as an angular velocity. This case is shown in Fig. 8.5(a), and the velocity image is shown in Fig. 8.5(b). The acceleration image is shown in Fig. 8.5(c). The image of point T, T'', is found without difficulty and the image of point S can then be located by referencing it to points O and T. Point S has a normal component and a Coriolis component relative to T, both in a direction normal to $V_{S/T}$. However, in order to determine the normal component $a^n_{S/T}$, we must know the path of S on link "b." To simplify the analysis we will use the method discussed in the previous chapter, where it was shown that

$$(a^n_{S/T} + a^c_{S/T}) = -(a^n_{T/S} + a^c_{T/S})$$

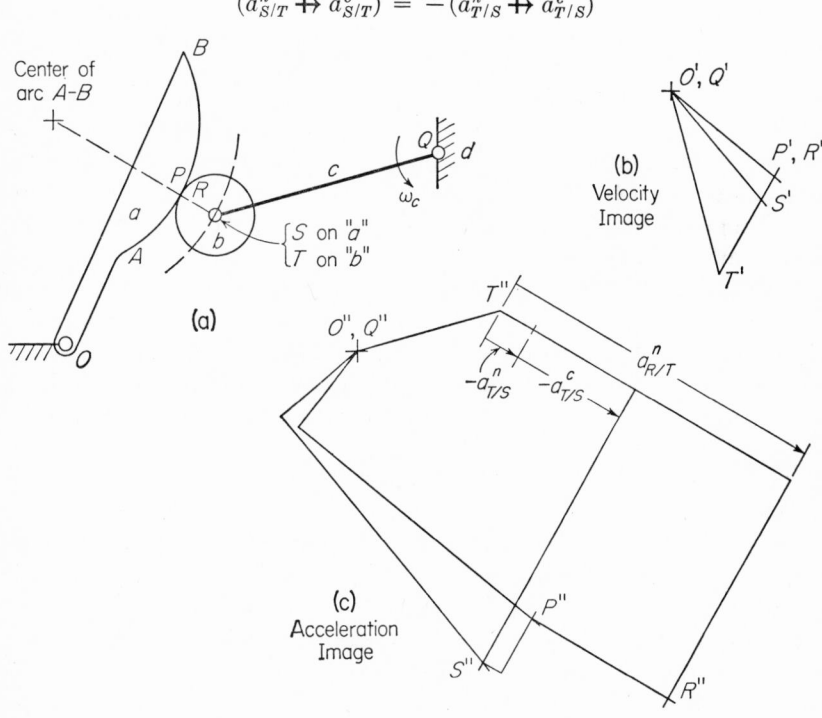

FIGURE 8.5

Then the component of acceleration of S relative to T perpendicular to the sliding velocity can readily be determined as shown in the figure since the path of T on link "a" is known. The only unknown component of S relative to T then is a tangential component in the direction of $V_{T/S}$. Point S can also be referenced to point O and can be located as shown in the figure. The image of point P, on link "a," can now readily be located by referencing it to points O and S, both on link "a." Now we can locate the image of point R on the roller by referencing it to points T on the same link, and to P on link "a," with which it has rolling contact. Referring R to T, we can calculate the normal acceleration and then draw the line in the direction of the tangential acceleration on which R'' lies. Although points R and P are not on the same link, we know from the previous discussion of rolling contact that the *total* acceleration of R relative to P is in a direction normal to the path of rolling contact at point P. We draw a line from P'' in that direction, and the intersection of this line with the line in the direction of the tangential acceleration of R relative to T is the image of point R, or R''.

We find then that the acceleration analysis of mechanisms which contain links in rolling contact offer no particular difficulty so long as we know the center of the arcs in rolling contact and keep in mind that the total acceleration of the points in contact is always normal to the surface at the contact point.

8.4 Higher Sliding Contact

In concluding our discussion on the graphical analysis of acceleration we will take up the case of mechanisms containing links with higher sliding pairs. In general the analysis of links with higher sliding contact is the most difficult analysis which we will encounter. The analysis of these cases will be based on the concepts already discussed but as we progress it will be found that analyses based on these concepts are tedious and time consuming in many cases. A large majority of the mechanisms which contain links with higher sliding pairs are cam type mechanisms, of which gears are a special case. A majority of the mechanisms which contain links in rolling contact are also cam type mechanisms. In the next Article we will discuss a method of circumventing the tedious part of the analysis of these mechanisms in many cases, but the methods discussed in the present and previous Articles can always be used for a complete analysis.

Two examples of the simpler mechanisms containing higher sliding pairs are shown in Fig. 8.6(a) and 8.6(b) with their velocity and acceleration images. Figure 8.6(a) is a disc cam with a knife-edge reciprocating follower, and Fig. 8.6(b) is a similar mechanism with both links having rotation. In both these cases the path of the knife-edge on its mating link is clearly defined and the acceleration analysis is easily handled by use of the Coriolis

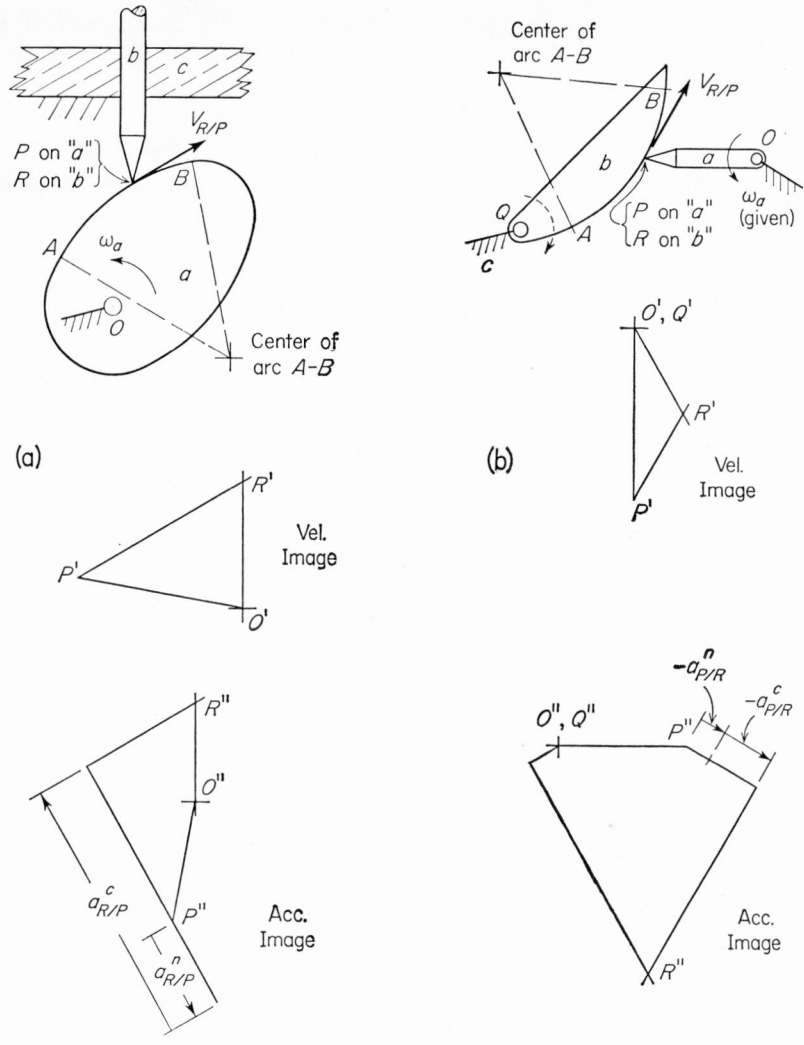

FIGURE 8.6

component of acceleration together with the normal acceleration of one point with respect to the other.

An example of another mechanism containing a higher sliding pair is shown in Fig. 8.7(a). In this example we have two links rotating relative to the fixed body and in sliding contact along curved surfaces. The angular velocity of link "a" is known and we wish to draw the acceleration image of the contact points P and R on the two links. The velocity image is shown in Fig. 8.7(b) and the acceleration image in Fig. 8.7(c). The acceleration image of point P on link "a" can be readily found since the motion of link

"a" is known, and the image of point R on link "b" can then be referenced to points Q and P. The equation of the acceleration of R relative to P is

$$a_{R/P} = a_{R/P}^n \mathrel{+\!\!\!\!+} 2V_{R/P}\omega_a \mathrel{+\!\!\!\!+} a_{R/P}^t$$

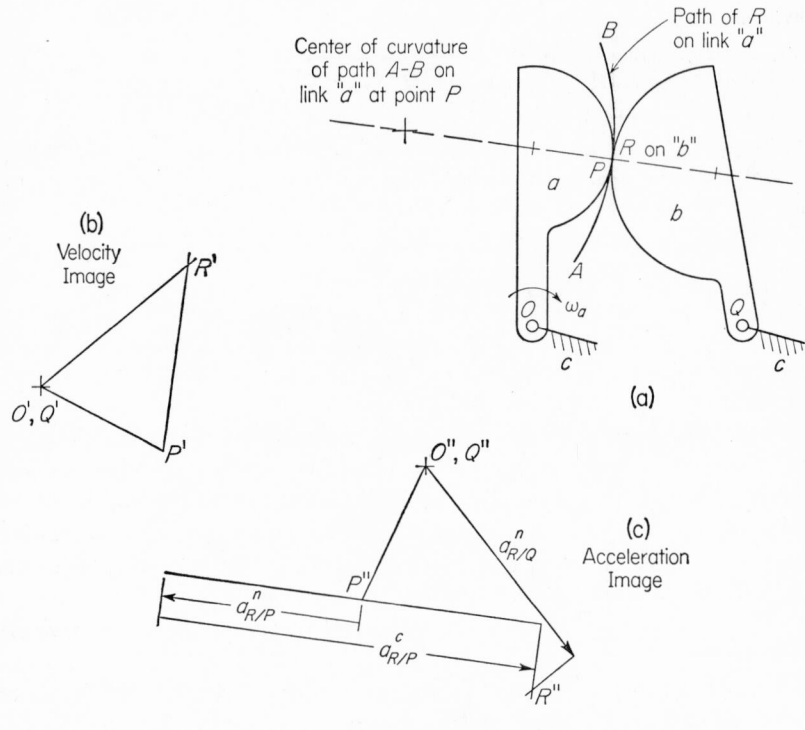

FIGURE 8.7

The Coriolis acceleration, the second term in the right hand side of the above equation, can be easily determined from the known velocities. The first term is determined from the relation

$$a_{R/P}^n = \frac{V_{R/P}^2}{r}$$

where r is the radius of curvature of the path (at point P) that point R describes on link "a." From these relations the image of point R can be determined as shown in the figure. However, to quote a time worn phrase, this is easier said than done. The difficulty lies in the determination of the radius of the path A–B at point P. The path of motion of point R on link "a" is not clearly defined in this case and must be determined graphically. The radius of curvature can be determined once we have found the path.

The path of motion of point R on link "a" can be determined as shown in Fig. 8.8. Since we wish to determine the path of the point on link "a," the simplest procedure is to invert the mechanism, making link "a" the fixed link and moving links "c" and "b" to new phase positions, always keeping link "b" in contact with the curved surface of link "a." Now if for each phase position we mark the position of point R on link "a" (now the fixed link) a smooth line through the points indicating the positions of point R will be the path of point R on link "a." The figure shows two different phase positions with point R falling on the curve A–B. The quickest method of

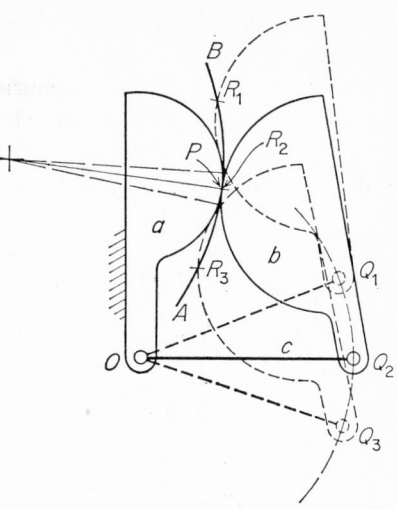

FIGURE 8.8

drawing the path A–B is to draw the locus of the point Q, which is an arc of radius O–Q about point O. Then, with link "b" drawn on transparent tracing paper, the tracing paper is placed so that point Q lies at some point on the arc with the curves in contact and the location of point R pricked for that position. This process is repeated for various positions, and the path A–B can be drawn through these points.

The radius of curvature of the path at point P can now be approximated by drawing normals to the path at points close to P and taking the average distance from the curve to the intersections of these normals as the radius of curvature. The accuracy of this method of determining the radius of curvature depends on the amount of curvature of the arc. For large curvature, fairly good accuracy can be obtained, but if the radii are large, considerable error could be expected. Since the normal acceleration of R relative to P is directly proportional to the radius of curvature, the accuracy of the acceleration image of point R will be determined by the accuracy of the radius. At best, this gives us an approximation of the acceleration of point R and should be used with this in mind, although if the radius of curvature can be accurately determined, then the analysis is perfectly good. It should be pointed out that the above analysis is only good for the phase position shown; for any other phase position, since points other than P and R are in contact, another path must be determined and a new radius of curvature found. Therefore if we desire an analysis of the mechanism for various phase positions, the analysis becomes time consuming and is still an approximation. However, this gives us a general method of analyzing the acceleration of mechanisms containing higher sliding pairs in which the path of motion of the point on one link relative to the mating link is not clearly defined and must be determined graphically. Since we will find a means of overcoming most of these difficulties in the next Article, we will not spend more time on this method of analysis.

8.5 Equivalent Mechanisms

In many cases the acceleration analysis of mechanisms containing links with rolling contact and/or higher sliding contact can be greatly simplified by replacing the mechanism with an equivalent mechanism whose links have the same relative motion as the original mechanism. As considered in this Article, an equivalent mechanism is one that has the same relative motion of links as the mechanism whose acceleration we wish to determine. In some cases the equivalent mechanism will be equivalent only for one phase position but in many cases it will be equivalent for all phase positions. This will be discussed further as we develop equivalent mechanisms for various types of systems.

As an example of an equivalent mechanism consider the mechanism already analyzed in Figs. 8.4 and 8.5, which is redrawn in Fig. 8.9(a) togetherer with the equivalent mechanism, Fig. 8.9(b). In the discussion of the acceleration analysis of the mechanism the image of point T was found by referring it to the point S on link "a" using the two component accelerations, $a_{T/S}^n$ and $a_{T/S}^c$. In the equivalent mechanism, link "a" has been replaced by a link with a curved surface corresponding to the path of point T on link "a," which will be referred to as the pitch line, and a knife-edge on link "c" in contact with that surface. It is obvious that the motions of the two links "a" and "c" are the same for the equivalent mechanism; if the motion of link "c" is all that we are interested in, which is the case in many mechanisms, the equivalent mechanism is sufficient for the analysis. In this case the two mechanisms are equivalent for all phase positions. Actu

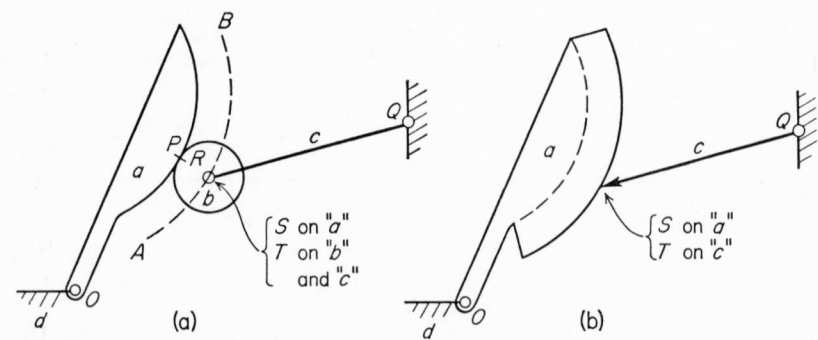

FIGURE 8.9

ally, in the original analysis, we used the equivalent mechanism as a basis for the analysis, and in that case the equivalent mechanism does not simplify the analysis if we need to determine the acceleration of point R. In later cases to be discussed the use of an equivalent mechanism will greatly simplify the analysis.

Another case in which we have made use of an equivalent mechanism without pointing out the fact is the case of the Geneva stop mechanism, Fig. 7.6. This mechanism is redrawn in Fig. 8.10(a) and the equivalent mechanism is shown in Fig. 8.10(b). The Geneva stop mechanism is a case containing a higher sliding pair but was used in the discussion of Coriolis acceleration because the equivalent mechanism is immediately obvious. It will be noted in referring to the analysis in Fig. 7.6 that we did not find the image of the points in contact but only the points corresponding to the equivalent mechanism. Having found the image of point R on link "b," we can easily find the image of the contact point on link "b," point T, by referring it to the points R and Q. In this example, the use of the equivalent mechanism greatly simplifies the analysis. If we had made the analysis

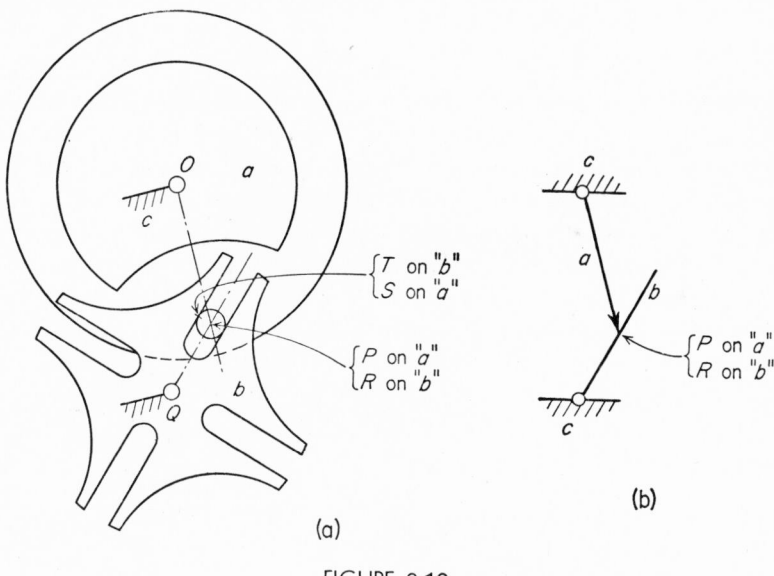

(a)

(b)

FIGURE 8.10

using the contact points S on link "a," and T on link "b," the path of either T on link "a" or S on link "b" would have been necessary to complete the analysis. It would have had to be plotted as discussed in the previous Article since the points have curved paths. In this case, as in the preceding case, the two mechanisms are equivalent for all phase positions.

Some other examples of equivalent mechanisms are shown in Fig. 8.11. The solid lines show the original mechanism and the dashed lines show the corresponding equivalent mechanism. Figure 8.11(a) shows a circular cam with a reciprocating roller follower. Since both the cam, link "a," and the roller, link "b," are circles, the centers of these links must remain a constant distance apart for all phase positions. It becomes obvious that a slider

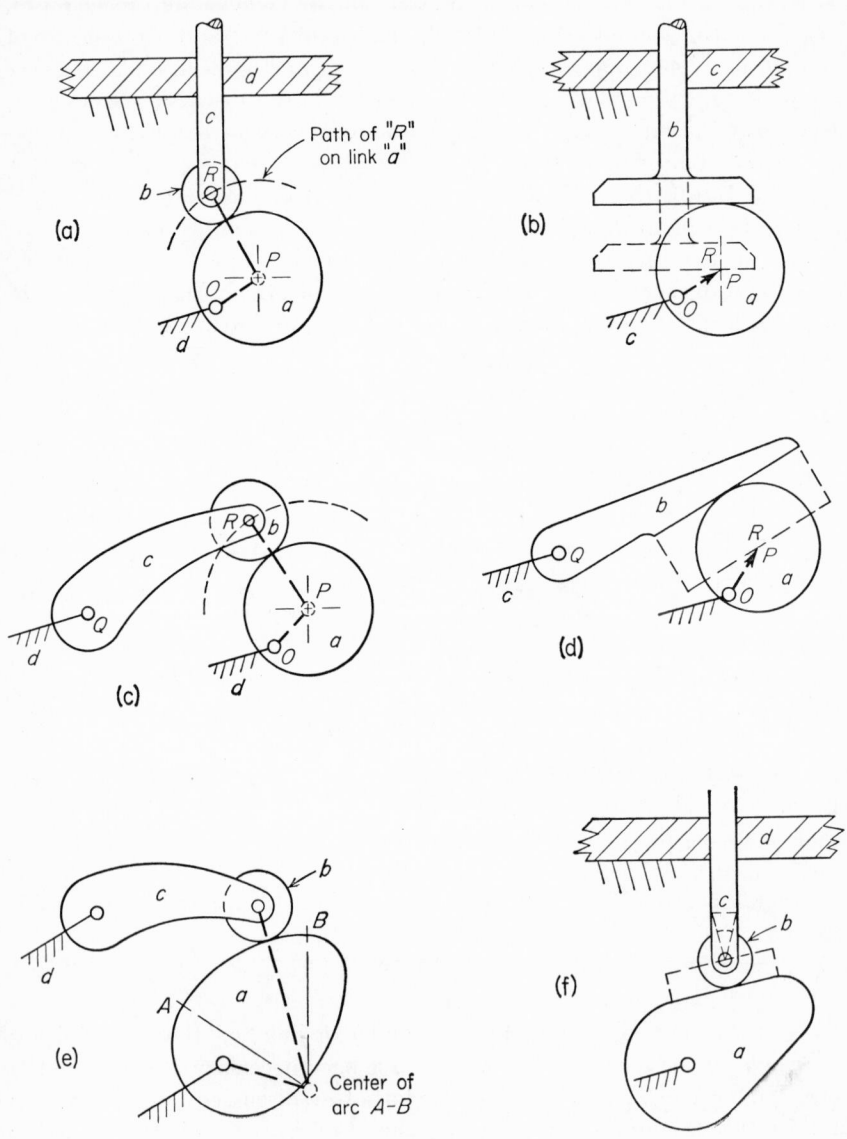

FIGURE 8.11

crank mechanism as shown by the dashed lines will give the same motion to link "c" that it would have in the original mechanism if the crank connected the fixed point on link "a" with its center P and a connecting rod were pin jointed to P and R, the center of link "b." This would be an equivalent mechanism for all phase positions, and the equivalent mechanism would greatly simplify the analysis since use of it would eliminate the need of determining the Coriolis acceleration of point R, the center of the roller, relative to the coincident point on the cam, link "a." Having the image of point R from the equivalent mechanism, we could determine the image of the contact point on link "b" as previously discussed in the sections on rolling contact. It should be pointed out that another equivalent mechanism would be obtained by replacing link "c" with a knife-edge in contact with the pitch surface of link "a" (the pitch surface being the path of point R on link "a" as shown in the figure). We will remember that in the discussion of rolling contact we made use of this equivalent mechanism without pointing out the fact that we were using an equivalent mechanism. However, such an equivalent mechanism would require the use of a Coriolis acceleration in the analysis.

A similar mechanism is shown in Fig. 8.11(b) where we have the same cam. In this case the reciprocating follower has a flat face, a type of follower that is sometimes called a mushroom follower. The equivalent mechanism in this case is a knife-edge pinned at point O with the knife-edge at point P, the center of the cam, and in higher sliding contact with a flat surface parallel to the original follower surface, as shown by dashed lines in the figure. Again the equivalence of the two mechanisms is obvious if we note that the point P must always remain at a constant distance from the original follower surface. In the acceleration analysis of the equivalent mechanism we still make use of a Coriolis acceleration, but the analysis will be greatly simplified because we would have to determine the path on link "a" of the contact point on link "b," and then determine the radius of curvature of that path if we did not make use of the equivalent mechanism. In the equivalent mechanism we make use of the path of point P, the knife-edge, on link "b" and this is a straight line. Again we note that the mechanism is equivalent for all phase positions.

Figure 8.11(c) shows a circular cam with a pivoted or rotating roller follower. The equivalent mechanism in this case is a quadric crank mechanism connecting the three pin joints on the original mechanism and a fourth pin joint located at the center of the circular cam, as shown. The equivalence of the mechanism comes in consequence of the fact that points P and R always remain a constant distance apart and the quadric crank maintains this condition. The equivalent mechanism eliminates the necessity of plotting the path of a point on either link "a" or "b" and determining its radius of curvature. It also bypasses the Coriolis acceleration. Another equivalent mechanism for this case would be a knife-edge follower resting on the pitch surface of the cam at point R, but this would require a Coriolis acceleration for the analysis. Both equivalent mechanisms would be equivalent for all phase positions.

A pivoted follower with a flat face and a circular cam is shown in Fig. 8.11(d) with its equivalent mechanism. As in Fig. 8.11(b) the equivalent mechanism is a knife-edge resting on a surface parallel to the flat face of the follower and in contact at point P, the center of the circular cam, and the mechanism is equivalent for all phase positions.

In all the cases of equivalent mechanisms discussed so far, the mechanisms have been equivalent for all phase positions. Figures 8.11(e) and 8.11 (f) are two cases where the equivalent mechanism is equivalent only for a limited number of phase positions. The cam profile in Fig. 8.11(e) is made up of circular arcs and for each arc a new equivalent mechanism must be used. For the arc A–B shown in the figure the equivalent mechanism is a quadric crank with a pin joint at the center of the arc. For each different arc this pin joint shifts to the center of the new arc. At the point where the two arcs meet, the cam profile is discontinuous (having two radii of curvature), and a plot of acceleration versus phase position would also be discontinuous at that point, there being two different values of acceleration for the same point. If the cam had a straight line for a part of the profile as in Fig. 8.11(f), the equivalent mechanism would be a knife-edge resting on a surface parallel to the straight portion, passing through the center of the follower as shown.

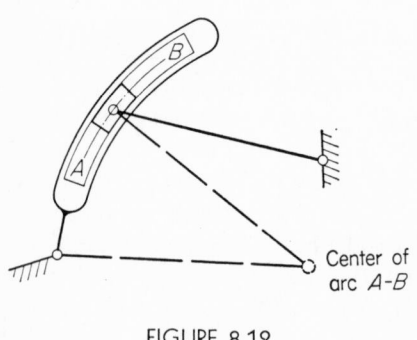

Center of
arc A–B

FIGURE 8.12

The mechanism in Fig. 7.7, which we analyzed for acceleration in the chapter on Coriolis accelerations, can be replaced by an equivalent mechanism which will simplify the analysis. This mechanism is shown in Fig. 8.12 with its equivalent mechanism. The equivalent mechanism is a quadric crank with a pin joint at the center of the arc A–B.

The last example of equivalent mechanisms which we will discuss is shown in Fig. 8.13(a) which is the same mechanism analyzed in Article 8.4 (Fig. 8.7). The equivalent mechanism is the quadric crank shown in the figure and it does not need any further discussion. However we will use the original mechanism to point out the equivalence of mechanisms which have links in higher sliding contact along circular arcs and mechanisms which have links in rolling contact. Note that in Fig. 8.13(b) we have replaced

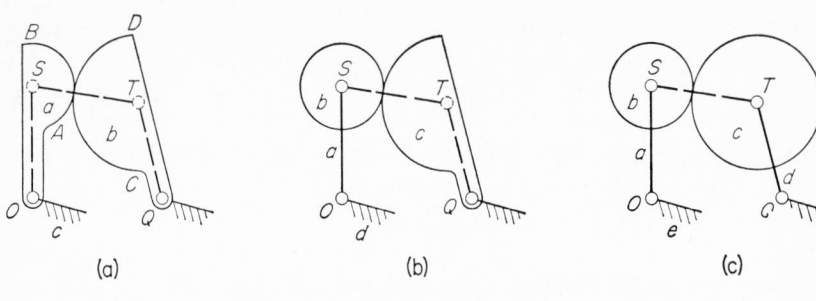

FIGURE 8.13

link "a" in the previous figure with a roller pinned to link "a" at the center of arc A–B and of the same radius as arc A–B. This mechanism is obviously equivalent to the original mechanism. Also in Fig. 8.13(c) we have a similar mechanism which now contains two rollers. From this we can see that anytime we have a link with a circular arc in contact with another link, either with higher sliding or rolling contact, that link can be replaced with a roller with center at the center of curvature of the arc and with radius equal to the radius of the arc. In many cases this will lead to simpler equivalent mechanisms and in the case discussed it is easy to see that the quadric crank mechanism is equivalent to the original mechanism. Sometimes the equivalent mechanism is a little difficult to see without the use of this procedure.

We have not discussed all the possible equivalent mechanisms but have covered enough that the student should realize the advantages of using equivalent mechanisms in acceleration analyses. Also the student should now be able to draw equivalent mechanisms for most cases of mechanisms which contain higher sliding or rolling contact in which an equivalent mechanism would simplify the acceleration analysis. Equivalent mechanisms are a powerful tool in acceleration analysis, and although we have shown methods of analysis without the use of the equivalent mechanisms, in many cases the use of equivalent mechanisms will greatly simplify the analysis. In cases of higher sliding, where the path of contact is not well defined, the equivalent mechanism gives us a most accurate method of determining the acceleration.

PROBLEMS

For the problems below construct the acceleration polygon for the figures indicated, locating the acceleration image of all labeled points. Select any appropriate scale for the acceleration vectors.

8.1 Fig. P5.2, with ω_a constant at 500 rpm counter clockwise. Determine the angular velocity and angular acceleration of links "b" and "c."

156   PROBLEMS | Chap. 8

8.2   Fig. P5.3, with ω_a constant at 1000 rpm counter clockwise. Determine the angular velocity and angular acceleration of links "b" and "c."

8.3   Fig. P5.4, with ω_a constant at 1800 rpm counter clockwise. Determine the angular velocity and angular acceleration of links "b" and "c."

8.4   Fig. P4.9, with ω_a constant at 300 rpm clockwise. Determine the angular velocity and angular acceleration of links "b" and "c."

8.5   Fig. P5.5, with ω_a constant at 200 rpm counter clockwise. Determine the angular velocity and angular acceleration of links "b" and "c."

8.6   Fig. P5.6, with ω_a constant at 500 rpm clockwise. Determine the angular velocity and angular acceleration of all links.

8.7   Fig. P5.7, with ω_a constant at 1000 rpm clockwise. Determine the angular velocity and angular acceleration of all links.

8.8   Fig. P5.9, with ω_a constant at 300 rpm clockwise. Determine the angular velocity and angular acceleration of all links.

8.9 (a) Fig. P8.1, with ω_a constant at 100 rpm counter clockwise. Use method outlined in Article 8.4.

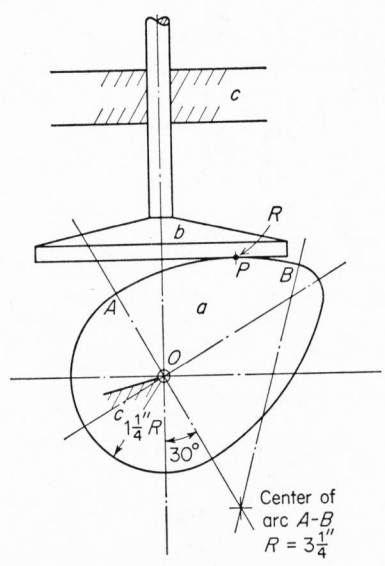

FIGURE P8.1

(b) Check the results in part **(a)** by use of an equivalent mechanism.

8.10 (a) Fig. P8.2, with ω_a constant at 2400 rpm counter clockwise. Use method outlined in Article 8.4.

(b) Check the results in part **(a)** by use of an equivalent mechanism.

8.11 (a) Fig. P8.3, with ω_a constant at 2000 rpm counter clockwise. Use method outlined in Article 8.4.

(b) Check the results in part **(a)** by use of an equivalent mechanism.

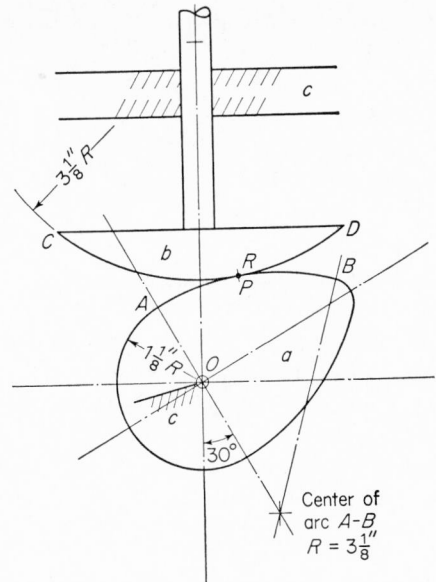

FIGURE P8.2

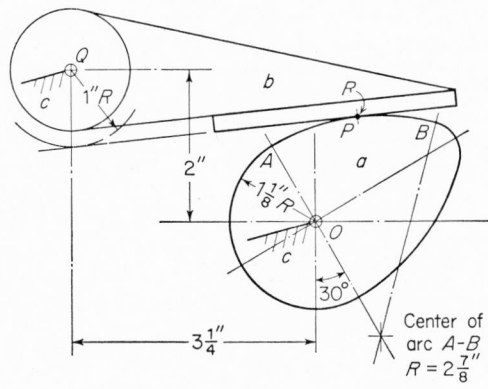

FIGURE P8.3

8.12 Check the results of Prob. 7.8 by use of an equivalent mechanism.

8.13 Check the results of Prob. 7.9 by use of an equivalent mechanism.

Chapter 9

Kinematic Analysis by
Analytical Methods

9.1 Introduction

We have now covered three different methods of determining velocities in mechanisms: graphical differentiation, instant centers, and velocity image; and two methods of determining acceleration: graphical differentiation, and the acceleration image. All of these have been graphical methods. Another method of analysis which does not require graphical means is available for determining velocities and accelerations in mechanisms. This is the analytical method, and consists of finding the equation of motion of the links of the mechanism as a function of time, or establishing the position of the driving link and differentiating the equation with respect to time, in order to get equations for the velocity and acceleration of the driven links.

The analytical method has many advantages over the graphical methods but has the great disadvantage that in all but the simpler mechanisms it is extremely complicated and time consuming. In fact, for complex mechanisms, the time required becomes prohibitive and the result is such a complicated equation that it is of little value. However, the analytical method lends itself very well to some of the simpler mechanisms and is coming into use more and more. It is especially useful in the synthesis of mechanisms, when it is available, and the dynamic analysis of some of the more common mechanisms is dependent on an analytical solution of the motions. Therefore a knowledge of analytical methods is essential to the student of dynamics.

Since there is no general method of attack in the analytical solution of the various mechanisms which would apply to all, each mechanism will be dealt with as an entity. Three mechanisms will be analyzed so as to give the student a grasp of the method and its advantages.

9.2 *The Simple Harmonic Motion Cam*

For the first example we will use the simple harmonic cam and follower shown in Fig. 9.1(a). This consists of a circular cam, pinned to the fixed link at some point away from the center of the circle, driving a flat-faced follower which moves in translation. This type cam is sometimes called an eccentric cam because the center of rotation is offset from the geometric center. This

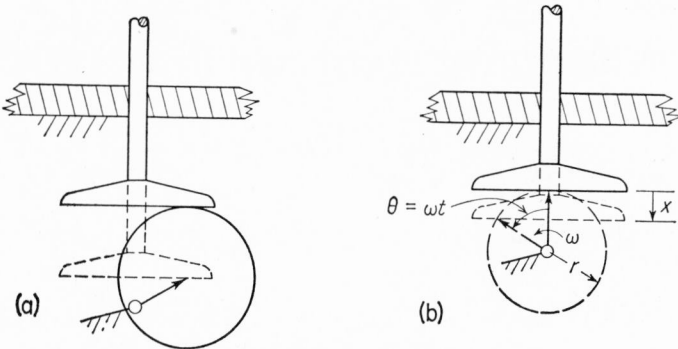

FIGURE 9.1

is the same mechanism for which we found the equivalent mechanism in the previous chapter, Fig. 8.11(b), and the equivalent mechanism will be used in deriving the equation of motion. We will use this simple mechanism as a first example because the equations are obvious and were discussed in detail in Chapter 1. The equivalent mechanism is redrawn in Fig. 9.1(b) and we assume that the cam (represented by the knife-edge) is rotating at constant angular velocity ω. As a reference we will start measuring time from the instant the follower is in its topmost position and the position of the knife-edge will be determined by the angle θ it makes with the vertical position. Letting r be the length of the knife-edge link (the eccentricity of the cam center from the center of rotation) and x represent the displacement of the follower at any time, we see from the figure that

$$x = r - r \cos \theta = r(1 - \cos \theta)$$

This equation holds for any angle θ, and we now have the equation of motion of the follower. The equations for the velocity and acceleration of the follower are now easily obtained by taking derivatives of the displacement with respect to time, or

$$v = \dot{x} = r \sin \theta \, \dot{\theta} = r\omega \sin \theta$$

and
$$a = \ddot{x} = r\omega^2 \cos \theta$$

We stated at the beginning of the chapter that there was no general method which would apply to all mechanisms. This statement should be restricted to mean that there is no means of determining the displacement equation which would apply to all mechanisms. In all cases the analytical analysis is dependent on determining the equation of displacement of the driven link as a function of the displacement of the driving link and then determining the velocity and acceleration equations by differentiation. Developing the displacement equation is usually the most difficult part of the analysis, although, if the equation is complicated, the successive differentiations can become quite difficult and lengthy. This will be seen in the next two examples.

9.3 The Slider Crank Mechanism

The slider crank mechanism is so common that a great deal of effort has gone into the analytical analysis of this mechanism. Since the mechanism is used in reciprocating engines and compressors and we will make use of the analysis later in discussing the balancing of such systems, we will discuss the analysis at length.

A drawing of the mechanism is shown in Fig. 9.2. Link "a," of length r, is called the crank, link "b," of length l, is the connecting rod, and link "c" is the slider or piston. Since the center of the piston moves along a line through the pin joint O, this is called an in-line system. If the line of motion

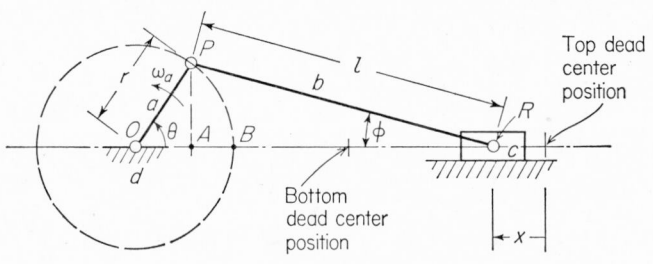

FIGURE 9.2

of the piston were parallel to, but displaced to either side of, this line it would be called an offset system. Since most reciprocating engines are in-line we will analyze the in-line system, although an offset system could be analyzed quite readily in the same manner.

We will make the assumption that the crank rotates counterclockwise with uniform angular velocity, ω, and use the angle θ, which the crank makes with the line of action of the piston, as the independent variable. We will develop the equation of motion of the piston as a function of the crank angle θ. The position of the piston when farthest from the center of rotation of the crank is called top dead center, and the position when closest to the center of rotation is called bottom dead center. The top dead center position will be used as a reference at which the angle θ is zero. The distance x, measured from top dead center, will represent the position of the piston at any time. If the connecting rod were of infinite length, the piston displacement would be distance A–B on the figure and the equation of motion would be

$$x = r(1 - \cos \theta)$$

which is the equation for simple harmonic motion as discussed in the previous article. A correction must be added to account for the finite length of the connecting rod. This correction is the difference between the length of the rod and its projection on the path of motion of the piston. Then the true displacement becomes:

$$x = r(1 - \cos \theta) + l(1 - \cos \phi) \tag{9.1}$$

where ϕ is the angle that the connecting rod makes with the center line of the piston. This equation holds true for any angle θ and is therefore the required equation of motion. However we have now introduced a new variable, ϕ, which must be eliminated in order to get the displacement as a function of θ only. From the figure we see that the relation between ϕ and θ is

$$l \sin \phi = r \sin \theta$$

or

$$\sin \phi = \frac{r}{l} \sin \theta$$

and

$$\cos \phi = \sqrt{1 - \sin^2 \phi} = \sqrt{1 - \left(\frac{r}{l}\right)^2 \sin^2 \theta}$$

Substituting this into Eq. (9.1) we get the equation of x as a function of θ only, or

$$x = r(1 - \cos \theta) + l\left[1 - \sqrt{1 - \left(\frac{r}{l}\right)^2 \sin^2 \theta}\right] \tag{9.2}$$

This exact expression for the piston displacement can be differentiated with respect to time to obtain exact expressions for the velocity and acceleration of the piston as a function of the crank position θ and the lengths of the crank and connecting rod (which are constant for any given system). Noting that $d\theta/dt = \omega$, the constant angular speed of the crank, these equations are

$$v = \dot{x} = r\omega\left[\sin \theta + \frac{r}{2l}\left(\frac{\sin 2\theta}{\sqrt{1 - \left(\frac{r}{l}\right)^2 \sin^2 \theta}}\right)\right] \tag{9.3}$$

and, after a great deal of algebraic manipulation and simplification

$$a = \ddot{x} = r\omega^2 \left[\cos\theta + \frac{\frac{r}{l}\cos^2\theta\left[1 - \left(\frac{r}{l}\right)^2\right] + \left(\frac{r}{l}\right)^3 \cos^4\theta}{\left[1 - \left(\frac{r}{l}\right)^2 \sin^2\theta\right]^{3/2}} \right] \tag{9.4}$$

Equations (9.3) and (9.4), while giving exact relationships for the velocity and acceleration, are quite cumbersome and unwieldy. A great simplification can be achieved by expanding the term under the radical in Eq. (9.2) into a power series by means of the binomial expansion. The resulting series converges rapidly for values of r/l which are found in practical applications, and the results of using only the first few terms as an approximation are satisfactory for engineering applications. The binomial expansion is

$$(x + y)^n = x^n + nx^{n-1}y + \frac{n(n-1)}{2!}x^{n-2}y^2$$

$$+ \frac{n(n-1)(n-2)}{3!}x^{n-3}y^3 + \cdots$$

and for the term $\left[1 - \left(\frac{r}{l}\right)^2 \sin^2\theta\right]^{1/2}$

$$x = 1$$

$$y = -\left(\frac{r}{l}\right)^2 \sin^2\theta$$

$$n = 1/2$$

The expansion then becomes

$$\left[1 - \left(\frac{r}{l}\right)^2 \sin^2\theta\right]^{1/2} = 1 - \frac{1}{2}\left(\frac{r}{l}\right)^2 \sin^2\theta - \frac{1}{8}\left(\frac{r}{l}\right)^4 \sin^4\theta$$

$$- \frac{1}{16}\left(\frac{r}{l}\right)^6 \sin^6\theta + \cdots$$

Values for the ratio of r/l are usually small, being of the order of $\frac{1}{4}$ or less for most practical engines. Using this value, $(\frac{1}{4})$, and the maximum value of $\sin\theta = 1$ in the above series, the terms become

$$1 - \frac{1}{32} - \frac{1}{2048} - \frac{1}{65,536} + \cdots$$

and for our purposes all but the first two terms can be dropped giving the approximation

$$\left[1 - \left(\frac{r}{l}\right)^2 \sin^2\theta\right]^{1/2} \approx 1 - \frac{1}{2}\left(\frac{r}{l}\right)^2 \sin^2\theta$$

Substituting this in Eq. (9.2) we get the approximate equation for the displacement

$$x = r(1 - \cos \theta) + \frac{l}{2}\left(\frac{r}{l}\right)^2 \sin^2 \theta \tag{9.5}$$

Differentiation with respect to time gives us

$$v = r\omega \sin \theta + \frac{r^2}{2l} \omega \sin 2\theta$$

$$= r\omega\left(\sin \theta + \frac{r}{2l} \sin 2\theta\right) \tag{9.6}$$

and

$$a = r\omega^2\left(\cos \theta + \frac{r}{l} \cos 2\theta\right) \tag{9.7}$$

We will note that the second term in the parentheses shows the effect of the finite length of the connecting rod on the motion. These equations will be used later in our discussion of balancing of reciprocating engines.

9.4 The Geneva Stop Mechanism

The last mechanism which we will analyze by the analytical method is the Geneva mechanism shown in Fig. 9.3(a). This mechanism was analyzed graphically in Chapter 7; the analytical method will give us a means of comparing the two methods.

Figure 9.3(b) is a kinematic sketch of the mechanism on which the analysis will be based. The driving link "*a*" is turning with constant

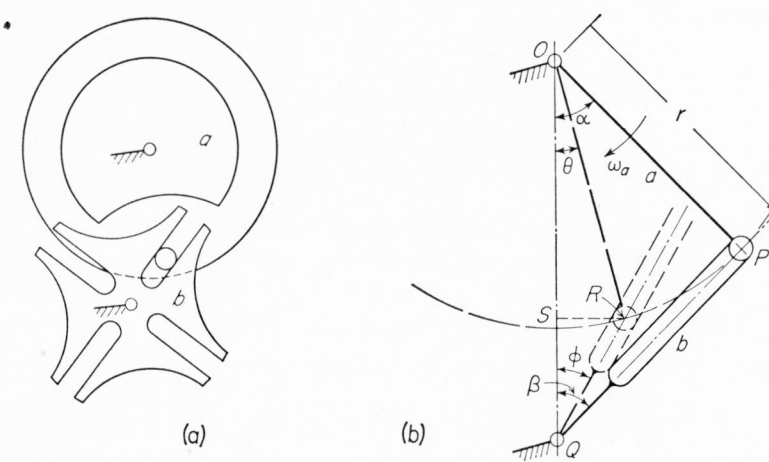

(a)   (b)

FIGURE 9.3

angular velocity ω, and we will develop equations for the angular velocity and angular acceleration of the driven link "b" as a function of the position of the driver.

The sketch is drawn for a four station system but the Geneva mechanism is not limited to this number of stations. The number of stations could vary from a minimum of three to any larger number. We will develop equations for the general case of n stations.

The following nomenclature will be used (see figure):

r = distance from fixed center of driving member, link "a," to center of driving pin.

α = angle driving link makes with center line, joining the fixed pin joints, at first contact with one station; a constant for any given number of stations.

β = angle driven link makes with center line at beginning of motion.

θ = angle driving link makes with center line at any time.

ϕ = angle that driven link makes with center line at any time.

n = number of stations.

From the figure, where the solid lines indicate the position of the links at the beginning of motion and the dashed lines indicate the positions at any given time, the angle between the driving link and the center line of the slot at the beginning of motion must be 90° since the center line of the slot must be tangent to the path of the driving pin. Also the angle β is one-half the angle of rotation of the driven link per revolution of driver and is fixed by the number of stations. The angle β then is given by the relation

$$\beta = \frac{360°}{2n} = \frac{180°}{n} \qquad (9.8)$$

Since triangle POQ is a right triangle,

$$\alpha = 90° - \beta = 90° - \frac{180°}{n} \qquad (9.9)$$

Since we wish to determine the equations as a function of θ we must get ϕ, defining the position of the driven link, as a function of θ. This relation can be developed from the figure

$$\tan \phi = \frac{S\text{–}R}{S\text{–}Q} = \frac{S\text{–}R}{(O\text{–}Q) - (O\text{–}S)}$$

where

$$S\text{–}R = r \sin \theta$$

$$O\text{–}Q = \frac{r}{\cos \alpha}$$

and

$$O\text{–}S = r \cos \theta$$

so that

$$\tan \phi = \frac{r \sin \theta}{\dfrac{r}{\cos \alpha} - r \cos \theta} = \frac{\sin \theta \cos \alpha}{1 - \cos \alpha \cos \theta}$$

and

$$\phi = \tan^{-1}\left(\frac{\cos \alpha \sin \theta}{1 - \cos \alpha \cos \theta}\right) \tag{9.10}$$

Now the angular velocity of the driven link is

$$\omega_b = \frac{d\phi}{dt} = \frac{d\phi}{d\theta} \cdot \frac{d\theta}{dt} = \omega_a \frac{d\phi}{d\theta}$$

Taking the derivative of ϕ with respect to θ we find (after considerable algebraic manipulation and simplification) that

$$\frac{d\phi}{d\theta} = \frac{\cos \alpha \, (\cos \theta - \cos \alpha)}{1 - 2 \cos \alpha \cos \theta + \cos^2 \alpha}$$

so that

$$\omega_b = \omega_a \left[\frac{\cos \alpha \, (\cos \theta - \cos \alpha)}{1 - 2 \cos \alpha \cos \theta + \cos^2 \alpha} \right] \tag{9.11}$$

The angular acceleration can now be obtained from the relation

$$\alpha_b = \frac{d^2\phi}{dt^2} = \frac{d\omega_b}{dt} = \frac{d\omega_b}{d\theta} \cdot \frac{d\theta}{dt} = \omega_a \frac{d\omega_b}{d\theta}$$

Performing this differentiation we get for the angular acceleration of the driven link

$$\alpha_b = \omega_a^2 \left[\frac{\cos \alpha \, (\cos^2 \alpha - 1) \sin \theta}{(1 - 2 \cos \alpha \cos \theta + \cos^2 \alpha)^2} \right] \tag{9.12}$$

With Eqs. (9.11) and (9.12) we can readily determine the angular velocity and angular acceleration of the driven link for any phase position of the driving link for any Geneva mechanism.

9.5 Discussion of the Analytical Method

The many advantages of the analytical method are obvious if a large number of similar mechanisms of varying dimensions are to be analyzed. The equations for the velocity and acceleration are general, with the dimensions, or dimension ratios, as parameters. The general equations will satisfy any number of similar mechanisms. The phase position for the maximum velocity and acceleration can be determined by a further differentiation of the velocity and acceleration equations with respect to the independent variable. Setting these equations equal to zero and solving for the value of the independent variable which satisfies the resulting equation will give the positions at which the velocity and acceleration are at a maximum (or minimum). Generally the resulting equation is fairly complex and the best method of solving for the value of the independent variable is plotting the function against the independent variable. The maximum and minimum points will then be the points at which the resulting curve crosses the independent axis.

The synthesis of mechanisms is readily accomplished if the velocity and acceleration equations are available. It is quite easy to check any number of different mechanisms of the same type by means of the equations, while the graphical analysis would at best be time consuming and tedious.

PROBLEMS

9.1 (a) Find an approximate equation for the piston displacement, similar to Eq. (9.2), for an offset slider crank mechanism if the path of motion of the crank is offset downward a distance "b" (see Fig. 9.2). Let the displacement, x, represent the horizontal distance from the center of crank rotation, point O, to point R.

(b) By differentiation determine the equations for velocity and acceleration.

9.2 Plot the velocity-time and acceleration-time curves for the Geneva mechanism using Eqs. (9.11) and (9.12). Use data as given in Prob. 1.6, and plot points for every $7\frac{1}{2}°$ of the driving link. Compare these curves with those obtained by graphical differentiation in Prob. 1.6.

Chapter **10**

Discussion of Kinematic Analysis

10.1 Comparison of Various Methods

We have now completed the study of the various methods of kinematic analyses. The methods which have been discussed are sufficient to allow us to analyze any mechanism which we might encounter in practice. The question now arises as to which method is the best for any particular analysis. There is no fixed answer to this question. In general the method which will give us the required information in the shortest time and with the least amount of effort should be used.

The analytical method will always give us the most complete information about a mechanism. But the time required for such an analysis is often not justified and a graphical method will give us the necessary information in a much shorter time and to the accuracy required for engineering work. However, if extreme accuracy is required, the analytical method should be attempted because the accuracy of this method is limited only by the number of significant figures we wish to use in the computations.

In many instances the maximum velocity and maximum acceleration are of primary concern, but we have no way of knowing at which phase positions these occur without resorting to an analysis of the various phase positions. This becomes a tedious and time-consuming chore if the instant center or image methods are used. The use of graphical differentiation will quickly determine the positions of the maximum velocity and acceleration. But, as found in our discussion of that method, the accuracy of the method is poor, especially at the points of maximum velocity and acceleration. Usually these show up as peaks in the curves, and peaks are points of maximum inaccuracy. By finding the positions of the maximums by graphical differentiation, we can determine the velocity and acceleration accurately at these positions by use of the other graphical methods. In this manner two or three graphical analyses at phase positions in the neighborhood of the indicated maximums will give us the information that we desire.

Graphical differentiation also serves well as a quick means of obtaining an over-all picture of the velocity and acceleration characteristics of a mechanism. It can also serve as a rough check for gross errors in more accurate analyses.

10.2 Presentation of Results

In all the graphical methods of analysis that we have discussed, with the exception of the method of graphical differentiation, the velocities and accelerations have been found for only one phase position. In a complete analysis of a mechanism all phase positions must be analyzed through a complete cycle. This should present no difficulty since all that is required is the drawing of the mechanism in the various phase positions and analyzing the mechanism for each phase position. The number of phase positions necessary for a complete analysis will depend on many factors, the most important being the accuracy needed. As a general rule the analysis should be made for every 15° position of the crank or driving member and then for smaller intervals in the vicinity of positions which are of particular interest. The results of such a complete analysis must then be presented in such a way that a comparison of the velocities and accelerations at the various phase positions can be made without the necessity of looking at the whole group of analyses.

The usual method of presenting the results is a graph with the velocity or acceleration plotted as a function of the position of the driving link. Since the driving link usually rotates with a constant angular velocity, this would also be a plot as a function of time since a given angular displacement corresponds to a certain time interval. It might also be desirable in some instances to plot the velocity or acceleration of some given point as a function of the position of that point. We will use some examples to show the various ways in which this information could be presented.

Velocity diagrams of the quadric crank mechanism are shown in Fig. 10.1. The mechanism is shown in Fig. 10.1(a) with velocity diagrams for the pin joints P and R. For any phase position of the point P, the magnitude of its velocity is plotted radially outward along the line $O–P$ extended. The locus of P for any phase position is the circle passing through P with center at O. Since link "a" has a constant angular velocity, the magnitude of the velocity of P is constant. A radial graph of the velocity of P will be as the concentric circle shown. The velocity of P at any position is the radial distance between the two circles at that position. The direction of the velocity is obviously perpendicular to the crank $O–P$, and directed in the direction of rotation.

This graph is of little use but serves as an introduction to a similar graph for the velocity of point R which is drawn in the same figure. Point R

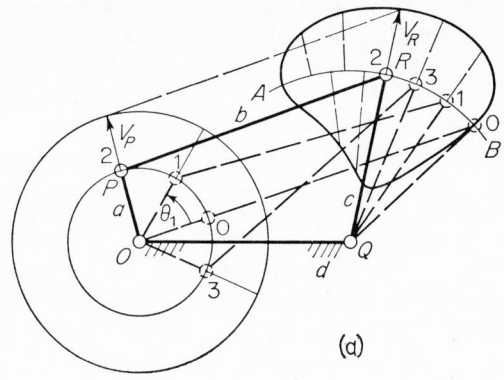

(a)

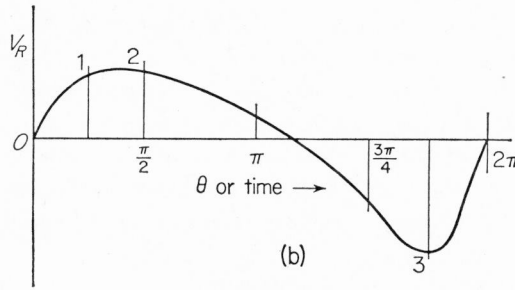

(b)

FIGURE 10.1

oscillates along the arc A–B. The magnitude of the velocity of R is plotted radially outward from this arc for motion to the left, and radially inward for motion to the right. Points of the curve are found by drawing a line, through the point on the circle which represents the velocity of P parallel to line P–R and intersecting the line Q–R. This construction of the velocity of R was discussed in Article 4.3 in connection with instant centers. This radial velocity-space graph then gives us a complete picture of the velocity of R for any position. Also by numbering the phase positions of the velocities of P and R, as in the figure, we can readily find the velocity of R corresponding to any position of the crank. These diagrams can be drawn to any scale that we might choose; however, in many cases the scale is of little importance since only the relative values of the velocities at the various phase positions are desired.

Figure 10.1(b) is a plot of the velocity of point R as a function of crank position (or time, since the crank is rotating with uniform velocity) using rectangular coordinates.

It should be noted that since angular velocities of links "a" and "c" are obtained by dividing the velocities of points P and R by the radii of rotation relative to the fixed link, these radial velocity-space graphs also represent the angular velocities of the links to some scale. In cases where the angular velocity curves are desired it is much easier to draw the curves as shown and then determine the scale to which they represent angular velocity than to fix an angular velocity scale and then draw such a graph to that scale.

Various velocity and acceleration graphs for the slider crank mechanism are shown in Fig. 10.2. The velocity-space graph for the slider, link "c," can be obtained in the same manner as in the previous example. But since the instant center of velocity "bd" lies on a vertical line through the pin joint connecting the slider and connecting rod, the construction can be simplified by extending the line R–P until it intersects a vertical through O to determine the velocity for any phase position. In doing this we must let

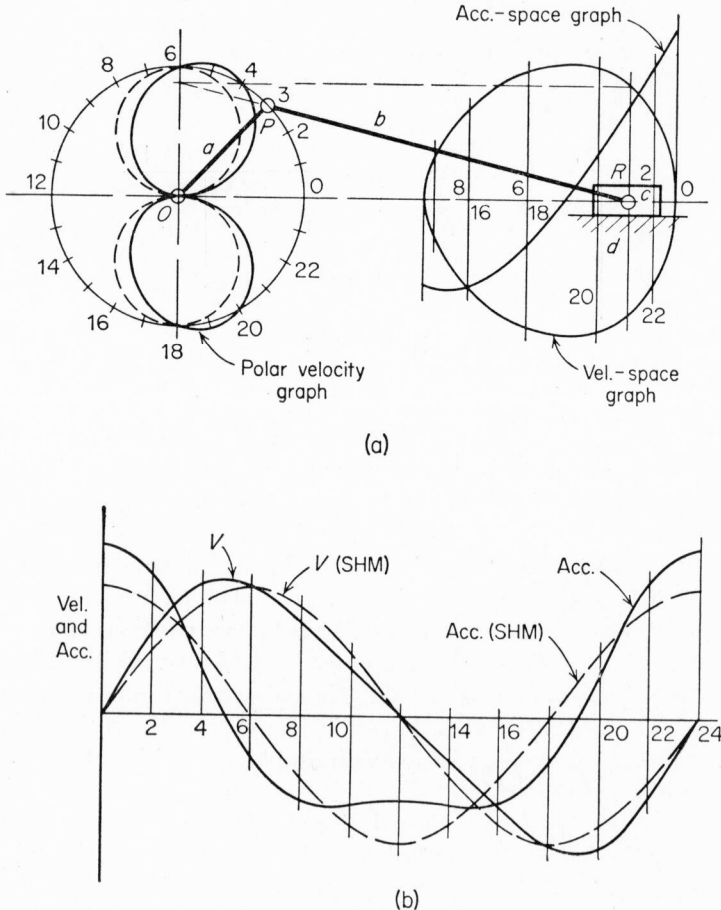

(a)

(b)

FIGURE 10.2

the length of the crank, $\overline{O-P}$, represent the velocity of point P. Projecting the intersection of R–P and a vertical through O onto the vertical through the point R will then give us points on the velocity-space curve, as shown in the figure. The polar velocity graph can be constructed by laying off the length corresponding to the velocity along the crank at its various phase positions, letting point O be the pole about which the graph is drawn. This polar velocity graph shows us the velocity of the slider as a function of the angular position of the crank. The magnitude of the velocity of the slider can be determined for any crank position by drawing a line along the crank position. The intersection of this line with the curve gives the velocity (measured from the pole, O). The upper curve gives the velocity as the slider moves to the left; the lower curve, the velocity as the slider moves to the right. As a comparison, the dashed circles are polar graphs for the slider if it moved with simple harmonic motion. From the previous chapter we know that as the connecting rod increases in length, the crank remaining of fixed length, the polar graph will approach the simple harmonic motion graph as a limit.

The acceleration space curve shown in the figure is obtained by plotting the acceleration for the various phase positions as obtained analytically from the equations developed in the previous chapter. All accelerations with sense towards the crank pin are plotted above the path of motion of the slider and those away from the crank pin are plotted below the path. In the velocity-space graph the sense is indicated in the same manner. Several graphical constructions have been developed for determining the acceleration of the slider in the slider crank mechanism, but they offer no particular advantage over the analytical method and will not be covered here. (Klein's construction is the best known of these constructions.)

In Fig. 10.2(b) the velocity and acceleration of the slider have been plotted as a function of the crank position (or time) in rectangular coordinates. For comparative purposes simple harmonic motion curves for the velocity and acceleration have also been plotted in the figure in dashed lines. All the curves have been plotted for a complete cycle of motion.

As a final example of velocity and acceleration graphs, Fig. 10.3 shows the velocity and acceleration graphs for the Geneva stop mechanism plotted as a function of time, or the position of the driving link, on rectangular coordinates. In this figure both the velocity and acceleration have been determined by means of graphical analyses using the image method.

The mechanism is shown in Fig. 10.3(a) and the various phase positions of points P and R are numbered from zero, at the position of initial contact, to four, corresponding to the phase position at the midpoint of the cycle, to eight, at the position where contact is broken. The velocity and acceleration images corresponding to symmetrical phase positions are also symmetrical and need not be drawn beyond the midpoint. This will be obvious as

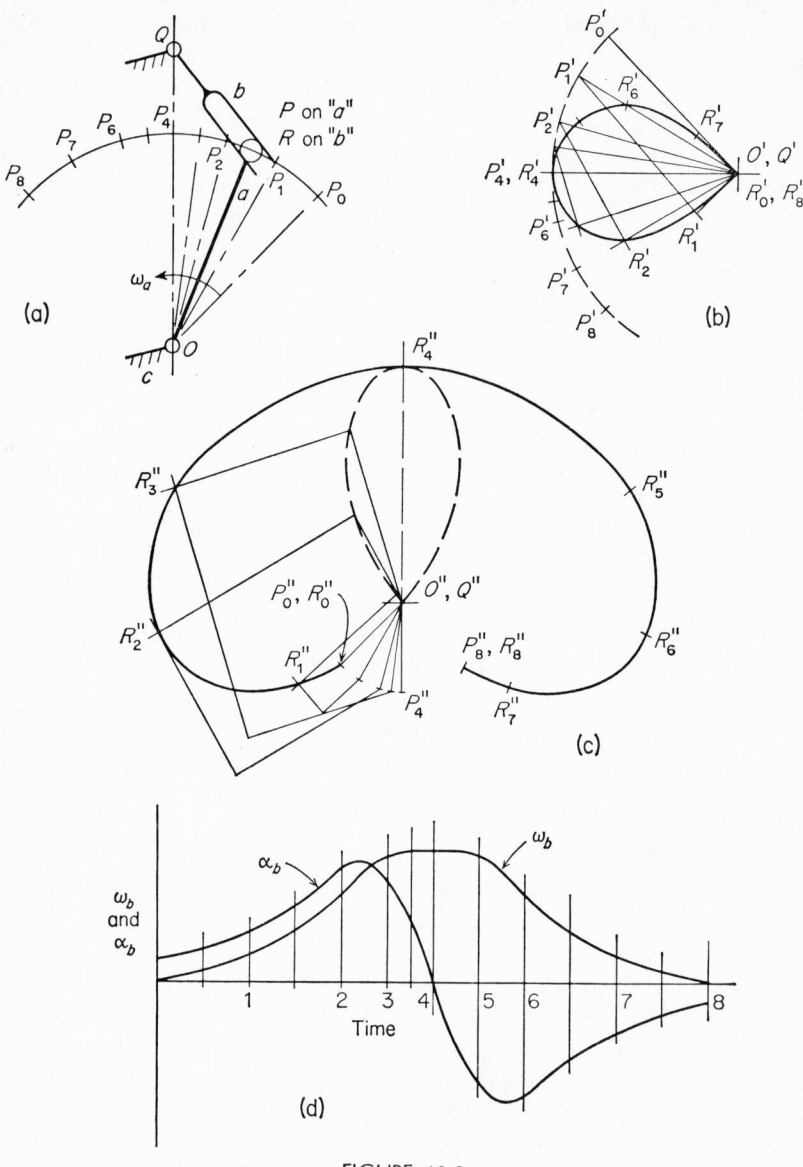

FIGURE 10.3

we discuss the images. The velocity images are drawn in Fig. 10.3(b) using a common pole, O', and the images of points P and R carry a subscript corresponding to the numbered phase positions. The solid curved line in the figure is the locus of the image points of point R for the various phase positions. The acceleration images are also drawn from a common pole, O'', in Fig. 10.3(c), and the locus of the images of point R is also indicated by a solid curved line. These curves indicate the symmetry of the figures. We see that for the velocity images the symmetry is about the horizontal line through O' and for the acceleration images the vertical line through O'' is the line of symmetry.

The angular velocity and acceleration of the driven link, "b," are plotted on rectangular coordinates as a function of time (angular position of link "a," the driving link) in Fig. 10.3(d). The ordinates of the angular velocity curve are obtained by dividing the velocity of point R at a phase position by its distance from the pin joint Q at that particular phase position. Note that point R is a different point on link "b" for each phase position, and therefore its radius from the center of rotation is different for each phase position. The ordinates of the angular acceleration curve are obtained by dividing the tangential acceleration of R relative to Q by its radius from Q. These ordinates are then plotted on the coordinates to some given scale.

Two points on the acceleration curve should be noted. One is the acceleration at the beginning and end of the motion, where the angular acceleration is finite and the velocity zero. The other is the midpoint position where the acceleration is zero. At both these points the acceleration image might be difficult to draw without a little thought about the location of the image of point R. At the first point, at which the pin just comes in contact with the slot, it is seen from the acceleration image that the image of points P and R are coincident, indicating that the acceleration of the two points is the same at this instant. This acceleration of P, on the pin, is a normal acceleration. The acceleration of point R, on link "b," is a tangential acceleration, which indicates an angular acceleration of link "b." We note that there is no Coriolis acceleration of R relative to P since link "b" has no angular velocity at this instant and for the same reason there is no normal acceleration of R relative to the fixed point. Therefore we see that the accelerations of the two points are the same. However, an instant later link "b" does have an angular velocity indicating both a Coriolis acceleration and a normal acceleration, both of which will be small, so that P'' and R'' are very close to the same point, and R'' will approach P'' as a limit as we move back towards the point of initial contact. The fact that P'' and R'' are coincident at this point can be verified by checking the angular acceleration of link "b" at the instant of initial contact using the equations developed in Chapter 9.

The other point on the curve which should be noted is the midpoint position at which there is no Coriolis acceleration since there is no linear velocity of R relative to P along the path of motion. We can also see there is no tangential acceleration of link "b" at this position since the angular velocity curve has zero slope at that position. Then the only acceleration that R can have at this instant is a normal acceleration towards Q. This can also be verified by referring to the equations developed in the previous chapter.

The velocity and acceleration images were drawn for 15° intervals of the driving link position, giving us seven points on the velocity and acceleration curves. These are not enough points to determine the curves very accurately. Especially is this true for the acceleration curve in the neighborhood of the midpoint position. Enough points should be determined so that the curves can be accurately drawn; in regions where the curves are rapidly changing, a large number of points are desirable. For the curves shown, points should be determined at $7\frac{1}{2}°$ intervals over the whole cycle and at every $3\frac{3}{4}°$ in the neighborhood of the midpoint position so that an accurate acceleration curve could be drawn.

The curves of velocity and acceleration for the Geneva mechanism are theoretical curves and it should be pointed out that in an actual mechanism, due to tolerances in the manufactured components, there will be some backlash and the actual curves will deviate more or less from those shown, especially at the beginning, the midpoint, and at the end of the motion. The amount of deviation will depend on the accuracy of the manufactured parts. We should also point out that because of the finite acceleration at the beginning of the motion of the driven link there will be an impact between the pin and the slot, causing high stresses. This sudden change of acceleration from zero to a finite value indicates an infinite change in acceleration at that instant, undesirable for high speed mechanisms. The change in acceleration with respect to time is called jerk and it is an important quantity in vibration studies and in the design of cams. This will be discussed in more detail when we discuss cams in a later chapter.

PROBLEMS

10.1 Plot the angular velocity of link "c" in Fig. P10.1 as ordinates against the angular position of link "a." Link "a" rotates counter clockwise at 45 rpm. Use

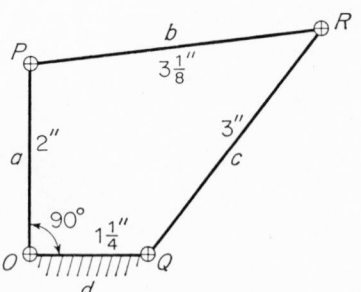

FIGURE P10.1

velocity images with a common pole to determine the velocity of point R. Compare the results with the velocity curve gotten by graphical differentiation in Prob. 1.5.

10.2 Plot the angular acceleration of link "c" in Fig. P10.1 as ordinates versus the angular position of link "a." Link "a" rotates counter clockwise at 45 rpm. Use acceleration images with a common pole. Compare the results with the acceleration curve obtained in Prob. 1.5.

10.3 Plot angular velocity and angular acceleration curves as a function of time for the Geneva mechanism using data as given in Prob. 1.6. Use velocity and acceleration images as shown in Fig. 10.3 and compare the curves with those obtained in Prob. 1.6 and Prob. 9.2.

Chapter 11

Static Force Analysis

11.1 Introduction

A study of dynamics of machinery cannot be undertaken without a thorough understanding of the basic principles of statics. In this chapter we will review some of these principles of statics and apply these principles to static analysis of machines. We shall discuss static force analysis at length since the same type of analysis will be used in dynamic problems, to be covered later. We shall also discuss the friction forces which are of importance in most moving machinery, and the method of analyzing the static forces in machines by use of the velocity analysis. This latter method is of particular advantage in determining the mechanical advantage of certain pieces of equipment.

The graphical method of force analysis is a powerful tool and is particularly applicable to the analysis of machinery where the analysis is usually quite complicated. This method will be used in most cases in the analyses to follow. The graphical method has the advantage of being much quicker in most cases, and it usually gives us a better understanding of the forces involved. In dynamic analysis of machinery which we will take up in later chapters, dynamics problems will be reduced to statics problems by the use of inertia forces.

Forces are vector quantities in that they have magnitude, direction, and sense. However we should note one important factor in force vectors which has not been emphasized in velocity and acceleration vectors: the line of action of a force vector, which indicates its direction and position relative to the body on which it acts, is very important in force analysis. Its point of action, the point at which a force acts on a body, is also important as we shall see in the discussion on equilibrium. Moments or couples can also be treated as vectors as will be explained in the Article on couples.

Since most mechanisms which we encounter are plane mechanisms, we can analyze the forces as though they were plane forces. Because of the fact that the links do not always lie in the same plane (the links in many cases being offset to avoid interference) the forces do not actually lie in the same plane but lie in parallel planes. Therefore such forces can be handled as though they were in the same plane by projecting them all into one plane. The moments caused by the offset, if they are appreciable, can be considered after the plane force analysis is completed.

11.2 Equilibrium

A rigid body is said to be in equilibrium if while at rest it tends to remain at rest or if while moving (in translation, rotation, or a combination of the two) its linear and angular velocity tends to remain constant. The effect of a single force acting on a body is to change the linear velocity of the body, or to accelerate it, and the effect of a moment acting on a body is to change its angular velocity, or to give it an angular accleration. The only way the velocity of a body can be changed is by the application of a force or a moment. Therefore if the summation of all forces acting on a body is zero and the summation of all moments acting on a body is zero, the body is in equilibrium. The conditions of equilibrium can then be stated mathematically as

$$\Sigma F = 0$$
$$\Sigma M = 0 \qquad (11.1)$$

where it is understood that the forces are added vectorially. Since we will be dealing primarily with plane systems it is quite often convenient to resolve the forces into rectangular components in the x and y directions. Then the forces in the two directions and the moments can be added algebraically. The equations of equilibrium then are

$$\Sigma F_x = 0$$
$$\Sigma F_y = 0 \qquad (11.2)$$
$$\Sigma M = 0$$

In our static analysis of mechanisms we shall make use of free-body diagrams of the individual links. Each link must be in equilibrium under the applied forces and moments and this condition of equilibrium for each free-body will give us sufficient information to determine the forces acting on each individual link. Therefore we need to review the conditions of equilibrium for bodies under various force systems.

Before we consider particular cases let us look at the case of a body under the influence of a general force system as shown in Fig. 11.1(a). The body has the four forces, F_1, F_2, F_3, and F_4; acting on it as shown. These forces can be combined into a single resultant which will have an equivalent

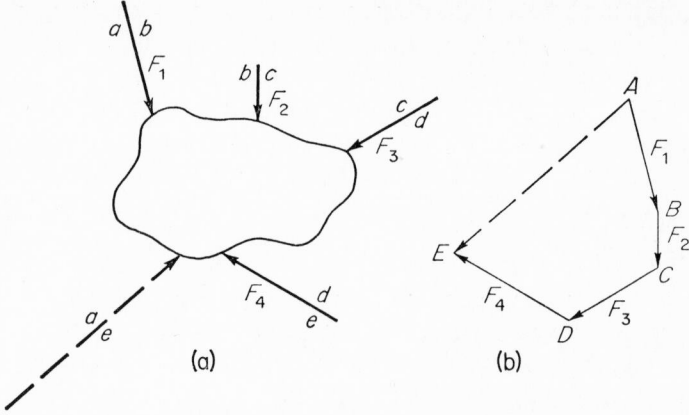

FIGURE 11.1

effect on the body by adding the forces vectorially as shown in Fig. 11.1(b). In order to simplify the discussion of the vectors, each vector in the space figure will be labeled with two lower-case letters, one on each side of the vector as shown in the space figure. In the vector diagram, in which the vectors are added, the vectors will be labeled with the same letters but capitals, one at each end of the vector. (This method of labeling the forces is called Bow's notation.) The sense of the force vectors in the diagram can be indicated by using the letters in alphabetical order, always placing the earlier letter at the tail of the vector. Then the resultant of the forces acting on the body is the force AE. Although the force diagram or force polygon gives us the magnitude, direction, and sense of the resultant, it does not give us the line of action of the resultant in the space figure. The line of action is very important, and we will discuss methods of determining the line of action later.

We see that the body is not in equilibrium because the first of Eqs. (11.1) is not satisfied; i.e., the summation of forces is not zero. In order to satisfy this condition of equilibrium, a force EA equal in magnitude and in the same direction as force AE but opposite in sense, must be applied to the body as shown in Fig. 11.1(a). Then with the force ea acting on the body, the body is in equilibrium *if the force ea lies on the line of action of the resultant* of the four original forces. This condition must be satisfied in order to satisfy the second of Eqs. (11.1) which states that the summation of moments must be zero. If the force ea has a different line of action from the resultant ae the summation of forces is zero but a moment is acting on the body as the result of two equal and opposite forces with their lines of action separated. Such a moment is called a couple. The concept of a couple will be discussed in some detail.

11.3 *Couples*

Consider a body with two equal parallel forces of opposite sense acting on it, as shown in Fig. 11.2, a distance h apart. Such a pair of forces is called a couple. The resultant force of the couple is zero, but the two forces impose a moment on the body. The magnitude of the moment is equal to the product of one of the forces and the distance h between the forces. This moment of the couple is constant regardless of the point about which the moment is taken. If

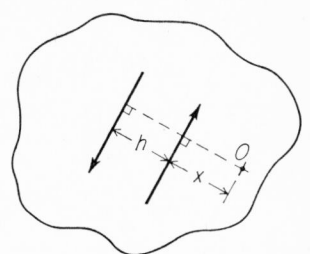

FIGURE 11.2

the moment is taken about a point on the line of action of one of the forces, its magnitude is Fh and its direction is counter clockwise. If the moment is taken about an arbitrary point, say point O on the figure, the moment of the closest force is clockwise and of magnitude $Fx;$ the moment of the other force is counter clockwise and of magnitude $F(x + h)$. Since both moments are in the same plane they can be added algebraically and the sum of the moments is $F(x + h) - Fx$ which is of magnitude Fh and counter clockwise in direction, the same as if the moments were taken about a point on the line of action of one of the forces.

A couple can be represented by a vector normal to the plane of the couple, where the magnitude of the couple is represented by the length of the vector and the sense follows the right hand rule which states that if the fingers of the right hand are bent in the direction of the couple (clockwise or counter clockwise) the extended thumb will indicate the sense of the vector. Then a clockwise vector will have a sense subsiding into the paper away from the reader, and a counter clockwise vector will be arising out of the paper. For plane systems a counter clockwise couple is usually considered positive in the United States, and this convention will be used in this text. The vector representation of a couple will prove useful later in the text.

Since a couple has constant magnitude and the resultant force is zero, the couple can be represented by any two equal parallel forces of opposite sense regardless of magnitude or direction so long as the moment of the couple remains constant. Another way of saying this is that the vector representing the couple has no fixed line of action relative to the body on which the couple acts.

11.4 *Bodies in Equilibrium*

We will now consider bodies or links in equilibrium under specific systems of forces. First we will take up the case of a link in equilibrium under the action of two forces, as shown in Fig. 11.3. The vector sum of the

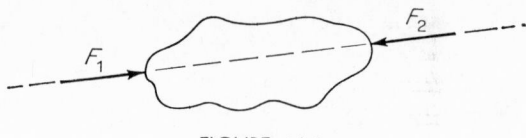

FIGURE 11.3

two forces must be zero and this requires that the forces must be equal in magnitude and direction but with opposite sense. But this limitation is not sufficient to insure equilibrium because these equal but opposite forces could constitute a couple. The two forces must have the same line of action if they do not form a couple, so the required conditions for a body to be in equilibrium under the action of two forces is that the two forces be equal in magnitude, opposite in sense, and collinear.

Next we will consider the case of a link in equilibrium with three non-parallel forces acting on it, as shown in Fig. 11.4(a). One condition for equilibrium is that the vector sum of the forces be zero, or the force polygon must close, as shown in Fig. 11.4(b). Again this condition does not insure that the summation of moments is zero because the resultant could be a couple. In order to find the necessary condition that the resultant is not a couple, we will reduce the problem to a two-force problem by combining two of the forces, say forces bc and ca, into a resultant force and determine its line of action. This can be done by the familiar parallelogram of forces, from which we conclude that the line of action of the resultant must pass through the intersection of the lines of action of its component forces. This

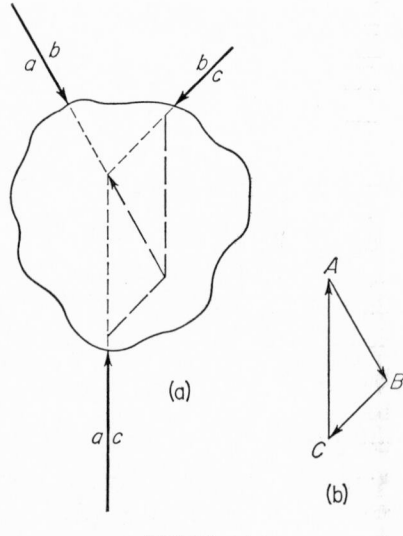

(a)

(b)

FIGURE 11.4

is shown in the figure. Then the necessary condition that the resultant and the force *ab* do not form a couple is that they have the same line of action. From this we see that the three forces must intersect at a common point. Therefore, if a body is in equilibrium under the action of three forces the resultant force must be zero and the lines of action of the forces must intersect at a common point.

Any body in equilibrium under the action of more than three forces which are non-parallel can be reduced to the three force problem by combining forces by means of the parallelogram of forces, taking two at a time, until only three equivalent forces remain and these three equivalent forces must be concurrent. This is the basis of a graphical method of determining equilibrium for a link under the action of any number of forces. This method makes use of a funicular polygon. The funicular polygon can be used to determine the line of action of the resultant of a system of forces. Therefore the funicular polygon, together with the force polygon, will serve to determine the equilibrium of a body under the influence of a system of forces.

11.5 The Funicular Polygon

The funicular polygon will be developed as a means of determining the line of action of the resultant of a system of forces in general. Consider a system of forces, *ab*, *bc*, *cd*, *de*, acting on a body as shown in Fig. 11.5(a). We wish to determine the resultant of these forces and its line of action. First we will draw the force polygon, as shown in Fig. 11.5(b), which will give us the magnitude and direction of the resultant, which is force *AE*. In order to find the line of action of this resultant we will replace each force

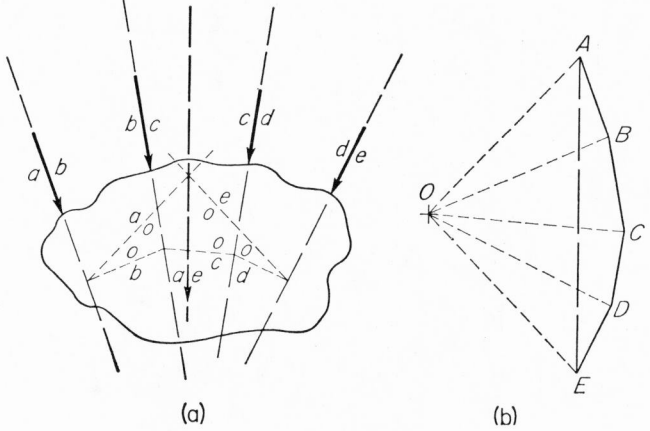

(a)   (b)

FIGURE 11.5

by two equivalent forces. From any point O, lines are drawn to the ends of the vectors in the force polygon (the corners of the force polygon). These lines are called rays and represent components of the various forces so that $AO \rightarrowtail OB = AB$, $BO \rightarrowtail OC = BC$, etc. The forces acting on the body will be replaced by these components, making use of the fact that the lines of action of the components of a force intersect each other on the line of action of the force from which they are derived. This may be seen by referring to the parallelogram of forces.

Then through any point of any force, say force ab, we draw the lines of action of its components ao and ob parallel to AO and OB respectively until they intersect the line of action of the next force, bc, (following the order of the letters). These components then replace ab. This can be done for any of the forces, but if we draw the components of bc through the point where ob intersects bc, its component bo will balance the component ob of force ab. By continuing in this manner, oc may be cancelled by co and od by do. Thus we have replaced all the given forces and cancelled all the components except ao and oe. We now extend the line of action of ao and oe until they intersect and the line of action of their resultant must pass through this intersection. From the force polygon we see that their resultant is the resultant of the four given forces. Therefore the line of action of the four given forces must pass through the intersection of ao and oe and its direction and magnitude is obtained from the force polygon.

The pole O could be taken anywhere and the funicular polygon could start at any point on any of the forces with the same result. In this manner we may adjust the position of the funicular polygon so as to make it fit more conveniently on the drawing.

Figure 11.6 shows how this method can be applied to a system of parallel forces. The force polygon, Fig. 11.6(b), in this case becomes a straight line

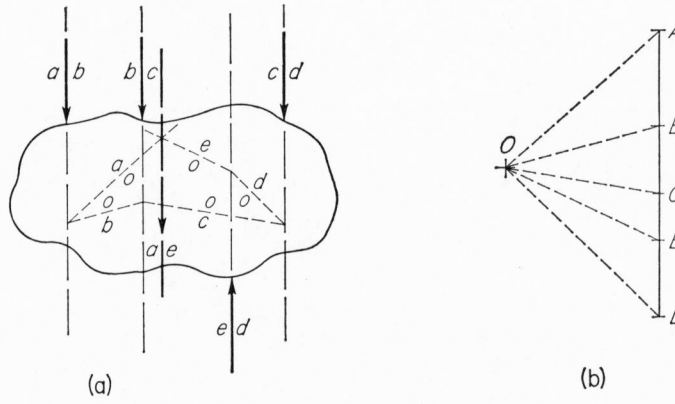

(a)   (b)

FIGURE 11.6

(a polygon of zero area) and the resultant is found in the same way as in the previous figure. The construction is shown in the figure.

In both the above cases the body would be in equilibrium if a force equal in magnitude and direction to the resultant, but with opposite sense, were applied to the body along the lines of action of the resulting force. This balancing force is the force EA in both examples.

We have already seen that one of the requirements of equilibrium is that the force polygon must close. However, we also found that the resultant could be a couple even though the force polygon closes. The funicular polygon can be used to determine whether a couple does exist.

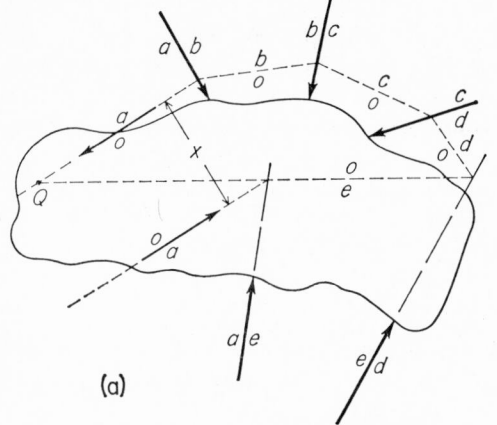
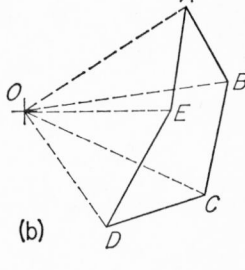

FIGURE 11.7

Consider the body in Fig. 11.7(a) under the influence of a system of forces which form a closed polygon, Fig. 11.7(b). Starting the funicular polygon on force ab and proceeding to bc, cd, etc., we find after replacing all the forces with their components that the two components ao and oa, being components of the original forces ab and ea respectively, form a couple with arm x. Therefore the resultant of the forces is a counter clockwise couple of magnitude $(ao) \cdot x$. The only way that the body could be in equilibrium under the action of the given forces is to shift one or more of the lines of action of the forces to a position which will cause the distance x to become zero. As an example of this the line of action of force ea could be shifted until it passes through the point Q in the figure. Then we see that if the body is in equilibrium under the action of a system of forces, the force polygon must close and the funicular polygon must close.

The funicular polygon is a powerful tool in graphical force analysis, and will be used throughout the remainder of the text for such analyses. It should be pointed out, however, that there are other graphical methods and analytical methods which will be used if they prove more convenient.

11.6 Transmission of Forces in a Machine

A machine, as defined in Chapter 2, is a mechanism which transmits forces. In the design of the machine the designer must know the forces which act on the individual links of the machine so that he can proportion these links in such a manner that they will not fail under the applied loads. In our force analysis of machines we will determine the forces that act on the individual links. In order to do this we must know the manner in which the forces are transmitted through the individual links. These forces are transmitted through the various pairs which connect the links, and the links themselves. For the present we will disregard the effects of friction in the various types of pairing and consider it in a later section.

In general the force transmitted from one link to another is always normal to the surfaces in contact, if friction is not considered. We will consider each type of pair individually and see how the forces are transmitted through these pairs.

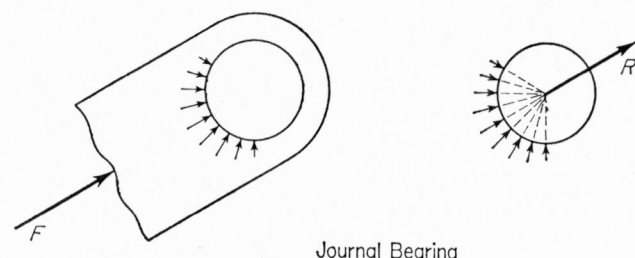

Journal Bearing

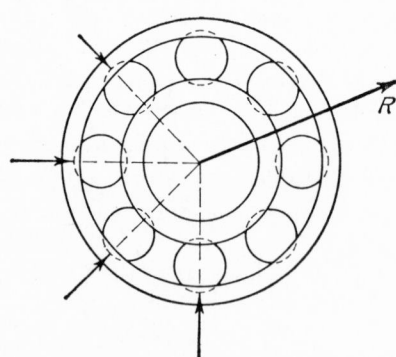

Ball or Roller Bearing

FIGURE 11.8

The turning pair or pin joint in machines we recognize as a bearing composed of a circular pin or shaft fitting in a hole in the link. Ball and roller bearings are also turning pairs. Since the forces transmitted through these bearings are always normal to the surfaces in contact, the resultant always passes through the center of the bearing. This can be seen from the examples shown in Fig. 11.8.

The lower sliding pair is represented by a piston, or any link sliding relative to another with surface contact. The resultant force transmitted through the sliding pair is always normal to the surface of contact, but its line of action cannot be determined from a consideration of the joint alone. The other pairs on the sliding link usually determine its line of action. In the case of a sliding link with a single pin joint as the only other pair, as shown in Fig. 11.9, the resultant can be considered to pass through the

FIGURE 11.9

pin joint. This will be discussed in more detail when we discuss the force analysis of a slider crank mechanism.

In higher pairs (rolling pairs and higher sliding pairs), the resultant of the force transmitted through the pair must be normal to the surfaces at the point or line of contact and will pass through the center of the arc defining the surface at the point of contact. The individual elements in a ball or roller bearing represent rolling contact (Fig. 11.8) as well as a wheel rolling along a flat surface as shown schematically in Fig. 11.10(a). Higher sliding pairs are represented by two gear teeth in mesh or a cam with flatfaced follower as shown in Fig. 11.10(b). In actual machine members point or line contact never exists so long as a force is transmitted through the pair. The members in contact deform under the load so that an area of

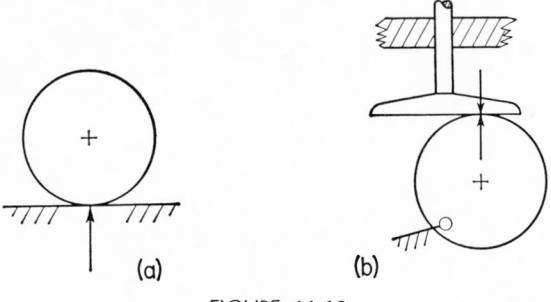

FIGURE 11.10

contact exists, and we really have surface contact for either rolling or higher sliding pairs. The contact area is extremely small, however, and the forces can be assumed to act at a point.

11.7 Force Analysis of Machines

We are now ready to start analyzing the forces in complete mechanisms, making use of the principles developed in the preceding sections. The force analysis will consist of determining all the forces and couples acting on each individual link and the forces acting on all the pairs in order that the designer has enough information to proportion the links and joints so that they will not fail under the imposed forces. In the present chapter we will consider only the effect of *external* forces applied to the mechanism; we will not be concerned with the forces which cause acceleration of the mechanism. These latter forces will be discussed later. Such an analysis, ignoring the forces concerned with accelerations, is called a static analysis. Friction forces will not be considered at present but will be dealt with in Article 11.9. The weights of the individual links, while usually considered static forces in mechanics, especially in structures, will also be left until we discuss acceleration forces. These weights are actually associated with the acceler- ation of gravity and their line of action will be covered in our discussion of dynamic forces.

Then, from our viewpoint, a static analysis will be concerned only with the forces associated with the useful work done by the machine, or the forces associated with the primary functions of the machine. Examples of such forces are the gas pressure on the piston of an internal combustion engine, the forces imposed on the jaws of a rock crusher by a stone being crushed, or, as a simple example, the forces on the jaws of a pair of pliers.

As a first example we will consider the slider crank mechanism shown in Fig. 11.11(a) with an external force F_c acting on the slider, link "c." The mechanism is kept in equilibrium by an external couple applied to the crank, link "a." We wish to determine the forces acting on all the pin joints, the normal force between the slider and the fixed link and the external torque applied to the crank to hold the mechanism in equilibrium.

In the force analysis of all machines the first thing we will do is isolate each individual link and make a free-body diagram of the link with the forces acting thereon. This method of attack will be used in both static and dynamic force analysis. Figure 11.11(b) shows the free-body diagrams for the links of the mechanism. For each link all the forces acting on the link are indicated, regardless of what is known about these forces. If the forces are completely known (i. e., known in magnitude, direction and sense), they are shown in solid lines along the proper line of action with the arrowhead, indicating sense, at the point of application of the force,

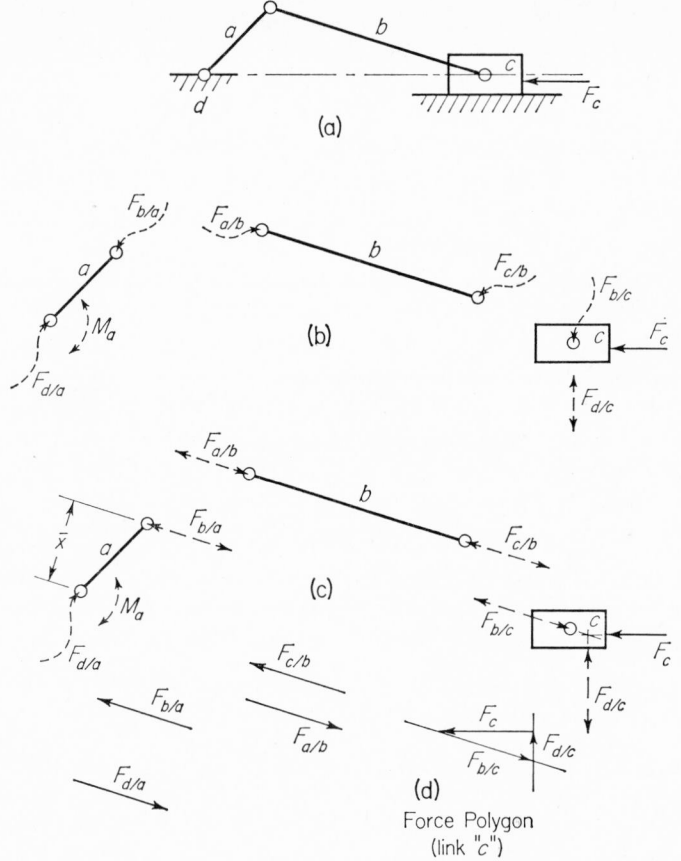

FIGURE 11.11

such as force F_c acting on link "c." If only the direction of the force is known, the force is represented by a straight dashed line in the direction of the force, but not in contact with the link, with arrowheads at each end of the dashed line indicating the sense is not known such as the force of link "d" on link "c." Note that when the line of action or point of application of the force is not known, the force is not drawn in contact with the link. If only the point of application of a force on a link is known, it is represented by a curved dashed line with the arrowhead at the point of application, as the force of link "b" on link "c" which must be applied at the pin joint. An unknown couple acting on a link will be indicated by a dashed arc with arrow heads at each end, as the moment acting on link "a."

We will label the forces in the following manner. External forces will be labeled with capital letters and a subscript to indicate the link on which they act. Forces imposed by one link on another will be labeled with a capital F and subscripts with a solidus between them, as $F_{b/c}$, indicating the force exerted by link "b" on link "c," or the force of "b" on "c." Couples will be labeled with a capital M.

Now returning to our free-body diagrams we find that link "c" has three forces acting on it; the external force F_c which is completely known, the force applied by link "d," $F_{d/c}$, known in direction only, and the force exerted by link "b," $F_{b/c}$, which is completely unknown except for its point of application (the pin joint). Link "b" has two forces acting on it, $F_{c/b}$ and $F_{a/b}$. The only thing known about these forces is the point of application at the pin joints. Link "a" is acted upon by the two forces, $F_{b/a}$ and $F_{d/a}$, and the external moment M_a.

Each of these links must be in equilibrium under the influence of the forces applied to it. We also know from Newton's third law that the forces exerted by two links on each other have the same magnitude and direction but opposite sense. The condition of equilibrium and Newton's law give us sufficient information to determine the forces acting on all the links. In some cases the forces on a link can be determined by considering only the single link in equilibrium, but in many cases we must deal with two or more links simultaneously in order to determine the forces, making use thereby of Newton's third law.

Consider the free-body diagram on link "c." There are four unknown quantities which must be determined in order to completely define the forces acting on the link. These are: (1) the magnitude of $F_{b/c}$; (2) the direction of $F_{b/c}$; (3) the magnitude of $F_{d/c}$; and (4) the line of action of $F_{d/c}$. The equations of equilibrium can be used to determine only *three* unknown quantities. If we refer to Eqs. (11.2) we see that we can set up three simultaneous equations, involving the forces and moments acting on a body in equilibrium, from which only three unknowns may be determined. Therefore we cannot determine the forces acting on link "c" by considering only equilibrium.

Link "b" also has four unknowns, the magnitude and direction of $F_{c/b}$ and the magnitude and direction of $F_{a/b}$, and therefore cannot be analyzed by equilibrium considerations alone. Link "a" has five unknowns, the magnitude and direction of $F_{b/a}$, the magnitude and direction of $F_{d/a}$ and the moment of M_a. So we find that none of the links can be analyzed by considering equilibrium alone, and our analysis must be made by considering two of the links simultaneously.

If we take links "a" and "b" together we know from Newton's third law that $F_{b/a}$ must be equal and opposite to $F_{a/b}$. This eliminates two of the unknowns from the combination leaving a total of seven unknowns for the two and the equilibrium equations for the two give us only six equations, not sufficient for the determination of the seven unknowns. However if we consider links "b" and "c" simultaneously, since $F_{b/c}$ is equal and opposite to $F_{c/b}$, we have a total of only six unknowns for the combination and the six equilibrium equations are sufficient to determine these six unknowns.

Knowing that we can analyze links "b" and "c" by considering them simultaneously, we will start our analysis with these two. Looking at link "b" we see that it is a two force member and for it to be in equilibrium under the action of two forces, they must be collinear. Then, since the point of application of the two forces is at the pin joints, their direction must be as shown in the free-body diagram shown in Fig. 11.11(c). It should be noted that in the absense of friction a torque cannot be applied to a link through a pin joint; therefore, link "b" has no couple acting on it. The magnitude of the forces acting on link "b" cannot be determined from equilibrium conditions since the only condition necessary for equilibrium is that the two forces be equal and opposite and forces of any magnitude will satisfy these conditions.

Turning now to link "c," we know by Newton's third law that the direction of $F_{b/c}$ must be the same as the direction of $F_{c/b}$ and a free-body diagram can be drawn for "c" as shown in Fig. 11.11(c). Now the forces on link "c" contain only three unknown quantities and they can be determined from the equations of equilibrium. A force polygon can be drawn to determine the magnitudes of $F_{b/c}$ and $F_{d/c}$ as shown in Fig. 11.11(d) by remembering that for a body in equilibrium the force polygon must close. The magnitude and direction of one force and the direction of the other two is enough information to draw the closed polygon. The line of action of $F_{d/c}$ must pass through the intersection of the other two forces, F_c and $F_{b/c}$, since link "c" is a three force member. A funicular polygon could have been used to determine the line of action of $F_{d/c}$, but for a three force member the funicular polygon would add unnecessary work.

The magnitude and sense of the forces acting on link "b" are now readily determined since $F_{c/b}$ is equal and opposite to $F_{b/c}$ and $F_{a/b}$ is equal and opposite to $F_{c/b}$ and we see that link "b" is in compression.

Turning now to link "a," $F_{b/a}$ is equal and opposite to $F_{a/b}$ (from Newton's third law). Since only three unknowns remain, they can be determined from the equilibrium equations. Since the external moment M is a couple, the resultant of $F_{b/a}$ and $F_{d/a}$ must be a couple which balances the external couple. The two forces must balance, so $F_{d/a}$ is equal and opposite to $F_{b/a}$ and the external couple necessary to hold the mechanism in equilibrium will be equal and opposite to the couple which is the resultant of these two forces. The magnitude of M_a then is equal to the force $F_{b/a}$ multiplied by the distance $\bar{x}$ as shown in the free-body diagram; its direction will be clockwise.

The above example was covered with considerable detail and in most dynamic analyses this amount of detail would not be necessary. Generally we will draw the free-body diagram as shown in Fig. 11.11(c) at the beginning of our analysis, putting all that we know about the forces into the free-body diagrams. For example the directions of the forces $F_{a/b}$, $F_{c/b}$, $F_{b/a}$ and $F_{d/a}$ we immediately know from the fact that link "b" is a two-force body, considered with Newton's third law. However, if there is some question as to which links we must start with in the analysis, the free-body diagrams as shown in Fig. 11.11(b) are usually best to work with. In general we must start the analysis with the link on which the known external forces are acting, or this link in combination with an adjoining link.

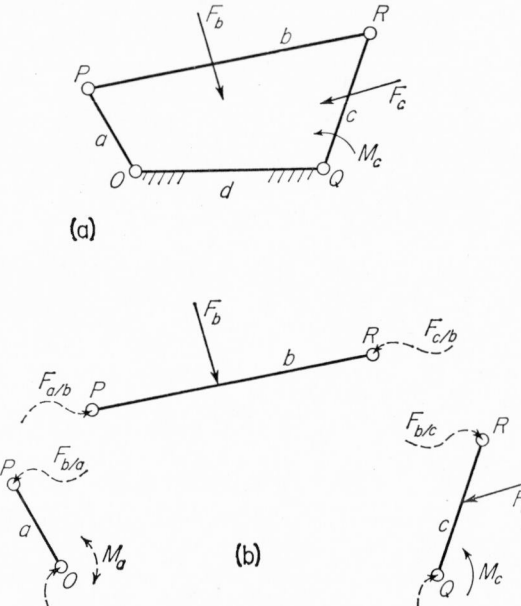

FIGURE 11.12

In order to show that the link on which the known external forces are acting must be used in the beginning of our analysis, let us make the false assumption that we could analyze the links "a" and "b" in the above mechanism before we need determine the forces acting on link "c." We could then determine the forces acting on links "a" and "b" and the external moment on "a" and they would be independent of the external force on link "c." Obviously this is not possible and we see that we must consider the link "c" at the beginning of the analysis.

As another example let us consider the quadric crank mechanism shown in Fig. 11.12(a) with the external torque M_c applied at the pin joint Q and the external forces F_c and F_b acting on the links "c" and "b." We wish to find the forces acting on all the pin joints and the external couple which must be applied to link "a" to hold the mechanism in equilibrium. Free-body diagrams of the links are shown in Fig. 11.12(b). Link "a" contains five unknowns, link "b" has four unknowns and link "c" has four unknowns. From our previous discussion we know that we must start our analysis with link "c," but since it contains four unknowns we must consider it and link "b" simultaneously. For the two we see that there are six unknowns ($F_{b/c}$ is equal and opposite to $F_{c/b}$) and therefore we can determine these from the equilibrium equations.

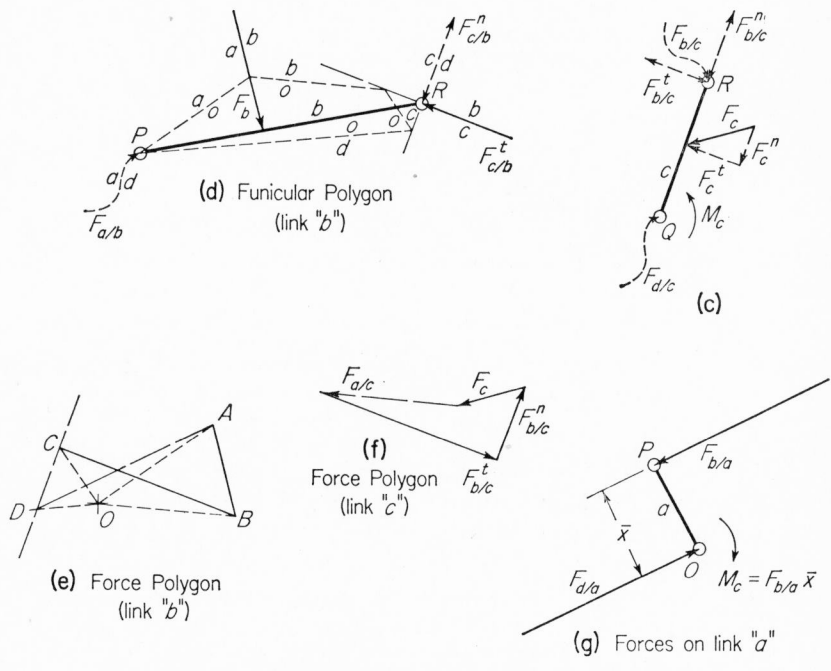

(d) Funicular Polygon (link "b")

(c)

(e) Force Polygon (link "b")

(f) Force Polygon (link "c")

(g) Forces on link "a"

FIGURE 11.12 (Cont.)

Since link "b" is a three-force member in this case, we cannot find the directions of the forces acting on it as we did in the previous case, and therefore we must start our analysis in a different manner. Consider the free-body diagram of link "c." If we resolve the forces $F_{b/c}$ and F_c into components perpendicular to line Q–R and along the line Q–R, we can take moments about Q and find the perpendicular component of $F_{b/c}$. These components are shown in Fig. 11.12(c) where the perpendicular component tangential to the path of R is labeled $F_{b/c}^t$ and the component with line of action passing through Q is labeled $F_{b/c}^n$. We will refer to these components as tangential and normal components. In summing moments about Q we note the normal components do not contribute to the moment since their line of action passes through Q, but we must consider the external moment M_c. This is as far as we can go in the determination of forces on link "c," since there are still three unknowns and we used one of the equilibrium equations in finding $F_{b/c}^t$. But remembering the law of action and reaction, we can transfer the components of $F_{b/c}$ to link "b" as shown in Fig. 11.12(d) and then we know one of the components of $F_{c/b}^t$ and the direction of the other component, $F_{c/b}^n$. Now link "b" has only three unknowns and they can be determined from the equilibrium equations.

We will make use of a funicular and force polygon to determine the magnitude of $F_{c/b}^n$ and the magnitude and direction of $F_{a/b}$. We recall that the force polygon is sufficient to determine the *forces* acting on a link, so that a force polygon is equivalent to solving the force equations of equilibrium, and the funicular polygon then is equivalent to solving the moment equation. If we look at the free-body diagram of link "b" with the components of $F_{c/b}$ as shown in Fig. 11.12(d), we see that if we take moments about point P we can determine $F_{c/b}^n$. The funicular polygon can be used for the same purpose. In order to do this we label the known forces consecutively, using Bow's notation as shown in the figure, then label the force $F_{c/b}^n$ and the force $F_{a/b}$ last. The reason for labeling the forces in this manner will be seen as we draw the force and funicular polygons. The force polygon for the known forces is now drawn, as shown in 11.12(e), and a dashed line indicates the force $F_{c/b}^n$ or force cd. We cannot locate the point D on this vector diagram since we do not know its magnitude. The funicular polygon will be used to locate D and thereby determine the magnitude of force cd. In order to draw the funicular polygon we pick a pole point O on the force polygon as shown to give us the components of the known forces. We recall that the funicular polygon must be drawn through points on the line of action of the forces and since we only know the point P at which $F_{a/b}$ acts, the funicular polygon must be started at that point. The force components oa and ob of the funicular polygon are drawn as shown and the component oc is then drawn until it intersects the line of action of cd. The funicular polygon now contains all the components of the forces with the exception of od. If the link is in equilibrium, the funicular polygon must close and therefore the component od must connect the intersection of oc and cd with the point P. The component OD, in the force polygon, must be parallel to od and drawing a line through O parallel to od until it intersects the dashed line through C will locate the point D and therefore determine the magnitude and sense of force cd. For equilibrium the force polygon must close and the line DA gives us the force da or $F_{a/b}$.

In picking a point for the pole O, we can choose any point and we try to use a point such that the funicular polygon is compact and does not run off the paper. We may have to make two or three choices before we find a point that gives us a satisfactory funicular polygon.

Returning now to link "c" we find that the only unknowns (we have $F_{b/c}^n$ from the analysis of link "b") are the magnitude and direction of $F_{d/c}$. These can be determined by a force polygon as shown in Fig. 11.12(f). Link "a," being a two-force member with an external couple, can be handled in the same manner as was link "a" in the previous example; the forces are as shown in Fig. 11.12(g). We see that an external couple must be applied clockwise of magnitude $F_{b/a}\bar{x}$ in order to hold the mechanism in equilibrium under the action of the forces given.

As a final example of static analysis let us consider the mechanism shown in Fig. 11.13(a), where we have a known external force acting on links "c" and "d" and an external couple acting on link "e." Again we wish to determine all the forces on the pin joints and the external couple which must be applied to link "a" to hold the mechanism in equilibrium. The

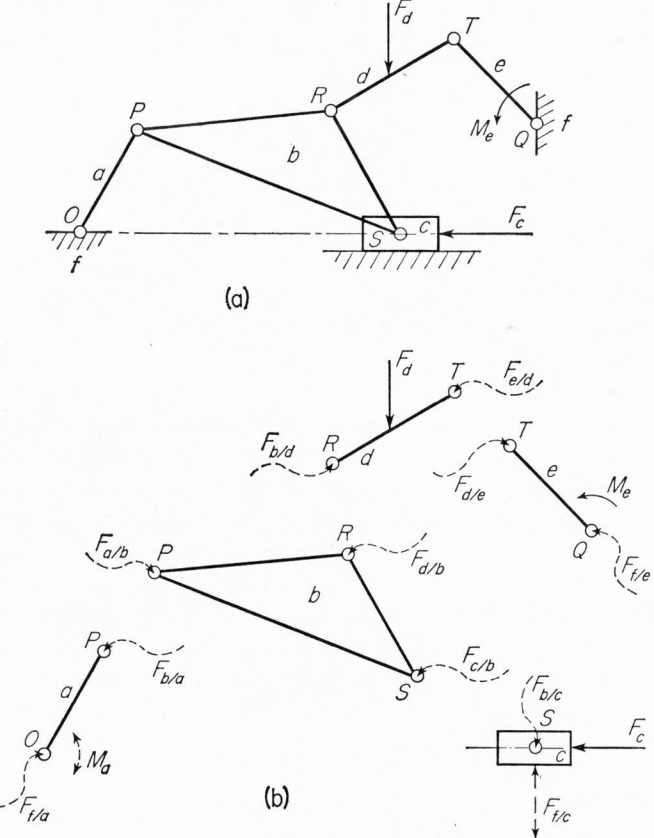

FIGURE 11.13

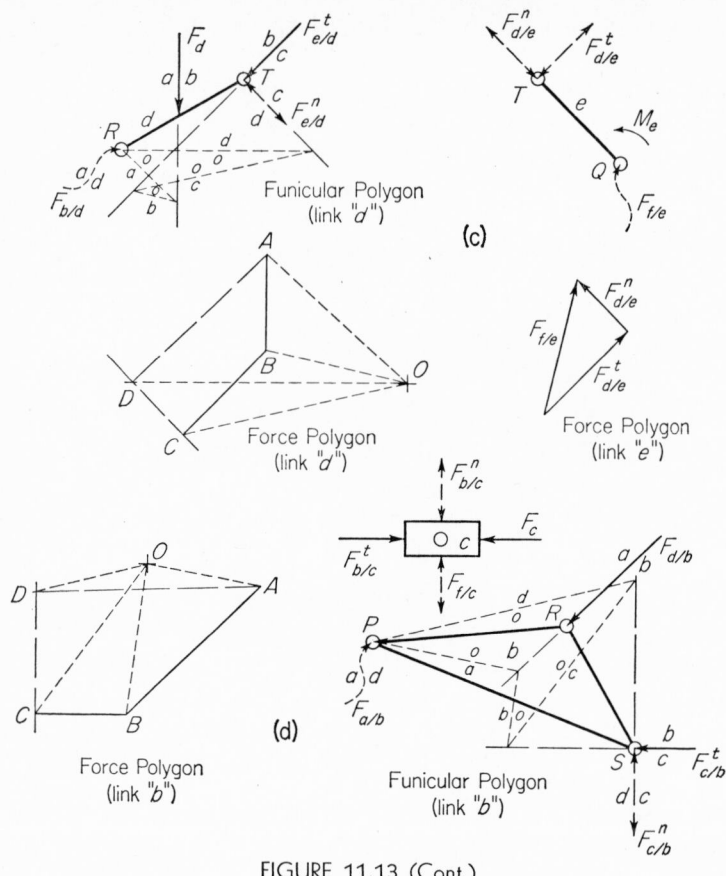

FIGURE 11.13 (Cont.)

free-body diagrams of all the links are shown in Fig. 11.13(b). From our previous discussion we know that our analysis must start with links "c" or "e." Considering link "c," we find that it contains only three unknowns as shown. But in this case we know the line of action, or the point of application, of force $F_{f/c}$ only because the line of action of the external force F_c passes through the pin joint S which is also the point of application of $F_{b/c}$. Therefore, since link "c" is a three-force member, all forces must intersect at a common point. Then we cannot analyze link "c" from the equations of equilibrium alone, even though there are three unknowns, because the moment equation has been used in determining the line of action of $F_{f/c}$. If we take links "c" and "b" together, we find that there are seven unknowns and they cannot be analyzed simultaneously.

If we consider links "d" and "e" together we find that the two contain only six unknowns so that we can analyze these links. These links can be handled in the same manner that links "b" and "c" in the previous example

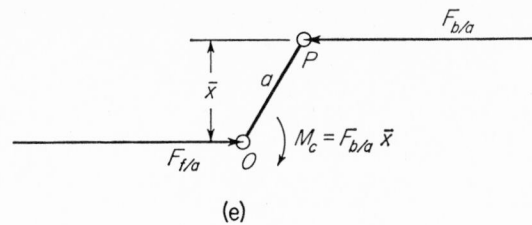

(e)

FIGURE 11.13 (Cont.)

were handled. The analysis of these links are shown in Fig. 11.13(c). $F_{d/e}$ is resolved into the two components $F_{d/e}^{n}$ and $F_{d/e}^{t}$ and moments taken about Q to find the magnitude of $F_{d/e}^{t}$. Transferring this known component to link "d" the forces on link "d" can then be found with a funicular and force polygon. Then the forces on link "e" can be determined with a force polygon.

Now transferring the known force $F_{b/d}$ to link "b" as $F_{d/b}$, we find that the two links "b" and "c" in combination contain only five unknowns and we have five equilibrium equations from which to determine them. (The summation of moments for link "c" was used to determine the line of action of $F_{f/c}$.) The analysis is shown in Fig. 11.13(d) where the free-body diagrams are redrawn for the two links. $F_{b/c}$ is resolved into two components, one in the direction of F_c and one normal to it. $F_{b/c}^{t}$ must be equal and opposite to F_c since they are the only forces in the horizontal direction. Then by transferring $F_{b/c}^{t}$ to link "b" we can determine the forces on link "b" with a funicular and force polygon as shown in the figure. The force $F_{f/c}$ can now be determined by transferring $F_{c/b}^{n}$ to link "c," and we see that $F_{f/c}$ must be equal and opposite to $F_{b/c}^{n}$.

The analysis of link "a" follows the procedure used in both the preceding examples, and will not be discussed in detail. It is shown in Fig. 11.13(e).

11.8 Force Analyses in General

From the examples just discussed we can set up a general procedure for the force analysis of mechanisms. The procedure is as follows.

1. Draw free-body diagrams of all the links in the mechanisms; be sure that all forces acting on each link are included. For two- and three-force members the directions of the forces can usually be determined, and these should be shown in the diagram.

2. Start the analysis with the links farthest along the chain from the links on which the unknown external forces or moments are acting. Usually these will have to be considered simultaneously with an adjoining link, and the analysis can be started with any two links which contain only six

unknown quantities in combination, making use of Newton's law of action and reaction.

3. These two links can then be analyzed by the use of a funicular polygon and force polygons.

4. Proceed along the chain from link to link making use of the known forces found in preceding analyses to the link containing the unknown external moment or force.

11.9 Friction Forces

Friction forces are encountered in machines at all points where there is a relative sliding of two members or where there is rolling contact between two members. In a large majority of machines the friction forces are so small in relation to the static or dynamic forces that they can be ignored in a force analysis. However in some cases the friction forces are of such magnitude that they must be considered in the force analysis. Friction forces are always associated with relative motion between parts, or impending relative motion, and the question might arise as to why they are included in the chapter on static analysis. There are two primary reasons for including a discussion of friction forces in the study of static forces: (1) although friction forces are present only when there is relative motion, or impending motion, between parts of a mechanism, the magnitudes of the friction forces are usually considered as independent of the velocity or acceleration and they can therefore be considered as static forces, and (2) in cases where the dynamic forces are the significant forces, the friction forces are usually negligible in relation to the dynamic forces. When the dynamic forces are relatively large, the relative velocities are generally of such a magnitude that proper lubrication must be provided, thereby reducing the friction forces to a small value.

In the discussion of friction forces we will assume that the coefficient of friction is known. Consider a block sliding along a surface as shown in

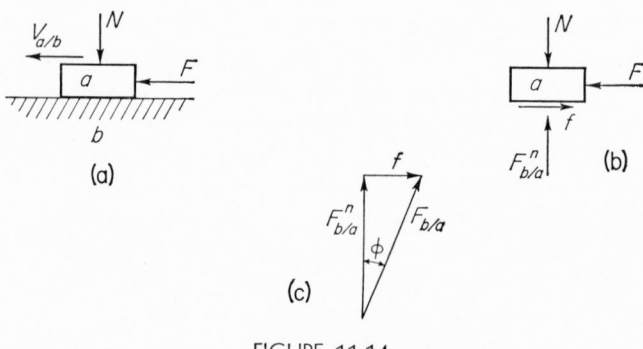

FIGURE 11.14

Fig. 11.14(a). The normal force between the two bodies is N and the force F, in the direction of sliding, is just sufficient to balance the friction force and keep the block sliding with a constant velocity. It has been found experimentally that the relation between the forces F and N is expressed by the equation

$$F = \mu N$$

where μ is the coefficient of friction, a dimensionless number. The coefficient of friction is dependent on the materials in contact, the lubrication at the contact surfaces, the temperature, the humidity and other factors, and must be determined experimentally for any given case.

Also it should be pointed out that the force necessary to start motion is greater than that required to maintain motion once it has been initiated, or the static coefficient of friction is higher than the sliding coefficient of friction.

The friction force acts at the surfaces in contact and always in a direction tending to resist the motion. A free-body diagram of the block is shown in Fig. 11.14(b) where the friction force is labeled with a lower case f. The friction force is a component of the force of link "b" on "a," and for equilibrium, the friction force must be equal and opposite to the external force F. The normal component, $F_{b/a}^n$ must be equal and opposite to N. The resultant of the friction force and the normal component is shown in Fig. 11.14(c) and we see that the resultant makes as angle ϕ with the normal component. This angle ϕ is dependent only on the coefficient of friction as can be seen from the relation

$$\phi = \tan^{-1}\left(\frac{f}{F_{b/a}^n}\right) = \tan^{-1}\left(\frac{\mu F_{b/a}^n}{F_{b/a}^n}\right) = \tan^{-1}(\mu) \qquad (11.3)$$

The angle ϕ is called the friction angle and we will make use of it in our analysis of friction forces. Particular note should be made of the fact that friction angle, ϕ, is independent of the magnitudes of the forces so that the direction of the force $F_{b/a}$ is fixed once the coefficient of friction is known, and $F_{b/a}$ must pass through the intersection of the lines of action of F and N.

It is not our purpose here to discuss in detail the value of the coefficient of friction and how it varies under various conditions but rather to show how it can be used in the force analysis of mechanisms if its value is known. However, some knowledge of the characteristics of the coefficient is necessary in order to intelligently use it in force analyses. Its value is usually small where it is encountered in machines, ranging from a maximum of 0.3 for rough, dry, metal-to-metal sliding, to 0.002 for well lubricated bearings. The coefficient is dependent on so many factors that its value should be taken as an approximation at best; we are not justified in using extreme accuracy in an analysis where friction forces are of appreciable value.

However our analysis is quite rigorous, assuming the value of the coefficient of friction is known.

In the above discussion the effect of the friction force on lower sliding pairs was shown, and the friction force can be handled in the same manner for higher sliding pairs and for rolling pairs, in each case making use of the friction angle. But we need to discuss the friction forces in pin joints in more detail. Consider Fig. 11.15(a) which shows a pin, link "*a*," in a bearing which is part of link "*b*." The clearance between the pin and

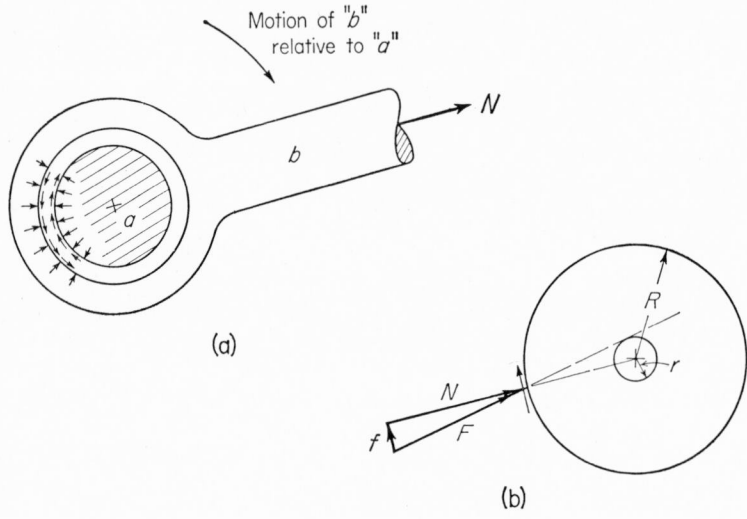

FIGURE 11.15

bearing is greatly exaggerated so that the force vectors can be shown. Assuming that motion or impending motion of link "*b*" is clockwise relative to the pin, the friction forces will be as shown in the figure, tending to oppose the motion. A large view of the pin is shown in Fig. 11.15(b) with the summation of the normal forces and the friction forces as single force vectors, and the resultant of the two, F. The resultant F must cause the same moment about the center of the pin that the friction force causes. If the moment arm of the resultant is r, the following condition must exist

$$Fr = fR$$

where R is the radius of the pin, or

$$[N^2 + (\mu N)^2]^{1/2}r = \mu NR$$

so that

$$N(1 + \mu^2)^{1/2}r = \mu NR$$

then

$$r = \frac{\mu}{(1 + \mu^2)^{1/2}} R = \frac{\tan \phi}{(1 + \tan^2 \phi)^{1/2}} R$$

$$= \frac{\tan \phi}{\sec \phi} R = R \sin \phi \tag{11.4}$$

From this we see that the resultant must be tangent to a circle about the center of the pin of radius $R \sin \phi$. This circle is called the friction circle and we note that the friction circle radius is independent of the force, being a function of the bearing radius and the friction angle only. In an analysis where we are considering friction, we will always draw in the friction circle at each pin joint and the forces at the pin joint must then be tangent to the friction circle instead of passing through the center of the pin. Since the friction angle is small and the friction coefficient is never exact, we use an approximation of the friction circle radius in our analysis. For small angles the sine of the angle is very nearly equal to the tangent of the angle. Making this substitution in Eq. (11.4)

$$r = R \tan \phi = \mu R \tag{11.5}$$

This gives us a quick means of determining the friction circle radius with sufficient accuracy once we have selected the coefficient of friction.

11.10 Force Analysis with Friction Included

We are now ready to analyze mechanisms with the friction forces included in the analysis. As an example we will use the slider crank mechanism already analyzed (with friction ignored) in Article 11.7. The mechanism is redrawn in Fig. 11.16(a) and the free-body diagrams of the various links are shown in Figs. 11.16(b) and 11.16(c) with the friction circles drawn at the pin joints. The radii of the friction circles are greatly exaggerated for clarity. Note that the coefficient of friction and the radii of the pins must be known before we can draw in the friction circles. Our primary problem in an analysis where friction forces are considered is to determine the position of the forces relative to the friction circles. The rule used to determine the position is that the friction force always tends to oppose the relative motion between the two members; therefore the forces must be tangent to the friction circles at a point such that the moment of the force about the center of the pin will oppose the relative angular motion. Figure 11.16(b) shows the forces in the free-body diagrams corresponding to the case in which the motion, or impending motion, of link "c" is towards the left. The approximate direction and sense of the forces are obtained from the previous analysis (the friction forces will cause a slight change in direction) and the relative angular motion of the links can be obtained by inspection of the mechanism, assuming motion of "c" to the left as stated.

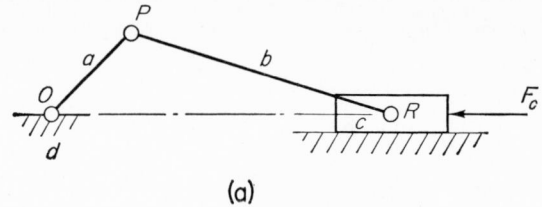

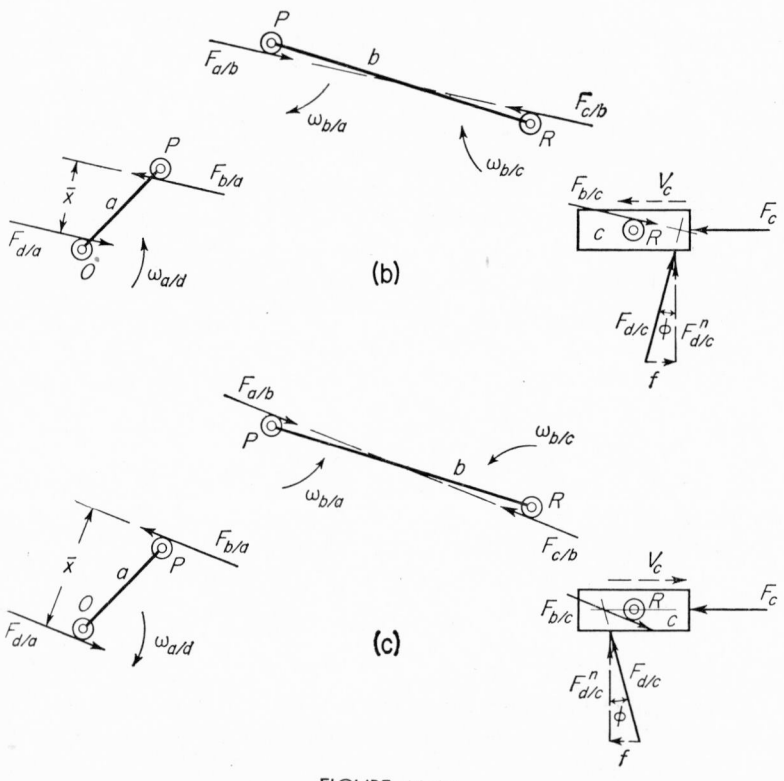

FIGURE 11.16

If we look at point R on link "b" we see that since the link is in compression and $\omega_{b/c}$ is clockwise, the force $F_{c/b}$ must be tangent to the friction circle as shown in order to cause an opposing counter clockwise torque. Also, the force $F_{a/b}$ must be as shown since $\omega_{b/a}$ is clockwise. Since the link "b" is a two-force member, the two forces must be collinear as shown, thereby fixing the direction of the forces. The forces on link "c" are shown in their correct positions and directions where $F_{d/c}$ is at an angle ϕ, the friction angle, relative to the normal, so as to oppose the motion of the slider. $F_{d/c}$ must also pass through the intersection of the other two forces. Now going to link "a" we see that the two forces acting on it are closer together because of the friction forces than they were when friction was not considered. This decrease in the distance $\bar{x}$ is caused by the forces being tangent to the friction circles and also by the change in direction of the forces. This means that the external moment applied to the link in order to hold the mechanism in equilibrium is smaller than in the previous case, where friction was ignored. This would be expected since the friction forces tend to oppose the motion and this motion was assumed in the direction of the external force F_c.

If we assume that link "c" is moving towards the right, the free-body diagram will be as shown in Fig. 11.16(c). (The student should go through the reasoning to understand that the forces are as shown.) Note that in this case the external moment on link "c" is greater than in the previous case because the moment must overcome not only the force F_c but also the friction forces which now have the effect of an increased external force.

The same mechanism is shown in a different phase position in Fig. 11.17, and assuming motion of the slider to the left, the direction of the forces on link "b" will be as shown in the figure.

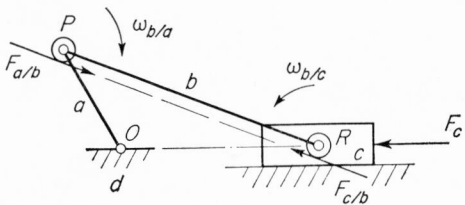

FIGURE 11.17

The analysis of any mechanism where friction is considered would be handled in the same manner. The direction of the forces on sliders and rollers are determined by the friction angle, always opposing the motion, and the forces at the pin joints are always tangent to the friction circles, again opposing the relative angular motion of the links. In complicated mechanisms where the direction of the relative motions cannot be determined by inspection, a rough velocity analysis can be quickly made to determine these directions. If the direction and sense of the forces between links cannot be determined by inspection, these can be determined by a rough force analysis ignoring the friction. The sense of the forces will not be changed by the friction forces and the direction of the forces will not be greatly affected by the friction forces.

11.11 *Determining Static Forces by Means of Velocity Image*

In many cases the mechanical advantage of a mechanism is desired and in such cases, a force analysis, as given in this chapter, can be used to determine the mechanical advantage. Making a complete analysis, however, requires the determination of the forces at each pin joint and between all sliding members. This entails considerable work in order to determine only the ratio of two forces. We can make use of the velocity image to determine the mechanical advantage, and usually it is much easier to draw a velocity image than it is to make a complete force analysis.

The principle of virtual work allows us to make use of the velocity image in the determination of forces. We will not develop the principle of virtual work in detail but will show how it can be used in relation to the velocity image. Most books on elementary mechanics cover the theory and the reader is referred to those for a complete development. For our purposes the principle can be stated as follows: if a mechanism is in equilibrium under the action of external forces, the sum of the work done on the mechanism by these forces is zero under a small change in phase position, if the friction forces be neglected. The small change in phase position causes a small displacement of all points in the mechanism and these small displacements are called virtual displacements.

This principle can be demonstrated by a lever, as shown in Fig. 11.18, hinged to the fixed body at O and in equilibrium under the external forces

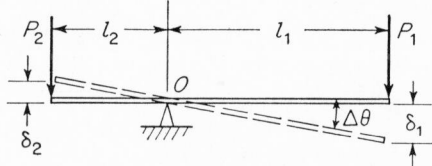

FIGURE 11.18

P_1 and P_2. The principle of virtual work states that if we let the lever rotate through a small angle $\Delta\theta$, causing the forces to move through small displacements δ_1 and δ_2, the work done by the forces in moving through these small displacements is zero, or

$$P_1\delta_1 + (-P_2\delta_2) = 0$$

Note that the force P_1 does positive work on the lever since the displacement has the same sense as the force and the force P_2 does negative work, the displacement being of opposite sense to the force. The displacement must be infinitesimal in magnitude for the equation to hold, since the work is the product of the force and its displacement in the direction of the force. If the displacement is of finite magnitude, it will have a component normal to the force and the force does no work in moving normal to its direction. The force at the pin joint does no work since the point has no motion and we have assumed zero friction. From the above equation we can get the ratio of the forces

$$\frac{P_1}{P_2} = \frac{\delta_2}{\delta_1} \tag{11.6}$$

showing that the forces are inversely proportional to their displacements.

We can also show that the ratio of the displacements is the same as the ratio of the velocities of the points of action of the forces if we assume an angular velocity of the lever. The ratio of the displacements can be written as

$$\frac{\delta_2}{\delta_1} = \frac{l_2 \Delta\theta}{l_1 \Delta\theta} = \frac{l_2}{l_1} \tag{11.7}$$

and the ratio of the velocities with an assumed angular velocity is

$$\frac{V_2}{V_1} = \frac{\omega l_2}{\omega l_1} = \frac{l_2}{l_1} = \frac{\delta_2}{\delta_1} \tag{11.8}$$

Substituting Eq. (11.8) into Eq. (11.6) we see that

$$\frac{P_1}{P_2} = \frac{V_2}{V_1} \tag{11.9}$$

showing that the forces are inversely proportional to the instantaneous velocities of the points of action of the forces. It should be pointed out that the velocities in this case are in the direction of the forces, and in cases where the velocities are not in the direction of the forces, only the component along the force direction should be used in the above equation, since the velocity in the direction of the work absorbing component of displacement is the only velocity associated with work.

Let us now consider the slider crank mechanism shown in Fig. 11.19(a). The crank and connecting rod are of the same length, l, and the crank angle is 45°. We wish to determine the magnitude of the force, F_a, acting vertically at the midpoint of the crank, necessary to hold the mechanism in equilibrium with a known force, F_c, acting horizontally on the slider. Let the slider move a small amount, δ, to the right doing negative work on the force, F_c. The force F_a will move downward and towards the right. Point P will move horizontally to the right a distance $\delta/2$ and point S, the point of application of force F_a, will move horizontally to the right half the distance of P, or $\delta/4$. Since the displacement was small, point S will also move downward a distance $\delta/4$ and this downward displacement is the work absorbing component of the displacement of F_a, and the work is positive. Then the work done on the mechanism by the external forces must be zero, or

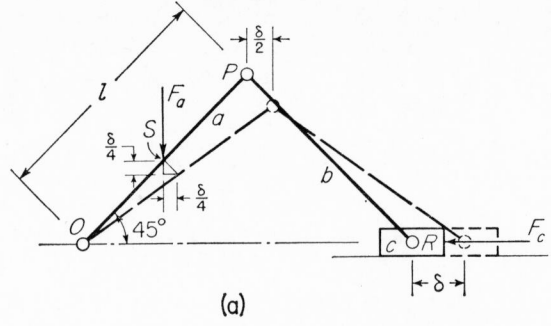

(a)

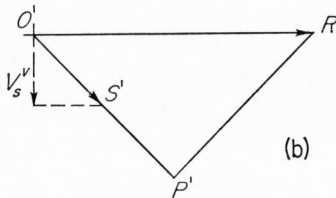

(b)

FIGURE 11.19

$$F_a\left(\frac{\delta}{4}\right) + (-F_c\delta) = 0$$

or
$$F_a = 4F_c$$

Now if we draw a velocity image for the mechanism, as in Fig. 11.19(b) we see by observation that the vertical component of the velocity of point S is one-fourth the velocity of point R in the direction of F_c and the force F_a could have been determined from the velocity image by using Eq. (11.9), giving us the relation

$$F_a = F_c \frac{V_R}{V_S^v} = 4F_c$$

The scale of the velocity image is unimportant since only velocity ratios are needed. If F_a is the only information desired, this method of determining F_a is much quicker than making a complete force analysis of the mechanism.

We will now use the method of virtual work in a practical example. Fig. 11.20(a) shows a rock crusher mechanism with a stone between the jaws which are links "f" and "e." The stone is in contact with link "e" at point W and we wish to determine the relation between the force normal to the jaw at W and the torque applied to the crank, link "a." If a force were applied at point P normal to the crank the torque on the crank would be the force times the length of the crank. The ratio of this force to the normal force on the jaw at W will be inversely proportional to the velocity of P and

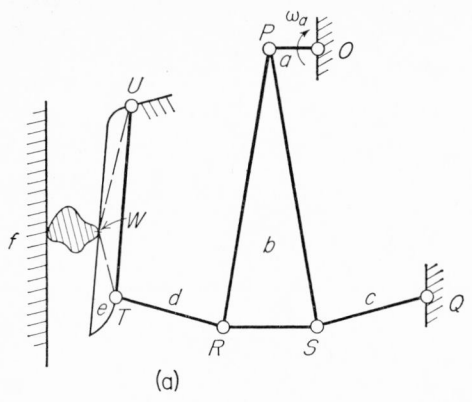

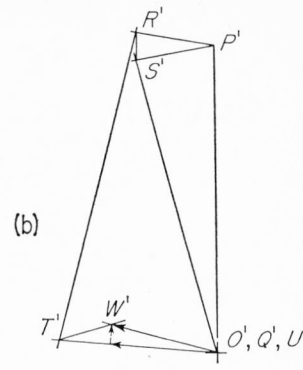

FIGURE 11.20

the component of the velocity of W normal to the jaw. From the velocity image of the mechanism, shown in Fig. 11.20(b), we can get these velocities and thereby determine the desired relationship. Note that there is a component of velocity of W parallel to the jaws and this component tends to move the stone upward. Another advantage of the virtual work method, making use of a velocity image, is the ease with which we can rearrange the mechanism to give us the desired ratio if the force relationship is not satisfactory. By observation of the velocity image and the mechanism we can readily see what various changes in the dimensions of the links will do to the force ratio.

PROBLEMS

11.1 If a force of 100 lb is acting horizontally to the left on slider "d" in Fig. P4.6, determine the torque on link "a" necessary to hold the mechanism in equilibrium. Also determine the forces acting at all pin joints, and the force between links "c" and "d."

11.2 A force of 1000 lbs is acting horizontally to the left on link "e" and a force of 500 lb is acting horizontally to the left at point U in Fig. P4.12. What torque is required on link "a" to hold the mechanism in equilibrium?

11.3 If a clockwise torque of 1600 lb-in. is acting on link "a" in Fig. P4.4, what force must be applied to the slider, link "d," to keep the mechanism in equilibrium? What are the forces between all links of the mechanism, under the given conditions?

11.4 If a force of 1500 lb is acting horizontally to the left on link "e" in Fig. P5.8, determine the torque of link "a" necessary to hold the mechanism in equilibrium. Also determine the forces between all links of the mechanism.

11.5 In Fig. P4.8, a force of 150 lb is acting horizontally to the right on link "c," a force of 150 lb is acting horizontally to the left along the center line of link "d," and a force of 75 lb is acting horizontally to the right at point R on link "d."

Determine the torque on link "a" necessary to hold the mechanism in equilibrium. Also determine the force $F_{d/e}$ and the couple $M_{d/e}$.

11.6 In Fig. P4.10, a force of 200 lb is acting vertically downward on link "d." Determine the torque necessary on link "a" to hold the mechanism in equilibrium and determine the forces acting between all links.

11.7 In Fig. P4.3 a vertical force of 500 lb is acting upward on link "e." Determine the torque on link "a" necessary to hold the mechanism in equilibrium. Determine the forces between all links.

11.8 A clockwise torque of 200 lb-in. is acting on link "e" in Fig. P5.9. Determine the necessary torque on link "a" to hold the mechanism in equilibrium.

11.9 In Fig. P4.11 a horizontal force of 1500 lb is acting horizontally to the left on link "e." Determine the torque on link "a" necessary to hold the mechanism in equilibrium and determine the forces acting between all the links.

11.10 A force of 100 lb is acting downward and parallel to the motion of the slider, link "e," in Fig. P4.13. Determine the torque on link "a" necessary to hold the mechanism in equilibrium.

11.11 A clockwise torque of 100 lb-in. is acting on link "e" in Fig. P5.10. Determine the torque on link "a" necessary to hold the mechanism in equilibrium.

11.12 In Fig. P5.5 links "c" and "d" represent a gear and rack. If the gear teeth are 20° involute (indicating that the line of action of the force between the gear and rack makes an angle of 20° with the common tangent) determine the necessary torque on link "a" to hold the mechanism in equilibrium under a vertical force of 500 lb upwards acting on the rack.

11.13 Considering sliding friction but ignoring friction of the pin joints make a static force analysis of the mechanism in Fig. P4.4 if a clockwise torque of 1600 lb-in. is acting on link "a." Assume impending motion of link "a" is clockwise, and a coefficient of friction of 0.2.

11.14 Repeat Prob. 11.13 assuming impending motion is counter clockwise.

11.15 Considering sliding friction and friction in the pin joints, make a static force analysis of the mechanism in Fig. P4.11 if a horizontal force of 1500 lb is acting to the left on link "e." Assume a coefficient of sliding friction of 0.2 and a coefficient of 0.15 for the pin joints. The pins of all pin joints are to be taken as one-half inch, and impending motion of link "e" is to the left.

11.16 Repeat Prob. 11.15 for impending motion of link "e" to the right.

11.17 Considering sliding friction, but ignoring friction of the pin joints, make a static force analysis of the cam mechanism in Fig. P8.3 for a counter clockwise torque of 1500 lb-in. acting on link "b." Assume impending motion of link "a" is counter clockwise and a coefficient of friction of 0.15.

11.18 A horizontal force of 100 lb is acting to the left on link "d" in Fig. P4.9. Link "b" is to roll on link "e." If friction is negligible except between links "b" and "e," what friction force is necessary between links "b" and "e" to assure rolling contact?

Note: The following problems are to be solved by means of a velocity image making use of the principle of virtual work.

11.19 Determine the torque on link "*a*" in Fig. P4.3 if a vertical force of 500 lbs is acting upward on link "*e*."

11.20 Determine the torque on link "*a*" in Fig. P4.6 if a force of 100 lb is acting horizontally to the left on slider "*d*."

11.21 Determine the torque on link "*a*" in Fig. P5.10 if a clockwise torque of 100 lb-in. is acting on link "*e*."

11.22 Determine the torque on link "*a*" in Fig. P4.12 if a force of 1000 lb is acting horizontally to the left on link "*e*" and a force of 500 lb is acting horizontally to the left at point *U*.

11.23 Determine the torque on link "*a*" in Fig. P4.8 if a force of 150 lb is acting horizontally to the right on link "*c*," a force of 150 lb is acting horizontally to the left along the center line of link "*d*" and a force of 75 lb is acting horizontally to the right at point *R* on link "*d*."

Chapter 12

Dynamics of Particles and Rigid Bodies in Plane Motion

12.1 Introduction

A thorough understanding of Newton's laws and their application to rigid bodies is necessary before we can start discussing the dynamic analysis of systems of bodies or mechanisms. In a review of these laws we will develop the dynamic equations of motion on a somewhat higher level than that usually taught in undergraduate courses in mechanics. However, since most mechanisms move in plane motion, our discussion will be restricted to plane motion here, with a few exceptions.

12.2 Mass Point

We will start our discussion of Newton's laws with the idea of a mass point. A mass point, as its name would imply, is a point which has mass. A point, which we will define as the intersection of two lines, has no dimensions. Therefore, since we have defined rotation as a change in direction of a line and we cannot draw a line on a point, a point cannot have rotation. It can have only a linear motion. The definition of mass becomes a little more difficult. Possibly the best way to define mass is by use of Newton's second law. For purposes of defining mass we will use Newton's law in a very restricted sense; however this restricted concept of Newton's law is the statement as usually found in elementary texts. We will state the law as follows: if a force is applied to a small rigid body the body is accelerated in the direction of the force, and the magnitude of the acceleration is proportional to the magnitude of the force. This can be written in equation form as:

$$F = ma$$

where m is a proportionality constant and is given the name mass. Now we can define mass as the ratio of force to acceleration, or

$$m = \frac{F}{a}$$

and the units of mass are lb-sec²/in.

A mass point is a particle or body with zero dimensions but having a definite mass. Such a particle does not exist but the abstract idea of a mass point is quite useful in the development of the laws of dynamics. In many cases finite bodies can be treated as mass points. The particular property which makes mass points useful is that they cannot rotate; in dealing with them we need only consider linear motion.

We should also point out that Newton's law, as we have used it, is restricted to the case in which mass is a constant. For our purposes in the analysis of machinery the law as stated is quite satisfactory because the links of most machinery have constant mass. However in many instances this narrow viewpoint is not satisfactory. The general statement of the law is

$$F = \frac{d}{dt}(mV)$$

where the product mass times velocity, is called momentum. We will use a general statement, that force is equal to the change in momentum with respect to time, in our development of the general laws of motion; we will consider the case of rigid bodies as a special case.

It is necessary that we know the mass of the particles and bodies which we will discuss and since we consider mass as a defined quantity, we need some means of determining the mass of a body by using some quantity which has physical significance to us. The weight of a body is the force which tends to pull the body towards the Earth's surface and, since it is a quantity with which we are familiar, we will use it as a means of determining mass. By experiment we find that if we drop a body it is accelerated towards the Earth's surface with an acceleration of 32.2 ft/sec² or 386 in./sec². This acceleration is designated "g," the acceleration of gravity. The value of g varies with position of the Earth's surface and with height above the Earth's surface. Weight varies in the same manner so that the ratio of force to acceleration, or the mass, is always a constant. For various positions on the Earth's surface and for altitudes up to 50,000 ft the value of g will vary from 32.06 to 32.26 ft/sec². The values first given are average values for the 45° latitude and if we use those values, the maximum error in mass determined with these values is less than one per cent and this accuracy is quite satisfactory for engineering calculations. In fact we would be quite happy if we could expect this accuracy in all our calculations.

Therefore we will consider the mass of a body as the weight in pounds divided by a g value of 386 in./sec².

12.3 Principle of Linear Momentum for a System of Mass Points

Let us now consider a system of n mass points in space. We will designate the points as $m_1, m_2, \ldots, m_n$ and their respective velocities as $v_1, v_2, \ldots, v_n$ and any arbitrary mass point as m_i, or m_k. Any one of the mass points can be acted on by a force outside the system and a force exerted by any other of the mass points. The force from outside the system is called an external force, and the forces exerted by any mass point on any other mass point are called internal forces. For example if we had a system composed of a small magnet and a small piece of steel the force exerted between the magnet and piece of steel would be an internal force. Any other force not associated with either piece, such as a push with a rod, would be an external force. Then the equation of motion for any mass point m_i is

$$\frac{d}{dt}(m_i v_i) = F_i + \Sigma F_{k/i} \qquad (12.1)$$

where F_i is the external force acting on the mass point and $\Sigma F_{k/i}$ is the sum of all the forces exerted on m_i by the other mass points in the system. The reason for separating the internal and external forces will be brought out in the discussion of Newton's third law.

Newton's third law states that if a body A exerts a force on body B, then body B exerts an equal but opposite force on body A, both forces having the same line of action. It is sometimes referred to as the law of action and reaction. (We have already made use of this law in our study of static forces where we said that the force exerted on link "a" by link "b" is equal and opposite to the force exerted on link "b" by link "a.")

If we now add Eqs. (12.1) for all the mass points of the system, the internal forces cancel each other, since $F_{k/i} = -F_{i/k}$ (from Newton's third law) with the result

$$\frac{d}{dt}(\Sigma m_i v_i) = \Sigma F_i \qquad (12.2)$$

The vector sum of the momentum vectors for all the mass points is called the total or resultant linear momentum of the system. Equation (12.2) states that the rate of change of the linear momentum of the system is equal to the resultant of the external forces acting on the system, and is independent of the internal forces; this is the principle of linear momentum. From this principle we conclude that we can't lift ourselves by our own bootstraps because the forces applied in such a case are internal forces,

In order to better realize the significance of this principle, we will place the mass points in a rectangular coordinate system and rewrite Eq. (12.2) as three equations for the components in the x, y, and z directions, and make use of the concept of mass center. The equations become

$$\frac{d}{dt}\left(\Sigma\, m_i V_i^x\right) = \Sigma\, F_i^x$$

$$\frac{d}{dt}\left(\Sigma\, m_i V_i^y\right) = \Sigma\, F_i^y \qquad (12.3)$$

$$\frac{d}{dt}\left(\Sigma\, m_i V_i^z\right) = \Sigma\, F_i^z$$

The superscripts indicate the direction and should not be mistaken for powers.

Let us now introduce the concept of mass center. The mass center of a system of particles is defined as a point in the system which we will call G whose x, y, and z coordinates are given by the equations

$$x_G = \frac{\Sigma\,(m_i x_i)}{\Sigma\, m_i}, \qquad y_G = \frac{\Sigma\,(m_i y_i)}{\Sigma\, m_i}, \qquad z_G = \frac{\Sigma\,(m_i z_i)}{\Sigma\, m_i} \qquad (12.4)$$

in which m_i denotes any mass point and x_i, y_i, and z_i its coordinates. The mass center is also called the center of gravity of the system of mass points because in a homogeneous gravity field the resultant of all the gravity forces acting on the masses $m_1, m_2, \ldots, m_n$ passes through the mass center. The summation of the individual masses, $\Sigma\, m_i$, is the total mass of the system. Denoting the total mass by m with no subscript, we can rewrite Eqs. (12.4) as

$$m x_G = \Sigma\,(m_i x_i), \qquad m y_G = \Sigma\,(m_i y_i), \qquad m z_G = \Sigma\,(m_i z_i)$$

If we assume that the masses of the individual particles are constant and take derivatives of the above equations with respect to time we find

$$m V_G^x = \Sigma\,(m_i V_i^x), \qquad m V_G^y = \Sigma\,(m_i V_i^y), \qquad m V_G^z = \Sigma\,(m_i V_i^z)$$

Substituting these relations into Eqs. (12.3) we can write the linear momentum equations in terms of the velocity of the mass center, as

$$\frac{d}{dt}\left(m V_G^x\right) = \Sigma\, F_i^x, \qquad \frac{d}{dt}\left(m V_G^y\right) = \Sigma\, F_i^y, \qquad \frac{d}{dt}\left(m_i V_G^z\right) = \Sigma\, F_i^z \quad (12.5)$$

These equations are extremely important and many problems of mechanics can be handled by the use of these equations alone. The equations state that the mass center has the motion of a particle of mass equal to the total mass of the system and acted upon by a force equal to the vector sum of all *external* forces acting on the individual mass points. Or, taking another viewpoint, we see from the equations that the only thing that can change the motion of the center of gravity of a system is an external force.

By the use of the principle of linear momentum alone we are able to draw important conclusions regarding the motion of a system without having to deal with each individual particle of the system. If we consider a rocket in the absence of air resistance, we see that if we fire the rocket at rest, the center of gravity or mass center of the rocket body and its propellent will remain at rest. The so-called propellent forces are internal forces and therefore they cannot affect the motion of the mass center. In the same manner if we ignore air resistance, we conclude that once a diver has left the diving board he cannot change the path of motion of the center of gravity of his body. Friction forces are the external forces which cause many systems at rest initially to be able to start moving. In the absence of friction most of our so-called self-propelled vehicles would never get started. Without friction our automobiles would just spin their wheels and never move.

We can use the principle of linear momentum to determine the relative velocities of a gun and a bullet fired from it. Consider a gun at rest mounted on wheels or on a frictionless surface. When the gun is fired the burning gases exert equal forces on the bullet and the gun (Newton's third law) and the bullet moves in one direction with a certain velocity while the gun moves in the other direction with a different velocity. Since there is no external force the mass center of the two bodies remains fixed and the momentum of the system must be zero, or the momentum of the bullet must be equal and opposite to the momentum of the gun. From this relation we find that the ratio of the velocities is inversely proportional to the masses. Therefore, the heavier the gun for a given cartridge, the lighter the recoil, the "kick." The kick is the external force which the shooter applies to change the momentum of the gun.

We will make use of the momentum principle in a later chapter when we discuss the balancing of machines. A balanced machine means that no disturbing forces are imposed on the foundation when the machine is running. For this to be so we see, from the principle of linear momentum, that the center of gravity of all the moving parts or links must have no motion, indicating that the sum of the external forces (forces on the foundation) is zero.

12.4 Principle of Angular Momentum for a System of Mass Points

In the last Article the effect of an external force on a system of mass points was developed. The question immediately arises as to the effect of an external couple on a system of mass points, in which case the external force is zero. From the preceding discussion we immediately know that the mass center of the system remains fixed if it had no initial motion. In this Article we will develop the equations for a mass system under the action of external moments, of which the external couple is a special case.

The equations will be developed for the case of plane motion in which the system of mass points can move only in the x-y plane or planes parallel to it, and the forces acting on the mass points must also lie in these planes. If we multiply the momentum of a particle by the normal distance from the momentum vector to some point in the plane we obtain the moment of momentum of the particle about that point. For a system of mass points in the x-y plane as shown in Fig. 12.1, if we consider the mass point m_n with

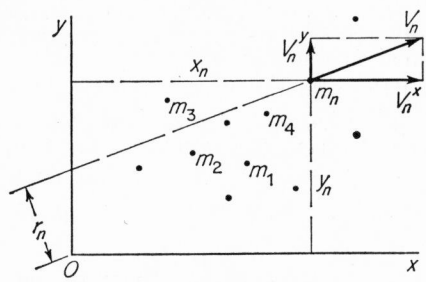

FIGURE 12.1

velocity V_n, its moment of momentum about the origin O is $m_n V_n r_n$. If we resolve the velocity into x and y components and consider a counter clockwise moment as positive, the moment of momentum is

$$H_n = m_n(V_n^y x_n - V_n^x y_n)$$

where H_n is the angular momentum of m_n, and x and y are the coordinates of the mass point. The sum of the moments of momentum of all the mass points is the moment of momentum of the system and will be designated by H with no subscript. Then

$$H = \Sigma\, m_i(V_i^y x_i - V_i^x y_i) \tag{12.6}$$

Now if we take the first of Eqs. (12.3) and multiply it by y, the second and multiply that by x, and then subtract the first product from the second the result is

$$\Sigma\, x_i \frac{d}{dt}(m_i V_i^y) - \Sigma\, y_i \frac{d}{dt}(m_i V_i^x) = \Sigma\, F_i^y x_i - \Sigma\, F_i^x y_i \tag{a}$$

By performing the indicated differentiation we can show that

$$\frac{d}{dt}[\Sigma\, m_i(V_i^y x_i - V_i^x y_i)] = \Sigma\, x_i \frac{d}{dt}(m_i V_i^y) - \Sigma\, y_i \frac{d}{dt}(m_i V_i^x)$$

Making this substitution in Eq. (a) we find that

$$\frac{d}{dt}[\Sigma\, m_i(V_i^y x_i - V_i^x y_i)] = \Sigma\, (F_i^y x_i - F_i^x y_i) \tag{12.7}$$

or using H for the resultant angular momentum of the system, from Eq. (12.6)

$$\frac{d}{dt}(H) = M \tag{12.8}$$

where
$$M = \Sigma \, (F_i^y x_i - F_i^x y_i)$$

and we recognize M as the moment of the external forces about the origin. We see from Eq. (12.8) that the rate of change of the angular momentum of a system about any axis is equal to the moment of all external forces acting on the system about the same axis and is independent of the internal forces; this is called the principle of angular momentum. The principle explains why a spinning ice skater can change his angular velocity by moving his arms out from his body or in close to his body. Since there is no external moment acting on the skater's body, the angular momentum must remain constant for the system (which in this case is the skater). The moving of the limbs changes the moment arm of some of the mass points of the system. To keep the same moment of momentum, the linear velocity of the mass points of the system must change so that the summation in Eq. (12.6) can remain constant. Since the linear velocity is equal to the angular velocity times the radius, the angular velocity must change.

12.5 *Plane Motion of a Rigid Body*

We will now apply the principles of linear and angular momentum to a rigid body in plane motion and thereby develop the equations of motion for rigid bodies under the influence of external forces and moments. The results will be directly applicable to the study of dynamic forces in machinery. Consider a rigid body moving in the x-y plane as shown in Fig. 12.2. The rigid body is composed of a system of mass points, but now the position of the mass points relative to each other is fixed and the relative motion of

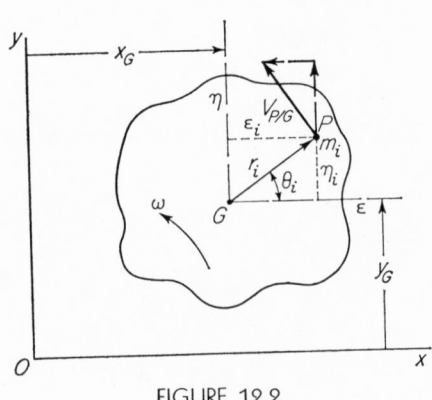

FIGURE 12.2

the mass points must follow the rules of kinematics as already developed. For this reason, since the motion of the individual mass points is determined by the principles of momentum, the equations of motion for the body as a whole can be found as a function of the external forces and moments.

Using the mass center of the rigid body, as defined by Eqs. (12.4), as an origin we will draw another set of coordinates parallel to the x-y coordinates and label them as the ϵ-η coordinates. The coordinate system moves with the body, but remains parallel to the x-y coordinates. Remembering that the body can have angular and linear motion relative to the x-y axes we will develop the dynamic equations of motion of the body relative to these fixed axes. We will consider the body as composed of mass points but the position of the mass points relative to each other is fixed since it is a rigid body. The total velocity of all points on the body will be given as the velocity of the C.G. plus the velocity of the point relative to the C.G. The velocity of the point relative to the C.G. will be given as functions of the ϵ-η coordinates.

Consider a mass point m_i at point P, its position relative to the C.G. fixed by the coordinates ϵ_i-η_i, or its radius r_i and the angle θ_i it makes with the axis. From the principle of linear momentum we have

$$\frac{d}{dt}(m_i V_i^x) = F_i^x + \Sigma F_{k/i}^x$$

$$\frac{d}{dt}(m_i V_i^y) = F_i^y + \Sigma F_{k/i}^y \tag{12.9}$$

But

$$V_i^x = V_G^x - \omega r_i \sin \theta_i = V_G^x - \omega \eta_i$$
$$V_i^y = V_G^y + \omega r_i \cos \theta_i = V_G^y + \omega \epsilon_i \tag{12.10}$$

then

$$\frac{d}{dt}[m_i(V_G^x - \omega \eta_i)] = F_i^x + \Sigma F_{k/i}^y$$

$$\frac{d}{dt}[m_i(V_G^y + \omega \epsilon_i)] = F_i^y + \Sigma F_{k/i}^y \tag{12.11}$$

Now summing Eqs. (12.11) for all the mass points of the body the internal forces balance leaving

$$\frac{d}{dt}[\Sigma m_i(V_G^x - \omega \eta_i)] = \Sigma F_i^x$$

$$\frac{d}{dt}[\Sigma m_i(V_G^y + \omega \epsilon_i)] = \Sigma F_i^y$$

Since V_G and ω are the same for all mass points these equations can be written as

$$\frac{d}{dt}\left[V_G^x \Sigma\, m_i - \omega \Sigma\, m_i \eta_i\right] = \Sigma\, F_i^x$$

$$\frac{d}{dt}\left[V_G^y \Sigma\, m_i + \omega \Sigma\, m_i \epsilon_i\right] = \Sigma\, F_i^y \tag{12.12}$$

Remembering that the C.G. was taken as the origin of the ϵ-η coordinate system we see that

$$\Sigma\, m_i \eta_i = \Sigma\, m_i \epsilon_i = 0 \tag{12.13}$$

since every mass point with coordinates ϵ, η relative to the C.G. is balanced by a mass point with coordinates $-\epsilon$, $-\eta$, then Eqs. (12.11) reduces to

$$\frac{d}{dt}(mV_G^x) = F^x$$

$$\frac{d}{dt}(mV_G^y) = F^y \tag{12.14}$$

where m is the total mass of the body and F^x and F^y are the resultant external forces acting on the body in the x and y directions. As would be expected these equations agree with Eqs. (12.5) for a system of unrestrained mass points. For a rigid body the mass is invariable with time and the equations can be written as

$$ma_G^x = F^x$$

$$ma_G^y = F^y \tag{12.15}$$

Or, taking the vector sum of the acceleration and force components, we end up with the well known equation

$$ma_G = F \tag{12.16}$$

For analytical work Eqs. (12.15) will usually be found most useful but for graphical work the form as given by Eq. (12.16) will prove the best.

We see from these equations that as far as the motion of the center of gravity of a rigid body is concerned, it can be dealt with as if it were a mass point of mass equal to the total mass of the body and acted on by the sum of all external forces. If the body moves with translation, the motion of the body can be determined by the motion of the center of gravity under the influence of all forces acting on the body.

In order to determine the angular motion of a rigid body we need to apply the principle of angular momentum to the body. Again we will consider the body in Fig. 12.2. The moment of momentum of the body about the origin of the fixed axes is given by Eq. (12.6) and writing the equation in terms of the two coordinate systems, x_i becomes $(x_G + \epsilon_i)$, y_i becomes $(y_G + \eta_i)$ and V_i^x and V_i^y are defined by Eqs. (12.10). Then the moment of momentum of the rigid body is

$$H = \Sigma \, m_i(V_i^y x_i - V_i^x y_i)$$
$$= \Sigma \, m_i[(V_G^y + \omega\epsilon_i)(x_G + \epsilon_i) - (V_G^x - \omega\eta_i)(y_G + \eta_i)]$$

Multiplying the terms in parentheses and grouping them (remembering that V_G, x_G, y_G and ω are independent of the summation being the same for all mass points in the body) we have

$$H = m(V_G^y x_G - V_G^x y_G) + \omega \Sigma \, m_i(\epsilon_i^2 + \eta_i^2)$$
$$+ V_G^y \Sigma \, m_i \epsilon_i - V_G^x \Sigma \, m_i \eta_i$$
$$+ \omega x_G \Sigma \, m_i \epsilon_i + \omega y_G \Sigma \, m_i \eta_i$$

From Eqs. (12.13) the last four terms are zero and we find that the moment of momentum of the body about the origin O is

$$H = m(V_G^y x_G - V_G^x y_G) + \omega \Sigma \, m_i(\epsilon_i^2 + \eta_i^2) \qquad (12.17)$$

Substituting this equation into Eq. (12.8)

$$\frac{d}{dt}[m(V_G^y x_G - V_G^x y_G) + \omega \Sigma \, m_i(\epsilon_i^2 + \eta_i^2)]$$
$$= \Sigma \, F_i^y(x_G + \epsilon_i) - \Sigma \, F_i^x(y_G + \eta_i)$$
$$= \Sigma \, (F_i^y x_G - F_i^x y_G) + \Sigma \, (F_i^y \epsilon_i - F_i^x \eta_i)$$
$$= (F^y x_G - F^x y_G) + \Sigma \, (F_i^y \epsilon_i - F_i^x \eta_i) \qquad (12.18)$$

If we now return to Eqs. (12.14) and multiply the first by y_G and the second by x_G and then subtract the first from the second we get

$$\frac{d}{dt}[m(V_G^y x_G - V_G^x y_G)] = F_y x_G - F_x y_G \qquad (12.19)$$

This equation corresponds to the first terms on each side of the equality sign in Eq. (12.18). We see from this that the last terms on each side of the equality sign must be equal, or

$$\frac{d}{dt}[\omega \Sigma \, m_i(\epsilon_i^2 + \eta_i^2)] = \Sigma \, (F_i^y \epsilon_i - F_i^x \eta_i) \qquad (12.20)$$

Now from Fig. 12.2 we see that

$$(\epsilon_i^2 + \eta_i^2) = r_i^2$$

so that Eq. (12.20) reduces to

$$\frac{d}{dt}(\omega \Sigma \, r_i^2 m_i) = \Sigma \, (F_i^y \epsilon_i - F_i^x \eta_i) \qquad (12.21)$$

The summation $\Sigma \, r_i^2 m_i$ is called the mass moment of inertia of the body about the C.G., and is designated as I_G. In integral form I_G is then defined as

$$I_G = \int r^2 dm \qquad (12.22)$$

where r is the distance from the center of gravity to differential mass dm. This quantity is a function only of the configuration of the rigid body and is invariable with time. The right-hand term of Eq. (12.21) is the moment of all the external forces about the C.G., and Eq. (12.21) reduces to

$$I_G \frac{d\omega}{dt} = M_G \tag{12.23}$$

or

$$I_G \alpha = M_G \tag{12.24}$$

From this equation we see that the angular velocity of a rigid body can only be changed by an external moment about the C.G., and therefore if the resultant of all external forces passes through the C.G. the angular velocity of the body will remain constant. This equation will prove quite useful in our dynamic analysis of mechanisms.

We will make use of the angular momentum equation of a rigid body written about some axis other than the axis through the C.G. in some of our analyses. Substituting Eq. (12.23) into Eq. (12.18) we find

$$\frac{d}{dt} [m(V_G^y x_G - V_G^x y_G) + I_G \omega] = (F^y x_G - F^x y_G) + M_G$$

This can be written as

$$\frac{d}{dt} (mV_G r_o + I_G \omega) = M_o \tag{12.25}$$

where $V_G r_o = (V_G^y x_G - V_G^x y_G)$

V_G = resultant velocity of the C.G.

r_o = moment of V_G about O (see Fig. 12.1)

$M_o = (F^y x_G - F^x y_G) + M_G$

= resultant moment of the external forces about O.

Equations (12.16) and (12.24) are the basis of all dynamic force analyses of machines, since they establish the motion of all rigid bodies. The motion of a rigid body is determined by (1) the linear acceleration of the center of gravity, and (2) the angular acceleration of the body. The linear acceleration of the C.G. is determined by Eq. (12.16) and the angular acceleration is determined by Eq. (12.24). The application of these equations to the analyses of mechanisms will be considered in later chapters.

12.6 Rotation of a Rigid Body About a Fixed Axis

The motion of a rigid body in plane motion in the general case is covered in the preceding section. If we consider the rotation of a rigid body about a fixed axis, we have a special case of the general motion. Since this case comes up quite often in analyses of mechanisms, we will discuss this particular case. It should be remembered, however, that the equations for the general case can be used for any rigid body but these may be simplified if we have rotation about a fixed axis.

Consider the rigid body in Fig. 12.3 constrained to rotation about the point O on the fixed body. Point O is then a pin joint between the rigid body and the fixed link. We will draw our fixed axis through the pin joint as shown in the figure. Now if we use Eq. (12.7), which is the principle of moment of momentum of a system of particles about some axis, we see from the figure that for a rigid body rotating about a fixed axis the velocity components of the individual mass points are (remembering counter clockwise motion is considered positive)

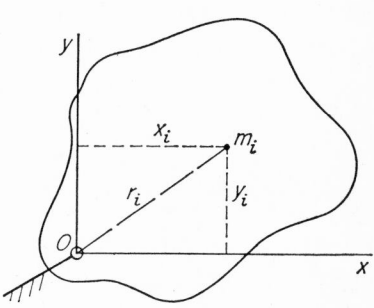

FIGURE 12.3

$$V_i^x = -y_i\omega, \qquad V_i^y = x_i\omega$$

Substituting these into Eq. (12.7) we find

$$\frac{d}{dt}\left[\Sigma\, m_i\omega(x_i^2 + y_i^2)\right] = \Sigma\,(F_i^y x_i - F_i^x y_i)$$

and remembering that ω is the only quantity that is a function of time

$$\alpha \Sigma\, m_i r_i^2 = \Sigma\,(F_i^y x_i - F_i^x y_i)$$

or
$$I_O\alpha = M_O \qquad\qquad (12.26)$$

where I_O is the mass moment of inertia of the body about O, and M_O is the resultant moment of all the external forces about O. In integral form the moment of inertia of a rigid body about any axis O is

$$I_O = \int r^2 dm \qquad\qquad (12.27)$$

where in this case r is the distance from the origin O to the differential mass dm. Since in most mechanisms one or more of the links are pin jointed to the fixed link, we will find that for such links Eq. (12.26) will usually be more convenient for purposes of analysis than the general equations.

The use of the general equations will give us the same result as can be shown by applying Eq. (12.18) to the rigid body rotating about a fixed axis. Equation (12.18) can be simplified by using Eqs. (12.19) and (12.24). Equation (12.19) can be further simplified using the relations

$$V_G^x = -y_G\omega, \qquad V_G^y = x_G\omega$$

so that
$$m r_G^2\alpha = F^y x_G - F^x y_G$$

and Eq. (12.18) becomes

$$(mr_G^2 + I_G)\alpha = (F^y x_G - F^x y_G) + M_G$$

The first term on the right of the equality sign represents the moment of the external forces as if they were acting at the C.G. and then the two terms on the right-hand side of the equation represent the resultant moment of the external forces about the origin O. Then the equation can be written

$$(mr_G^2 + I_G)\alpha = M_O \qquad (12.28)$$

and comparing this equation with Eq. (12.26) we see that

$$I_O = (mr_G^2 + I_G) \qquad (12.29)$$

This is known as the parallel-axis theorem and can be used to determine the moment of inertia about any axis if we know the moment of inertia about some other axis. These relations should be kept in mind and we should always remember to use the right moment of inertia corresponding to the particular equations we use in our analysis.

12.7 *Conclusion*

The equations developed in this chapter are sufficient for the dynamic force analysis of machines composed of rigid bodies. The particular equations which we will use in the dynamic analysis of rigid body mechanisms are as follows:

For a link pin jointed to the fixed body we will use the equation

$$I_O \alpha = M_O \qquad (12.26)$$

where I_O is the moment of inertia of the link about the pin joint O and M_O is the resultant moment of the external forces about the pin joint. For all other links we will use the two equations

$$ma_G = F \qquad (12.16)$$

$$I_G \alpha = M_G \qquad (12.24)$$

where F is the resultant of all external forces with a line of action passing through the C.G., I_G is the moment of inertia of the link about the C.G. and M_G is the resultant moment of the resultant external forces about the C.G.

These equations will be used throughout the remainder of the text in dynamic force analysis and balancing of mechanisms.

Chapter 13

Work, Energy, and Impulse

13.1 Introduction

In the preceding chapter we developed the necessary relations for determining the dynamic forces in machines if we know the accelerations of the machine members. Now, if we know the required motion of a mechanism, we can determine the accelerations of the links by kinematic analysis, and we can find the moments and forces acting on the links required to give us the prescribed motion by use of the relations developed in the preceding chapter.

However there are other analyses which are necessary in the design of machinery for which the preceding relations are not sufficient. In the design of clutches, brakes, and flywheels we will need to use work and energy relationships, and at times we will find that impulse and momentum relationships are useful. Energy relationships will also prove useful in the analysis of critical speeds of shafting. The concept of work has already been used in Chapter 11 for determining the mechanical advantage in mechanisms.

In this chapter we will develop the relationship between work and energy and the relationship of impulse and momentum. Since we are primarily concerned with rigid bodies, we will devote most of our time to rigid bodies.

13.2 Impulse and Momentum

Let us consider first a body moving with rectilinear translation. Eqs. (12.14) completely defines the motion, since there is no rotation. If we set up our axes so that the motion is along one of the axes, we can write the momentum equation as

$$\frac{d}{dt}(mV) = F$$

Multiplying both sides of this equation by dt and integrating we get

$$m(V_2 - V_1) = \int_{t_1}^{t_2} F \, dt \tag{13.1}$$

where V_1 is the initial velocity at time t_1 and V_2 is the velocity at time t_2. The time integral of the external force is called linear impulse. Then the change in momentum in any direction is equal to the impulse of the external forces in that direction. This equation is used in the study of motions of bodies under impact. Impact is defined as the sudden collision of bodies. During this impact, which is usually of very short duration, extremely large forces act for a very short time and the accurate determination of these forces is generally impossible. However, the change in velocity of the bodies can be determined from the above equation, as we shall see later. It should be pointed out that this equation is perfectly general and is not restricted to cases of impact where the forces act for only a short interval of time.

For the case of general motion of a rigid body where the body has both translation and rotation, we make use of the principle of angular momentum as given by Eq. (12.25). Again multiplying both sides of the equation by dt and integrating we get

$$(mV_G r_O + I_G \omega)_2 - (mV_G r_O + I_G \omega)_1 = \int_{t_1}^{t_2} M_O \, dt$$

and by rearranging terms

$$m[(V_G r_O)_2 - (V_G r_O)_1] + I_G(\omega_2 - \omega_1) = \int_{t_1}^{t_2} M_O \, dt \tag{13.2}$$

where O is any point which we may choose as the origin and r_O is the moment arm of the linear momentum vector representing the momentum of the C.G. and M_O is the moment of all external forces about the origin.

If the body has a fixed axis of rotation and we choose that axis as the origin, Eq. (13.2) becomes

$$(mr_G^2 + I_G)(\omega_2 - \omega_1) = I_O(\omega_2 - \omega_1) = \int_{t_1}^{t_2} M_O \, dt \tag{13.3}$$

and if the fixed axis passes through the C.G.

$$I_G(\omega_2 - \omega_1) = \int_{t_1}^{t_2} M_G \, dt \tag{13.4}$$

The impulse-momentum relations will be found useful in the analysis of brakes, clutches and gearing, and also in other cases where shock loads are encountered. The application of these equations to the analysis of these elements will be demonstrated at the end of the chapter, where we will also discuss the application of the work-energy equations to the same type of elements. A better understanding of the principles can be obtained by discussing the applications after we have studied the work-energy relations.

13.3 Work and Kinetic Energy

Before we start to develop the relations of work and energy, we need to review our definition of work. Work is defined as the product of a force and the displacement of its point of action in the direction of the force. It is defined mathematically as

$$W = Fs \cos \theta \qquad (13.5)$$

where s is the displacement and θ is the angle between the line of action of the force and the direction of the displacement. We could also say that the work is the product of the displacement and the component of force along the line of action of the displacement. Note that this definition also satisfies Eq. (13.5). Work is considered positive if the component of the force in the direction of the displacement has the same sense as the displacement and the work is negative if the force opposes the displacement. From our definition we see that a couple acting on a body does no work when the body moves linearly, since the couple is composed of two equal and opposite forces. One force will do positive work and the other will do negative work and therefore the sum of the work is zero. However a couple will do work on a body having angular motion. The work done by a couple acting on a body is

$$W = M\phi \qquad (13.6)$$

where M is the value of the couple and ϕ is the angular displacement of the body. We can see that this equation is the correct relation for the work done by a couple from Fig. 13.1. The figure shows a body with a couple of magnitude Fh acting on it. If we assume that the body rotates about point O on the line of action of one of the forces of the couple, then during a small displacement the other force of

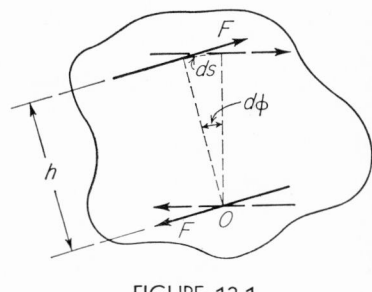

FIGURE 13.1

the couple will move through a distance ds or $hd\phi$ and since the forces rotate with the body, the force will always be in the direction of the displacement. Then the work done by the force will be

$$dW = Fhd\phi$$

or
$$W = M\phi$$

Remembering that a couple can be shifted to any position relative to the body without affecting the magnitude of the couple, we can always shift the couple so that the line of action of one force passes through the center of rotation of the body and we see that the equation holds for rotation about any axis.

The units of work are force times distance and, in the units used in the text, are in.-lb. Since work is a quantity having magnitude only, it is a scalar quantity and can be added and subtracted as an algebraic number.

Let us consider a mass point acted on by a force while moving through a differential displacement ds. The x and y components of the force are F^x and F^y, and the components of the displacements are dx and dy. The total work done on the point by the force is

$$dW = F \cos \theta \, ds = F^x dx + F^y dy \qquad (13.7)$$

The force will be composed of internal and external forces and from Eqs. (12.9) we can substitute for the force components.

$$F^x = m \frac{dV^x}{dt}$$

$$F^y = m \frac{dV^y}{dt}$$

where F_x and F_y are the total forces acting on the mass point, or

$$dW = m \frac{dV^x}{dt} \, dx + m \frac{dV^y}{dt} \, dy$$

$$= m dV^x \frac{dx}{dt} + m dV^y \frac{dy}{dt}$$

$$= m(V^x dV^x + V^y dV^y)$$

$$= \frac{m}{2} [d(V^x)^2 + d(V^y)^2]$$

$$= \frac{m}{2} d[(V^x)^2 + (V^y)^2]$$

$$= d\left(\frac{1}{2} m V^2\right) \qquad (13.8)$$

where V is the total velocity of the mass point. The term $\frac{1}{2} m V^2$ is called the kinetic energy of the mass point. Since the velocity is squared the kinetic energy is always positive or zero.

Considering now a system of mass points, we find that in general the internal forces do work since the particles can have relative motion. However if we take the system of mass points as making up a rigid body, then there is no relative motion between the individual mass points and the internal forces do no work. Then for a rigid body moving from a position A to another position B under the action of an external force F which is the resultant of the forces on all mass points

$$F \cos \theta \, ds = \Sigma \, d\!\left(\frac{1}{2}m_i V_i^2\right) = d\,\Sigma\left(\frac{m_i V_i^2}{2}\right) \qquad (13.9)$$

Letting T represent the total kinetic energy of the body

$$dT = F \cos \theta \, ds \qquad (13.10)$$

and integrating

$$T_B - T_A = \int_A^B F \cos \theta \, ds \qquad (13.11)$$

This is the general energy equation for a rigid body which indicates that the total change in kinetic energy from position A to position B is equal to the work done by all forces acting on the body during the change in position. If the work is positive, the kinetic energy increases. If the work is negative, the energy decreases.

The kinetic energy of a rigid body can be presented in a more useful form by introducing the idea of mass center or center of gravity. Using a fixed coordinate system and a moving coordinate system with origin at the center of gravity as shown in Fig. 12.2, the velocity of the individual mass points can be resolved into two components, the velocity of translation of the C.G., and the velocity relative to the C.G. The x and y components of the velocity are then given by Eqs. (12.10) as

$$V_i^x = V_G^x - \omega \eta_i$$
$$V_i^y = V_G^y + \omega \epsilon_i$$

so that

$$T = \frac{1}{2}\Sigma\, m_i V_i^2 = \frac{1}{2}\Sigma\, m_i[(V_i^x)^2 + (V_i^y)^2]$$

$$= \frac{1}{2}\Sigma\, m_i[(V_G^x)^2 + (V_G^y)^2] + \omega(V_G^y \Sigma\, m_i\epsilon_i - V_G^x \Sigma\, m_i\eta_i)$$

$$+ \frac{1}{2}\omega^2 \Sigma\, m_i(\epsilon_i^2 + \eta_i^2) \qquad (13.12)$$

From the definition of mass center the second term to the right of the equality sign is zero, and remembering that

$$V_G^2 = (V_G^x)^2 + (V_G^y)^2$$
$$r_i^2 = \epsilon_i^2 + \eta_i^2$$

Equation (13.12) reduces to

$$T = \frac{1}{2}m V_G^2 + \frac{1}{2}\omega^2 \Sigma\, m_i r_i^2$$

$$= \frac{1}{2}m V_G^2 + \frac{1}{2}I_G \omega^2 \qquad (13.13)$$

For the case of a rigid body rotating about a fixed axis O, a distance r_G from the C.G., we find from Eq. (13.13)

$$T = \frac{1}{2}m(r_G\omega)^2 + \frac{1}{2}I_G\omega^2$$

$$= \frac{1}{2}\omega^2(mr_G^2 + I_G)$$

$$= \frac{1}{2}I_O\omega^2 \tag{13.14}$$

If we have a system of rigid bodies which make up a mechanism, we can expand Eq. (13.11) so as to relate the change in total kinetic energy of the mechanism to the external work done on the mechanism. The internal forces, between links of the mechanism, which are the reactions at the various pairs connecting the links, produce no work during motion of the mechanism if the friction is neglected. This is true because there is no relative motion in the direction of the forces of the points in contact. Then summing Eq. (13.11) for all the links

$$\Sigma\,\Delta T = \Sigma\,W_e \tag{13.15}$$

where $\Sigma\,\Delta T$ is the total change in kinetic energy of the system and $\Sigma\,W_e$ is the total external work done on the mechanism.

The relations developed in this section will be used in the analysis of clutches and brakes which will be discussed at the end of this chapter.

13.4 Potential Energy

Consider the various types of forces encountered in machinery. These forces can be listed as

1. Weights or gravity forces.
2. Elastic forces such as spring forces.
3. Forces normal to the surfaces on which they act such as forces exerted on a sliding member by its guide where the force is normal to the direction of motion.
4. Friction forces.
5. Forces caused by hydraulic or gas pressure on pistons.
6. Impact forces.
7. All other forces such as external forces from members not a part of the machine.

If we consider these types of forces from the viewpoint of the work done by the forces while acting on a body in motion, we will find that the first two types of forces have certain properties which distinguish them from the others. These forces are called potential forces for reasons which will be shown later in the discussion. The third type of force is also unique in that it does no work on the moving body, since there is no component in the direction of the motion, while all the other forces can do work on the body.

Taking now the gravity forces we note that the work done by these forces is dependent only on the vertical displacement of the body on which they act and is independent of the *path* of motion of the body. If a body moves above some horizontal reference or datum plane a vertical distance h, the gravity force will do work on the body equal to $-Wh$, the negative sign indicating the force opposes the motion. Some other external force must be applied to the body to cause it to move through the distance h. If the body moves slowly so that no dynamic forces are involved, the force moving the body upward will be equal and opposite to the weight, and will do positive work Wh on the body. The work done by the upward force is recoverable if we let the body descend to the datum plane while pulling another body of equal weight upward by means of a cable and pulley while it descends, or, by letting it fall freely, the gravity force will do positive work on the body and thereby increase its kinetic energy by the amount of the original work done on the body. This recoverable work which is produced by the gravity force in returning to the datum plane, the work being equal to Wh, is called the potential energy of the body at the height h above the datum. From the above discussion we see that the difference in potential energy of a body (which is its ability to do work or its stored energy) while moving from one position to another is equal to the work done by the gravity force during this motion with reversed sign. If the gravity force does negative work, the potential energy increases and vice versa. Letting U represent the potential energy of the body the relation can be represented mathematically as

$$dU = -dW \qquad (13.16)$$

Forces such as the gravity force whose work on a body is dependent only on the initial and final positions of the body are called potential forces and Eq. (13.16) holds only for such forces.

Elastic forces are also potential forces. Consider a body attached to a spring and resting on a frictionless surface as shown in Fig. 13.2. The force exerted on the body by the spring is proportional to the deflec- tion of the spring and in direction

FIGURE 13.2

opposing the deflection. If the deflection, x, is measured from the un- stressed condition of the spring, the spring force is represented by the equation

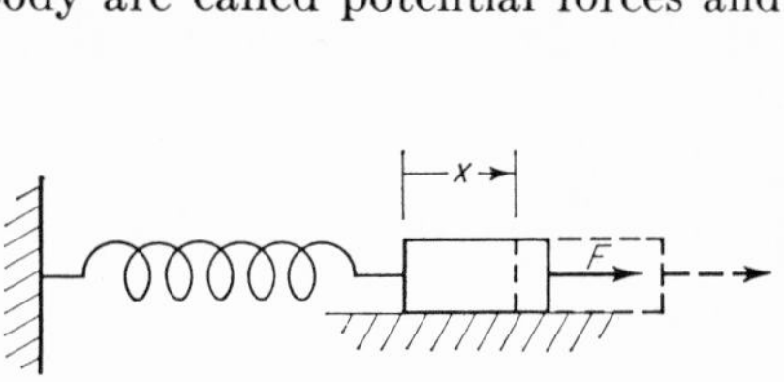

$$F = -kx \tag{13.17}$$

where k is the proportionality constant in lb/in. called the spring rate and is dependent on the stiffness of the spring. An external force causing the spring to deflect is equal and opposite to the spring force, and the work done by an external force in compressing or extending the spring then is

$$W = \int_0^x F dx = \int_0^x kx dx = \frac{1}{2} kx^2 \tag{13.18}$$

The work done by the spring on the body is equal to the work done by the external force in deflecting the spring with the sign reversed, and from the equation we see that this work is dependent only on the displacement of the spring, therefore the spring force is a potential force. The deflected spring can do work on the body in returning to the undeflected position and therefore energy has been stored in the spring. This potential energy is sometimes called the elastic energy of the spring. Equation (13.16) holds for this case also. We should note that the spring force is an internal force if we consider the system as made up of the spring, moving body and the fixed body.

Now considering friction forces, we find that these forces are entirely different from the preceding forces. The friction force always opposes the motion and if the motion is stopped, the friction force disappears and there is no tendency for the body to return to its initial position or to return the work done by the forces used to overcome the friction forces. Such forces are called dissipative forces and the work is used in heating up the bodies on which the friction forces act. The same is true for the last three types of forces in general although under certain conditions these forces can be potential forces.

If impact forces are potential forces this means that the bodies acted on by the impact forces are perfectly elastic and there is no dissipation of energy; we could say that the bodies act as springs. Actually no materials are perfectly elastic and even in springs there is some dissipation of energy, although for most metals this energy loss is small in springs and can be neglected for practical problems. For most impact forces encountered in machine members, however, we will find that there is considerable loss in energy and they cannot be considered as potential forces. This will be discussed further when we consider problems involving impact later in the chapter.

If we now consider a machine or mechanism as composed of rigid bodies and elastic bodies such as springs, Eq. (13.15) can be rewritten to include the internal elastic forces as

$$dW_e + dW_i = dT \tag{13.19}$$

where the work is separated into work done by external forces represented as dW_e and internal forces represented as dW_i. If the external and internal forces are potential forces only, the work can be replaced by the potential energy and Eq. (13.19) reduced to

$$- dU_e - dU_i = dT$$

or $$d(U_e + U_i + T) = 0 \qquad (13.20)$$

This equation is quite important. It states that the sum of the potential and kinetic energies for a system acted on only by potential forces remains a constant. The equation represents the law of conservation of energy, and systems for which this equation holds are called conservative systems. At first thought we might say that no machine satisfies this definition, since there are always friction forces in machines, but in cases where the friction forces are small in relation to the potential forces, the work of the friction forces can be neglected in relation to the work done by the potential forces, and Eq. (13.20) can be used for all practical purposes.

The law of conservation of energy is the basis of a large part of the study of vibrations. In our study of virtual work in Chapter 11, the whole analysis assumed that we were dealing with conservative systems, and actually was based on the law of conservation of energy. We will also make use of the law in our discussion of critical speeds of rotating shafts in a later chapter.

13.5 *Applications of the Work, Energy, and Impulse Relations*

Noting that impulse is a function of time, and work is a function of displacement, we can make the general statement that those problems in which velocity is given or desired as a function of time are best solved by the impulse-momentum relations and those involving velocity as a function of displacement lend themselves to the work-energy relations. However this should not be taken as a rigid rule. We will now consider some typical problems encountered in the design of machinery.

As a first example we will consider the analysis of clutches and brakes used to bring a machine up to operating speed or to stop a machine which is at operating speed. At present we will restrict our discussion to mechanisms which are rotating about an axis passing through their center of gravity such as electric motors and gear trains. Mechanisms which contain large flywheels, such as punch presses, could also be considered as satisfying this restriction if the total kinetic energy of the various links is negligible in relation to the energy of the flywheel.

In order to design brakes and clutches for such machines, we need to know the energy which must be dissipated (or the work that must be done) by the brake or clutch, and the torques that the brake or clutch must apply to the machine.

230

Consider a machine rotating at some given speed which must be brought to a stop by means of a friction brake. Equation (13.14) can be used to determine the energy which must be dissipated and this work must be absorbed by the brake as friction work if we ignore the friction work done by the bearings in the machine, which is generally negligible in relation to the kinetic energy of the rotating parts. Then the brake must do negative work on the machine of the amount

$$W = \frac{1}{2}I_G\omega^2 \tag{13.21}$$

where I_G is the moment of inertia of the rotating parts relative to the rotating axis which passes through the C.G. and this work will be dissipated in the brake as heat energy.

The torque which the brake must apply to the machine in order to dissipate the energy will be dependent on the time in which the machine is to be brought to a stop. Then in order to determine the torque which must be applied by the brake we must specify the time in which the machine must be brought to a stop. The time could be specified directly or we could specify the angle through which the machine will turn from the time of application of the brake until the machine is brought to rest. If the angular displacement is specified, the work-energy equation can be used to determine the required torque, as mentioned at the first of this article and our equation would be

$$W = \int_{\theta_0}^{\theta_1} M d\theta = \frac{1}{2}I_G(\omega_0^2 - \omega_1^2)$$

where θ_0 is the angular position of the machine when the brake is first applied, at which time the angular velocity is ω_0, and θ_1 is the angular position of the machine corresponding to an angular velocity ω_1. For our case we have assumed that the machine is to be brought to rest, therefore ω_1 will be zero. In order to evaluate the integral we must have the torque M as a function of the angular displacement θ. For most practical problems the torque can be considered constant and the equation becomes

$$M(\theta_1 - \theta_0) = \frac{1}{2}I_G\omega_0^2$$

or

$$M = \frac{I_G\omega_0^2}{2\Delta\theta} \tag{13.22}$$

where M is the uniform torque required to bring the machine to a stop in an angular displacement $\Delta\theta$.

If the time in which the machine must be brought to rest is specified we will make use of the impulse-momentum equation

$$\int_0^t M dt = I_G(\omega_0 - \omega_1)$$

and again assuming constant torque

$$M = \frac{I_G \omega_0}{t} \qquad (13.23)$$

where t is the time in which the machine is brought to a stop.

Let us now consider a friction clutch used to bring the same machine or rotor to operating speed from rest. In order to bring the rotor up to operating speed the clutch must do the same amount of work on the rotor that the brake did in stopping the rotor, although the work must be positive work in this case. The work then is given by Eq. (13.21) where ω is the operating speed, and this amount of energy must be supplied to the rotor by the clutch. If we assume that the clutch is driven by a motor rotating at the operating speed of the motor at all times, there will also be energy dissipated in the clutch in the form of heat at the same time that the clutch is doing work on the rotor. When the clutch is first engaged, the friction surfaces of the clutch have a relative velocity equal to the operating speed of the rotor, and when the rotor has been brought up to speed the relative velocity of the friction surfaces is zero. This is an exact parallel to the conditions existing between the friction surfaces of the brake while it is stopping the rotor and therefore the clutch must dissipate in the form of heat the same quantity of energy that was dissipated in the brake. We see then that the motor must supply energy equal to twice the kinetic energy of the rotor at operating speed.

The torque which the clutch must apply to the rotor can be determined in the same way that the torque applied by the brake was found, and again the torque is dependent on the time required to bring the rotor up to speed.

Since the motor must supply energy equal to twice the kinetic energy of the rotor if we use a friction clutch, the thought might occur to us that if we use some other kind of clutch which dissipated no energy, then we would have a more efficient system. Such a system is not possible if the driving motor is rotating at operating speed when the clutch is engaged as will be shown in the following discussion.

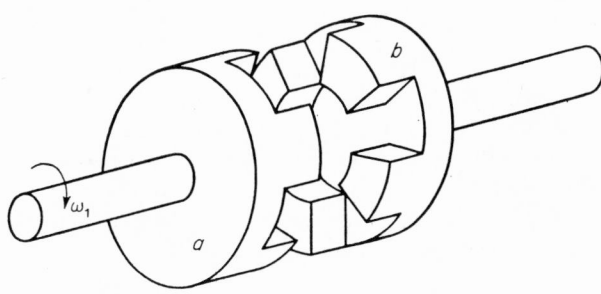

FIGURE 13.3

Consider a positive acting clutch such as the jaw clutch shown in Fig. 13.3. If link "a" is attached to the driving motor and link "b" attached to the rotor which must be brought up to operating speed, when the two links are engaged by sliding one along the shaft, there will be impact between the jaws of the two links. The angular impulse corresponding to the impact forces is given by the equation

$$\int_{t_0}^{t_1} T dt = I_G \omega_1 \qquad (13.24)$$

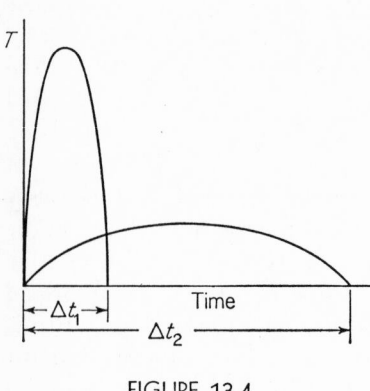

FIGURE 13.4

where ω_1 is the operating speed reached at time t_1. For cases of impact, the elapsed time is extremely short, and the torque-time relation as well as the actual time is not generally known. However the value of the integral is definitely known and we can draw some general conclusions from this equation. Figure 13.4 is a plot of the assumed torque as a function of time for two time increments. The area under the curves represents the value of the impulse integral and although the curves are assumed we can see from the figure that the shorter the time increment, the greater the torque must be. In cases of impact, the forces on the jaws and the torque are extremely high. For this reason a positive acting clutch should be engaged only at slow relative speeds, so that the torque does not become excessive. In cases where impact loads are necessary in machinery, the force-time relations can be obtained experimentally with modern instrumentation and this experimental analysis should be used in the design of such mechanisms.

For any type of clutch used to bring a rotor up to operating speed with the driving motor running at this speed when the clutch is engaged, there is always a relative angular velocity between the motor and the rotor until the rotor is at the operating speed. The torque acting on the rotor must be equal and opposite to the torque acting on the motor at all times and since the motor will turn through a greater angle during any increment of time than the rotor, the motor must do more work than is absorbed by the rotor in increasing its kinetic energy. This extra work then must be absorbed by the clutch in the form of heat. The work which must be absorbed by the clutch is equal to the kinetic energy of the rotor at operating speed. This can readily be shown if we assume that the motor turns at a constant speed while the rotor is being brought up to speed. The impulse which must be applied to the rotor to bring it up to speed is given by Eq. (13.24), and this impulse must be supplied by the motor. The work which the motor does on the clutch is

$$W = \int_{t_0}^{t_1} T d\theta = \int_{t_0}^{t_1} T \frac{d\theta}{dt} dt = \omega_1 \int_{t_0}^{t_1} T dt$$

and substituting Eq. (13.24)

$$W = I_G \omega_1^2$$

and since the kinetic energy of the rotor at operating speed is half this value, the clutch must absorb an amount of energy equal to the kinetic energy of the rotor.

Let us now consider a general mechanism in which the links may have rotation, translation or a combination of the two as shown in Fig. 13.5, with the driving link "a" rotating at constant velocity. We wish to determine the energy which must be absorbed by a brake

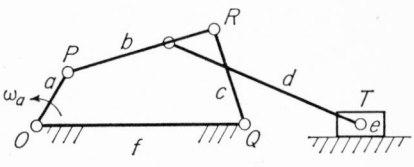

FIGURE 13.5

attached to the shaft passing through point O and driving link "a," and the torque which the brake must apply to the shaft in order to bring the mechanism to rest. The total energy of the mechanism is the sum of the kinetic and potential energies of the individual links and will vary with the phase position of the drive shaft, so long as it is rotating at constant velocity, and there will be a transfer of energy from the driving motor to the mechanism during each cycle of operation, the net transfer over the cycle being zero. If the driving torque is removed at any time, the total energy of the mechanism will remain a constant and the driving link "a," or crank, will then vary in angular velocity over a cycle but have its original velocity when it returns to the position at which the torque was removed. In the design of the brake we must assume that the brake may be applied at any position, and therefore the brake must be designed to absorb the maximum total energy of the mechanism. The only way to determine the maximum energy of the mechanism is to determine the energy for all phase positions, or plot a curve of energy as a function of phase position.

In machines made up of rigid bodies, since the potential energy of the various links is that associated with the gravity forces, the potential energy is negligible in relation to the kinetic energy in most cases and therefore the total energy can be taken as the kinetic energy of the individual links. The kinetic energy of the individual links can be determined by applying Eq. (13.13) to each link. Note that the velocity of the center of gravity and the angular velocity of each link must be known in order to apply this equation, and these must be determined from a velocity analysis. The sum of the kinetic energies of the individual links then is the total energy of the machine for the phase position analyzed, and this energy must be absorbed by the brake in bringing the machine to a stop.

In order to determine the torque which must be applied by the brake to stop the machine, we must use the work-energy relations as given by Eq. (13.15) or the impulse-momentum relations as given by Eq. (13.2). However we will find that for this case of a general mechanism the determination of the required torque by use of the impulse-momentum relations is much more complicated than for the previous example and that generally the work-energy equation should be used to determine the torque required to stop the mechanism for a given angular displacement of the crank.

Considering the impulse-momentum relations we will take the origin of the system at point O and will assume that the torque is known as a function of time. This torque-time relation would have to be found experimentally for the particular brake, and for convenience we will take the torque as constant. Rewriting Eq. (13.2) for the conditions which we have imposed we find it must be written as

$$\Sigma \, mV_{G}r_O + \Sigma \, I_G\omega = \int_0^t M_O dt$$

where the summation indicates the sum of the moments of momentum of all the individual links relative to O at the instant the brake is applied, V_G and ω are the velocity of the center of gravity and angular velocity of the links and M_O is the moment of all external forces about O. The difficulty of using this equation for the determination of the required torque applied by the brake arises from the fact that M_O, the moment of all external forces, is not just the moment applied by the brake. An external moment is also applied to the mechanism by the normal reaction between the slider, link "e," and the fixed body as well as the reaction at Q between the fixed body and link "c." Then the external moment M_O is the sum of these two moments and the torque applied by the brake. For both these external forces, the force as well as the moment arm of the force will vary with time so that the external moment becomes a complex function of time and the integral cannot be readily evaluated. There are approximate methods of evaluating this integral but these methods are beyond the scope of this text and will not be discussed.

If now we consider the work-energy relations as given by Eq. (13.15) we can write the equation for our case as

$$\Sigma \, \frac{1}{2}mV_G^2 + \Sigma \, \frac{1}{2}I_G\omega^2 = \int_0^\theta M_O d\theta$$

where the summation is for all the links and M_O now is the torque applied by the brake. We need not include the external moment caused by the external forces on link "c" and "e" in this case because these forces do no work on the mechanism. Now if we assume that the torque is constant we find from the equation that the required torque to bring the mechanism to a stop in a given angular displacement of the crank, θ, is

$$M_O = \frac{\Sigma \, mV_G^2 + \Sigma \, I_G\omega^2}{2\theta}$$

Then we find that in setting up specifications for a brake or clutch for mechanisms other than those composed of purely rotating members, we should specify the angular displacement of the crank in which the mechanism must be brought to rest or brought up to speed, rather than the time.

PROBLEMS

13.1 (a) What is the angular momentum about the center of gravity of the system of gears shown in Fig. P13.1 if link "a" is rotating at 2000 rpm?

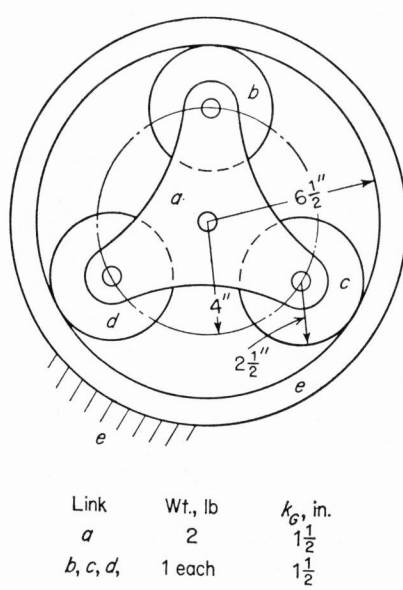

Link	Wt., lb	k_G, in.
a	2	$1\frac{1}{2}$
$b, c, d,$	1 each	$1\frac{1}{2}$

FIGURE P13.1

(b) What is the kinetic energy of the above system?

(c) What constant torque must be applied to link "a" in order to stop the motion of the system in 5 sec?

13.2 (a) Three gears are mounted on a platform as shown in Fig. P13.2. The motor housing is attached to the platform, which is free to rotate about a vertical axis. All friction in the system is negligible. If the motor is rotating at a speed of

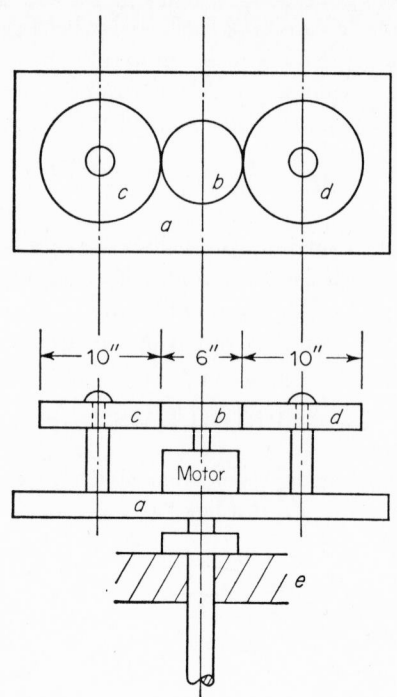

Link	Wt., lb	k_G, in.
a	6	8
b(including motor rotor)	3	$1\frac{3}{4}$
c	3	3
d	3	3

FIGURE P13.2

3600 rpm clockwise and the platform is rotating at a speed of 1800 rpm counter clockwise, what is the angular momentum of the system?

(b) Determine the kinetic energy of the system.

(c) If, while the system is at rest the motor is brought up to a speed of 3600 rpm clockwise determine the absolute angular velocity of all members of the system.

13.3 A block weighing 10 lbs is attached to a cord passing through a hole in a horizontal frictionless surface, as shown in Fig. P13.3. The block is initially revolving in a circle with a 24 in. radius and with a constant tangential velocity of 140 in./sec. The cord is slowly pulled from below, shortening the radius of the circular path of the block. At what radius of the circular path will the cord break if its breaking strength is 140 lb?

13.4 A bullet of mass m_1 is fired into a wooden block of mass m_2 resting on a horizontal surface. The coefficient of friction between the block and the surface is

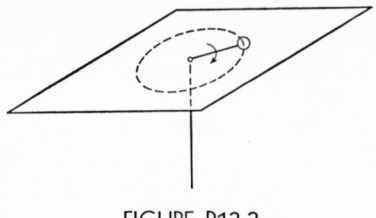

FIGURE P13.3

0.2. The bullet remains embedded in the block which slides a distance x under the impact. Express the distance x in terms of the given quantities.

13.5 (a) A spring-loaded stop is to be installed at the end of a package chute as shown in Fig. P13.4. The packages are pushed onto the chute by a conveyer which

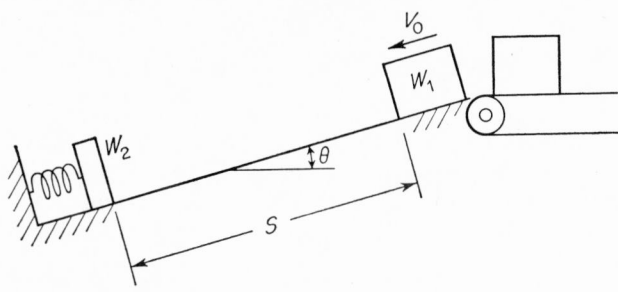

FIGURE P13.4

gives them an initial velocity of V_0. The coefficient of friction between box and chute is 0.1. Determine the velocity V_1 of a package, just before it hits the stop, in terms of the given quantities.

(b) Determine the energy that the springs must absorb if the package, of weight W_1, hits the mass in front of the springs, of weight W_2, with inelastic impact. Neglect the friction loss after impact.

13.6 Three boxcars are on a horizontal spur track. A stop at the end of the track has springs attached to it to absorb the shock when cars hit it. The three cars are initially disconnected, and the car farthest from the stop is moving with a velocity of 3 mph towards the stop while the other two cars are at rest. As the cars collide, they are automatically connected (inelastic impact). If the cars weigh 10,000 lbs each determine the value of the spring rate k so that the maximum spring force exerted on the stop is 3500 lb.

13.7 (a) In an automobile accident car 1 hit car 2, which was standing still. The cars were locked together after the impact and skidded 20 ft in a straight line with wheels locked. Tests indicate that the coefficient of friction between the wheels and road was 0.5. If car 1 weighs 3000 lbs and car 2 weighs 4000 lbs determine the velocity of the two cars immediately after impact.

(b) The driver of car 1 contended he was driving under the 60 mph speed limit at the time of the accident. Skid marks indicated the wheels on car 1 were locked for a distance of 20 ft before the collision. From the given information, would you say that the driver was correctly reporting his speed?

13.8 (a) A shaft and disc, initially at rest, is connected by means of a friction clutch to a shaft and disc rotating at 1800 rpm. If the moment of inertia of the rotating shaft and disc is I_1 and that of the other shaft and disc is I_2, what will be the common speed of the two shafts when the clutch has ceased to slip and if no external torque is applied?

(b) How much energy is absorbed in the clutch?

13.9 Figure P13.5 shows a system consisting of a flywheel A connected to one element of a positive action clutch by means of a torsional spring, and a flywheel B

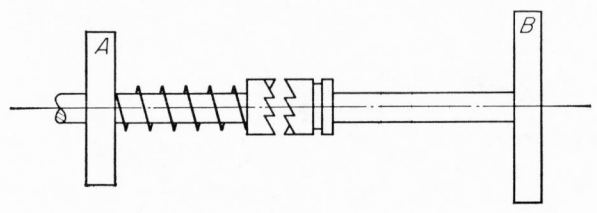

FIGURE P13.5

attached to the other element of the clutch by means of a shaft on which the clutch element can slide axially. Flywheel A weighs 50 lbs and has a radius of gyration of 10 in. Flywheel B weighs 100 lbs and has a radius of gyration of 12 in. The spring has a torsional spring rate of 1500 lb-in./rad. When flywheel A is rotating at 100 rpm and flywheel B is at rest, the clutch is suddenly engaged. Neglecting all friction and the moments of inertia of the shaft and clutch elements, determine

(a) The maximum angular deflection of the spring.

(b) The speeds of the flywheels at the instant the angular deflection in the spring is a maximum.

(c) The common speed of the flywheels when the spring regains its initial unstrained condition.

Chapter **14**

Dynamic Analysis of Mechanisms

14.1 Inertia Forces

We are now ready to study dynamic-force analysis of machinery. Dynamic forces are those associated with accelerations of machines. The analysis of the accelerations in mechanisms has been covered in detail in the earlier chapters, and in Chapter 12 the relationship between accelerations and forces has been discussed. Dynamic-force analysis is the application of these principles to various mechanisms to the end of determining the forces necessary to act on the various links of the mechanism to cause a prescribed motion.

Dynamic forces are proportional to the accelerations of the links of the mechanisms, and for high speed machines dynamic forces are very large in relation to the static forces which do useful work. For example, in modern high speed reciprocating engines such as the automobile engine the dynamic forces may be equal to or greater than the gas pressure force on the piston, and in a gas-turbine rotor with a small unbalance the inertia force is many times greater than the weight of the rotor. In such cases the dynamic forces must be considered in the design of the machine; in slow speed machines the dynamic forces may be negligible.

In developing the equations of motion, we found that the effect of a set of external forces on a body was a linear acceleration of the center of gravity as given by the equation

$$F = ma_G$$

and an angular acceleration of the body as given by the equation

$$M_G = I_G\alpha$$

Considering the first of these equations we see that if a force equal in magnitude to the resultant of the external forces and in the same direction but with opposite sense to the resultant is applied to the center of gravity, the acceleration of the center of gravity will be zero. Likewise, if we apply a moment about the center of gravity equal in magnitude to the resultant moment of the external forces but opposite in sense, the angular acceleration will be zero; under these conditions the body will be in static equilibrium.

The equations of motion can be rewritten as

$$F - ma_G = F + (- ma_G) = 0$$
$$M_G - I_G\alpha = M_G + (- I_G\alpha) = 0 \qquad (14.1)$$

If we think of the terms ma_G and $I_G\alpha$ respectively as a force acting through the center of gravity and a moment about the center of gravity, then Eqs. (14.1) state that the summations of forces and moments on the body are zero and therefore the body is in static equilibrium. Forces and moments defined in this manner are called inertia forces and inertia torques, respectively. The negative signs in the equations indicate that the inertia force must have opposite sense to the acceleration of the center of gravity and the inertia torque must be in opposite sense to the angular acceleration. If the force equation is satisfied the resultant of the forces acting on the body is a couple and therefore the inertia moment is a couple when the inertia force is applied at the center of gravity.

Let us now consider a link of a mechanism as a free-body under the influence of two external forces F_1 and F_2 as shown in Fig. 14.1(a). The resultant of these external forces is the force R, found in Fig. 14.1(b), and its line of action is a distance r from the center of gravity as shown. The effect of this resultant is an acceleration of the center of gravity and a clockwise angular acceleration of the body, as shown in the figure. In Fig. 14.1(c) the same link is shown with the resultant, the inertia force (labeled F_i) and the inertia torque (labeled T_i) acting on it. The inertia force passes through the center of gravity and is equal but opposite in sense to R. The sum of these two forces is zero, but they comprise a clockwise torque on the link of magnitude Rr. The inertia torque is a counter clockwise torque (of opposite sense to the angular acceleration) and, since the link must be in static equilibrium with the inertia force and couple acting, it must be equal in magnitude to Rr. Therefore if we treat any link as a free-body and apply the inertia force and inertia torque to the body the link is in static equilibrium under the influence of these inertia forces, and the external forces can be analyzed in the same manner that the static analysis was made in Chapter 11.

The inertia force and inertia torque can be replaced by a single force which has the same effect on the body as the force and couple, and is therefore equivalent to the inertia force and couple. This simplifies our force analysis since the inertia effects can then be taken care of by a *single* force.

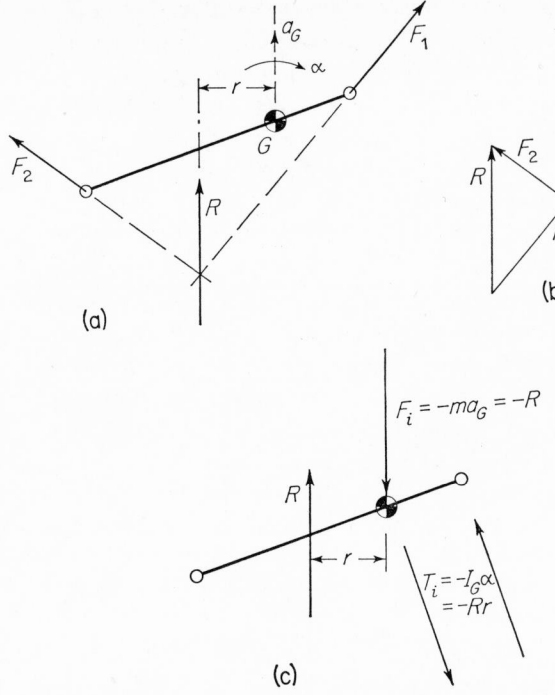

FIGURE 14.1

In order to show how the couple and force can be replaced by a single equivalent force, let us consider the body in Fig. 14.2, which has a clockwise angular acceleration and whose center of gravity has a linear acceleration as shown. The inertia force and inertia couple are indicated on the body. We remember that the couple can be replaced by any other couple composed of two equal forces of any magnitude and direction so long as the

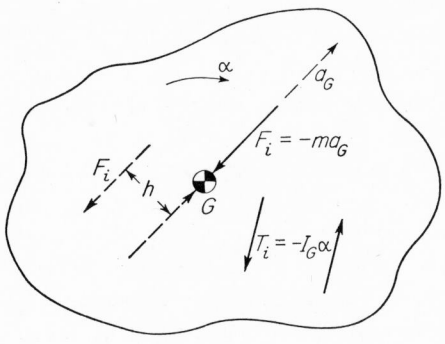

FIGURE 14.2

distance between the forces is such that the distance or arm of the couple multiplied by the force is equal to the magnitude of the couple and the sense of the couple does not change. Let us then replace the given couple by a couple in which the forces are of magnitude equal to the magnitude of the inertia force, and shift this equivalent couple to the position shown by the dashed forces in the figure, so that one of the forces of the couple is along the same line of action as the inertia force but is of opposite sense. The equal and opposite forces cancel, and the single force labeled F_i remains and is equivalent to the original inertia force and couple. The arm of the couple, h, is given by the equation

$$h = \frac{T_i}{F_i} = \frac{I_G \alpha}{F_i} \tag{14.2}$$

Now the inertia force and inertia couple can be replaced by a single force equal in magnitude, direction, and sense to the inertia force. The line of action of this single force is shifted from the center of gravity by a distance h. Note that the line of action is shifted in a direction from the center of gravity so that the moment of the force about the center of gravity is in the same direction as the inertia torque. Referring to Fig. 14.1(c) again, we see that the equivalent force will be equal and opposite to the resultant of the external forces and have the same line of action so that the summation of all the forces on the link will be zero.

14.2 Dynamic Analysis

As the first example of a dynamic force analysis we will analyze the quadric crank mechanism shown in Fig. 14.3(a) with link "a" rotating with constant velocity, ω_a. We will consider only the forces on the pin joints and that external moment on "a" necessary to give the mechanism the pre-scribed motion. It will be assumed that the weights of the links, or the gravity forces, are negligible and that there are no external forces applied to the mechanism. The analysis will therefore consider only the effects of the inertia forces.

We must first determine the inertia forces on the individual links and their lines of action. The locations of the centers of gravity of the links are shown on the figure and it is assumed that the masses and moments of inertia of the links are known. The accelerations of the links must be known in order that the inertia forces can be determined. This requires an acceleration analysis and the acceleration image is shown in Fig. 14.3(b) in which the images of the various centers of gravity have been indicated. The inertia forces can now be calculated from the equation $F_i = ma$.

Free-bodies of the various links are now drawn as shown in Fig. 14.3(c) with the inertia forces acting on each link shown at their correct positions.

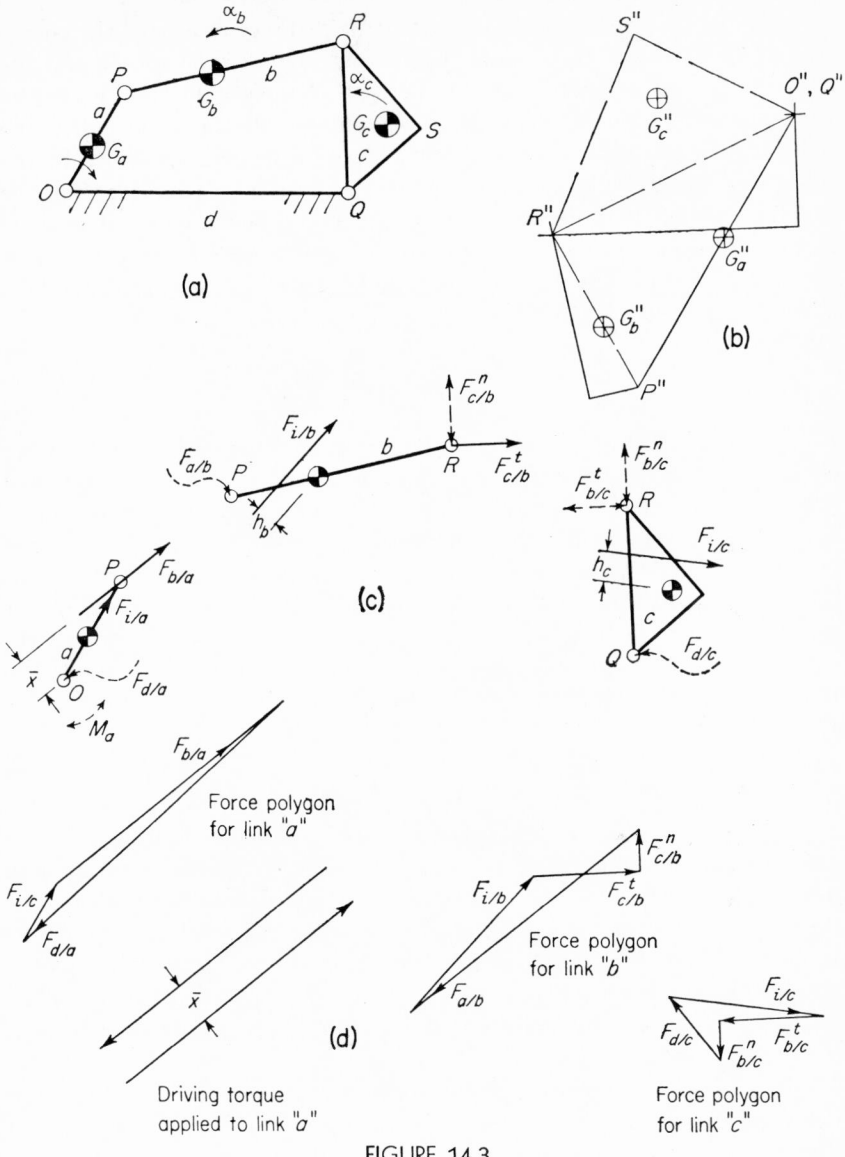

FIGURE 14.3

Considering the free body of link "c," we note that the inertia force has the same direction as the acceleration of the center of gravity of the link but with opposite sense. The distance from the center of gravity to the line of action of the force, h_c, is found from the relation

$$h_c = \frac{I_G \alpha}{ma}$$

The force is shifted in a direction such that the moment of the inertia force about the center of gravity is opposite to the sense of the angular acceleration. In this case the inertia moment is clockwise since the acceleration is counterclockwise. For convenience and in order to save time, the direction of the angular acceleration of each link is indicated on the drawing of the mechanism, immediately after the acceleration image has been completed, as shown in the figure. This gives us a quick check of the position of the inertia force. The inertia force on the free-body of link "b" is located in the same manner. Since link "a" has no angular acceleration, the inertia force passes through the center of gravity and is directed away from the center of rotation, point O. This force is caused by a normal acceleration only and we recognize it as a centrifugal force.

The inertia forces are treated as known external forces and each link is in equilibrium under the action of the inertia forces and the unknown reaction forces. The determination of the unknown forces then is the same as for a static analysis as discussed in Chapter 11. (The student is advised to review that chapter.)

Starting with link "c" we can take moments about Q and thereby find $F_{b/c}^{t}$. Then applying this known force to the free body of link "b," as shown in the figure we can determine all the forces on link "b" by means of a force and funicular polygon. Knowing $F_{b/a}$ from the solution of link "b" the force $F_{d/a}$ can be found by a force polygon and the external moment on "a" can be found by taking moments about O. Also from the solution of the forces on link "b," we know $F_{b/c}^{n}$ and the force $F_{d/c}$ can be found with a force polygon of the forces on link "c." Force polygons for all the links and the required external torque on link "a" are shown in Fig. 14.3(d). Note that since $F_{i/a}$ applied no torque about O the torque required to drive the mechanism at the given speed is equal in magnitude to $F_{b/a} \cdot \bar{x}$ but in opposite sense.

Other methods could have been used in analyzing the forces on the mechanism. Since link "c" is rotating about a fixed axis, we could have used the equation

$$M_Q = I_Q \alpha$$

and taking moments about Q, $F_{b/c}^{t}$ could have been found without determining $F_{i/c}$ or h_c, although $F_{i/c}$ would have to be determined in order to draw a force polygon to determine $F_{d/c}$. Also, link "b" could have been analyzed by taking moments about P to determine $F_{c/b}^{n}$ and then using a force polygon to determine $F_{a/b}$. The moment arms of the various forces would have to be scaled from the drawing in such an analysis. Any method of analysis is satisfactory and usually the quickest one is preferable; however, for a link with a large number of forces acting on it, the funicular polygon will generally prove the simplest.

Let us now consider the effects of the inertia forces on the fixed link or frame of the mechanism. The mechanism is redrawn in Fig. 14.4(a) with the inertia forces acting on the various links and also the forces that links "*a*" and "*c*" exert on the frame, as found from the analysis, are shown.

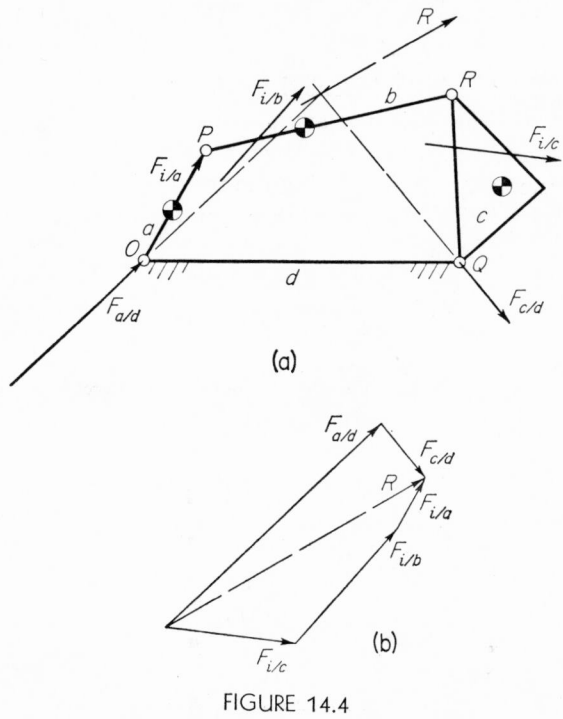

(a)

(b)

FIGURE 14.4

These forces on the frame, caused by the inertia forces *only*, are called shaking forces. These forces are important in that the frame or support must be made strong enough to withstand them. Also these forces may set up vibrations in the support or the surroundings. If the machine is placed in a building, these shaking forces are transmitted to the floor of the building and might prove troublesome. From Eq. (12.2) we see that the resultant of these shaking forces is equal to the resultant of the inertia forces, as can also be shown by the force polygon in Fig. 14.4(b) where we see that the inertia forces and the shaking forces have the same resultant. Then if we are interested only in the magnitude and direction of the resultant shaking force, all we need do is determine the resultant of the inertia forces. But if we are interested also in the line of action of the resultant shaking force, it must be determined from the individual forces acting on the frame, as shown in the figure, and therefore a complete analysis is necessary. The line of action of the resultant of the inertia forces shown in the figure will not be the same as the line of action of the individual forces acting on the frame since the inertia forces are transmitted to the frame through the links directly connected to the frame.

It will be noted that the external torque on link "a" which is required to give the mechanism the prescribed motion is counter clockwise while the angular velocity of "a" is clockwise, indicating that the mechanism is doing work on the driving motor rather than requiring that the motor do work on the mechanism. The net work done through a complete cycle must be zero since the energy of the system at any phase position is fixed if the velocity of the crank is constant. Therefore the external work will be positive during part of the cycle and negative during the rest of the cycle, the sum being zero. Then at some phase positions other than that shown the motor will do work on the mechanism.

14.3 Combined Static and Dynamic Force Analysis

We have now discussed the static force analysis and the dynamic force analysis of machines as separate analyses. In many cases there is no need to separate these analyses and they can be combined into one single analysis. The total forces acting on the links of a mechanism are the sums of the static and dynamic forces, and in the design of individual links for strength the links must be so proportioned that they will withstand the total forces. The slider-crank mechanism will be used to demonstrate a combined static and dynamic analysis.

The mechanism is shown in Fig. 14.5(a). We assume that the crank, link "a," is rotating with constant angular velocity, ω_a, and that the motion is caused by a known external force F_c applied to link "c." (The external force might be as the gas pressure on the piston of an internal combustion engine.) The weights of the links will also be included in the analysis. The weights of the links always act through the center of gravity and always have the same direction (towards the center of the Earth). They are handled as known external forces, although they are actually inertia forces also, being caused by the acceleration of gravity. The acceleration image is shown in Fig. 14.5(b) and the free-body diagrams of the links are shown in Fig. 14.5(c), with the known and unknown forces acting on them. The inertia force, $F_{i/b}$, and its moment arm relative to the center of gravity and the forces $F_{i/a}$ and $F_{i/c}$ are determined as in the previous example and are drawn in as shown.

Starting with link "c" the horizontal component of $F_{b/c}$ can be found by setting the sum of the horizontal forces equal to zero. We must next go to link "b" and with $F^h_{c/b}$ known we can determine $F^v_{c/b}$ and $F_{a/b}$ by means of a funicular and force polygon or by taking moments about P together with a force polygon. Then with $F_{b/a}$ known, $F_{d/a}$ can be found by means of a force

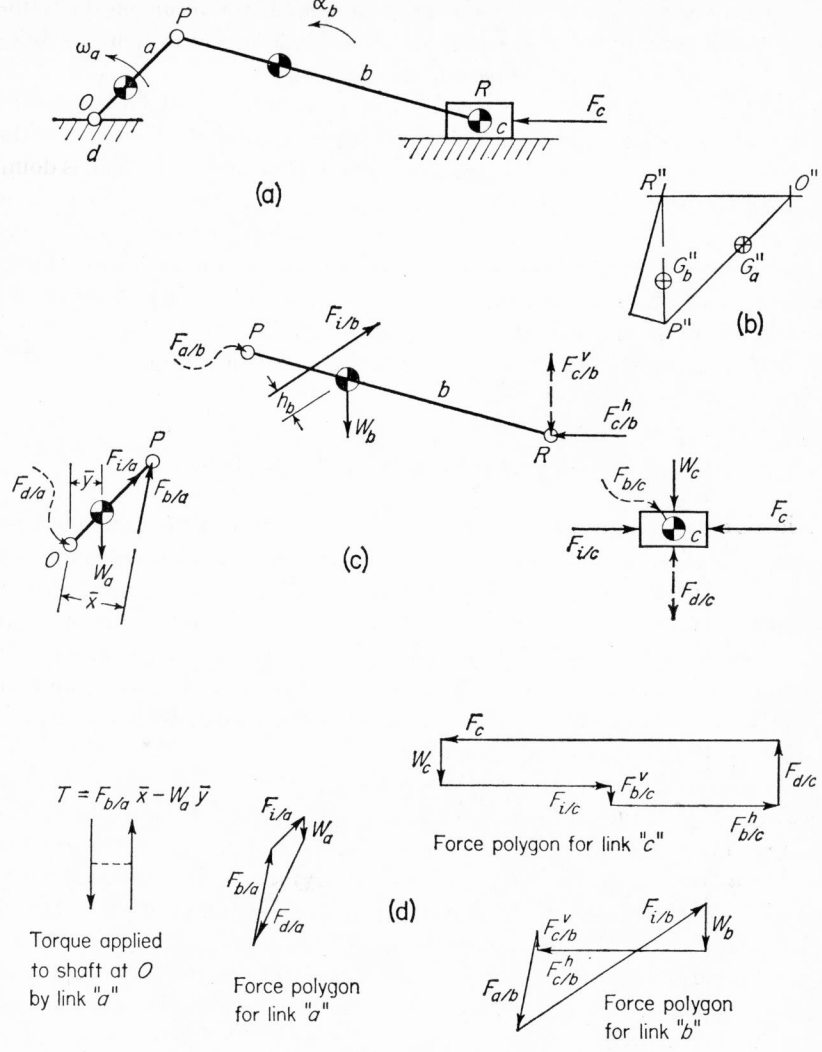

FIGURE 14.5

polygon, and the external moment on link "a" can be determined by taking moments about O. Returning to link "c," we can find $F_{d/c}$ by means of a force polygon since all other forces on the link now are known.

Force polygons for all the links and the torque applied to the shaft at O by link "a" are shown in Fig. 14.5(d). Note that the counterclockwise torque on the shaft at O can be used to drive some other mechanism attached to the shaft. In this case the external force, F_c, is greater than that necessary to drive the mechanism at the prescribed crank velocity so that work can be done on the shaft through O. If the force had been too small to drive the mechanism, the torque applied by link "a" would have been clockwise indicating that a counter clockwise torque would have to be applied to the crank to give the prescribed motion. If the torque on link "a" turned out to be zero, the external force would be just sufficient to give the mechanism the prescribed motion. If the force on link "c" necessary to give the mechanism the prescribed motion were required, we would start our analysis with link "a" and determine the necessary external force on link "c" to bring its free body into equilibrium.

It should be noted that the analysis of the mechanism shown in Fig. 14.5 could have been made by considering links "b" and "c" combined as a free-body. A funicular and force polygon could then be used to determine $F_{a/b}$ and $F_{a/c}$ and it would not be necessary to consider components of $F_{b/c}$.

One other example will be used to demonstrate the combined analysis of a mechanism. Figure 14.6(a) shows a quick-return mechanism driven by the crank, link "a", which rotates with constant angular velocity ω_a. The motion is opposed by a force F_e applied to the slider "e" as shown. We wish to determine the forces at all the pairs or joints and the torque required to drive the mechanism. It is assumed that the weight forces are negligible. We choose this particular mechanism because the analysis becomes somewhat involved when we get to links "b" and "c." The acceleration image is shown in Fig. 14.6(b) and the free-body diagrams of the various links are shown in Fig. 14.6(c). Note that the line of action of the force $F_{b/c}$ is indicated as unknown. The reasons for this will be discussed when we get to that point in our analysis.

The analysis is started with link "e" and we find $F^h_{d/e}$ by a summation of horizontal forces as in the previous example. Then knowing $F^h_{e/d}$ the forces on link "d" can be found by means of a funicular and force polygon. Going now to link "c" we find that there are four unknowns, the magnitude and line of action of $F_{b/c}$ and the magnitude and direction of $F_{f/c}$, and since there are only three equations of equilibrium, these forces cannot be determined by considering link "c" only. We also find that link "b" contains four unknowns, but for the combination of links "b" and "c" we have only six unknowns and they can be analyzed in combination. If we examine the free-body of link "b" we see that $F_{a/b}$ causes no torque about the center of gravity and therefore $F_{c/b}$ must be of such a magnitude as to balance the forces and its line of action must be displaced from the center of gravity enough to balance the inertia torque. This force can then be resolved into a force passing through the pin joint P and a pure torque about P (the center of gravity) sufficient to balance the inertia torque. The equal but opposite force and torque on link "c" as shown in Fig. 14.6(d) make link "c" a free body with three unknowns and these can be determined with a funicular and force polygon. We can readily see that link "c" must apply a torque to

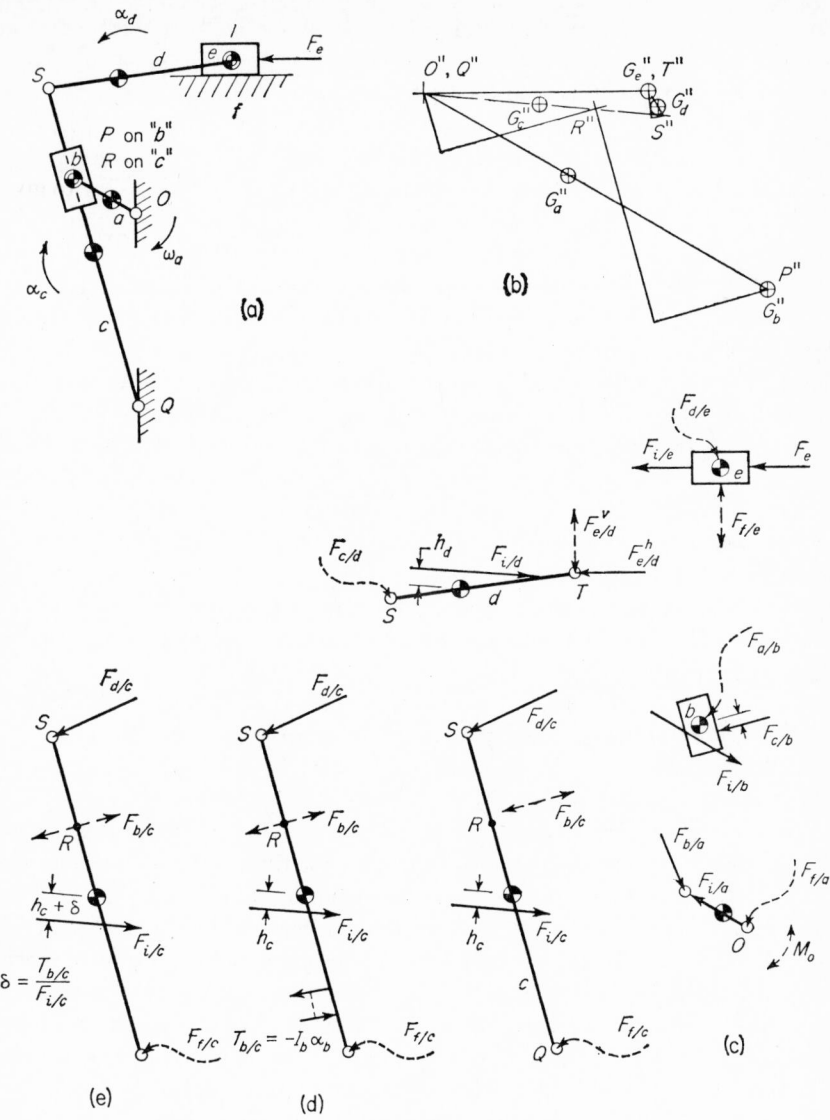

FIGURE 14.6

link "b" sufficient to give link "b" its angular acceleration since it is the only link that can apply a torque to link "b." In order to simplify the analysis of link "c" we could displace the inertia force $F_{i/c}$ enough to take care of the torque caused by link "b" as shown in Fig. 14.6(e) where the added distance is

$$\delta = \frac{T_{b/c}}{F'_{i/c}}$$

and it must be added or subtracted from h_c depending on the direction of the torque $T_{b/c}$. Knowing $F_{c/b}$ from the analysis of link "*b*" the force $F_{a/b}$ can be determined from a force polygon. The analysis of link "*a*" will be left to the student.

14.4 Dynamically Equivalent Systems

In dealing with various links of a mechanism we have seen that each link has certain properties which determine the accelerations of that link under the influence of a system of forces. These dynamic properties of the link or body are

1. The mass of the body
2. The location of the center of gravity
3. The mass moment of inertia

If two bodies have the same mass and moment of inertia, and same location of the center of gravity, they will have the same motion under the influence of a given system of external forces. Any two bodies which have the same mass, same moment of inertia, and same location of the C.G. are said to be dynamically equivalent. In our dynamic analyses of mechanisms we sometimes find it convenient to replace a link by a system of mass points which will simplify the analysis. The system must be dynamically equivalent to the link which it replaces and we call it a dynamically equivalent system.

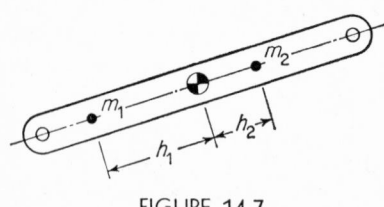

FIGURE 14.7

Consider the link which has a mass m and a moment of inertia I_G about the center of gravity, as shown in Fig. 14.7. We wish to determine a dynamically equivalent system; the simplest system will be one composed of two mass points. The system must be a rigid body, therefore we think of the two mass points as if they were connected by a massless rod. The two mass points, m_1 and m_2, are shown on the figure and their respective distances from the center of gravity of the link are h_1 and h_2. For the two mass points to be dynamically equivalent to the link the following equations must be satisfied

$$m_1 + m_2 = m$$
$$m_1 h_1 - m_2 h_2 = 0 \qquad\qquad (14.3)$$
$$m_1 h_1^2 + m_2 h_2^2 = I_G$$

The first equation states that the mass of the equivalent system must be equal to the mass of the link, the second states that the center of gravity of the system and the link must be at the same position and the third states that the moments of inertia of the two must be equal. The two mass point system will then be dynamically equivalent to the link for any possible combination of masses, m_1 and m_2, and distances, h_1 and h_2, so long as these three equations are satisfied. We have four quantities then which must satisfy three equations. Any one of the four quantities can be arbitrarily selected; the remaining three are fixed by, and can be determined from, the three Eqs. (14.3).

By replacing the link of a mechanism with a two-mass-point equivalent system the single inertia force and the position of its line of action relative to the center of gravity is replaced by two inertia forces acting on the two mass points. Then instead of determining the acceleration of the center of gravity we must determine the acceleration of the two mass points of the equivalent system and calculate the inertia forces corresponding to the two masses. It should be remembered that the two masses comprise the total mass of the equivalent system and they are connected by a massless rod which extends to join the equivalent system to the other links with the same pairs as the link it replaces. The equivalent system has some advantage in the analysis of a mechanism where the analysis must be made for various phase positions, since the positions of the masses of the equivalent system always remain the same relative to the link. The moment arm of the inertia force corresponding to the center of gravity will vary for various phase positions. We shall find that the equivalent system is quite useful in the discussion of balancing of the slider-crank mechanism in the next chapter.

In the slider crank mechanism shown in Fig. 14.8 we shall replace the connecting rod, link "b," with an equivalent system. Since we have a choice of one of the four quantities of the equivalent system we shall place one of the mass points, m_1, at the pin joint connecting the slider with the connecting rod. This will simplify our analysis since this mass can then be considered a part of the slider, having the same motion as the slider. We need then determine the acceleration of only the one point on the connecting rod corresponding to the mass m_2. Having chosen, then, the distance h_1, the masses m_1 and m_2 and the distance h_2 can be determined from Eqs. (14.3).

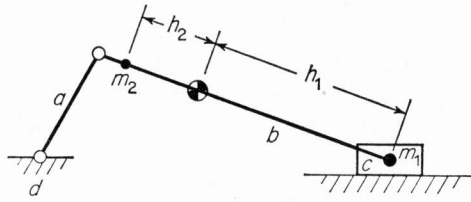

FIGURE 14.8

14.5 Determination of Moments of Inertia and Location of the Center of Gravity

The location of the center of gravity and the moment of inertia of all the links of a mechanism must be known before we can make a dynamic analysis of the mechanism. In this article we will discuss means of determining the location of the center of gravity and the mass moment of inertia of a link.

For bodies or links with simple geometric shapes such as rods of uniform cross section, the center of gravity and the mass moment of inertia can be determined quite accurately from the equations developed in Chapter 12. The location of the center of gravity is determined by Eqs. (12.4) which, in integral form, are

$$x_G = \frac{\int x\,dm}{m}$$

$$y_G = \frac{\int y\,dm}{m}$$

where x_G and y_G are the x and y distances from an arbitrary origin to the center of gravity. The mass moment of inertia about any axis can be determined from Eq. (12.27). Ordinarily the moment of inertia is desired about the center of gravity and we can then use the center of gravity as the axis about which the moment of inertia is determined. If it is more convenient to determine the moment of inertia about some other axis, we can use the parallel axis theorem, Eq. (12.29), to determine the moment of inertia about the center of gravity.

These equations are satisfactory for the determination of moments of inertia and location of centers of gravity for bodies having symmetry about two axes in the plane of motion. By observation we can see that the center of gravity of such bodies lies at the intersection of the axes of symmetry, and formulas can be found in handbooks for the calculation of the moments of inertia. Many machine elements or links such as sliders, flywheels, and gears fall in this category. However there are many machine elements which do not lend themselves to mathematical methods and we find that an experimental method is advisable. Two experimental methods of determining the moment of inertia will be discussed.

In the determination of the moment of inertia of a body experimentally the location of the center of gravity must be known. For most bodies the center of gravity can be readily located experimentally by suspending the body at some point so that it is free to rotate about the point of suspension and drawing a vertical line on the body through the point of suspension, then suspending the body at a different point and again drawing a vertical line through that point of suspension. The intersection of these two lines will usually locate, on the body, the center of gravity. It should be noted that for some odd-shaped bodies the lines so drawn may not intersect at a point on the physical body. However, the intersection of the lines drawn *on* the body will always locate the center of gravity and, remembering that kinematically all bodies extend indefinitely in all directions, the center of gravity is a point on the body. Since the gravity forces can be considered as acting through the center of gravity and the body is in equilibrium, the center of gravity must lie on a vertical line through the support. An even simpler and more accurate method of locating the center of gravity is supporting the link on two sets of scales as shown in Fig. 14.9. The sum of the reactions on the scales gives us the weight of the link. Knowing that the distributed weight of the link has a resultant equal to the total weight acting through the center of gravity, the summation of moments about either

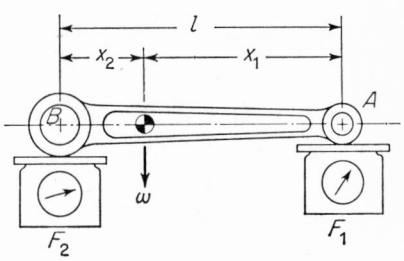

FIGURE 14.9

point of contact with the balances will locate the center of gravity between these two points. For example, taking moments about point A

$$wx_1 = F_2l$$

and
$$x_1 = \frac{F_2l}{F_1 + F_2}$$

Consider now a link of a mechanism, such as the connecting rod shown in Fig. 14.10, supported on a knife-edge at O. The center of gravity is a distance h_G from the point of support. Now if the rod is displaced a small angle θ and released it will oscillate as a pendulum about the support. By noting the time required for a given number of oscillations we can determine the moment of inertia about the support. The equation of motion by Newton's second law is

$$T_O = I_O\alpha \qquad (14.4)$$

and for the case shown the external torque is

$$T_O = -wh_G \sin \theta$$

The negative sign indicates that the torque is opposite in direction to the displacement θ. If the angle θ is small, the sine of the angle is approximately equal to the angle in radians and the torque becomes

$$T_O = -wh_G\theta \qquad (14.5)$$

The differential equation of motion can then be written

$$\frac{d^2\theta}{dt^2} + \frac{wh_G}{I_O}\theta = 0 \qquad (14.6)$$

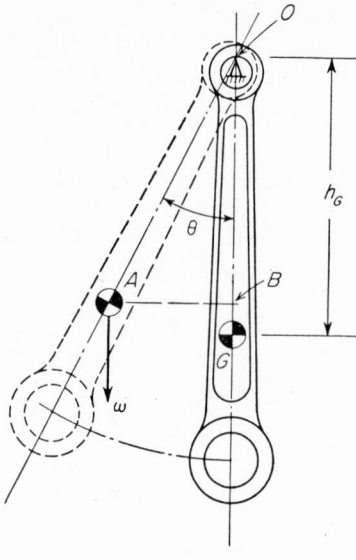

FIGURE 14.10

This is a linear differential equation of second order and the general solution to the equation is

$$\theta = A \cos \sqrt{\frac{wh_G}{I_O}}\, t + B \sin \sqrt{\frac{wh_G}{I_O}}\, t \qquad (14.7)$$

where A and B are constants of integration and must be determined from the initial conditions. Assuming that the rod is displaced from the vertical position by an angle θ_O and released with zero velocity, the constants are found to be

$$A = \theta_O$$
$$B = 0$$

and the solution becomes

$$\theta = \theta_O \cos \sqrt{\frac{wh_G}{I_O}}\, t \qquad (14.8)$$

In order to get a better idea of what this last equation means let us rewrite Eq. (14.4), using Eq. (14.5), in the form

$$\alpha = -\left(\frac{wh_G}{I_O}\right)\theta$$

From our discussion of simple harmonic motion in Chapter 1 we recognize this as the equation of simple harmonic motion for angular motion. This motion can then be represented by the projection of a rotating vector of length θ_O rotating at an angular velocity equal to the square root of the proportionality constant which in this case is $\dfrac{wh_G}{I_O}$. Then at any time t, the angular displacement is given by the equation

$$\theta = \theta_0 \cos \sqrt{\frac{wh_G}{I_O}} \, t = \theta_0 \cos \omega t$$

which is the same as the solution to the differential equation of motion. Then the number of complete oscillations per second, the frequency, is

$$f = \frac{\omega}{2\pi} \tag{14.9}$$

The period or time required for one cycle is

$$T = \frac{1}{f} = 2\pi \sqrt{\frac{I_O}{wh_G}} \tag{14.10}$$

The error in the period caused by taking $\sin \theta = \theta$ in Eq. (14.5) is less than 0.2 per cent for $\theta_0 = 10°$ which is certainly negligible for engineering calculations. Now solving for the moment of inertia

$$I_O = \left(\frac{T}{2\pi}\right)^2 wh_G \tag{14.11}$$

Using the parallel-axis theorem, Eq. (12.29), we find that the moment of inertia about the center of gravity is

$$I_G = I_O - \frac{w}{g} \, h_g^2$$

$$= wh_G \left[\left(\frac{T}{2\pi}\right)^2 - \frac{h_G}{g} \right] \tag{14.12}$$

This equation can be used to determine the moment of inertia of a body about the center of gravity if the period of oscillation about some point and the distance from the point to the center of gravity is known. The period can be determined quite accurately by suspending the body from a knife-edge as shown in the figure and noting the average frequency from a large number of oscillations.

Accuracy in the determination of the moment of inertia is dependent on accuracy in determining T and h_G. Note that the term in the brackets is the difference between two quantities. If these two quantities are of the same order of magnitude a small error in either quantity will cause a large error in the moment of inertia. In order to keep this error small it is desirable to make T large and h_G small. This can be done by suspending the body so that the center of gravity is close to the knife-edge; for the body shown in Fig. 14.10, higher accuracy would be obtained by suspending the crank from the end opposite that shown in the figure.

For odd-shaped links which cannot be readily suspended from a knife-edge, the moment of inertia can be determined by suspending the link on a light weight pendulum as shown in Fig. 14.11. The pendulum is a platform suspended by knife-edges along the axis O–O and the link is set on the platform so that the center of gravity is directly below the axis of sus-

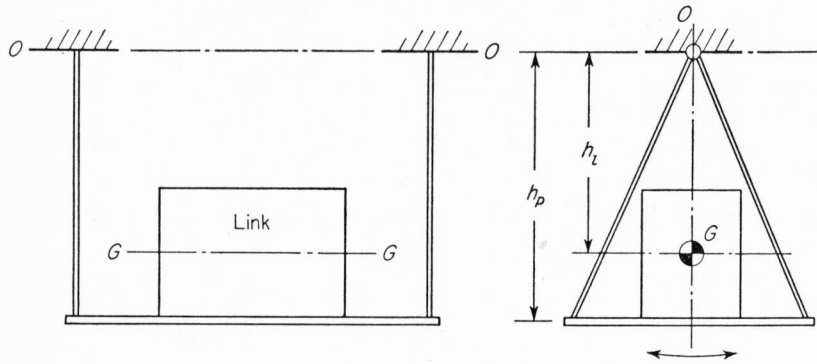

FIGURE 14.11

pension, and the axis about which the moment of inertia is desired, G–G, is parallel to the axis O–O. For this case we must determine the period of the platform with the link on it and also the period of the platform alone. The equation for the moment of inertia of the link about the center of gravity can be developed as follows. Equation 14.10 gives the period of the platform with the link on it, where I_O is the sum of the moments of inertia of the platform and link both about the O–O axis, w is the total weight of the platform and link, and h_G is the distance from O–O to the C.G. of the combination. From the figure and Eqs. (12.4)

$$h_g = \frac{w_l h_l + w_p h_p}{w_l + w_p}$$

Then Eq. (14.10) becomes, for this case,

$$\frac{T}{2\pi} = \sqrt{\frac{I_l + I_p}{w_l h_l + w_p h_p}}$$

Solving for I_l (about the O–O axis), using Eq. (14.11) for I_p, and using the parallel axis theorem, we find that the moment of inertia of the link about its C.G. is

$$I_G = w_l h_l \left[\left(\frac{T}{2\pi} \right)^2 - \frac{h_l}{g} \right] + \frac{w_p h_p}{4\pi^2} (T^2 - T_p^2) \qquad (14.13)$$

where I_G = moment of inertia of link about its center of gravity

   w_l = weight of link

h_l = distance from axis of rotation to center of gravity of link

T = period of platform with link on it

w_p = weight of platform

h_p = distance from center of rotation to center of gravity of platform

T_p = period of platform alone

In this case also the length h_l should be small for good accuracy and the weight of the platform should be small so that its period is small in relation to the period of the platform and link.

Since the mass moment of inertia has the units of mass times a distance squared, it is quite convenient to define the mass moment of inertia of a body as

$$I_G = mk_G^2 \tag{14.14}$$

where m is the total mass of the body and k_G has the units of length and is called the radius of gyration of the body about the center of gravity. Then k is the root mean square of the radii of all the mass points comprising the body. The use of the radius of gyration in defining the moment of inertia gives a better means of visualizing the moment of inertia of a body. If the body were replaced by a thin circular ring having the mass of the body and of radius k_G about the center of gravity, the moment of inertia of the ring would be the same as the original body relative to the center of gravity. We could also define the moment of inertia of a body about any point, with a radius of gyration about that point, with a similar equation.

14.6 Center of Percussion

Another concept which is quite useful in the design of machine members is the idea of center of percussion. We will develop the idea of center of percussion by means of simple and compound pendulums. A simple pendulum is defined as a pendulum composed of a mass point suspended from some point by a massless rod as shown in Fig. 14.12(a). All other pendulums are called compound pendulums. The period of the simple pendulum is

$$T = 2\pi \sqrt{\frac{I_O}{wl}} = 2\pi \sqrt{\frac{\bar{l}}{g}} \tag{14.15}$$

and we note that the period is a function only of the length l. If we take a compound pendulum, as the connecting rod in Fig. 14.12(b), we can find the length of a simple pendulum which will have the same period, and we say

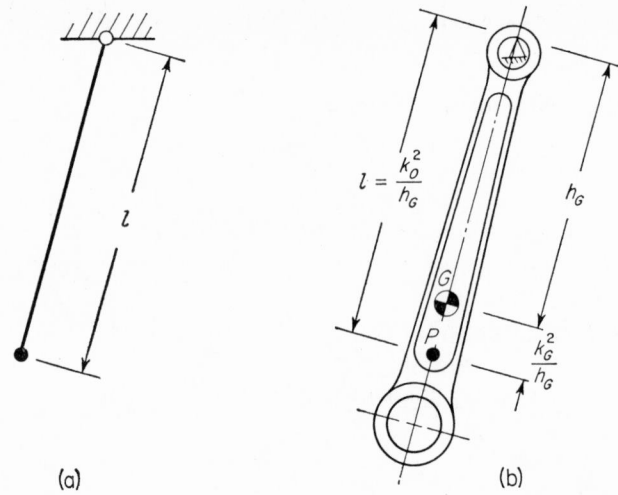

(a)   (b)

FIGURE 14.12

that the simple pendulum is equivalent to the compound pendulum. Writing the period of the compound pendulum in terms of the radius of gyration about point O, the support, and setting it equal to the period of the equivalent simple pendulum we find

$$2\pi \sqrt{\frac{\bar{l}}{g}} = 2\pi \sqrt{\frac{mk_O^2}{wh_G}} = 2\pi \sqrt{\frac{k_O^2}{gh_G}}$$

or
$$l = \frac{k_O^2}{h_G} \qquad (14.16)$$

Then the equivalent simple pendulum would be a mass point at P on the compound pendulum, as shown in the figure, oscillating about O. The point P is called the center of percussion of the compound pendulum relative to point O. Note that we cannot speak of the center of percussion of a link but must always refer it to some other point on the link. If the connecting rod were supported at some other point, the center of percussion would be at some point other than P.

By using the parallel-axis theorem in terms of the radius of gyration we can determine the distance from the center of gravity to the center of percussion. The parallel axis theorem in these terms is

$$mk_O^2 = mk_G^2 + mh_G^2$$

or
$$k_O^2 = k_G^2 + h_G^2 \qquad (14.17)$$

Substituting this into Eq. (14.16)

$$l = \frac{k_G^2}{h_G} + h_G$$

and we see that the distance from the center of gravity to the center of percussion is k_G^2/h_G.

If a body rotates about a fixed axis the resultant of the inertia force and the inertia moment will always pass through the center of percussion about the axis of rotation. In order to show this consider a link rotating about a fixed point O as shown in Fig. 14.13. The inertia force passing through the center of gravity is resolved into the two normal components corresponding to the normal and tangential acceleration as shown in the figure. The resultant inertia force will be a distance h from the center of gravity and will also pass through some point P on the line through the center of gravity and the axis of rotation. The distance h is given by Eq. (14.2) as

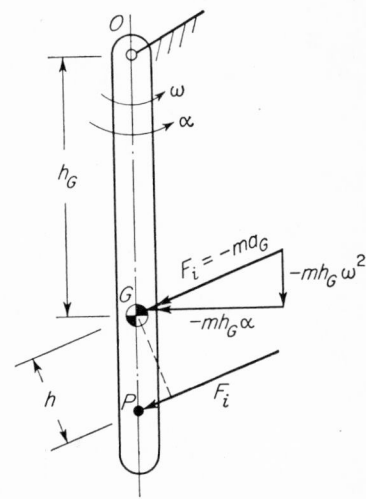

FIGURE 14.13

$$h = \frac{I\alpha}{F_i} = \frac{mk_G^2\alpha}{ma_G} = \frac{k_G^2\alpha}{a_G}$$

By similar triangles

$$\frac{G\text{–}P}{ma_G} = \frac{h}{mh_G\alpha}$$

and by substituting the above equation for h, the distance $G\text{–}P$ becomes

$$G\text{–}P = \frac{k_G^2}{h_G} \qquad\qquad (14.18)$$

and we see that this is the position of the center of percussion about the axis of rotation. From Eq. (14.18) we see also that the point O, the center of rotation, has become the center of percussion about the point P as an axis by reversing the positions of the distances $G\text{–}P$ and h_G in the equation.

If an external force is suddenly applied through the center of percussion normal to the line $O\text{–}G$, it will be exactly balanced by the equivalent inertia force and therefore no force will be exerted at the axis of rotation. This can be shown by applying a sudden force to a bar, as shown in Fig. 14.14, a distance b from the center of gravity. The force will cause a linear acceleration of all points on the bar of magnitude F/m, the same as if the force were applied at the center of gravity, and an angular acceleration to the bar of magnitude Fb/mk_G^2. The total linear acceleration of any point is the sum of

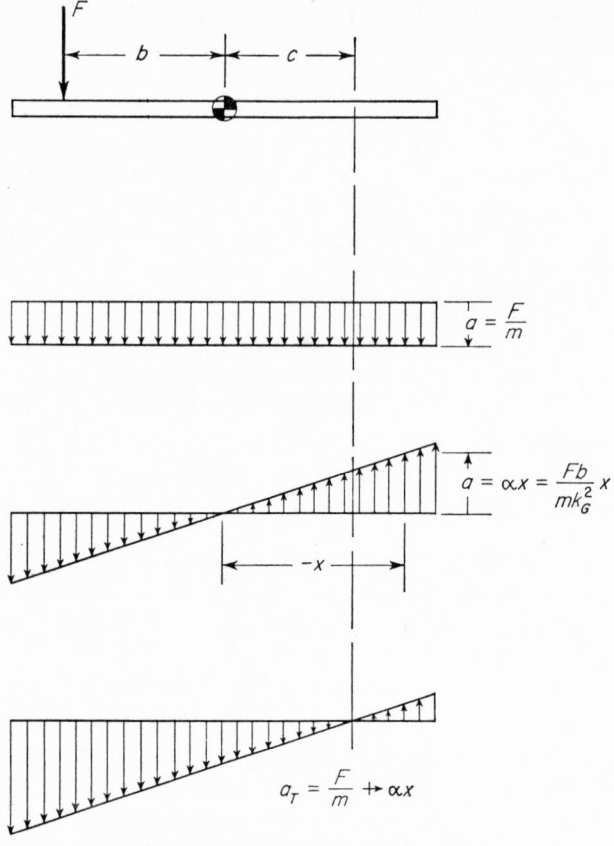

FIGURE 14.14

the two accelerations and the linear acceleration of any point caused by the angular acceleration is αx where x is the distance from the point to the center of gravity. At some point these two accelerations will be equal and opposite so that that point has zero acceleration. Letting the point of zero acceleration be a distance c from the center of gravity, we can find the distance c by setting the two accelerations equal

$$\frac{F}{m} = \frac{Fbc}{mk_G^2}$$

so that

$$b = \frac{k_G}{c}$$

and we see that the point at a distance c from the center of gravity has zero acceleration and if the body were forced to pivot about that point there would be no force at the pivot. Then for any force applied through the center of percussion of a body rotating about a fixed axis, the only force at the axis will be a force along the line joining the axis and the center of gravity equal to the component of the external force in that direction.

When we replace a link with a two mass point equivalent system, either mass point is at the center of percussion relative to the other mass point. This should be obvious since we can make a simple pendulum of the equivalent system by supporting it at one of the mass points and then the other mass point will be at the center of percussion about the support. It can be proved by substituting mk_G^2 for I_G in Eqs. (14.3) and eliminating the terms m_1, m_2, and m. In this way we find that

$$h_1 h_2 = k_G^2$$

which agrees with Eq. (14.18) for the location of the center of percussion.

We will make use of the center of percussion later in the discussion of balancing machines.

14.7 Dynamic Analysis in Design

In the discussion of dynamic analysis we have assumed that the mass, or weight, of the various links was known and that the position of the center of gravity and the mass moment of inertia of the links was known. This means that the size, shape, and material of each link must be known before we can make a complete dynamic analysis; these depend on the forces acting on the various members. We are then faced with the problem of which comes first, the design or the analysis. The general procedure is to assume a size and general shape for the various links, after the kinematic analysis has been completed, based on experience and common judgement. From this an estimate of the mass and location of the center of gravity can be made and then the mass moment of inertia can be estimated making use of the radius of gyration concept. One of the advantages of defining the moment of inertia in terms of radius of gyration is that we can usually estimate the radius of gyration fairly well from the dimensions of a body. These rough estimates are then satisfactory for making a first rough dynamic analysis of the mechanism. The forces found from this rough analysis then can form a basis for a more detailed design of the various links, after which a detailed dynamic analysis can be made. This process can then be repeated until a satisfactory design is completed. Usually one or two detailed analyses are sufficient for a satisfactory design.

In our analyses we have always taken the inertia forces as if they acted at a point on the various links. It should be noted that actually these inertia forces are distributed along the link and are not concentrated at one point. This fact is of no importance so long as we are concerned only with the forces at points where the various links are paired with other links. For any given link these forces are external forces on the link and the analyses as discussed give us the correct values of these external forces. However, if we are concerned with the internal forces in the individual links, which determine the stresses in the link, the distribution of the inertia forces along the link can be important.

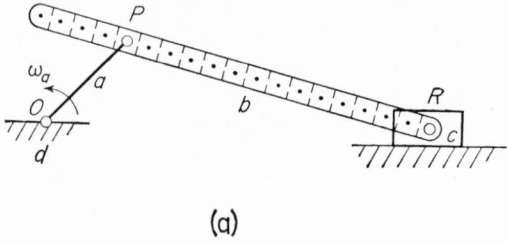

(a)

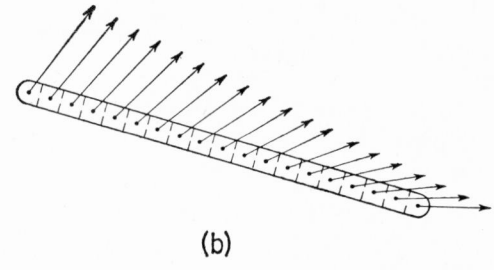

(b)

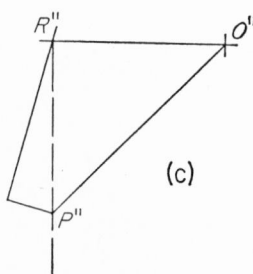

(c)

FIGURE 14.15

In most cases the stresses can be determined to engineering accuracy by replacing the distributed inertia forces with their resultant acting along the line of action of the resultant. This is the effective inertia force that we have found in the previous analyses acting at some distance h from the center of gravity. In cases where the distributed load must be used in determining stresses, the distributed load can be satisfactorily approximated by breaking the links into small elements and determining the inertia forces of each element. This will be demonstrated by an example.

For the slider-crank mechanism shown in Fig. 14.15(a) the connecting rod is shown as a uniform cross section bar for simplicity and is extended beyond the pin joint with the crank. The bar is broken up into equal length sections as shown and the inertia force for each section is determined from the mass of the section and the acceleration of the midpoint of the section. Figure 14.15(b) shows these inertia forces corresponding to the acceleration image in Fig. 14.15(c). This represents the distribution of the inertia forces along the bar. The stresses in the bar can now be determined since the bar is in equilibrium under the action of these distributed inertia forces and the forces exerted on the bar by links "a" and "c." In order to determine the stresses the various forces acting should be resolved into components along the bar and perpendicular to the bar. The forces along the bar cause pure normal stresses and the forces normal to the bar cause bending stresses. It should be noted that the normal stresses vary along the bar because of the inertia forces.

In cases where the links are not of uniform cross section, the bar should be broken into equal length sections but in these cases the masses of the various sections will not be equal. The accuracy of this approximation depends upon the number of sections that the link is broken into, the more sections the greater the accuracy. For engineering work, however, the sections need not be too large in number.

PROBLEMS

14.1 Make a complete dynamic force analysis of the mechanism shown in Fig. P14.1 for a constant angular velocity of link "a" of 180 rpm clockwise. An additional mass is attached to the shaft at Q, which has the same angular motion as link "c," whose C.G. is on the shaft and whose mass moment of inertia is 0.020 lb-in.-sec^2. Determine the forces on all joints and the torque which must be applied to link "a" to cause the given motion. Do not include the gravity forces in the analysis.

14.2 Make a combined static and dynamic force analysis of the mechanism shown in Fig. P14.2. An external force of 50 lbs is applied upward on link "e." Link "a" is turning at a constant speed of 100 rpm clockwise. Determine the forces acting between all links and the torque required on link "a" to cause the given motion.

14.3 Make a dynamic force analysis of the mechanism shown in Fig. P14.3 including the gravity forces on the links. Link "a" is turning at a constant speed of 100 rpm counter clockwise. Determine the torque on link "a" necessary to cause the given motion and the forces acting between all links.

14.4 Make a combined static and dynamic force analysis of the mechanism shown in Fig. P14.4, including the gravity forces on the links. Link "d" has an external force of 40 lbs to the left acting on it, and a velocity of 200 in./sec to the right and an acceleration of 100 in./sec^2 to the left. Determine the external torque acting on link "a" to cause the given motion, and the forces acting between all links.

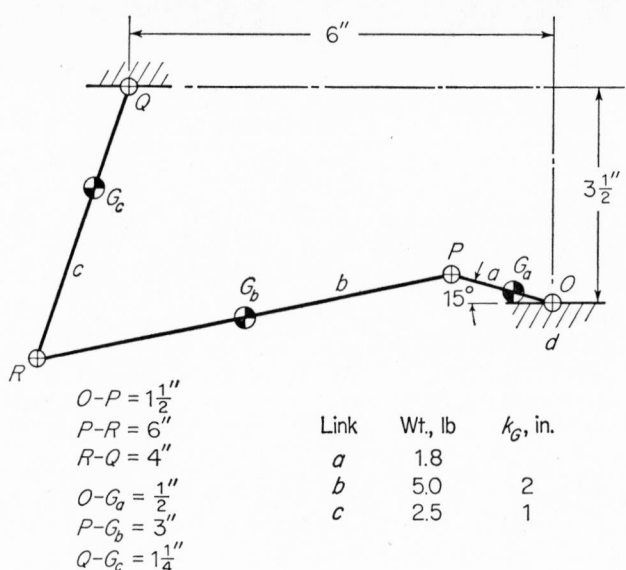

$O\text{-}P = 1\frac{1}{2}''$
$P\text{-}R = 6''$
$R\text{-}Q = 4''$
$O\text{-}G_a = \frac{1}{2}''$
$P\text{-}G_b = 3''$
$Q\text{-}G_c = 1\frac{1}{4}''$

Link	Wt., lb	k_G, in.
a	1.8	
b	5.0	2
c	2.5	1

FIGURE P14.1

$O\text{-}P = 3''$
$P\text{-}R = 9''$
$R\text{-}S = 7\frac{1}{2}''$
$R\text{-}T = 12''$
$O\text{-}G_a = 1\frac{1}{4}''$
$P\text{-}G_b = 4\frac{1}{8}''$
$S\text{-}G_c = 3''$
$R\text{-}G_d = 5\frac{1}{4}''$

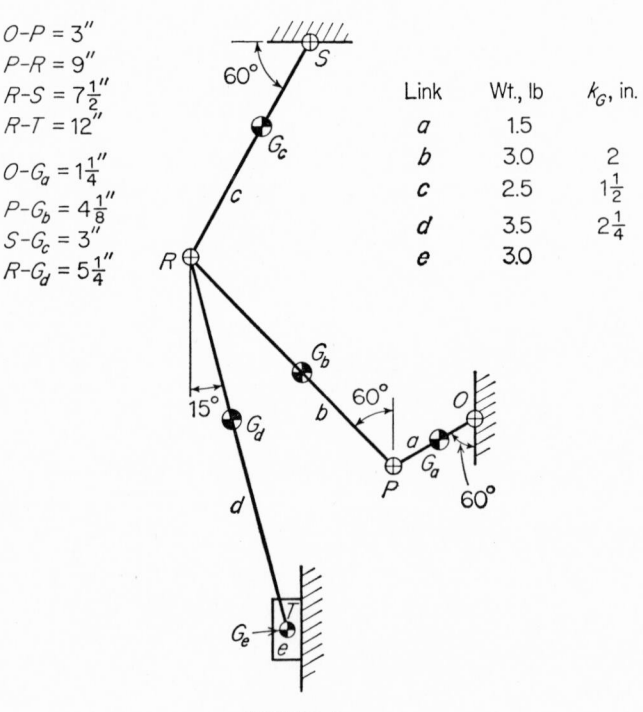

Link	Wt., lb	k_G, in.
a	1.5	
b	3.0	2
c	2.5	$1\frac{1}{2}$
d	3.5	$2\frac{1}{4}$
e	3.0	

FIGURE P14.2

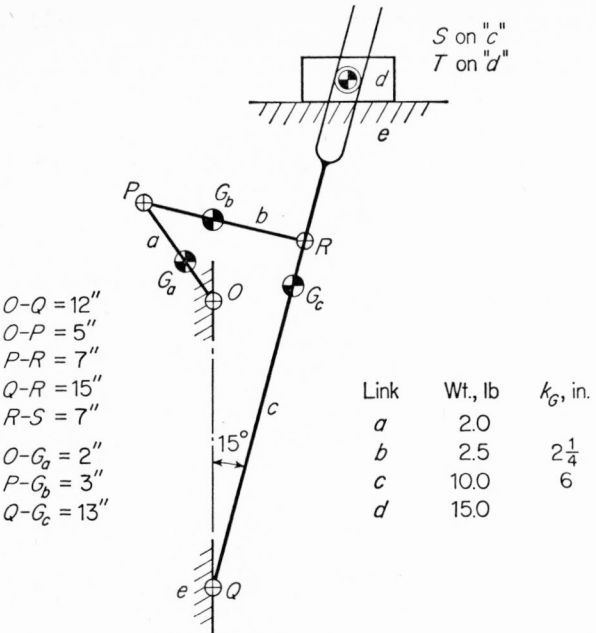

$O-Q = 12''$
$O-P = 5''$
$P-R = 7''$
$Q-R = 15''$
$R-S = 7''$

$O-G_a = 2''$
$P-G_b = 3''$
$Q-G_c = 13''$

Link	Wt., lb	k_G, in.
a	2.0	
b	2.5	$2\frac{1}{4}$
c	10.0	6
d	15.0	

FIGURE P14.3

$O-Q = 8''$
$Q-R = 12''$
$R-S = 8''$

$O-G_a = 3''$
$Q-G_c = 10''$

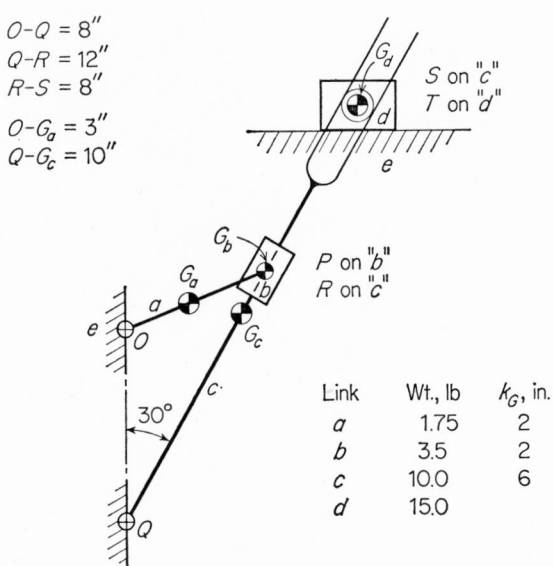

Link	Wt., lb	k_G, in.
a	1.75	2
b	3.5	2
c	10.0	6
d	15.0	

FIGURE P14.4

14.5 Make a combined static and dynamic force analysis of the mechanism shown in Fig. P14.5 including the gravity forces of the links. Link "e" has an external force of 50 lbs acting horizontally to the left. Link "a" is rotating at a constant speed of 2500 rpm clockwise. Determine the external torque on link "a" necessary to give the prescribed motion and the forces acting between all links.

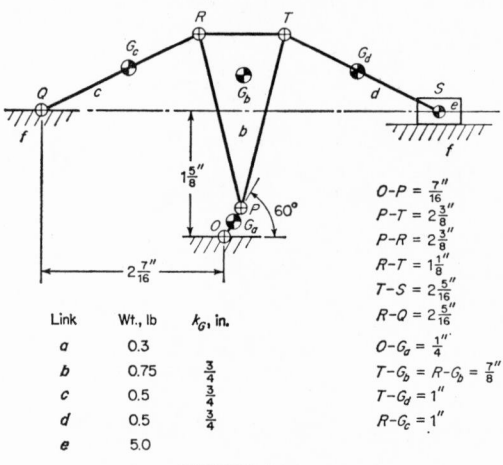

$$O\text{-}P = \frac{7}{16}''$$
$$P\text{-}T = 2\frac{3}{8}''$$
$$P\text{-}R = 2\frac{3}{8}''$$
$$R\text{-}T = 1\frac{1}{8}''$$
$$T\text{-}S = 2\frac{5}{16}''$$
$$R\text{-}Q = 2\frac{5}{16}''$$
$$O\text{-}G_a = \frac{1}{4}''$$
$$T\text{-}G_b = R\text{-}G_b = \frac{7}{8}''$$
$$T\text{-}G_d = 1''$$
$$R\text{-}G_c = 1''$$

Link	Wt., lb	k_G, in.
a	0.3	
b	0.75	$\frac{3}{4}$
c	0.5	$\frac{3}{4}$
d	0.5	$\frac{3}{4}$
e	5.0	

FIGURE P14.5

14.6 Make a dynamic analysis of the mechanism shown in Fig. P14.6 neglecting the gravity forces on the links. Link "a" is turning at a constant speed of 2000 rpm counter clockwise. Links "c" and "d" represent a 20° involute gear and rack. Determine the external torque on link "a" necessary to cause the given motion and the forces acting between all links.

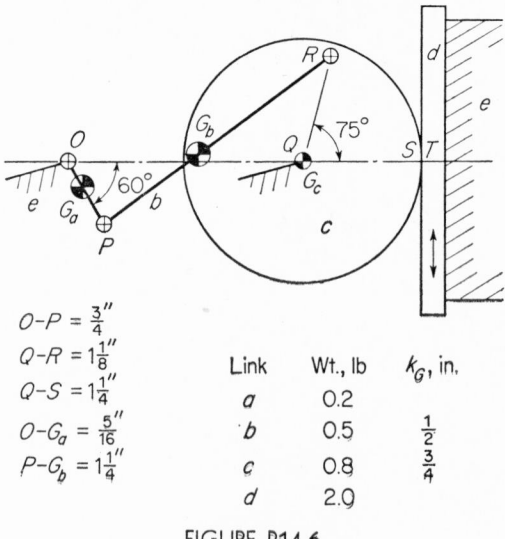

$$O\text{-}P = \frac{3}{4}''$$
$$Q\text{-}R = 1\frac{1}{8}''$$
$$Q\text{-}S = 1\frac{1}{4}''$$
$$O\text{-}G_a = \frac{5}{16}''$$
$$P\text{-}G_b = 1\frac{1}{4}''$$

Link	Wt., lb	k_G, in.
a	0.2	
b	0.5	$\frac{1}{2}$
c	0.8	$\frac{3}{4}$
d	2.0	

FIGURE P14.6

14.7 Make a dynamic analysis of the mechanism shown in Fig. P14.7 neglecting the gravity forces on the links. Link "*a*" is turning at a constant speed of 1000 rpm clockwise. Links "*c*" and "*d*" are 20° involute gears and gear "*d*" has attached to it an additional mass with C.G. at the center of rotation and mass moment of inertia of 0.060 lb-in.-sec². Determine the torque required on link "*a*" to cause the given motion and the forces acting between all links.

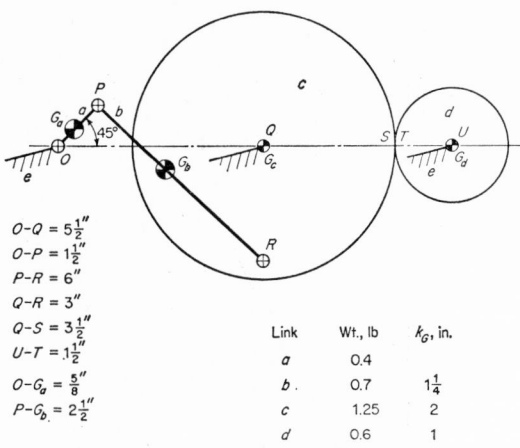

$O\text{-}Q = 5\frac{1}{2}''$
$O\text{-}P = 1\frac{1}{2}''$
$P\text{-}R = 6''$
$Q\text{-}R = 3''$
$Q\text{-}S = 3\frac{1}{2}''$
$U\text{-}T = 1\frac{1}{2}''$
$O\text{-}G_a = \frac{5}{8}''$
$P\text{-}G_b = 2\frac{1}{2}''$

Link	Wt., lb	k_G, in.
a	0.4	
b	0.7	$1\frac{1}{4}$
c	1.25	2
d	0.6	1

FIGURE P14.7

14.8 Make a dynamic analysis of the mechanism shown in Fig. P14.8 neglecting the gravity forces on the links. Link "*a*" is rotating at a constant speed of 300 rpm clockwise. Determine the horizontal force on link "*e*" necessary to cause the given motion and the forces acting between all links.

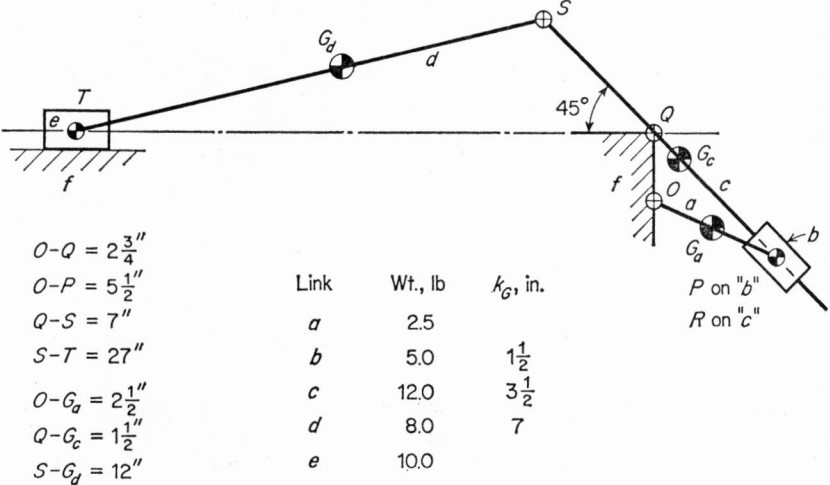

$O\text{-}Q = 2\frac{3}{4}''$
$O\text{-}P = 5\frac{1}{2}''$
$Q\text{-}S = 7''$
$S\text{-}T = 27''$
$O\text{-}G_a = 2\frac{1}{2}''$
$Q\text{-}G_c = 1\frac{1}{2}''$
$S\text{-}G_d = 12''$

Link	Wt., lb	k_G, in.
a	2.5	
b	5.0	$1\frac{1}{2}$
c	12.0	$3\frac{1}{2}$
d	8.0	7
e	10.0	

P on "*b*"
R on "*c*"

FIGURE P14.8

14.9 Make a dynamic force analysis of the mechanism shown in Fig. P14.9 neglecting the gravity forces. Link "a" is rotating at a constant speed of 1500 rpm counter clockwise. Determine the torque on link "a" necessary to cause the given motion and the forces acting between all links.

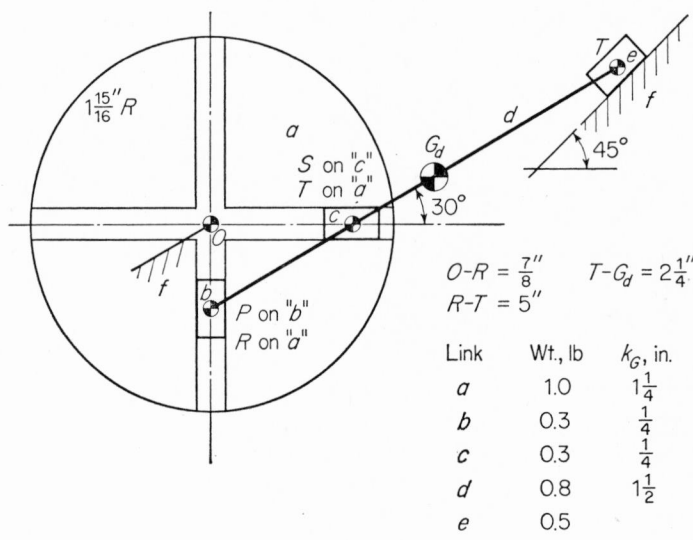

FIGURE P14.9

14.10 Repeat Problem 14.9 for link "a" rotating at 1500 rpm counter clockwise and an angular acceleration of 1000 rad/sec² clockwise.

14.11 Make a dynamic analysis of the mechanism shown in Fig. P14.10 neglecting the gravity forces. Link "a" is rotating at a constant speed of 600 rpm clockwise. Link "e" has attached to it a mass whose C.G. is at Q and whose mass moment of inertia is 0.10 lb-in.-sec². Determine the torque on link "a" necessary to cause the given motion, and the forces acting between all links.

14.12 (a) For the Geneva mechanism shown in Fig. 7.6(a), distance O–P is $2\frac{1}{4}$ in., link "a" is rotating at a constant speed of 250 rpm clockwise, and link "b" weighs 3 lbs and its radius of gyration is 1.2 in. Plot a curve of the normal force between the pin and slot as a function of the angular position of link "a." Plot the curve for 90° of motion of link "b" from the time the pin first comes into contact with the slot.

(b) Plot curves of the torques on links "a" and "b" as a function of the angular position of link "a."

14.13 In order to determine the moment of inertia of a small flywheel it was suspended in a vertical plane as a compound pendulum. The distance from C.G. to the knife-edge support is 10 in. and the flywheel made 100 oscillations in 134.4 sec. Determine the mass moment of inertia about an axis through the C.G. if the flywheel weighs 100 lbs.

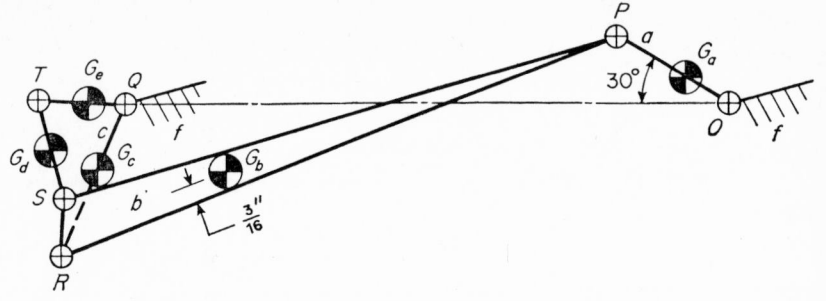

$O-P = 1\frac{9}{16}''$ $O-G_a = \frac{9}{16}''$

$P-R = 7\frac{3}{16}''$ $P-G_b = 4\frac{7}{8}''$

$R-S = \frac{23}{32}''$ $R-G_c = 1\frac{1}{8}''$

$P-S = 6\frac{7}{8}''$ $S-G_d = \frac{19}{32}''$

$Q-R = 1\frac{15}{16}''$ $T-G_e = \frac{19}{32}''$

$S-T = 1\frac{7}{32}''$

$Q-T = \frac{31}{32}''$

Link	Wt., lb	k_G, in.
a	0.3	
b	1.2	$1\frac{1}{4}$
c	0.3	$\frac{1}{2}$
d	0.15	$\frac{3}{8}$
e	0.15	$\frac{3}{8}$

FIGURE P14.10

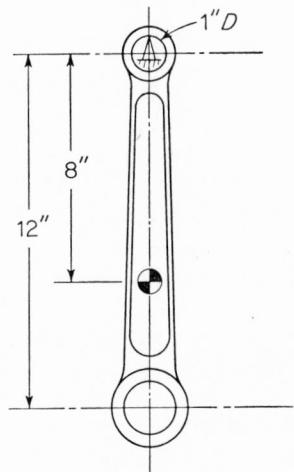

FIGURE P14.11

14.14 (a) The connecting rod shown in Fig. P14.11 was suspended on a knife-edge as shown and allowed to oscillate through a small angle. It completed 200 cycles in 114 sec. Determine the moment of inertia of the connecting rod.

(b) Find W_1, W_2, and h_2 of the two mass equivalent systems for the above connecting rod if W_1 is located at the center of the upper bearing.

(c) Locate the center of percussion of the above connecting rod about the center of the upper bearing.

Chapter 15

Balancing of Reciprocating
Mechanisms

15.1 Introduction

In the last chapter we found that the inertia forces in a mechanism cause shaking forces on the foundation or support. It was pointed out that these shaking forces are generally undesirable and, since in most cases they serve no useful purpose, it is desirable that they be eliminated or reduced to small values. When the shaking forces in a mechanism are zero we say that the machine is balanced, indicating that the inertia forces for all the moving parts of a mechanism are balanced or that their resultant is zero. In a perfectly balanced machine the center of gravity of all the moving parts, as they are taken as a system, remains fixed in space. This is sufficient to assure that there are no shaking *forces* but does not mean that a shaking couple would not exist.

Balancing is of two classifications: balancing of reciprocating mechanisms, and balancing of members having pure rotation. We will cover reciprocating mechanisms in this chapter and consider rotating mechanisms in the next.

15.2 Balancing the Quadric Crank Mechanism

We will begin our discussion of balancing with a consideration of the quadric crank mechanism. We will find that the dynamic forces in a quadric crank mechanism are readily balanced whereas the dynamic couple is quite difficult, if not impossible, to balance. Consider the mechanism shown in Fig. 15.1(a) where the crank, link "a," is rotating at a constant angular velocity and link "c" oscillates between positions θ_1 and θ_2. These links have pure rotation about the fixed link while the connecting rod,

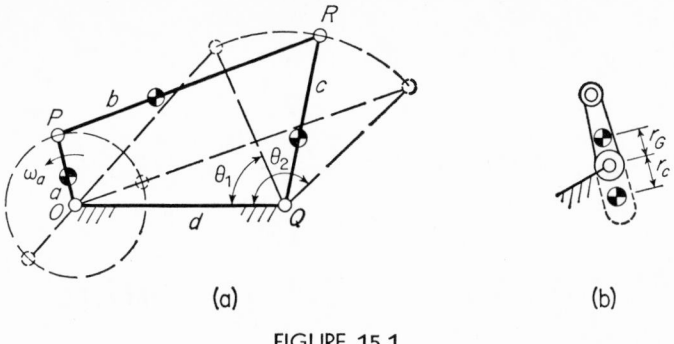

FIGURE 15.1

link "b," has a complicated motion consisting of a rotation and translation which vary with the time or crank position.

If we now look at the crank alone we see that the only inertia force is a centrifugal force of magnitude $m\omega^2 r$ and direction from O towards the center of gravity, where m is the mass of the crank and r is the distance from the pin joint O to the center of gravity. If now we extend the crank beyond the pin O as shown in Fig. 15.1(b) so that the distance of the center of gravity of the extension when multiplied by the mass of the extension is equal to mr, this extension will cause an inertia force exactly equal to the inertia force of the crank but with opposite sense, balancing thereby the inertia forces. Such an extension is called a counterbalance. This counterbalance has the effect of placing the center of gravity of the crank and counterbalance, as a single link, at the center of rotation. Since the center of gravity has no motion, there is no inertia force. For the center of gravity to be at the center of rotation the following relation must hold

$$r_G m_G = r_C m_C$$

and we see that we could use a large mass at a small radius or a small mass at a large radius to balance the crank, so long as the above equation holds. Since we will be dealing primarily with mass points in our discussion of balancing, we will usually think of counterbalances as concentrated masses at some distance from the center of rotation. We could replace the mass of the crank alone with another mass at some distance from the center of rotation, for the purposes of balancing, so long as the mass multiplied by the distance is the same as given by the above equation.

Link "c," since it is rotating about point Q, can be counterbalanced in the same manner. Turning now to link "b" we find that its motion is not pure rotation about some fixed axis and therefore it cannot be balanced by a single counterbalance. We will replace the connecting rod, or link "b," with a two-mass equivalent system in order to balance the inertia forces acting on it. We recall that we must satisfy the three Eqs. (14.3) to have an equivalent system, of which the first makes the masses equal and the second places the center of gravity of the original and equivalent system at the same position. The third equation makes the moment of inertia of the two systems equivalent, and since at the present we are concerned only with forces, the third equation, having to do with moments of inertia, does not have to be satisfied in order that the inertia forces will be the same for the two systems. These two equations which affect the inertia forces contain four unknowns of which we can assign values for two arbitrarily and use the equations to determine the other two. Thus if we replace the connecting rod with an equivalent system with one mass point at P and the other at R, the systems are equivalent so far as forces are concerned as long as we make the two masses such as to satisfy the first two Eqs. (14.3). The two mass points of the equivalent system remain at a given distance from a fixed axis and can be balanced by means of a counterbalance rotating about the same axis.

Then the inertia forces in a four-bar mechanism can be completely balanced by the use of two counterbalances as shown in Fig. 15.2. The mass

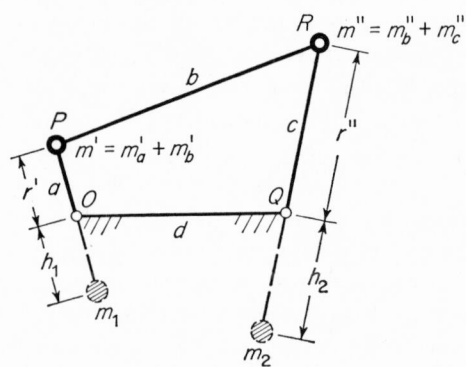

FIGURE 15.2

of the connecting rod is replaced by an equivalent system of two mass points located at points P and R, where the mass at P is designated as m'_b and the mass at R is m''_b. For simplification we will also replace links "a" and "c" with two mass equivalent systems placing the masses at the pin joints. The masses at points O and Q, since they have no motion, are of no importance. The mass of link "a" at P is designated m'_a and the mass of "c" at R is m''_c. We have now reduced the mechanism to two mass points with pure rotation relative to the fixed link. The sum of the masses at P is $m' = m'_a + m'_b$ rotating at a radius r' about the fixed axis O, and the mass at R is $m'' = m''_b + m''_c$ rotating about the fixed axis Q with a radius r''. These can be completely balanced with counterbalances as shown in the figure by satisfying the equations

$$m_1 h_1 = m'r'$$
$$m_2 h_2 = m''r''$$

where h_1 = distance to counterbalance m_1 from O;

h_2 = distance to counterbalance m_2 from Q.

The two counterbalances, or counterweights, as they are sometimes called, will completely balance the inertia forces in the original quadric crank mechanism and the frame or fixed link will be free of shaking forces.

We have not considered the balancing of moments in the plane of the mechanism. If we examine Fig. 15.1(a), we note that the angular velocity of link "c" is constantly varying and, except for the two positions where the velocity reaches a maximum, it will always have an angular acceleration. Although not so obvious, the same is true for link "b." A torque must be applied to these links to cause this angular acceleration and this torque will be applied by the various links as forces acting at the pin joints. These forces will be transmitted to the frame or fixed link at points O and Q. The above argument holds for the system with counterweights shown in Fig. 15.2, but in this case the sum of the forces acting on the frame is zero, therefore the forces acting at points O and Q in this case will result in a pure couple and the forces will be equal in magnitude and direction but with opposite sense. The magnitude and direction of this couple will vary with time, depending on the moment of inertia and angular acceleration of links "b" and "c."

This shaking couple cannot be eliminated completely for most mechanisms by simple means but can be reduced considerably in many cases by keeping the moment of inertia of the various links at a minimum. The analysis and elimination of shaking couples is beyond the scope of this text and in most engineering applications of mechanisms the shaking couple is not balanced because of the impracticality of the methods required. To exemplify such a method we could attach to the same frame an exact duplicate of the quadric crank mechanism shown in Fig. 15.2 in the same plane but so situated as to be a mirror image of the first mechanism. Then, by rotating the cranks with the same angular velocity but in opposite sense the couples of the two mechanisms would exactly balance and the frame would have no shaking forces or couples acting on it. In most actual cases the shaking torques are not balanced as previously mentioned. If they are of such a magnitude as to be objectionable, the machine should be isolated from its surroundings. (Methods of isolation can be found in texts on mechanical vibrations.)

In the discussion of the balancing of the quadric crank mechanism we have made the assumption that the crank is rotating at constant angular velocity. It is desirable that the crank rotate with constant angular velocity in most mechanisms, and we will not consider the case where the crank velocity varies. In our discussion of kinetic energy, however, we found that a varying driving torque was usually required over a cycle in order to keep the crank rotating at a constant velocity through a cycle. This imposes quite a problem for the driving motor. A flywheel is usually employed to keep the crank moving at a uniform velocity. Flywheels will be discussed in a later chapter; it is sufficient at present to state that the angular velocity can be held essentially constant by means of a flywheel.

15.3 Balancing the Slider-Crank Mechanism

Balancing of the slider-crank mechanism is accomplished in the same general manner as that given in the previous Article, but since we have the equations for the accelerations of the various links as developed in Chapter 9, we will make use of these equations and use analytical methods in discussing balance of the slider-crank mechanism. Since this mechanism is so widely used in various machines, such as internal combustion engines, considerable work has been done on the balancing of these mechanisms.

Consider the slider-crank mechanism shown in Fig. 15.3(a). The crank, link "*a*," has pure rotation; the slider, link "*c*," moves with rectilinear translation; and the connecting rod, link "*b*," has a complex motion

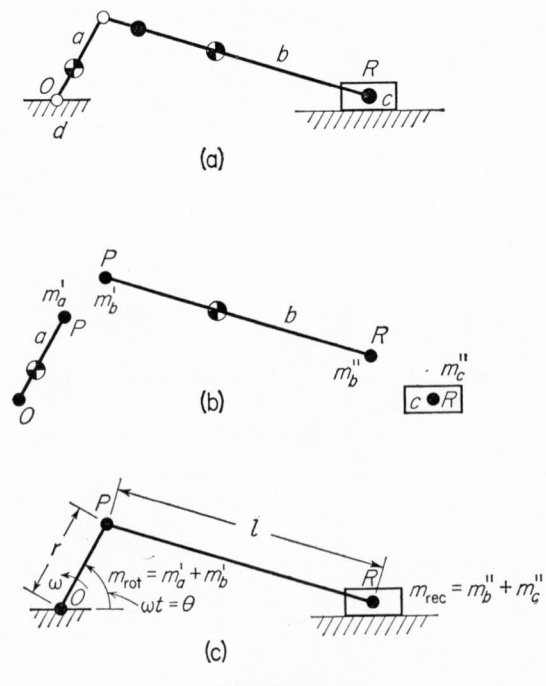

(a)

(b)

(c)

FIGURE 15.3

consisting of rotation and translation. As in the previous example we will assume that the crank rotates with uniform angular velocity. The crank will be replaced with a two-mass equivalent system with masses at the pin joints P and O as shown in Fig. 15.3(b). Since the slider moves with rectilinear translation it can be replaced with an equivalent system of one mass point, at R. The connecting rod will also be replaced with a two-mass equivalent system. If one mass is placed at R and all three of Eqs. (14.3) are satisfied, the other mass will be at some point between the center of gravity and P, as shown in Fig. 15.3(a). In most slider-crank mechanisms, however, the geometry of the actual connecting rod is such that the second mass point falls very close to the end of the crank, point P. If we place the mass point at P, the equation relating moments of inertia is very nearly satisfied, and as far as inertia forces are concerned the two systems can be made equivalent. The equivalent links are shown in Fig. 15.3(b) where m_a' and m_b' are the mass points of the equivalent links "a" and "b" respectively at P and m_b'' and m_c'' are the mass points of links "b" and "c" at R. The complete mechanism has now been replaced with two mass points at P and R as shown in Fig. 15.3(c).

The masses at point P comprise a single mass point which has pure rotation about O and therefore we will designate that mass point as m_{rot} while the combined mass point at R moves with rectilinear translation or reciprocates along a horizontal line and will be designated as m_{rec}. The acceleration of the rotating mass is $r\omega^2$ and is directed from P towards O for all phase positions. The acceleration of the reciprocating mass as obtained from Eq. (9.7) is

$$a = r\omega^2(\cos\theta + \frac{r}{l}\cos 2\theta)$$

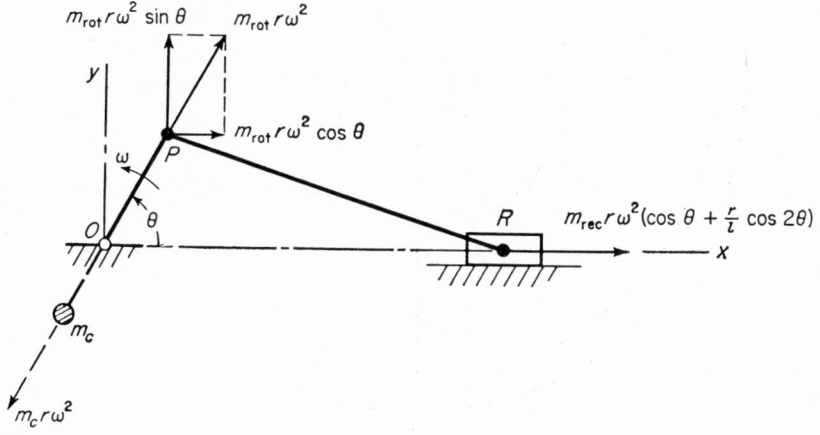

FIGURE 15.4

and is directed towards the crank for positive values and away from the crank for negative values, always being along the path of the slider.

The unbalanced inertia forces will then be as shown in solid lines in Fig. 15.4, and we will find it convenient to set up coordinate axes, as shown in the figure, with origin at point O. The x and y components of the inertia forces then are

$$F_x = (m_{\text{rot}} + m_{\text{rec}})r\omega^2 \cos \theta + m_{\text{rec}} \frac{r}{l} r\omega^2 \cos 2\theta \qquad (15.1)$$

and
$$F_y = m_{\text{rot}}r\omega^2 \sin \theta \qquad (15.2)$$

The rotating mass can be completely balanced by placing a counterweight on an extension of the crank through O just as in the case of the quadric crank mechanism, as shown by dashed lines in the figure, but the balance of the reciprocating mass is not so simple. In order to show the inertia forces better and to show the effect of counterbalancing, a polar diagram of the various forces will be drawn.

The polar diagram is drawn as shown in Fig. 15.5. Three concentric circles are drawn with the radius of the inner circle equal to the value of

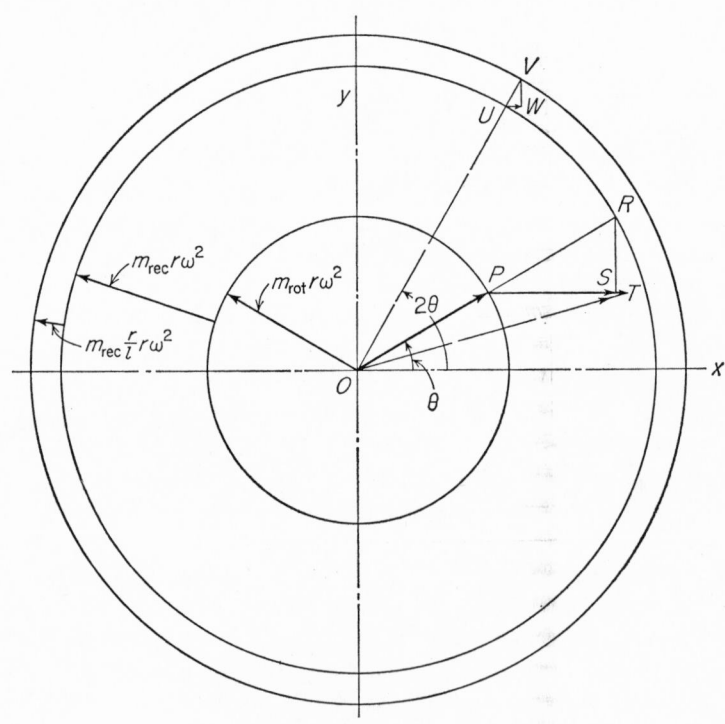

FIGURE 15.5

$m_{\mathrm{rot}} r \omega^2$ to some given scale, the radial distance from the first to second circle equal to $m_{\mathrm{rec}} r \omega^2$ to the same scale, and the radial distance from the second to the third circle equal to $m_{\mathrm{rec}} \dfrac{r}{l} r \omega^2$. The x-axis corresponding to the path of the slider is laid out horizontal from the center O and the crank angle, θ, is then measured from this axis or from top dead center position. The inertia force corresponding to the rotating mass can now be represented by a vector of magnitude $m_{\mathrm{rot}} r \omega^2$ and making an angle θ with the x-axis where θ is the crank angle as shown in Fig. 15.4. This vector is shown as $\overline{O\text{–}P}$ in the figure. The inertia force corresponding to the reciprocating mass has two components, both of which are in the x direction. Taking first the component, $m_{\mathrm{rec}} r \omega^2 \cos \theta$, we see that if the line $O\text{–}P$ is extended to R on the second circle the horizontal component of the line $P\text{–}R$ is equal in magnitude and direction to $m_{\mathrm{rec}} r \omega^2 \cos \theta$. Therefore, the vector $\overline{P\text{–}S}$ is this component of the inertia force for the reciprocating mass. The second component, $m_{\mathrm{rec}} \dfrac{r}{l} r \omega^2 \cos 2\theta$, can be obtained by drawing a radial line making an angle 2θ with the x-axis, from O to the outer circle, intersecting the second and outer circle at U and V. The horizontal projection of the line $U\text{–}V$ is $\overline{U\text{–}W}$. $\overline{U\text{–}W}$ is a vector representing the second component $m_{\mathrm{rec}} \dfrac{r}{l} r \omega^2 \cos 2\theta$. If we take this vector and lay if off at the end of the vector $\overline{P\text{–}S}$ as $\overline{S\text{–}T}$, we have added the three vectors representing the inertia forces of the mechanism, and the vector sum of these forces, vector $\overline{O\text{–}T}$, represents the unbalanced inertia forces, or the shaking force on the frame, in magnitude and direction when the crank is at angle θ. This process can be repeated for any crank angle, and if this is done for all phase positions we will have a polar diagram of the unbalanced shaking forces. This has been done in Fig. 15.6 for $30°$ intervals of the crank with the resultant curve $P\text{–}R\text{–}S\text{–}T\text{–}P$, of the shaking forces. The vector $\overline{O\text{–}P}$ is the shaking force at top dead center, $\overline{O\text{–}R}$ is the force for the crank at $90°$ and $\overline{O\text{–}S}$ is the force at bottom dead center.

From Eqs. (15.1) and (15.2) we see that if we balance the rotating mass with a counterweight as shown by the dashed lines in Fig. 15.4, all the vertical shaking forces are eliminated; the only unbalance is the unbalance in the horizontal direction caused by the reciprocating mass. This is represented in the polar diagram (Fig. 15.6) by the horizontal distance from the inner circle to the curve $P\text{–}R\text{–}S\text{–}T\text{–}P$ for any phase position. Vector $\overline{U\text{–}V}$ represents this force for the $30°$ crank position. Any additional counterweight would tend to balance the horizontal shaking forces, but would at the same time introduce unbalanced vertical forces, and we find that complete balancing cannot be achieved solely by applying counterweights to the crank. However, considerable improvement on the balance

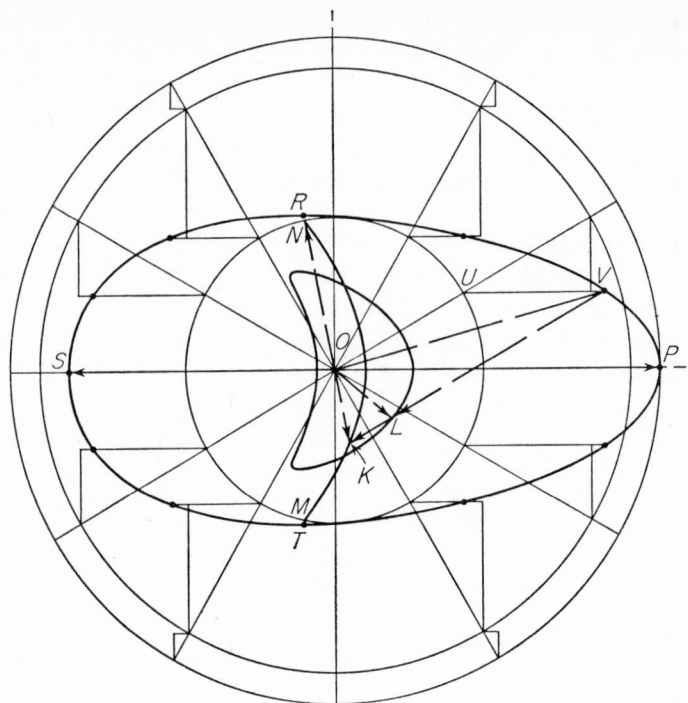

FIGURE 15.6

can be made by the judicious use of counterweights on the crank. We will assume that the counterweights are applied at a distance equal to the crank length from the center of rotation of the crank. It should be kept in mind that the same effect could be achieved by varying the mass of the counter-weight and its radius so long as the product of mass times radius remains constant.

Let us consider first the effect of using a counterbalancing mass equal to the sum of the rotating and reciprocating masses. The vector representing the inertia force of the counterweight would then be added to the initial unbalanced vector. This vector would be equal in magnitude to the radius of the second circle and parallel to the crank as shown by vector $\overline{V-K}$ in Fig. 15.6. The shaking force would then be $\overline{O-K}$ for a crank angle of 30° and the resulting polar diagram of the shaking forces would be the curve $M-K-N$. This would eliminate most of the horizontal shaking forces but would give fairly large vertical forces. A compromise, giving the smallest average shaking force, can be achieved by using a counterbalance with mass equal to the rotating mass plus some fraction of the reciprocating mass. The total mass of the counterweight which would give the best results would depend on the relative magnitudes of the rotating and reciprocating masses and the ratio r/l of the particular mechanism. For most actual reciprocating engines a counterbalance equal to the rotating mass plus one-half to two-thirds of the reciprocating mass would give a minimum shaking force. The resultant polar diagram of the unbalanced inertia forces would then be similar to the curve passing through point L in the figure which corresponds to a counterbalancing mass equal to the rotating mass plus two-thirds of the reciprocating mass. This is generally the only balancing that is done on single cylinder engines since by this method the unbalance can be reduced to a fairly small value, and any improvement would require a complicated and expensive mechanism.

An interesting but impractical method of completely balancing the inertia forces is shown in Fig. 15.7. The connecting rod is extended beyond

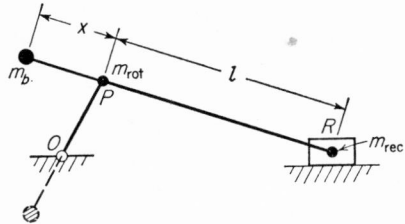

FIGURE 15.7

the pin joint P and enough mass is added so that the equivalent mass of the extension, m_b, multiplied by its distance from P, is equal to $m_{rec}l$. Then the center of gravity of the connecting rod and the slider taken together will fall at P. A counterbalance could be added to the crank as shown so as to make the center of gravity of the mechanism fall at O. Under these conditions the center of gravity has no motion, and the inertia forces are zero. This solution is impractical in that it would require a very large crankcase in order to inclose the connecting rod extension.

Another method of completely balancing the inertia forces by means of a gear arrangement will be discussed in a later section when we discuss the balancing of multicylinder engines. It will be found that this method is complicated and expensive and in general is not justified for single cylinder engines.

In general the inertia moments in the plane of the slider-crank are not balanced in actual mechanisms because these moments are usually small for mechanisms as ordinarily designed. If the mechanism is a prime mover, such as an internal combustion engine, the output torque of the engine must impose a torque on the frame and this torque is not constant. This output will impose a shaking couple on the support and the engine is usually isolated from the support in such a way to minimize the effects of this varying torque. This same isolation can be used to reduce the inertia torque and, since the inertia torque is small, elaborate means of balancing it are not justified. This isolation usually consists in placing springs between the engine and its support. This same type of torque, having to do with the work done, is found in other machines using the slider-crank mechanism, such as punch presses, and here also the inertia torque is a small part of the total.

However a fairly simple method is available for balancing the inertia torque of the slider-crank mechanism so long as the crank is rotating at constant angular velocity. Since in many cases a flywheel is used to keep the crank at very nearly constant velocity we will show how the inertia torques can be balanced in this case. It will be remembered that in replacing the connecting rod with an equivalent two-mass system one mass was placed at the pin joint (generally called the wrist pin) between the slider and connecting rod, and one at the pin joint (called the crank pin) between the crank and connecting rod. This does not give us a true equivalent system because the moment of inertia of the two systems is not the same. By using a true equivalent system with one mass at the wrist

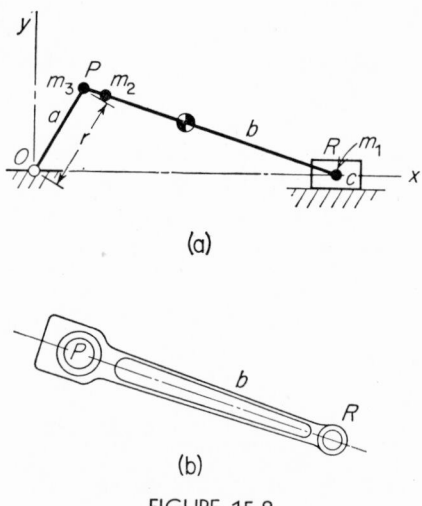

(a)

(b)

FIGURE 15.8

pin, the other mass point falls at a position somewhat removed from the crank pin, as shown in Fig. 15.8(a). If we now write the angular momentum equation for the system of mass points using point O as a reference, and x and y coordinates as shown in the figure [see Eqs. (12.7) and (12.8)], we have

$$M_O = \frac{d}{dt}[\Sigma m_i(V_i^y x_i - V_i^x y_i)] \qquad (15.3)$$

Considering each mass of the summation separately, we see that for mass m_1 the moment of momentum about O is always zero since y_1 is always zero and V_1^y is also always zero. The mass m_3 always remains the same distance from O, and we can therefore consider it as part of the crank which is a rigid body rotating about a fixed axis. Its moment of momentum (see Art. 12.6) can be written as

$$m_3(V_3^y x_3 - V_3^x y_3) = m_3 r^2 \omega$$

which is constant if ω is constant. Then we find that the two masses m_1 and m_3 have no inertia torque and therefore cause no unbalanced shaking moment. Any shaking moment then is caused by the mass m_2, and if we could have a true equivalent system for the connecting rod such that the two masses fell at points P and R then there would be no unbalanced shaking couple. This is easily done by making a connecting rod extend beyond the pin joints as shown in Fig. 15.8(b). The rod must be so proportioned that the center of percussion about the wrist pin is at the crank pin. Under these conditions the inertia torques are completely balanced so long as the crank turns at a uniform velocity.

15.4 *Balancing of Multicylinder Engines*

In multistage reciprocating compressors and internal combustion engines, two or more slider-crank mechanisms are arranged in parallel planes with the cranks attached to a single shaft. We will now discuss the balancing of such systems, and will find that in many cases the combination can be so arranged that the various inertia forces balance each other.

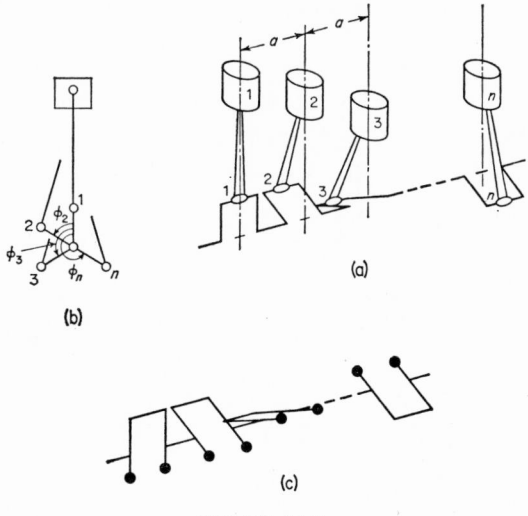

FIGURE 15.9

We will first consider the general case of an in-line multicylinder engine. An in-line engine is one in which all the cylinders are parallel and to the same side of the crankshaft as shown in Fig. 15.9(a). Figure 15.9(b) is an end view of the engine showing the relative position of the cranks. It will be noted that all cranks are referenced to crank number one by the angle they make with that crank. All cylinders will be assumed to be an equal distance "a" apart, and we will also assume that the piston assembly and connecting rods are identical for all cylinders, so that m_{rec} is the same for all cylinders.

Equations (15.1) and (15.2) can now be rewritten for each individual cylinder. It has been shown that the rotating mass can be balanced by a counterweight, and we will assume that counterweights have been added to each crank so as to balance the rotating masses. These counterweights will have to be arranged as shown in Fig. 15.9(c) so as to cause no interference with the connecting rod. Then the only unbalance existing is that caused by the reciprocating masses, and the unbalanced inertia force for each cylinder is a force along the axis of the cylinder. This can be expressed as

$$F = m_{rec}\, r\omega^2 \cos\theta + m_{rec}\, \frac{r}{l}\, r\omega^2 \cos 2\theta \qquad (15.4)$$

The two terms will be dealt with separately, and we call the force corresponding to the first term the primary force and the second term will be called the secondary force, it being of secondary importance since it is always smaller than the primary force. Since the forces for each cylinder are always in the same direction we can add them algebraically and the total inertia force for the engine can be written as

$$\Sigma\, F = m_{rec} r\omega^2 \left[\sum_{i=1}^{n} \cos\,(\theta_1 + \phi_i) + \frac{r}{l}\sum_{i=1}^{n} \cos 2(\theta_1 + \phi_i)\right] \qquad (15.5)$$

where θ_1 is the angle that crank one makes with the centerline of the cylinder, which in the case shown is vertical, and ϕ_i is the angle between crank i and crank one as shown in Fig. 15.9(b). Since ϕ_i is the angular position of the various cranks relative to crank one, ϕ_1 is zero.

Equation (15.5) can be arranged in a better form for the discussion of balancing by making use of the trigonometric relationship

$$\cos\,(\theta + \phi) = \cos\theta \cos\phi - \sin\theta \sin\phi$$

Substituting this relation into Eq. (15.5) we find that the sum of the inertia forces is

$$\Sigma\, F = m_{rec} r\omega^2 \left[\cos\theta_1 \sum_{i=1}^{n}\cos\phi_i - \sin\theta_1 \sum_{i=1}^{n}\sin\phi_i \right.$$
$$\left. + \frac{r}{l}\cos 2\theta_1 \sum_{i=1}^{n}\cos 2\phi_i - \frac{r}{l}\sin 2\theta_1 \sum_{i=1}^{n}\sin 2\phi_i\right] \qquad (15.6)$$

The first two terms in the brackets determine the primary forces and the last two terms determine the secondary forces.

In order that the inertia forces of the various pistons balance or counteract each other, Eq. (15.6) must reduce to zero, and the only condition which will make this true for any position of the crankshaft (independent of θ_1) is that the summations all be zero. Since in some crankshaft arrangements either the primary forces or secondary forces are balanced while the other is unbalanced, we will consider the two forces separately. The conditions necessary for complete balance of the primary forces then are

$$\Sigma \cos \phi_i = 0, \qquad \Sigma \sin \phi_i = 0 \tag{15.7}$$

and for complete balance of the secondary forces

$$\Sigma \cos 2\phi_i = 0, \qquad \Sigma \sin 2\phi_i = 0 \tag{15.8}$$

Before applying these equations to particular engines we need to examine another possibility of unbalance. In all our discussions so far we have been concerned only with plane mechanisms; but the in-line engine is not a plane mechanism, since each cylinder taken with its corresponding piston, connecting rod and crank comprise a separate slider-crank mechanism whose plane is separated from the plane of the adjacent cylinders by a distance "a." Therefore we must consider the moment of the forces in the plane containing the cylinders, and for complete balance of the engine it is necessary that not only the inertia forces be balanced but also the resultant of these forces must not result in a couple in the plane of the cylinders. This couple can be fairly large and must be considered in the balancing of multicylinder engines. It should be pointed out that this transverse couple is entirely different from the couple previously considered in single cylinder engines, which was in the plane of the individual slider-crank mechanisms.

In setting up equations for the transverse moment of the inertia forces, a reference axis passing through the intersection of the centerline of the crankshaft and the axis of cylinder one usually is used. Then moments will be taken about cylinder one. The moment equation can then be written by multiplying each force component by its moment arm as

$$M = m_{rec} r \omega^2 \left[\cos \theta_1 \sum_{i=1}^{n} a_i \cos \phi_i - \sin \theta_1 \sum_{i=1}^{n} a_i \sin \phi_i \right.$$
$$\left. + \frac{r}{l} \cos 2\theta_1 \sum_{i=1}^{n} a_i \cos 2\phi_i - \frac{r}{l} \sin 2\theta_1 \sum_{i=1}^{n} a_i \sin 2\phi_i \right] \tag{15.9}$$

where a_i is the distance from cylinder one to cylinder i. Then, for balance of moments caused by the primary forces which will be referred to as primary moments, the following equations must hold

$$\Sigma a_i \cos \phi_i = 0, \qquad \Sigma a_i \sin \phi_i = 0 \tag{15.10}$$

For the secondary moments to be zero

$$\Sigma \, a_i \cos 2\phi_i = 0, \qquad \Sigma \, a_i \sin 2\phi_i = 0 \qquad (15.11)$$

For the case where the cylinders are equally spaced, a_i becomes

$$a_i = -\,(1 - i)a$$

Then the necessary conditions for complete balance of an in-line multi-cylinder engine are that Eqs. (15.7), (15.8), (15.10), and (15.11) be satisfied. We should qualify the statement of complete balance in the above sentence, since the term complete balance as used does not include balance of moments about the crankshaft axis and is subject to the approximations made in obtaining the equations for the accelerations in the slider-crank mechanism. However complete balance is the term usually used to denote balance of the primary and secondary forces and moments, and it will be so used here. The possibility of balancing multicylinder in-line engines will be discussed in detail in the following sections where various crank arrangements will be analyzed by means of these equations.

15.5 The Four Cylinder In-Line Engine

The four cylinder in-line engine will be used to demonstrate the use of the above equations in analyzing the balance of engines. For internal combustion engines balance is not the sole consideration in the selection of a crank arrangement since uniformity or evenness of the power strokes is also important. The evenness of the power strokes depends on the firing order and therefore the smoothness of the torque applied to the crankshaft is dependent on the firing order. Therefore we must consider the firing order of the engine at the same time that we consider balancing. Both the two-stroke and the four-stroke cycles will be discussed in relation to the firing order.

In the four-stroke cycle gases are ignited at approximately top dead center for any one cylinder and power is delivered to the crankshaft for 180° rotation, until the piston is at bottom dead center, then the burned gases are exhausted during the next 180°, a fresh charge of the combustible mixture is sucked into the cylinder during the next 180°, this mixture is compressed during the next 180°, after which the cycle is repeated. Thus we have power delivered to the crankshaft over one-half revolution of every two revolutions of the crankshaft. Calling as a stroke the movement of the piston from one dead center position to the other, we can label the sequence of strokes as (1) power stroke, *P;* (2) exhaust stroke, *E;* (3) intake stroke, *I;* and (4) compression stroke, *C.* Charts of these strokes will be shown for the various engines discussed so that the uniformity of torque given by the power strokes can be noted.

For the two-stroke cycle the above train of events occurs during each revolution of the crankshaft, each occupying approximately one-quarter of a revolution, the power and exhaust both occurring in the course of the same stroke, and the intake and compression both occurring in the same stroke.

Various crank arrangements are possible for the four cylinder engine, but we will consider only two. Any other arrangement can be readily analyzed in the same manner as we will these. Consider first the engine with crank arrangement $0°, 90°, 270°, 180°$, or $\phi_1 = 0$, $\phi_2 = 90°$, $\phi_3 = 270°$, and $\phi_4 = 180°$, as shown in Fig. 15.10(a). The power strokes for the four- and two-stroke cycle are shown in Figs. 15.10(b) and 15.10(c), respectively.

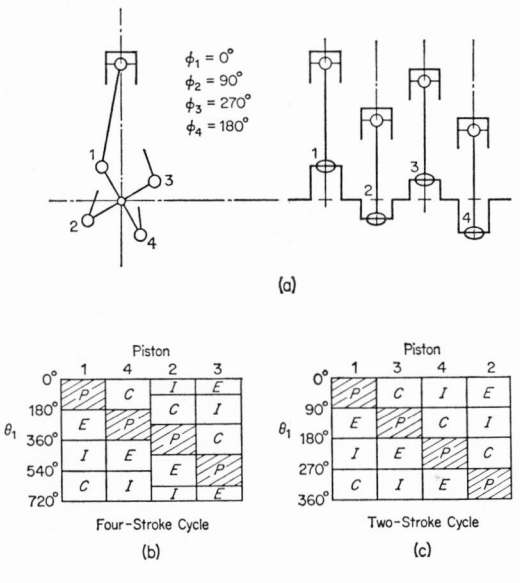

FIGURE 15.10

We see that the two-stroke cycle has power evenly applied while for the four-stroke cycle two of the power strokes overlap by $90°$ and there is a $90°$ lapse between the power strokes for the fourth and first pistons. Balance of the engine is analyzed in Table 15.1 making use of four sets of equations.

Then we see that the primary and secondary forces and secondary moments are completely balanced but the primary moments are unbalanced. Since the forces are all balanced, the unbalanced primary moment is a pure couple tending to rotate the engine about an axis normal to the plane of the cylinders. Substituting the summations into the moment equation, Eq. (15.9), we find that the primary couple is given by the equation

$$M = m_{\text{rec}} r \omega^2 [- 3a \cos \theta_1 + a \sin \theta_1]$$

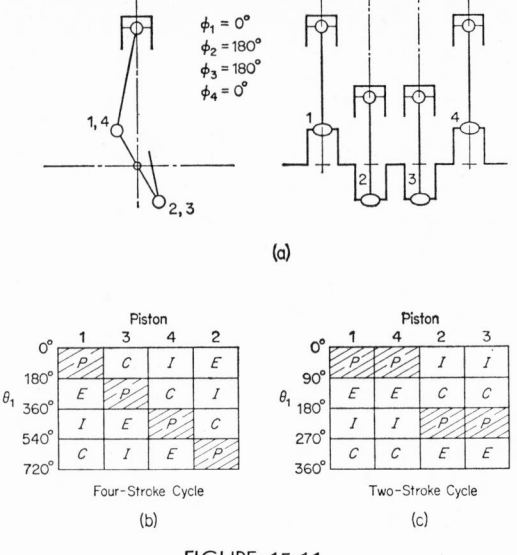

FIGURE 15.11

The conventional four cylinder automotive type engine is shown in Fig. 15.11(a) with crank arrangement 0°–180°–180°–0°. The power strokes are evenly spaced for the four-stroke cycle as shown in Fig. 15.11(b) but the power is uneven for the two-stroke cycle as shown in Fig. 15.11(c). Balance of the engine is analyzed in Table 15.2.

Table 15.1

Crank	ϕ	$\cos\phi$	$\sin\phi$	2ϕ	$\cos 2\phi$	$\sin 2\phi$	a	$a\cos\phi$	$a\sin\phi$	$a\cos 2\phi$	$a\sin 2\phi$
1	0°	1	0	0°	1	0	0	0	0	0	0
2	90°	0	1	180°	−1	0	a	0	a	$-a$	0
3	270°	0	−1	540°	−1	0	$2a$	0	$-2a$	$-2a$	0
4	180°	−1	0	360°	1	0	$3a$	$-3a$	0	$3a$	0
Σ		0	0		0	0			$-3a$	$-a$	0	0
		Primary forces balanced			Secondary forces balanced				Primary moments unbalanced		Secondary moments balanced	

The primary forces and moments are balanced but the secondary forces and moments are unbalanced. Substituting the summations into Eqs. (15.6) and (15.9) we find that the resultant unbalanced force is

$$F = m_{\text{rec}}r\omega^2\left(4\,\frac{r}{l}\cos 2\theta_1\right)$$

and the unbalanced moment is

$$M = m_{rec} r \omega^2 \left(6a \frac{r}{l} \cos 2\theta_1 \right)$$

Table 15.2

Crank	ϕ	$\cos \phi$	$\sin \phi$	2ϕ	$\cos 2\phi$	$\sin 2\phi$	a	$a \cos \phi$	$a \sin \phi$	$a \cos 2\phi$	$a \sin 2\phi$
1	$0°$	1	0	$0°$	1	0	0	0	0	0	0
2	$180°$	-1	0	$360°$	1	0	a	$-a$	0	a	0
3	$180°$	-1	0	$360°$	1	0	$2a$	$-2a$	0	$2a$	0
4	$0°$	1	0	$0°$	1	0	$3a$	$3a$	0	$3a$	0
	Σ	0	0		4	0		0	0	$6a$	0
		Primary forces balanced			Secondary forces unbalanced			Primary moments balanced		Secondary moments unbalanced	

Since the resultant moment is caused by the unbalanced forces and the moment is taken about cylinder one, the position of the resultant unbalanced force relative to cylinder one can be found by dividing the moment by the force or

$$z = \frac{M}{F} = \frac{3}{2} a$$

We see that the line of action of the unbalanced resultant is at a distance $1.5a$ from cylinder one, which puts it midway between cylinders two and three.

An interesting method has been used in some internal combustion engines to balance the secondary forces as given by the above analysis. This method consists of an arrangement of gears with counterweights, as shown in Fig. 15.12, where the two counterweighted gears are in the plane of the cylinders and driven at twice the speed of the crank by means of a helical gear on the

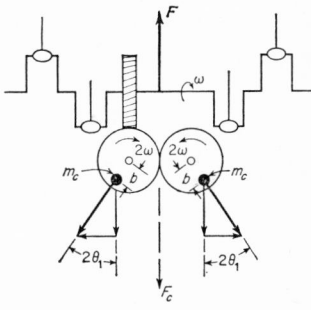

FIGURE 15.12

crankshaft. The horizontal components of the counterbalance forces balance and the vertical components add to give a total force

$$F_v = 2m_c (2\omega)^2 b \cos 2\theta_1$$

This force is always opposite to the unbalanced force in the engine; it has the same line of action as the unbalanced force if the gears are arranged as shown in the figure. The magnitudes of the forces can be made equal by varying the weight of the counterbalances and then the engine is completely balanced.

This same method of balancing also lends itself to the balancing of primary forces and primary and secondary couples. For the balancing of primary forces the gears containing the counterweights would be driven at the speed of the crankshaft and so arranged that the line of action of the counterweight forces is along the line of action of the unbalanced primary resultant. By the use of two sets of gears, one turning at the speed of the crankshaft and one turning at twice this speed, a single cylinder engine can be completely balanced. **Figure 15.13** shows the arrangements of the

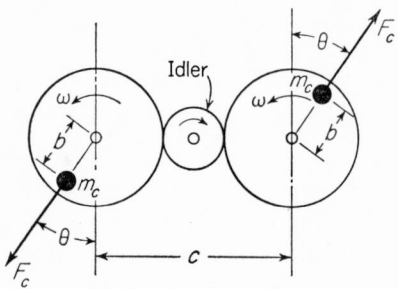

FIGURE 15.13

counterweights on the gears so that a pure couple is produced. The gears are separated by an idler so that the two gears turn in the same direction. The couple caused by the counterbalances is

$$M = m_c cb\omega^2 \cos \theta$$

For counterbalancing primary moments the angular speed of the gears would be the same as the crankshaft and for secondary moments it would be twice the crankshaft speed.

The analytical method of examining the balance of in-line engines can be used for engines of any number of cylinders by following the procedure demonstrated for the two four cylinder engines. In this manner it can be shown that the six cylinder engine with crank arrangement $0°–240°–120°–120°–240°–0°$ is perfectly balanced as regards primary and secondary forces and moments, as is the eight cylinder engine with crank arrangement $0°–180°–90°–270°–270°–90°–180°–0°$.

15.6 Rotating Vector Analysis

A quick and convenient method of analyzing the balance of multi-cylinder engines is letting the primary and secondary forces be represented as the projection of rotating vectors onto the centerline of the cylinders. Assuming again that the rotating masses are balanced by counterweights on the crankshaft, the only unbalance is the unbalance caused by the reciprocating mass and is a force along the axis of the cylinder. Equation (15.4), which represents the unbalanced inertia force for any one cylinder, can be rewritten as

$$F = m_{\text{rec}}\, r\omega^2 \cos \omega t + m_{\text{rec}}\, \frac{r}{l}\, r\omega^2 \cos 2\omega t$$

where θ has been replaced by ωt and time is counted as zero when the crank is at top dead center position. The primary force can now be represented as the projection on the axis of the cylinder of a vector of magnitude $m_{\text{rec}} r\omega^2$ rotating about its origin with an angular velocity ω, and the secondary force can be represented as the projection of a vector of magnitude $m_{\text{rec}} \frac{r}{l} r\omega^2$ rotating with an angular velocity of 2ω. Both the primary and secondary rotating vectors are pointing towards the piston when the crank is at top dead center position. The primary vector will always point in the direction of the crank since it rotates at the same velocity as the crank. The secondary vector, rotating at twice the velocity of the crank, will point towards the piston at top dead center and when the crank is at bottom dead center (having rotated 180°) the secondary vector will again point towards the piston since its angular velocity is twice the crank velocity.

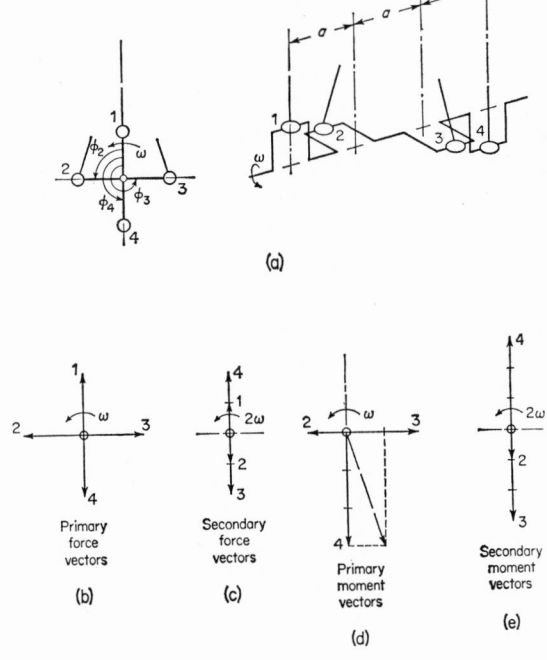

FIGURE 15.14

This method will be demonstrated by analyzing the four cylinder in-line engine with crank arrangement of 0°–90°–270°–180° which was analyzed analytically in the previous Article. The crank arrangement is shown in Fig. 15.14(a) where the cylinders are vertical and crank one is shown in top dead center position. Figure 15.14 (b) shows the rotating primary vectors with the vectors pointing in the direction of the corresponding crank. These vectors rotate at the angular velocity of the crank and the primary forces are the vertical projections of these vectors. It is obvious from the figure that the sum of the vectors is zero and therefore the primary forces are balanced.

The secondary force vectors are shown in Fig. 15.14(c) and they rotate at twice the speed of the crank. Since the primary and secondary vectors point in the same direction when the crank is at top dead center, secondary vector one will be pointing upward. Vector two was upward when crank two was upward, but since the vector rotates at twice the speed of the crank it will have rotated through an angle 2ϕ while crank rotated through angle ϕ, therefore it will be downward. Crank three has rotated 270° from top dead center and therefore vector three will have rotated 540° and is downward. By the same reasoning, vector 4 will be upward and we see from the vector diagram that the secondary forces are balanced. Note that the magnitude of these secondary vectors are all the same; i.e., vector three is measured from the arrow of vector two.

The primary and secondary moments can also be represented as the projections of rotating vectors. Taking moments again about cylinder one we see that the moment of any inertia force is equal to the force multiplied by its distance from cylinder one and is clockwise or counter clockwise depending on whether the force is upward or downward. Therefore the moment corresponding to any force can be represented by a rotating vector in the same direction as the force and of magnitude equal to the product of force times its distance from cylinder one. Figure 15.14(d) shows the rotating primary moment vectors. Vector three is twice the length of vector two since cylinder three is $2a$ inches from cylinder one and cylinder two is a inches from cylinder one; vector four is three times the length of vector two. The primary moments are not balanced as can be seen from the figure and the unbalance is the sum of the vertical projections of these vectors. These vectors can be combined into a single resultant, as shown in the figure, whose vertical component represents the unbalanced primary moment. If the component is downward the moment is clockwise and if upward the moment is counter clockwise when viewing the crankshaft from the aspect shown in the figure. The resultant as shown represents the moment when the crank one is at top dead center. The secondary moment vectors are shown in Fig. 15.14(e), and we see that the secondary moments are balanced.

The rotating-vector analysis can be made in the same manner for any other in-line engine, and has the advantage that any unbalance can readily be seen by noting the vector diagrams. This method can also be used in engines other than in-line engines. It is particularly useful in analyzing opposed engines which will be discussed in the next Article.

15.7 Opposed and Vee Type Engines

In order to decrease the length of multicylinder engines and thereby have a more compact engine, the cylinders are arranged in banks of in-line cylinders lying in radial planes containing the centerline of the crankshaft.

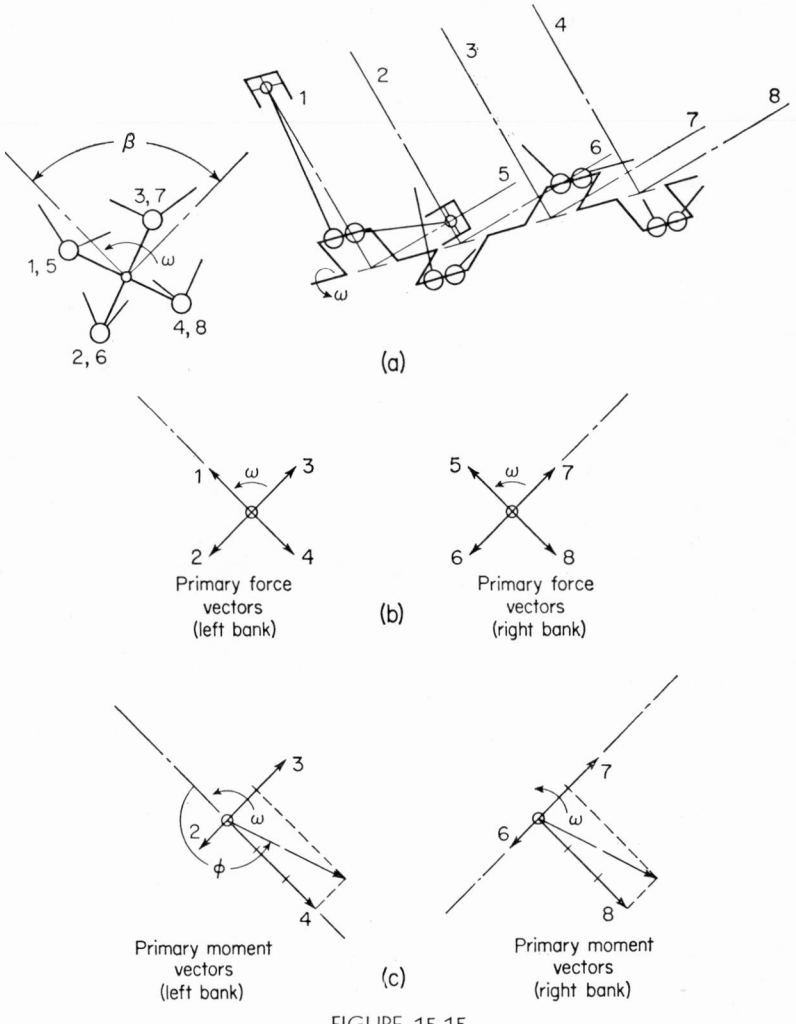

FIGURE 15.15

An example of such an engine is the V-8 engine shown in Fig. 15.15(a) consisting of two banks of four cylinders each driving a common four-crank crankshaft. One piston from each bank is connected to each crank, or throw as they are sometimes called. The connecting rods are usually pinned to the crank side by side so that the two pistons common to a single throw do not lie in the same transverse plane, but this small offset is usually ignored in analyzing the balance. The angle between banks of cylinders, angle β, is chosen so as to give evenly spaced power strokes. An angle of 90° usually is used for the V-8 automotive engine.

Another example of a two-bank engine is the four cylinder opposed engine shown in Fig. 15.17(a), where the two banks are 180° apart. This type of engine is used in light aircraft engines and in some automobile engines. Other engines of this type, such as the V-12, the V-16 and a W-18 having three banks of six cylinders each, have been built. We will examine the balance of the V-8 and four cylinder opposed in detail.

In the analysis of this type engine each bank can be analyzed separately as an in-line engine and then any unbalance of the banks can be combined vectorially.

Consider the V-8 engine shown in Fig. 15.15(a) with an angle between banks of 90°. It will be left to the student to show that the firing strokes are evenly spaced for four-stroke cycle operation with firing order 1–8–4–2–7–3–6–5 with 90° crank rotation between firings. Taking each bank separately we previously found that a four cylinder in-line engine with this crank arrangement is balanced except for the primary moments. Therefore with the two banks the only unbalance will be an unbalanced primary moment for each bank. The primary force vectors for each bank are shown in Fig. 15.15(b) for the crank position where piston one is at top dead center. The primary moment vectors are shown in Fig. 15.15(c) with the resultant moment vector for each bank. It will be noted that the unbalanced moment for the left bank is the projection of the resultant vector in the plane of the left bank. The projection of the resultant vector in the plane of the right bank is the unbalanced moment in that bank. The two resultant vectors are in the same phase position relative to the crank and of equal magnitude. Then the total unbalance in the engine, being the vector sum of the unbalance in each bank, can be represented as a single vector rotating at the angular speed of the crankshaft and of magnitude and phase position as given by either of the vectors in Fig. 15.15(c), since this vector has normal components in the plane of each bank corresponding to the moment in that bank. Since the forces are completely balanced, this vector represents a pure couple. The magnitude of the couple can be determined from the figure as

$$M = \sqrt{(3am_{rec}r\omega^2)^2 + (am_{rec}r\omega^2)^2}$$
$$= \sqrt{10}\, am_{rec}r\omega^2$$

and the phase angle measured counter clockwise from the crank for pistons one and five is

$$\phi = 180° + \tan^{-1}\left(\tfrac{1}{3}\right) = 198.43°$$

This unbalanced couple can be represented as two rotating forces attached to the crank as shown in Fig. 15.16 and they can be balanced by two counterweights attached to the crankshaft as shown. These two counterweights produce a pure couple which can be made to exactly balance the inertia couple if correctly proportioned.

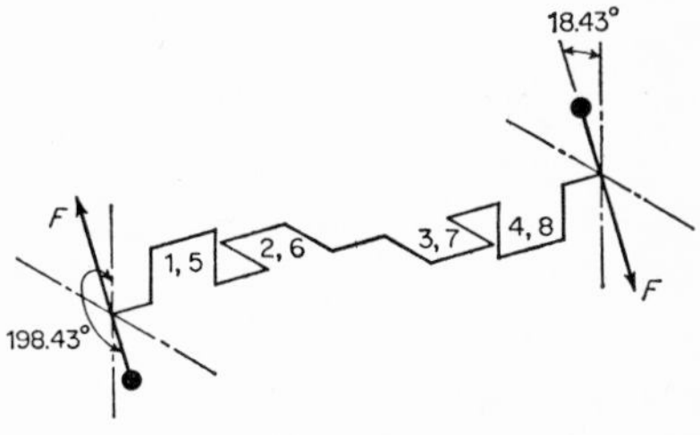

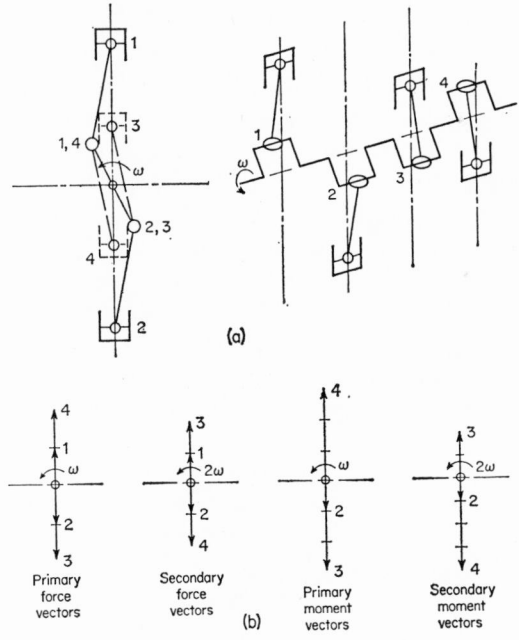

FIGURE 15.16

If we now consider the four cylinder opposed engine as shown in Fig. 15.17(a) we find that we can combine the rotating vectors representing the inertia forces into a single diagram since both banks are in the same plane. The vectors representing the primary and secondary forces and moments are shown in Fig. 15.17(b) and we should note that the secondary force vectors are in the same direction as the primary force vectors when the pistons are at top dead center. This engine

FIGURE 15.17

is in balance except for the secondary moment which is a pure couple. This can only be balanced by a gear arrangement rotating at twice the crankshaft velocity.

Although the V-8 and opposed engines were analyzed by means of rotating vectors, it should be pointed out that the analytical method would have served just as well by analyzing each bank separately. The rotating vector analysis was used only because it is easier to visualize the unbalance with rotating vectors.

15.8 Discussion

We have discussed only a few particular cases of balancing of mechanisms with reciprocating or oscillating motion. In the case of the engine mechanisms we consider only those cases where the masses of all pistons and connecting rods are the same and the distance between cylinders was uniform. The analytical and graphical methods can also be used for other cases in which these conditions do not hold, and the student should have no difficulty in applying these methods to systems with varying constants by changing the constants in the equations for the analytical method and by varying the length of the vectors for the graphical method.

The analytical method is in general more accurate but has the disadvantage that it is usually longer and often it becomes a process of mathematical manipulation in which all physical significance is lost. The graphical method overcomes these disadvantages and is especially useful as a check of the results.

Balancing of the inertia forces is practical in only a few reciprocating mechanisms. For those in which the forces cannot be balanced, one must resort to some means of isolating the mechanism from its surroundings so as to minimize the forces transmitted to the surroundings. This becomes a problem in mechanical vibrations, beyond the scope of this text. It should be pointed out that although we considered only primary and secondary forces in our analysis of reciprocating engines since they are the only forces of appreciable magnitude, small forces of higher frequency were ignored by use of the approximate equations of acceleration but these forces could excite vibrations in the surroundings.

PROBLEMS

15.1 In the mechanism shown in Fig. P10.1 link "a" weighs 2 lb with its C.G. along line O–P $\frac{3}{4}$ in. from O; link "b" weighs 2.5 lbs with its C.G. along line P–R $1\frac{1}{2}$ in. from P; and link "c" weighs 2.5 lbs with its C.G. along line Q–R and $1\frac{1}{4}$ in. from Q. Replace link "b" with a two-mass equivalent system, locating the masses at pin joints P and R. Determine the counter balance in in.-lb which must be attached to links "a" and "b" in order to eliminate the shaking forces in the mechanism.

15.2 The following data are for a single cylinder internal combustion engine:

Speed = 3600 rpm
Stroke = $2\frac{1}{2}$ in.
Connecting rod length = 6 in.
Weight of piston assembly = 1.5 lb
Weight of connecting rod = 2.25 lb
Equivalent unbalanced weight of crank at radius of $1\frac{1}{4}$ in. = 1.25 lb
Distance from C.G. of connecting rod to crank pin = 2.5 in.

Draw a polar diagram, similar to Fig. 15.6, of the inertia forces for the following cases.

(a) No counterbalancing weights.

(b) A counterbalancing weight at a radius of $1\frac{1}{4}$ in. and equal to the weight of the crank at the crank pin and the weight of the piston assembly.

(c) Using an equivalent two mass system for the connecting rod with masses at the crank pin and the piston pin, a counterbalancing weight equal to the rotating weight and the reciprocating weight.

(d) A counterbalancing weight equal to the rotating weight and two-thirds of the reciprocating weight.

15.3 Compare the results of Prob. 15.2(a) with the results obtained from a graphical force analysis for a crank angle 15° from top dead center.

15.4 Analyze the balance of the four cylinder engine shown in Fig. 15.11 by means of a rotating vector analysis.

15.5 Analyze the three cylinder radial engine shown in Fig. P15.1 for balance. All cylinders lie in the same plane and all pistons and connecting rods have the same mass. Assume that the rotating masses are balanced and determine the

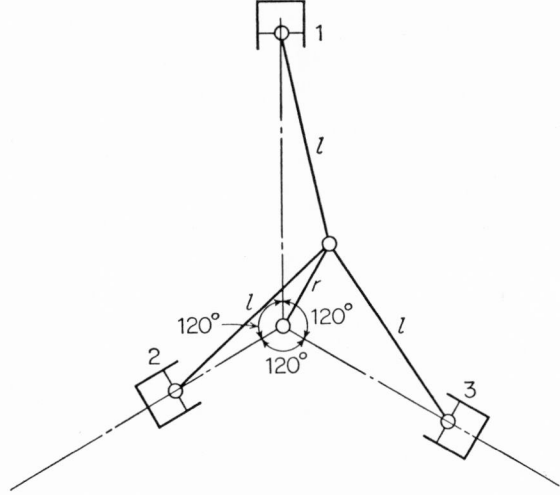

FIGURE P15.1

additional rotating counterbalance necessary to balance the primary forces in terms of the dimensions and reciprocating mass.

15.6 Determine the unbalance (forces and moments) in a two cylinder in-line engine, with cranks at 0° and 180°, analytically and check the results by means of a rotating vector analysis.

15.7 Determine the best crank arrangement as regards balance for an opposed six cylinder four-stroke cycle engine by means of a rotating vector analysis.

15.8 Show by means of a rotating vector analysis that a six cylinder in-line engine with crank arrangement 0°–240°–120°–120°–240°–0° is balanced as regards primary and secondary forces and moments.

15.9 A three cylinder in-line engine with equal spaced cylinders and crank arrangement 0°–120°–240°, has a crank length of 3 in., a connecting rod length of 8 in., and a reciprocating weight of 4 lb. Determine the magnitude and direction of the unbalanced primary and secondary couples when the crank on the left end is 30° past top dead center. Assume the rotating masses are balanced.

Chapter 16

Static and Dynamic Balance
of Rotating Bodies

16.1 Introduction

In Chapter 15 it was seen that only a few particular mechanisms could be completely balanced when the various links had reciprocating or oscillating motion. We will discuss the balancing of bodies having only rotation in this chapter. We will find that it is theoretically possible to completely balance any rotating body by the addition of counterweights to the body, so long as the body is rotating at constant angular velocity. Although it is theoretically possible to perfectly balance a rotating body, it is impossible practically to do so. We can approach perfect balance to any degree of accuracy, depending on the time and effort which we are willing to spend in the balancing process. With modern equipment balance can be achieved to such high degree that the unbalance is negligible for practical purposes.

16.2 Static and Dynamic Balance

Consider a rotor, resting on two horizontal knife-edges or ways, as shown in Fig. 16.1(a). We assume that the rotor is rigid and is perfectly balanced except for the mass m_u at radius r from the axis of rotation. If the rotor is placed on the ways so that the unbalance is in any position other than a vertical plane, the rotor will roll along the surface until the unbalance is on the bottom. If now a counterweight of equal weight and radius to the unbalance is placed anywhere along the top of the rotor, the rotor will be in indifferent equilibrium, or the rotor will have no tendency to roll, when placed in any position. The rotor is then said to be statically balanced. Assuming that the counterweight, m_c, is placed as shown in Fig. 16.1(b) and

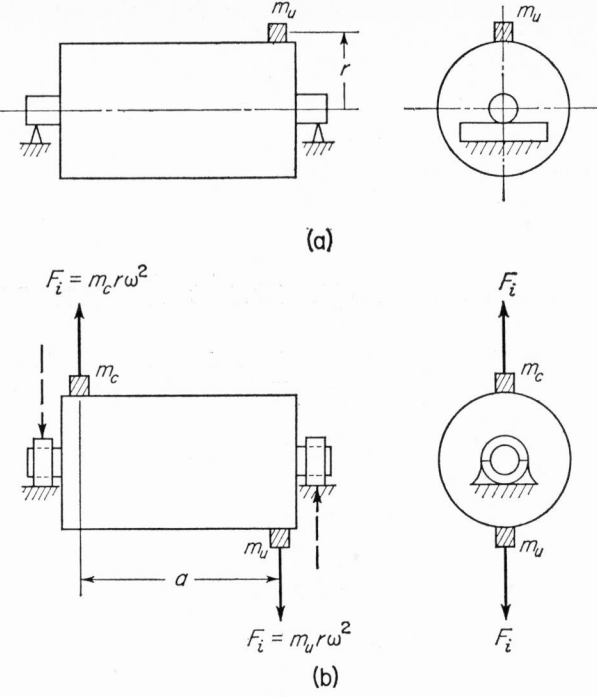

FIGURE 16.1

that the rotor is placed on bearings and rotated with some angular velocity ω, the inertia force of the two weights is

$$F_i = m_u r \omega^2 = m_c r \omega^2$$

and the direction is as shown in the figure. The forces are completely balanced but there is a resultant couple of magnitude $mr\omega^2 a$. Then the condition of static balance indicates that the forces are balanced. However if the rotor is rotating in bearings which hold the axis fixed, the bearings must exert a couple on the rotor equal and opposite to the inertia couple which rotates about the axis as the rotor rotates. Such a couple is called dynamic unbalance since the couple exists only when the rotor is rotating.

For complete balance the rotor must be balanced both statically and dynamically. It should be noted that if the rotor is balanced dynamically, it is also balanced statically. If the counterweight had been placed in the radial plane containing the original unbalance, the rotor would have been dynamically balanced. Many rotating members have small axial dimensions and for these cases static balancing is all that is needed, since the moment arm for a dynamic couple is necessarily small. Automobile wheels and airplane propellers are examples of members which are usually balanced only statically.

In the previous example it was mentioned that static and dynamic unbalance could have been achieved by placing the balance weight in the same transverse plane as the unbalance. However, because of interference with other parts of the mechanism, it is not always possible to place the balance weight in the plane of the unbalance, and other means must be used to achieve dynamic balance of rotating members.

16.3 Known Unbalance in Single Plane

In many cases the unbalanced masses in rotating members is of considerable magnitude and can be determined fairly accurately from a drawing of the member. An example of such cases is the crankshaft of engines as discussed in the previous chapter. The balancing of such members will be discussed in this chapter.

Consider first a rotating shaft with three masses attached to it as shown in Fig. 16.2(a), where the masses all lie in a single transverse plane. Static balance is all that is necessary and this can be achieved by the addition of a

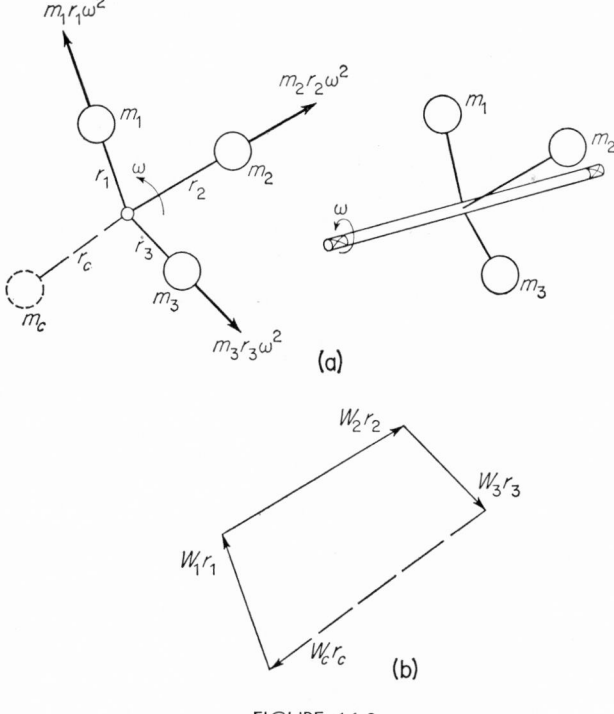

FIGURE 16.2

single counterbalance. The counterbalance is shown in the figure in dashed lines as m_c. The total unbalance is the vector sum of the inertia forces of the three weights, and the inertia force of the counterbalance must be such that it balances the resultant of the other three forces in order that the system be balanced. The vector equation for the balanced system is

$$(W_1r_1 \leftrightarrow W_2r_2 \leftrightarrow W_3r_3 \leftrightarrow W_cr_c)\, \frac{\omega^2}{g} = 0$$

Since the ω^2/g is common to all terms it is usually dropped in engineering work, and unbalance is given in units of a weight times a distance. In order to determine the counterbalance necessary a vector diagram of the inertia forces of the three weights is drawn as shown in Fig. 16.2(b) making the vectors equal in magnitude to the weights times their radii and directed in the direction of the inertia forces. The vector closing the polygon gives the W_cr_c of the required counterbalance, and it must be positioned on the shaft so that its inertia force is in the direction of the closing vector, as shown in the figure. Knowing the magnitude of W_cr_c, either the radius or the weight can be arbitrarily chosen and the other determined.

The counterbalance could be determined analytically by resolving the Wr vectors into horizontal and vertical or x and y components, as shown in Fig. 16.3. The sum of the horizontal and vertical components, including

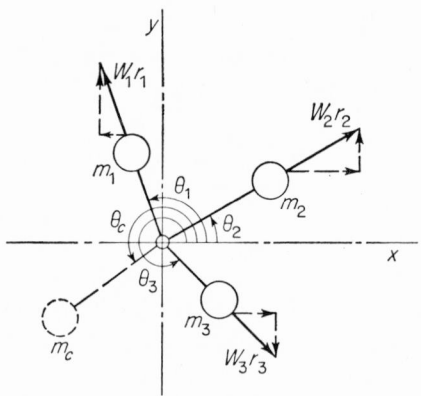

FIGURE 16.3

the components of the counterbalance, must be zero for balance, or

$$W_cr_c \cos \theta_c + \sum_{i=1}^{n} W_ir_i \cos \theta_i = 0$$

$$W_cr_c \sin \theta_c + \sum_{i=1}^{n} W_ir_i \sin \theta_i = 0$$

or
$$W_c r_c \cos \theta_c = - \sum_{i=1}^{n} W_i r_i \cos \theta_i \tag{16.1}$$

$$W_c r_c \sin \theta_c = - \sum_{i=1}^{n} W_i r_i \sin \theta_i \tag{16.2}$$

where the summation is over the original weights and the angle θ is the angle of the respective weights as measured from the horizontal to the right as shown in the figure. The direction of the counterbalance in terms of $\tan \theta_c$ is found by dividing Eq. (16.2) by Eq. (16.1), giving us

$$\tan \theta_c = \frac{- \Sigma W_i r_i \sin \theta_i}{- \Sigma W_i r_i \cos \theta_i} \tag{16.3}$$

The algebraic signs must be kept in the above equation so that the quadrant in which the counterbalance lies can be determined. Noting that the horizontal and vertical components of the counterbalance must be equal in magnitude to the summation of the components of the original unbalance, its magnitude is given by the equation

$$W_c r_c = \sqrt{(\Sigma W_i r_i \cos \theta_i)^2 + (\Sigma W_i r_i \sin \theta_i)^2} \tag{16.4}$$

16.4 General Case of Known Unbalance

Let us now consider the general case of unbalanced masses in various transverse planes. A single counterweight can be used to statically balance such a system, but we found in Article 16.1 that this could result in a dynamic couple. In order to balance the couple, two counterweights are necessary, each in a different transverse plane. Therefore, in general, counterweights must be placed in two planes in order to completely balance dynamically. We shall now prove that complete dynamic balance can be achieved by two counterweights, each in a different transverse plane.

Consider a shaft with two weights, W_1 and W_2, as shown in Fig. 16.4(a). We will show that complete static and dynamic balance can be obtained by single masses in the transverse planes A and B, which are arbitrarily placed along the shaft. Taking W_1 first at a distance a_1 from plane A and b_1 from plane B, we can consider the shaft to be rotating with uniform angular velocity, with imaginary bearings at the two planes. The inertia force of the rotating weight will cause reactions at the bearings. These reactions at the bearings could be canceled by counterweights in the two planes rotating with the shaft and so placed on the shaft that they counteract the reaction forces. This process could be repeated for W_2 and then we would have two counterbalances in each plane which would exactly balance the inertia forces and moments of W_1 and W_2. These two counterweights in each plane could be replaced by one equivalent counterweight in the manner

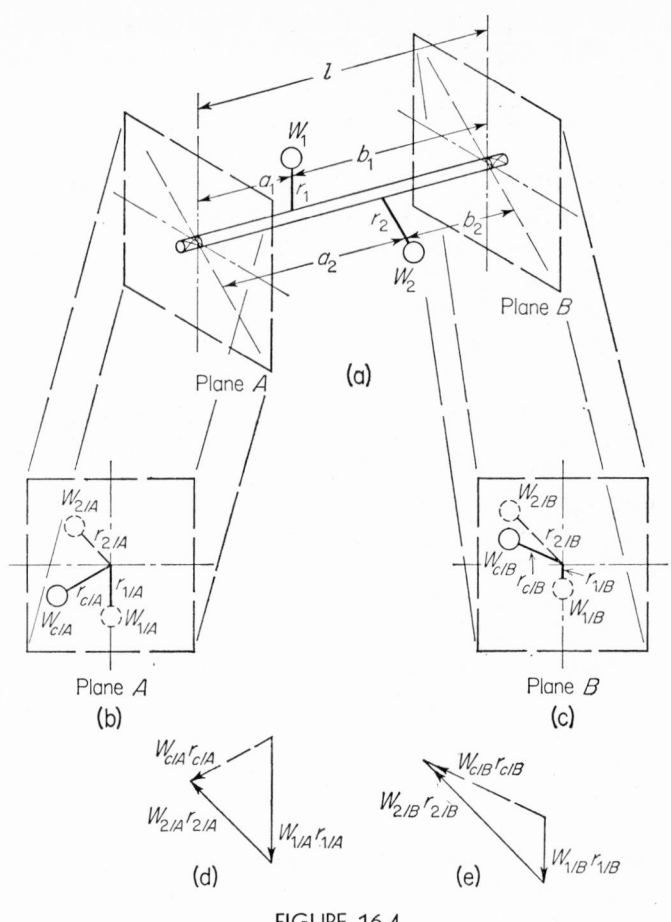

FIGURE 16.4

similar to that explained in Article 16.3. Then the system would be completely balanced by single counterweights in each of the two planes.

The counterweights in planes A and B necessary to balance weight W_1 can be determined by taking moments in the axial plane containing W_1 about the intersection of plane A or B and the shaft. The moment equation about plane A is

$$W_1 r_1 a_1 + W_{1/B} r_{1/B} l = 0$$

or

$$W_{1/B} r_{1/B} = -W_1 r_1 \frac{a_1}{l}$$

where $W_{1/B}$ = counterweight in plane B

$r_{1/B}$ = radius of counterweight in plane B

l = distance between planes A and B.

The negative sign indicates that the counterweight is in opposite direction to W_1 as shown in Fig. 16.4(c). The counterweight in plane A can now be found by taking moments about plane B *or* summing forces in the axial plane containing W_1. Summing forces give us

$$W_{1/A}r_{1/A} = -\,(W_1r_1 - W_{1/B}r_{1/B})$$

This counterweight is shown in Fig. 16.4(b). In the same way the counterbalance can be found in the planes for W_2. These are shown also in the Figs. 16.4(b) and (c).

The single equivalent counterweights in the two planes, $W_{c/A}$ and $W_{c/B}$, are shown also in the figures and is the resultant of the vectors corresponding to the two counterweights in each plane as shown in Figs. 16.4(d) and (e).

Although the above example only contained two unbalanced weights, it is readily seen that the process would be the same for any number of unbalanced masses and therefore any unbalance in a rotating member can be completely balanced by the addition of two counterbalances in any two transverse planes, which will be referred to as balancing planes. The balancing planes are usually located at convenient points on the shaft or rotor so that the counterweights can be easily attached. In large rotors or shafts containing flywheels balance is usually achieved by the removal of metal from the rotor or flywheel instead of the addition of balancing weights. This is usually accomplished by drilling holes in the members at the correct positions. The holes would obviously be drilled 180° away from the position where counterweights would be added.

16.5 Graphical Method of Dynamic Balancing

We will now show how a rotor or shaft with known unbalances can be balanced in two planes by graphical means. Consider the shaft with three unbalanced masses as shown in Fig. 16.5(a). We wish to balance the system with counterweights in planes A and B. The various quantities needed for balancing graphically are tabulated in Table 16.1. The quantities W, r, θ, a, and b are known quantities for the three unbalanced weights W_1, W_2, W_3, in planes 1, 2, and 3 respectively. The quantities Wr, Wra, and Wrb are calculated from these. Note that a_1 and $W_1r_1a_1$ are negative since W_1 is to the left of plane A. Therefore the moment of W_1 is opposite to the moments of W_2 and W_3 about plane A. The only quantities known for planes A and B are the distances between the planes. The underlined quantities for planes A and B are determined from the graphical analysis.

We start our analysis by taking moments about plane A and the sum of the moments of all the forces, including the force caused by the balancing weight in plane B, must be zero about plane A. Since moments are vector

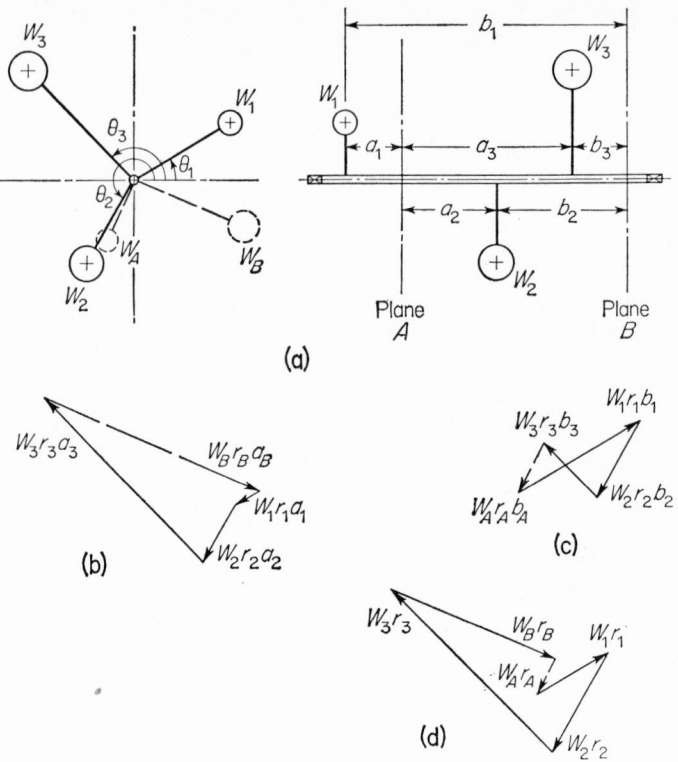

FIGURE 16.5

quantities, they can be represented as vectors, and the vector resultant must be zero. The vector representing a moment is normal to the plane of the moment and the sense of the vector follows the right-hand rule, which states that if the fingers of the right hand are closed in a fist with the thumb outside then, if the fingers are pointing in the direction of the moment, the thumb will point in the direction of the arrow head. In the vector diagram for moments about plane A, Fig. 16.5(b), the ω^2/g term has been dropped so that the moment is represented by a vector of magnitude Wra and the vectors have all been rotated 90° counter clockwise. There is quite an advantage in rotating the vectors because now they point in the radial direction of the corresponding weights. For example the vector $W_3r_3a_3$ has the same direction as the radial line from the shaft to W_3 and sense from the shaft to W_3. The vectors for the three known unbalances are drawn as shown. Note that the sense of the vector $W_1r_1a_1$ is from W_1 towards the shaft because it is a negative vector (a_1 being negative since it is to the left of plane A). For balanced moments about plane A, the moment vector

Table 16.1

Plane	W (lb)	r (in.)	θ	a (in.)	b (in.)	Wr	Wra	Wrb
1	5	6	30°	−3	15	30	−90	450
2	8	5	240°	5	7	40	200	280
3	10	8	135°	9	3	80	720	240
A			250°	0	12	14.5		177
B			337°	12	0	62.5	750	

diagram must close so that the vector $W_B r_B a_B$ representing the balance weight in plane B is as shown in the figure. The direction and sense of the vector determines the direction and position of the counterweight in plane B necessary to balance the moments about plane A. The magnitude of the counterbalance in plane B is found by dividing the magnitude of the vector $W_B r_B a_B$ by the distance between the planes, a_B. The counterweight W_B is shown in Fig. 16.5(a) in its correct position.

We now have a choice of two methods to determine the necessary counterweight in plane A. We can take moments about plane B in the same manner that we took moments about plane A, or we can use the summation of forces. Figure 16.5(c) shows the vector diagram of moments about plane B and the closing vector determines the counterweight in plane A. Note that the counterweight in plane A will not affect the moments about plane A, therefore those moments are still balanced. Instead of taking moments about plane B we could find the required counterweight in plane A by drawing a vector diagram for the centrifugal forces of all the weights, including the weight in plane B, as shown in Fig. 16.5(d). The vector closing the polygon indicates the magnitude, direction and sense of the counterbalance in plane A. It should be pointed out that we could not have started the balancing procedure by drawing the force vectors first since the closing vector would only give us the direction and magnitude of a single force necessary for balancing and we would have no means of determining the magnitudes or directions of the necessary weights in either plane. Such a diagram would only tell us the necessary weight for static balance, and two other vector polygons would still be necessary for determining the required weights in the two planes.

16.6 Dynamic Balancing by Analytical Methods

Balancing by analytical methods can readily be accomplished by taking components of the moments and forces in the horizontal and vertical axial planes including the counterweights as unknowns. The sum of these must be zero in each plane for dynamic balance. The position and magnitude of the counterweights in the two balancing planes can be determined by either of two methods: (1) taking moments about one plane and then balancing the forces, or (2) taking moments about both planes. The set of equations which must be satisfied where moments about one plane and forces are used are

$$Wra \sin \theta = 0, \quad Wra \cos \theta = 0, \quad Wr \sin \theta = 0, \quad Wr \cos \theta = 0 \quad (16.5)$$

where a is the distance from one plane to the various weights, θ is the angle as shown in Fig. 16.5(a) and the summation for moments includes the counterweight in the plane about which moments were not taken while the force summation includes both counterweights. If the forces are not considered the equations which must be satisfied are

$$Wra \sin \theta = 0, \quad Wra \cos \theta = 0, \quad Wrb \sin \theta = 0, \quad Wrb \cos \theta = 0 \quad (16.6)$$

As an example of the application of these two sets of equations they will be applied to the same rotor as used in the graphical analysis and shown in Fig. 16.5(a). Using Eqs. (16.6) where moments only are considered, the

Table 16.2

Plane	Wr	a	b	θ	$\sin \theta$	$\cos \theta$	$Wra \sin \theta$	$Wra \cos \theta$	$Wrb \sin \theta$	$Wrb \cos \theta$
1	30	-3	15	$30°$	0.500	0.866	-45.0	-78.0	225.0	390.0
2	40	5	7	$240°$	-0.866	-0.500	-173.2	-100.0	-242.5	-140.0
3	80	9	3	$135°$	0.707	-0.707	509.0	-509.0	169.7	-169.7
A		0	12				0	0	-152.2	-80.3
B		12	0				-290.8	687.0	0	0
						Σ	0	0	0	0

necessary information is tabulated in Table 16.2 for convenience. All the information for planes 1, 2, and 3 are known or can be calculated directly, while only the values of a and b are known for the balancing planes A and B. Knowing that the summations must be zero the appropriate values for $Wra \sin \theta$, $Wra \cos \theta$, $Wrb \sin \theta$, and $Wrb \cos \theta$ for planes A and B can be so determined as to make the summation zero and are shown underlined in the tabulation. These are the horizontal and vertical components of the moments about each plane and from these we can determine the angle θ and magnitude of Wr for the counterweights in the two planes. For plane B

$$\tan \theta_B = \frac{Wra \sin \theta}{Wra \cos \theta} = \frac{-290.8}{+687.0}$$

$$\theta_B = 336.1°$$

and the magnitude of the counterweight multiplied by its radius is the square root of the sum of the squares of the perpendicular components divided by the value of a, or

$$(Wr)_B = \frac{\sqrt{(290.8)^2 + (687.0)^2}}{12} = 62 \text{ lb-in.}$$

In the same manner, for plane A:

$$\tan \theta_A = \frac{-152.2}{-80.3}$$

$$\theta_A = 259.3° \qquad \text{and}$$

$$(Wr)_A = \frac{\sqrt{(152.2)^2 + (80.3)^2}}{12} = 14.34 \text{ lb-in.}$$

Equations (16.5) could be used to determine the counterbalance in a similar manner by first using the two moment equations to determine the counterweight in one of the planes and then using force equations to determine the counterbalance in the other plane. After the counterbalance in one plane has been determined the summation of forces including the known counterbalance must be zero leaving the counterbalance in the other plane as the only unknown and it could be solved for. Since there are no advantages in the use of these equations, it is usually preferable to use Eqs. (16.6).

16.7 Balancing

In the preceding sections the necessary counterbalance was determined as a weight multiplied by the radius of rotation. Having this we can then arbitrarily select either the radius or weight and then determine the other. In many practical cases balance weights are attached directly to the rotor, or holes are drilled in the rotor, at convenient locations and for these cases the radius is fixed, leaving only the weight to be determined. The counterweights should always be placed at the maximum radius available so that a minimum counterweight is needed. For the same reason it is generally desirable to locate the balancing planes as far apart as possible. In the design of rotating members which will require balancing, convenient locations should be made for the adding of counterweights or drilling of balancing holes.

Although any rotor can be balanced in two planes in order to remove dynamic bearing forces, such a method leaves bending moments in the rotor. In order to reduce these bending moments, it is quite often desirable to balance each unbalance in the plane of the unbalance. For example most crankshafts are balanced as shown in Fig. 15.9(c) by placing counterweights on extensions of the crank arms or webs in order to reduce bending moments in the shaft.

Although the analytical method of balancing is the more accurate method, it is usually desirable to use the graphical method also as a check. The graphical method is sufficiently accurate in most cases if a large scale is used for the vectors. For high speed applications neither method is sufficiently accurate for good balance, because the magnitude and location of the unbalances can not be determined with sufficient accuracy. For these cases other methods must be used which will be discussed in a later chapter. However, where large unbalances are known, they should be balanced by the above methods in the design of the member so that only small unbalances will be present for correction by other methods.

PROBLEMS

16.1 A rotor with three masses rotating in a common plane is shown in Fig. P16.1, where the dimensions and weights are as follows:

$$W_1 = 4 \text{ lb} \qquad r_1 = 3 \text{ in.} \qquad \theta_1 = 45°$$
$$W_2 = 3 \text{ lb} \qquad r_2 = 5 \text{ in.} \qquad \theta_2 = 225°$$
$$W_3 = 4 \text{ lb} \qquad r_3 = 6 \text{ in.} \qquad \theta_3 = 330°$$

Determine the weight and position of the counterweight which will balance the system at a radius of 4 in. analytically and check the results graphically.

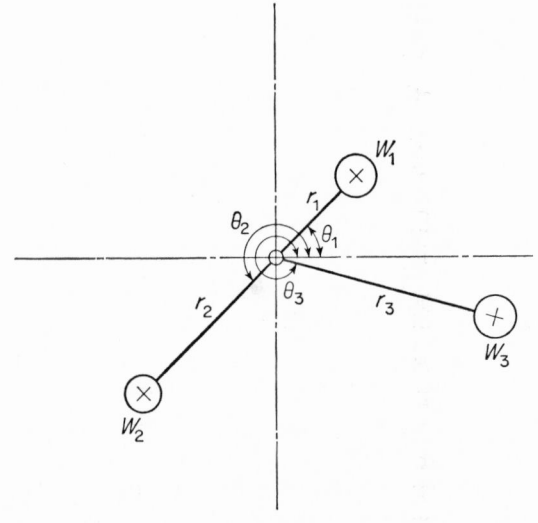

FIGURE P16.1

16.2 A rotor with three masses rotating in a common plane is shown in Fig. P16.1, where the dimensions and weights are as follows:

$$W_1 = 6 \text{ lb} \qquad r_1 = 4 \text{ in.} \qquad \theta_1 = 90°$$
$$W_2 = 5 \text{ lb} \qquad r_2 = 2 \text{ in.} \qquad \theta_2 = 180°$$
$$W_3 = 3 \text{ lb} \qquad r_3 = 5 \text{ in.} \qquad \theta_3 = 315°$$

Determine the weight and position of the counterweight which will balance the system at a radius of 3 in. analytically and check the results graphically.

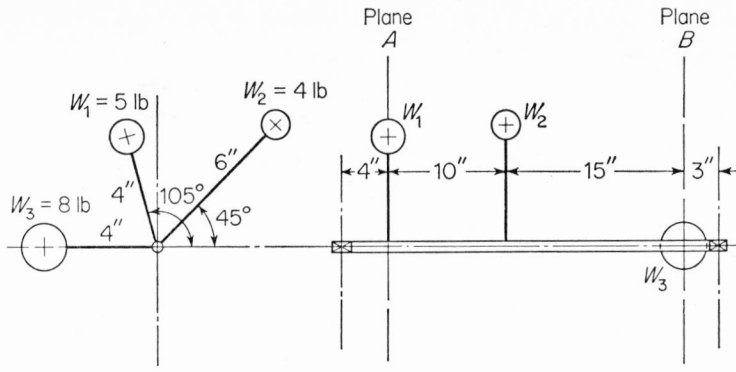

FIGURE P16.2

16.3 A rotor with three masses is shown in Fig. P16.2. Determine the magnitudes of the reactions at the bearings if the rotor is turning at a speed of 1800 rpm.

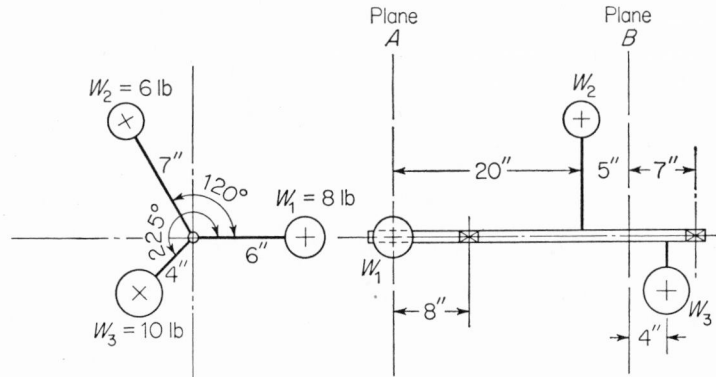

FIGURE P16.3

16.4 (a) Determine analytically the positions and magnitudes of the weights necessary to balance the system in Fig. P16.2 if the weights are placed in planes A and B and at a radius of 5 in.

(b) Check the results of part (a) graphically.

16.5 Determine the bearing reactions for the rotor shown in Fig. P16.3 if the shaft is turning at 2400 rpm.

16.6 (a) Determine analytically the positions and magnitudes of the weights in planes A and B which will balance the system in Fig. P16.3 if they are placed at a radius of 5 in.

(b) Check the results of part (a) by a graphical analysis.

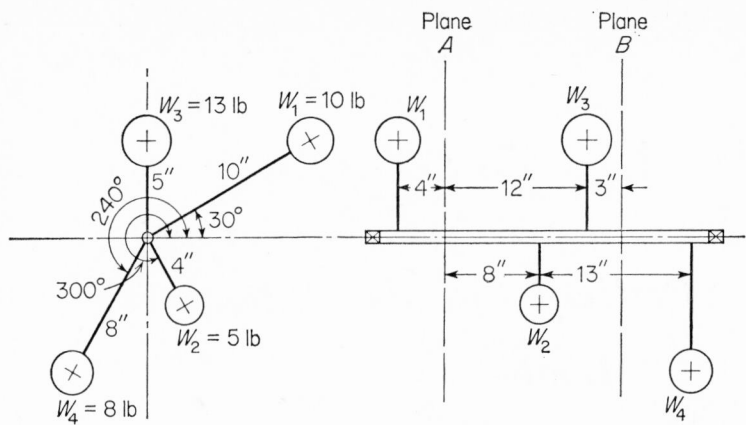

FIGURE P16.4

16.7 (a) The rotating system shown in Fig. P16.4 is to be balanced by a weight in plane A at a radius of 12 in. and a weight in plane B at a radius of 10 in. Determine the weights of the two counterbalances analytically.

(b) Check the results of part (a) by a graphical solution.

Chapter 17

Critical Speeds of Rotating

Members

17.1 Introduction

Before proceeding to a discussion of special machines for the determination of unbalance in rotors, which will be covered in the following chapter, we need to discuss another very important phenomenon which is closely related to the unbalance of rotating members. It has been observed in many rotating shafts or rotors that at certain speeds excessive vibrations occur which cause large bearing reactions and, in many cases, permanent deformation of the rotating member, while at speeds above or below this speed the rotor runs smoothly. In some cases the rotors have broken with great damage ensuing. The angular velocity at which this occurs is called the critical speed, the whipping speed or the critical whirling speed. This phenomenon occurs even for rotors which are very accurately balanced and therefore no rotating member should be operated for any length of time at a speed close to the critical speed. In this chapter we will show why this phenomenon occurs and discuss ways of determining the critical speed of rotating members, and means of changing this critical speed if it happens to be at the speed that a shaft is designed to operate. In the discussion of balancing machines in the next chapter we will make use of information developed in this chapter.

17.2 Single Disc on a Shaft

We shall first discuss a single disc rotating on a flexible shaft. We shall assume that the weight of the shaft is negligible in relation to the weight of the disc or rotor and that the center of gravity of the disc is offset from the center of the disc by a very small amount, e, called the eccentricity.

311

When the shaft starts to rotate this unbalance will cause a centrifugal force tending to bend the shaft in the direction of the center of gravity. Figure 17.1(a) shows the disc and shaft in the deflected position caused by an angular velocity of some given value. Figure 17.1(b) shows a side view of the disc where G is the center of gravity, S is the center of the disc through which the shaft passes and O is the point where the bearing axis intersects

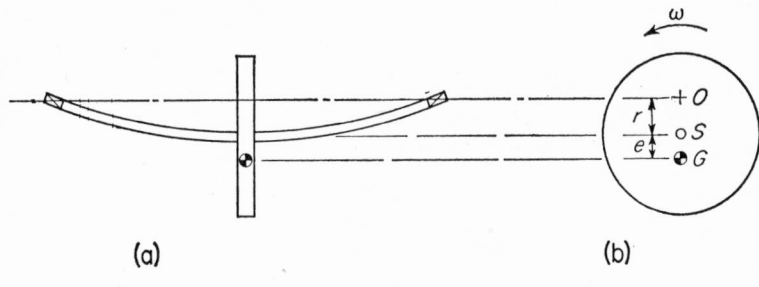

(a)   (b)

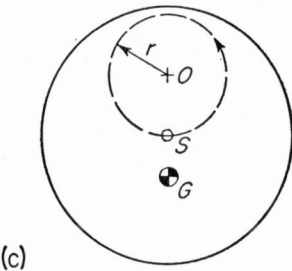

(c)

FIGURE 17.1

the disc. The distance $\overline{SG}$ then is the eccentricity, e, of the center of gravity and the distance $\overline{OS}$ is the deflection of the shaft, labeled r, caused by the centrifugal force. Both the eccentricity and the deflection are greatly exaggerated in the figure for clarity.

When the shaft is rotated at some fixed velocity, ω, the centrifugal force will cause the shaft to deflect in the direction of the eccentricity and the center of the disc will then whirl about the centerline of the bearings in a circle of radius r, as shown in Fig. 17.1(c). The center of gravity will then be rotating with a radius of $(r + e)$ and the centrifugal force will be $m(r + e)\omega^2$ where m is the mass of the disc. This force is balanced by the elastic pull of the shaft tending to straighten the shaft. This pull is proportional to the bending stiffness of the shaft and the deflection, r. This elastic force can then be written as kr where k is the force on the disc necessary to deflect the shaft a unit distance, or the spring rate of the shaft, as defined in Article 13.4. These two forces must be in equilibrium for a steady whirling motion, giving us the equation

$$kr = m(r + e)\omega^2 \tag{17.1}$$

Solving this equation for the shaft deflection r,

$$r = \frac{me\omega^2}{k - m\omega^2} = e \frac{\omega^2}{\dfrac{k}{m} - \omega^2} \tag{17.2}$$

From this equation we see that when the shaft is rotating at an angular velocity such that ω^2 is equal to k/m, the denominator of the fraction goes to zero and the deflection then becomes infinite. Such a condition is obviously impossible since the shaft would break before the deflection could go to extremely large values, but such a speed is called the critical speed of the shaft and we find it undesirable to operate rotating members at such speeds.

We will discuss what happens in actual cases if they are operated at the critical speed later but for the present let us define the critical speed as

$$\omega_c = \sqrt{\frac{k}{m}} \tag{17.3}$$

Substituting this equation into Eq. (17.2) we can rewrite it as

$$r = e \frac{\omega^2}{\omega_c^2 - \omega^2} = e \frac{\left(\dfrac{\omega}{\omega_c}\right)^2}{1 - \left(\dfrac{\omega}{\omega_c}\right)^2} \tag{17.4}$$

Figure 17.2 shows a plot of this equation with the deflection r as a function of ω/ω_c. This curve shows that when the shaft is running below the critical speed, ($\frac{\omega}{\omega_c} < 1$), the deflection of the shaft is as shown in Fig. 17.1 with the center of gravity lying on the line joining S and O and rotating about O with a radius of $(r + e)$. When the shaft is operated above the critical speed, r becomes negative indicating that r and e are in opposite directions. Figure 17.3 shows the deflection of the shaft under this condition, and we see that the center of gravity G now rotates in a circle about O with a radius $(r - e)$. If the shaft is running at a very high speed (many times the critical speed) r approaches the value of e as a limit, G and O become coincident and the center of the disc whirls about the center of gravity with a radius e. In this case the shaft runs smoothly, since there is no centrifugal force, and the only force exerted on the bearings is the force necessary to deflect the shaft by the amount e. For a well-balanced system, this force is negligible. It is easily seen that the center of gravity must remain fixed in space at extremely high speeds with the disc rotating about the center of gravity because otherwise the centrifugal force would become excessive

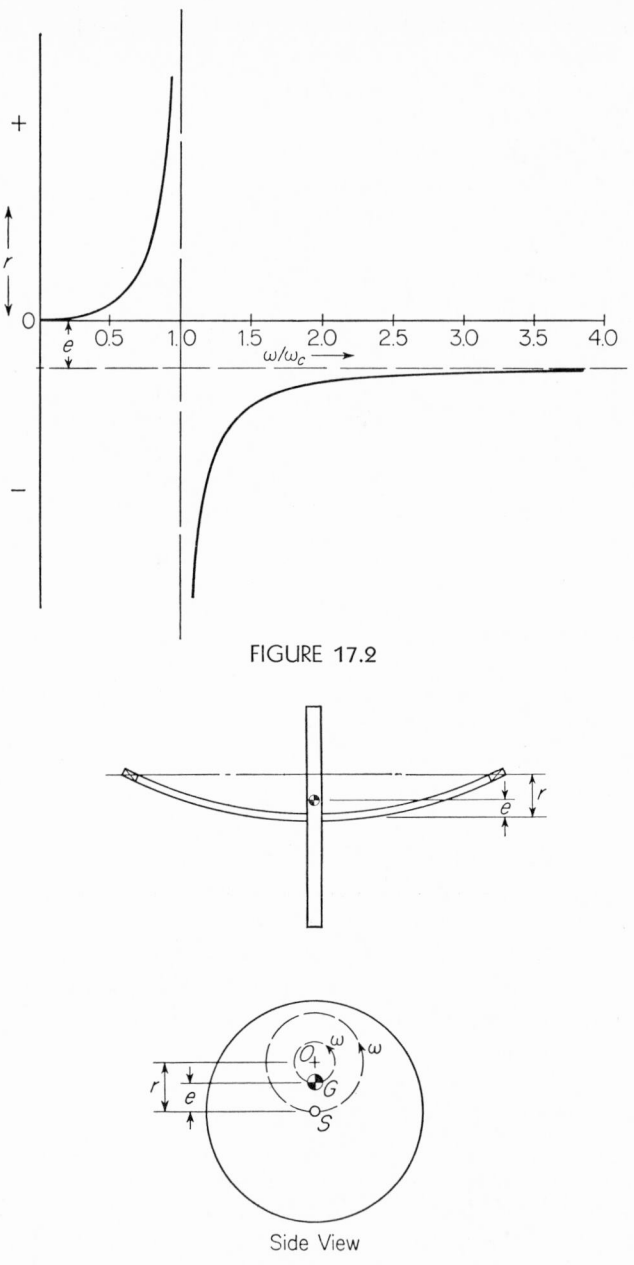

FIGURE 17.2

Side View

FIGURE 17.3

and, since all rotors run smoothly at speeds greatly exceeding the critical, the only explanation is that there is no centrifugal force. The tendency of rotating members to rotate about their centers of gravity at high speeds is used to achieve automatic balancing of rotating members. This will be discussed in the next chapter.

The whirling of the shaft is stable at speeds below and above the critical but is unstable at the critical speed. The above equations were developed on the basis of the rotor operating at some constant angular velocity. If an actual rotor is started from rest with slowly increasing speed, the radius of whirl will gradually increase until the critical speed is approached, at which time the shaft will whirl violently, resulting in large forces on the bearings. Because of some damping or friction in the system, the radius of whirl will be finite at the critical speed and as the speed increases above the critical (assuming that the whirling was not sufficient to cause failure) the radius of whirl will decrease until the rotor is operating quite smoothly and will continue to do so as the speed increases. If, however, the speed is increased rapidly as we pass through the critical, the shaft will pass through the critical speed without excessive whirl since the speed must remain near the critical for some time for the amplitude of whirl to build up to a high value.

17.3 Single Disc with Friction

In order to explain how the center of gravity shifts from a position outside the circle of motion of the center of the disc to a position inside this circle as the shaft goes through the critical speed, we must consider the effect of friction on the motion. In the previous equations the frictional forces were ignored. We will find that the friction forces do not appreciably affect the critical speed, but have a large effect on the relative positions of the points O, S, and G. Since our analysis will be used only to demonstrate the effects of friction on the whirling motion of shafts and rotors and the friction forces can at best be only approximations, we will take the liberty of making some assumptions at the beginning of the analysis. However the results of the analysis agree with the results found by actual observations of whirling rotors.

Consider a disc rotating about some point O other than the geometric center S as shown in Fig. 17.4(a). Friction forces caused by air resistance will tend to oppose this motion and we will assume that the friction forces are proportional to the velocity at any point. In the figure the friction forces around the periphery of the disc are shown. Since point A has the highest velocity (OA being the longest radius) and point B has the lowest velocity, the friction forces will vary along the periphery from a maximum at A to a minimum at B. By symmetry we see that the resultant of these forces is zero in the horizontal direction but they have a resultant F in the vertical direction downward. There will also be a resultant couple about O

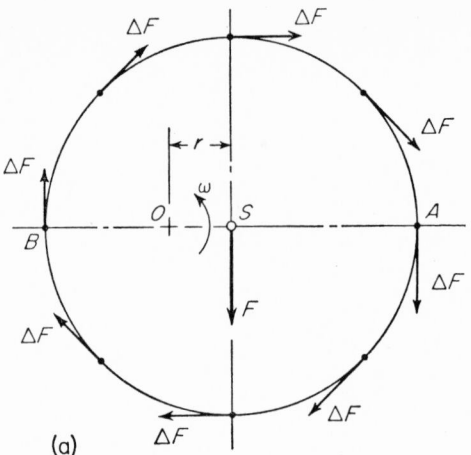

(a)

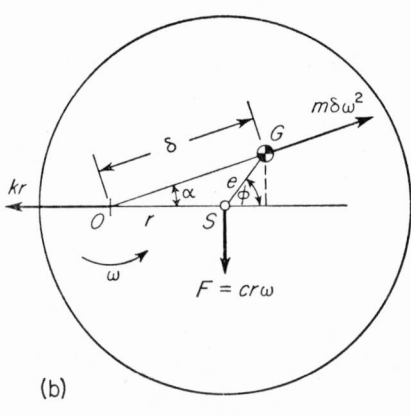

(b)

FIGURE 17.4

which must be balanced by a torque from the shaft. The resultant will then be a force downward through S and a couple. Note that the force F opposes the motion of the geometric center S. We can write this force as

$$F = cr\omega \tag{17.5}$$

where c is a constant of proportionality, called the damping constant, and $r\omega$ is the velocity of the center S. Figure 17.4(b) shows the forces on the rotating disc and we see that with the friction force the points O, S, and G cannot be collinear since there must be component of the centrifugal force balancing the friction or damping force, and the line SG must make an angle ϕ with the line OS. This angle, which is called the phase angle, represents the angle by which the center of gravity leads the displacement or line OS.

The phase angle can be determined as a function of the angular velocity of whirl from the figure by summing up the forces in the horizontal and vertical directions as

$$m\delta\omega^2 \cos\alpha = kr \tag{17.6}$$

$$m\delta\omega^2 \sin\alpha = cr\omega \tag{17.7}$$

The relation between angles ϕ and α as shown by the figure are

$$r = \delta\cos\alpha - e\cos\phi$$

$$\delta\sin\alpha = e\sin\phi$$

Using these equations to eliminate α from Eqs. (17.6) and (17.7)

$$m(r + e\cos\phi)\omega^2 = kr \tag{17.8}$$

$$me\omega^2 \sin\phi = cr\omega \tag{17.9}$$

Solving Eqs. (17.8) and (17.9) for $\cos\phi$ and $\sin\phi$, $\tan\phi$ can be determined as

$$\tan\phi = \frac{\sin\phi}{\cos\phi} = \frac{c\omega}{k - m\omega^2}$$

Dividing through by m and remembering that k/m is ω_c^2 and then dividing both numerator and denominator by ω_c^2 this equation can be reduced to

$$\tan\phi = \frac{\left(\dfrac{c}{m\omega_c}\right)\left(\dfrac{\omega}{\omega_c}\right)}{1 - \left(\dfrac{\omega}{\omega_c}\right)^2} \tag{17.10}$$

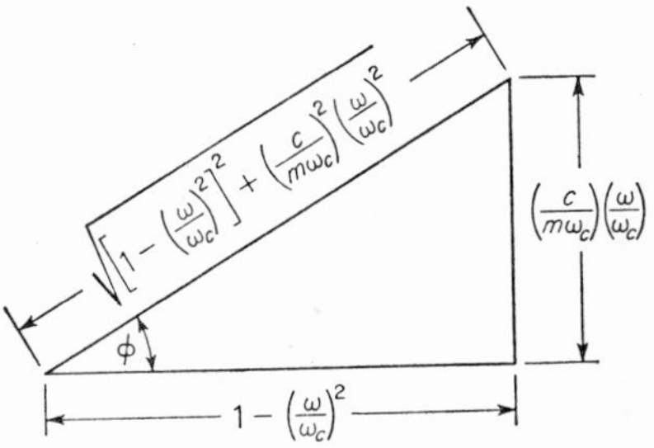

The radius of whirl of the center of the disc or the amplitude of the whirl can be found for the case where friction is considered by the use of Eq. (17.9). From Eq. (17.10) and Fig. 17.5

FIGURE 17.5

$$\sin\phi = \frac{\left(\dfrac{c}{m\omega_c}\right)\left(\dfrac{\omega}{\omega_c}\right)}{\sqrt{\left[1 - \left(\dfrac{\omega}{\omega_c}\right)^2\right]^2 + \left(\dfrac{c}{m\omega_c}\right)^2\left(\dfrac{\omega}{\omega_c}\right)^2}}$$

Substituting this in Eq. (17.9), solving for r and simplifying

$$r = \frac{e\left(\dfrac{\omega}{\omega_c}\right)^2}{\sqrt{\left[1 - \left(\dfrac{\omega}{\omega_c}\right)^2\right]^2 + \left(\dfrac{c}{m\omega_c}\right)^2\left(\dfrac{\omega}{\omega_c}\right)^2}} \tag{17.11}$$

Note that this equation reduces to Eq. (17.4), developed for the case with no friction, if c is zero.

These two equations, Eqs. (17.10) and (17.11), will prove useful not only in our study of critical speeds of shafting but also in the study of balancing machines. A plot of Eq. (17.10) is shown in Fig. 17.6 where the angle ϕ is

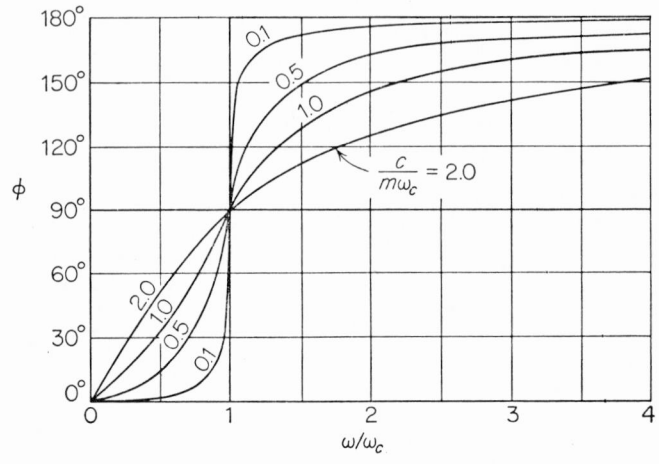

FIGURE 17.6

plotted as a function of ω/ω_c with $c/m\omega_c$ as a parameter. Note that for very low speeds the angle ϕ is very nearly zero, at the critical speed ϕ is 90° for any amount of damping and at higher speeds ϕ approaches 180° as a limit. In most cases the damping constant, c, is small and for these cases ϕ is almost zero for speeds up to one-half the critical. We say that "the heavy side flies out" while for speeds above one and one-half the critical ϕ is almost 180° and we say that "the light side flies out."

Figure 17.7 is a plot of Eq. (17.11) where r/e is plotted as a function of ω/ω_c, with $c/m\omega_c$ as a parameter, and here we see that damping is beneficial in that it reduces the amplitude of whirl at the critical speed. Since the relative direction of r and e is shown by Fig. 17.6, the absolute value of the ratio of the amplitudes of r to e is plotted in Fig. 17.7. As shown in the figure the maximum amplitude of whirl when damping is present does not occur at exactly the critical speed, but at slightly higher values. However, since no rotor should be operated at any speed close to the critical, the critical as determined in the case of no damping is satisfactory for practical cases.

In some cases it has been observed that a flexible shaft with a single disc whirls violently at some speed, seems to recover as the speed increases and then, at a slightly higher speed, whirls violently again before smoothing out

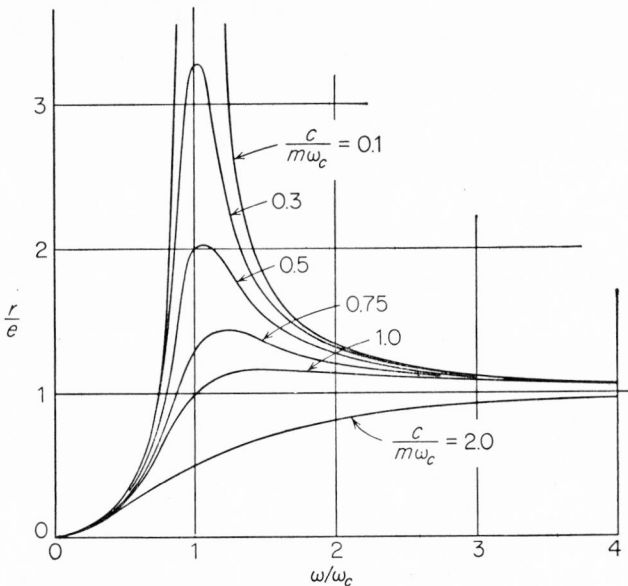

$$\frac{c}{m\omega_c} = 0.1$$

0.3

0.5

0.75

1.0

$$\frac{c}{m\omega_c} = 2.0$$

$\frac{r}{e}$

ω/ω_c

FIGURE 17.7

at still higher speeds, indicating two critical speeds. This can be explained
by the fact that most bearings do not have the same flexibility in the
horizontal and vertical directions. Since the spring constant, k, was defined
as the force per unit deflection, this indicates that the spring constant will
be slightly different in a horizontal and vertical direction, giving two critical
speeds. The shaft then will not actually whirl in a circle at these critical
speeds but will move in an oval or straight line with the axis or line being at
90° at one critical relative to the direction at the other critical. As the shaft
is brought up to speed it will whirl at the lowest critical, seem to recover and
then whirl again at the higher critical. Since these critical speeds are usually
close together, and it is desirable to operate at a speed quite removed from
the critical, we need consider only one of the critical speeds in most cases.

17.4 Natural Frequency of Transverse Vibration

Consider again the shaft with a single disc as redrawn in Fig. 17.8.
If, while the disc is standing still, a force is applied to the disc causing it to
deflect by an amount y_0 and then suddenly removed, the disc and shaft will
oscillate or vibrate in a transverse direction with an amplitude of y_0. We
will determine the natural frequency of this vibration and will find that it is
the same as the critical speed as found in the previous articles.

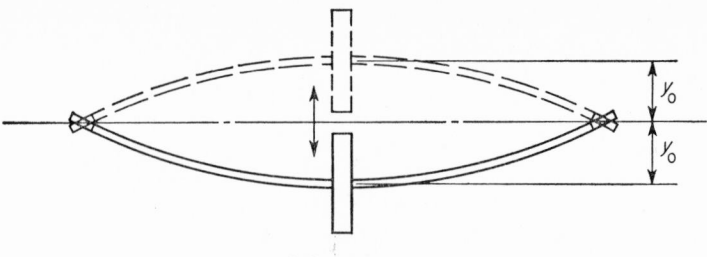

FIGURE 17.8

If we disregard friction the system is a conservative system as defined in Article 13.4 and we can develop the equation of motion by energy considerations. From the law of conservation of energy the sum of the kinetic and potential energies is a constant. If we consider first that the system is vibrating in a horizontal plane so as to eliminate the effects of gravity, the sum of potential and kinetic energies is

$$\tfrac{1}{2}mv^2 + \tfrac{1}{2}ky^2 = \text{constant}$$

where y is the deflection at any time. Taking the derivative of this equation with respect to time

$$mv\frac{dv}{dt} + ky\frac{dy}{dt} = 0$$

Noting that $v = dy/dt$, this can be written as

$$\frac{d^2y}{dt^2} = -\frac{k}{m}y \tag{17.12}$$

This is the equation defining simple harmonic motion and therefore the disc will oscillate with simple harmonic motion with a circular frequency (the angular velocity of the rotating vector representing the motion) of

$$\omega_n = \sqrt{\frac{k}{m}} \tag{17.13}$$

This frequency, ω_n, is called the natural frequency of free vibration and we see that it has the same value as the critical speed of whirl.

In order to show that gravity has no effect on the natural frequency we will also develop the equation of motion for vibration in the vertical direction. Using Eq. (13.20) we rewrite it as

$$\frac{d}{dt}(U_e + U_i + T) = 0 \tag{17.14}$$

Because of the weight of the disc, the shaft will deflect a small amount δ and using this equilibrium position as a reference for the displacements we can set up equations for the potential and kinetic energies. The only internal force is the spring force of the shaft and the total potential energy caused by the work it does on the disc is

$$U_i = + \frac{k}{2}(y + \delta)^2 \qquad (17.15)$$

where y is the deflection measured from the equilibrium position and taken as positive downward. The weight, an external force, does work on the shaft during a displacement and the potential energy of the system decreases for a positive or downward displacement so that

$$U_e = - W(y + \delta) \qquad (17.16)$$

The kinetic energy is the same as before, or

$$T = \tfrac{1}{2}mv^2 \qquad (17.17)$$

Expanding these terms and substituting then into Eq. (17.14)

$$\frac{d}{dt}(\tfrac{1}{2}ky^2 + ky\delta + \tfrac{1}{2}k\delta^2 - Wy - W\delta + \tfrac{1}{2}mv^2) = 0$$

Noting that $W = k\delta$, the terms Wy and $ky\delta$ cancel and we find upon taking the derivative

$$mv\frac{dv}{dt} + ky\frac{dy}{dt} = 0$$

or

$$\frac{d^2y}{dt^2} = - \frac{k}{m}y$$

which is the same equation of motion as found for the horizontal vibration. Then we see that the oscillations are the same in the vertical and horizontal directions when the displacements are measured from the equilibrium position in both cases, and that gravity does not affect the natural frequency of vibration.

Since the critical speed and the natural frequency of transverse vibration are the same, we can determine the critical speed by calculating the natural frequency. The natural frequency is fairly easy to determine for many cases as we will find in this chapter. The whirling of a shaft is often referred to as a vibration but in the strict sense it is not a true vibration. In the whirling shaft the heavy side always flies out below the critical so that the extreme longitudinal fiber on the heavy side is always in tension. The shaft whirls much in the manner of a jumping rope and since the shaft rotates about its centroidal axis at the same time that the shaft whirls, both with the same speed, the stress in any longitudinal fiber of the shaft remains constant during whirling. For transverse vibration, however, the shaft does not rotate and, as the deflection changes from one direction to another, the fiber stresses change from tension to compression. In the vibrating shaft the stresses in the shaft are the same that would occur if the load on the shaft were changing direction at the same frequency as the vibration while for the whirling shaft the shaft is stressed in the same manner as if a steady load were applied to the shaft.

Equation 17.13 can be written in a form better suited to the determination of the natural frequency by writing k as a function of the weight and the static deflection caused by this weight. This relation as noted previously is

$$W = k\delta$$

Then
$$\omega_n = \sqrt{\frac{W/\delta}{W/g}} = \sqrt{\frac{g}{\delta}} \qquad (17.18)$$

Then for a single disc on a shaft the natural frequency or critical speed can be determined by calculating the deflection of the shaft caused by the weight of the disc and substituting into Eq. (17.18). The critical speed as found by this equation is in terms of rad/sec and should be converted to rpm since the critical speed is usually given in rpm.

In the next Article we will consider the natural frequency for shafts and rotors in general which may have any number of discs or masses. We will again make use of energy methods but a much shorter method is available in which the maximum kinetic energies are used and we develop this method for the single disc system.

Consider the shaft and disc vibrating at its natural frequency with an amplitude of y_0. At the two extreme displacements the shaft comes to a complete stop as it reverses its direction of motion, and at these two positions, since the velocity is zero, the kinetic energy is also zero. The potential energy will be a maximum at these positions. We have shown that the potential energy due to the gravity force does not affect the natural frequency if we use the equilibrium position as a reference for the displacements. Therefore the total potential energy can be considered as the elastic energy of the shaft due to a displacement from the equilibrium position. Then at the equilibrium position the potential energy is zero and all the energy of the system is kinetic energy and obviously the kinetic energy is a maximum at this position. Since the total energy of the system remains a constant, the maximum kinetic energy must be equal to the maximum potential energy, or

$$\tfrac{1}{2}mv_{max}^2 = \tfrac{1}{2}ky_0^2 \qquad (17.19)$$

where y_0 is the amplitude or maximum displacement. We have shown that the disc and shaft vibrate with simple harmonic motion so we can write the displacement y at any time as

$$y = y_0 \sin \omega_n t$$

and the velocity then is

$$v = y_0\omega_n \cos \omega_n t$$

where ω_n is the natural frequency of vibration. The velocity will be at a maximum when $\cos \omega_n t = 1$, so that

$$v_{\max} = y_0 \omega_n$$

Substituting this into Eq. (17.19)

$$m y_0^2 \omega_n^2 = k y_0^2$$

Solving this equation for ω_n, we find

$$\omega_n = \sqrt{\frac{k}{m}}$$

This method of determining the natural frequency, known as Rayleigh's method, is much simpler than any other since we can set the maximum kinetic energy equal to the maximum potential energy and solve directly for the frequency. It should be noted that this method makes the assumption that the system vibrates with simple harmonic motion, but since a large majority of vibrations are of this type and for other vibrations it is a good approximation, this method is usually satisfactory for the determination of the natural frequency.

17.5 Multidisc Shaft

Although a single disc on a shaft was used to show that the critical speed of rotation and the natural frequency of transverse vibration are the same, the same is true for a shaft with any number of discs or for a heavy rotor. This can be seen by noting that if we deal with the center of gravity of a system of discs, the same equations hold as long as we use the spring rate corresponding to a load at the position on the shaft at which the center of gravity is located, then, for any shaft or rotor, the critical speed can be determined by determining the natural frequency of transverse vibration. However, instead of working with the center of gravity and the spring constant we will use Rayleigh's method which is much easier.

Consider the shaft with three discs as shown in Fig. 17.9(a) which is representative of a shaft with any number of discs. The shafts could vibrate transversely in any three possible modes as shown in Fig. 17.9 (b), (c), and (d), which show the deflection curve of the shaft for various modes of vibration. The frequency of the vibrations would be different for each mode of vibration. The mode shown in Fig. 17.9(b) would have the lowest frequency as can be seen by noting that the resistance of the shaft to deflections corresponding to the other modes is much greater. The greater stiffness would correspond to a greater spring rate and thereby, from Eq. (17.13), a higher frequency. As the number of discs increases, the number of modes of vibration would also increase and for a large single

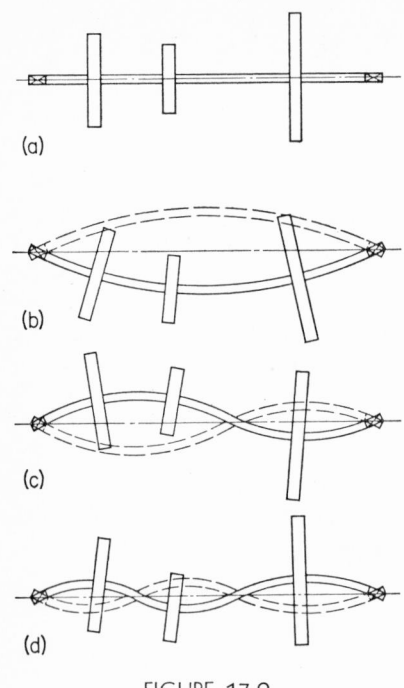

(a)

(b)

(c)

(d)

FIGURE 17.9

rotor, which could be considered as a shaft with an infinite number of discs, there would be an infinite number of modes of vibration with a corresponding infinite number of natural frequencies of vibration. For each mode of vibration or for each natural frequency there will be a corresponding critical speed. The lowest or first order critical speed is the most important in most cases, since the higher critical speeds are usually above the operating speed of rotating machinery. Therefore we will consider only the lowest or first order critical speed. However, in some cases, the second and even the third critical speed is in the range of operation for some high speed equipment and would need be considered in these cases.

Rayleigh's method consists of equating the maximum potential and maximum kinetic energy as shown in the preceding Article. He found that for the first natural frequency the beam-disc system vibrated in a manner such that the frequency became a minimum. Or stating it in another way, of all the possible deflection curves in a beam the curve corresponding to the least amount of constraint, consistent with the bearing constraints, is the curve that the shaft will take during vibration and this will correspond with the lowest natural frequency. Any other curve would necessitate additional constraints on the shaft, making the shaft stiffer and therefore having a higher natural frequency. However, Rayleigh found that any reasonable curve would correspond to a frequency quite close to the true frequency.

Rayleigh's method then consists of assuming some reasonable deflection curve, assuming that the discs vibrate with simple harmonic motion corresponding to that curve, and then equating the maximum potential and maximum kinetic energies. The shaft shown in Fig. 17.10 will be used for developing the equation for the natural frequency. The shaft is a simple shaft with bearings at the ends and containing any number of discs, n. The deflection curve during vibration is usually assumed as proportional to the static deflection curve imposed by the weights of the beams. The static deflection curve is fairly easy to develop and generally gives satisfactory

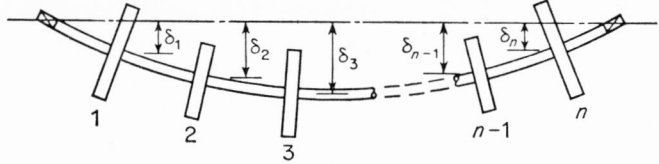

FIGURE 17.10

results. The potential energy of the system is the strain energy caused by weights of the discs and is equal to the work done on the shaft by forces equal to the weights of the discs applied at the position of the discs during this deflection. This energy corresponding to the maximum deflection for any disc is

$$\text{Potential energy} = \tfrac{1}{2}W_i\delta_i$$

where δ_i is the static deflection of the beam at disc i. All the discs are assumed to vibrate with simple harmonic motion with an amplitude of δ_i at the natural frequency and the motion for any disc can then be written as

$$y_i = \delta_i \sin \omega_n t$$

The maximum velocity for any disc will then be

$$v_i = \delta_i \omega_n$$

Then summing the maximum potential and maximum kinetic energies of the discs and equating them

$$\sum_{i=1}^{n} \frac{1}{2} W_i \delta_i = \sum_{i=1}^{n} \frac{1}{2} m_i v_i^2 = \sum_{i=1}^{n} \frac{1}{2}\frac{W_i}{g}\delta_i^2\omega_n^2$$

with the result

$$\omega_n = \sqrt{\frac{g \,\Sigma\, W_i\delta_i}{\Sigma\, W_i\delta_i^2}} \tag{17.20}$$

where the natural frequency is given in terms of rad/sec. The critical speed of a shaft is usually given in revolutions per minute and converting Eq. (17.20) to rpm, we find the critical speed to be

$$N = 187.7\sqrt{\frac{\Sigma\, W_i\delta_i}{\Sigma\, W_i\delta_i^2}} \tag{17.21}$$

where the acceleration of gravity has been brought from under the radical and combined with the coefficient. It should be remembered that this method usually gives a critical speed somewhat higher than the true critical. If the true deflection curve during vibration were used in determining the deflection, the result would be the true critical speed but since any other deflection curve could only be imposed by the addition of restraints, thereby increasing the rigidity of the shaft, the critical speed corresponding to a stiffer shaft would be higher than that actually encountered. However, for most engineering work the deflection curve caused by the weight of the discs is sufficiently accurate. A frequency within 5 per cent of the true frequency could ordinarily be expected by this method.

If greater accuracy is desired it can be achieved by using inertia loads to determine a new deflection curve instead of the static weight loads. Using the deflection curve and frequency as found in the above method the loads on the shaft caused by the discs can be taken as

$$F_i = m_i \delta_i \omega_i^2 \tag{17.22}$$

Using these loads instead of the weights of the discs we can determine a new deflection curve more nearly approaching the true curve and then, using the new deflection curve, Eq. (17.20) can be used again as

$$\omega_n' = \sqrt{\frac{g \, \Sigma \, W_i \delta_i'}{\Sigma \, W_i (\delta_i')^2}}$$

where δ_i' is the deflection for the ith disc from the new deflection curve. This process could be repeated any number of times to improve the accuracy but since the process converges rapidly only one or two are usually necessary to get the required accuracy. This process is a method of successive approximations.

The problem then reduces to the determination of the deflection curve of a shaft statically loaded by the weights of the discs and the substitution of the results into Eq. (17.20). If the weight of the shaft is large in relation to the discs, then the weight of the shaft should also be included in determining the deflection curve and in the substitution in Eq. (17.20). This can be handled by breaking the shaft into a large number of increments and finding the weight of each increment and then using these weights as concentrated loads on the shaft. This will be demonstrated in the next Article.

It is important to emphasize that in determining the critical speed or natural frequency from these equations that only loads caused by masses or weights acting on the shaft should be included in the static deflection curve. Loads caused by belts, or the forces transmitted by gears, are constant loads not affecting the kinetic energy of the shaft during vibration and therefore do not affect the critical speed.

17.6 Deflection of Non-Uniform Shaft

The deflection of a shaft of uniform cross section is a problem in strength of materials and can be handled analytically. However, if the cross section of the shaft is not uniform the determination of the deflection curve becomes quite a problem and most designers resort to a graphical method of determining the deflection curve. Although the deflection of shafts is not considered a part of dynamics, we will discuss the graphical method since the determination of the critical speed depends on the deflection curve. Also the graphical method is a process of graphical integration which is quite useful in many dynamic analyses.

The equations which relate load, shear, bending moment, slope and deflection of any beam are

$$\frac{dV}{dx} = -q \qquad (17.23)$$

$$\frac{dM}{dx} = V \qquad (17.24)$$

$$\frac{d^2y}{dx^2} = -\frac{M}{EI} \qquad (17.25)$$

$$\frac{dy}{dx} = \text{slope} \qquad (17.26)$$

where V = shear force, lb

  q = load, lb/in.

  M = bending moment, lb-in.

  y = deflection, in.

  E = Young's modulus of elasticity, lb/in.^{2}

  I = moment of inertia of cross section, in.^{4}

  x = distance along beam, in.

Differentiating Eq. (17.24) with respect to x, we relate the bending moment to the load or

$$\frac{d^2M}{dx^2} = \frac{dV}{dx} = -q \qquad (17.27)$$

and differentiating Eq. (17.25) twice with respect to x (assuming EI is constant), we get

$$\frac{d^3y}{dx^3} = \frac{1}{-EI}\frac{dM}{dx} = \frac{V}{-EI}$$

$$\frac{d^4y}{dx^4} = \frac{1}{-EI}\frac{dV}{dx} = \frac{q}{EI} \qquad (17.28)$$

and we have an equation of the deflection as a function of the load, q, and the determination of the deflection involves integrating the load, divided by EI, four times as long as EI is a constant along the beam.

We have assumed a uniform loading of the beam along its surface but it can be shown that the same equations hold for any type of loading, such as a load varying with x or a concentrated load.

From Eq. (17.23) we see that the shear force at any point is the integral of the load along the beam up to that point. Therefore when we draw a shear diagram we are graphically integrating the load along the beam. Also, from Eq. (17.24), when we draw a bending moment diagram we are graphically integrating the shear force along the beam.

This double integration can be done with a single graphical construction by drawing a funicular polygon of the loads. We will show that a funicular polygon of the forces on a beam is a bending moment diagram of the beam. Consider the simply supported beam with three loads shown in Fig. 17.11

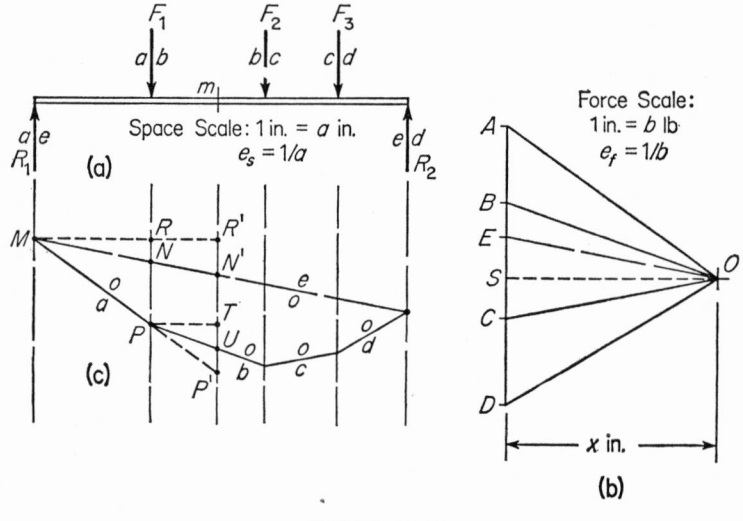

FIGURE 17.11

(a). Using Bow's notation for the loads, a force and a funicular polygon are drawn as shown in Figs. 17.11(b) and (c). The pole point, O, for the force polygon is x inches from the vertical forces. The beam is drawn to a scale such that one inch on the drawing is "a" inches on the beam and therefore the space scale is

$$e_s = \frac{1}{a}$$

and in the same manner the force scale is

$$e_f = \frac{1}{b}$$

where one inch of the force polygon represents "b" lbs.

The triangle MNP on the funicular polygon is similar to the triangle OEA on the force polygon (parallel sides) so that

$$\frac{NP}{EA} = \frac{MR}{OS}$$

and then
$$(NP)(OS) = (EA)(MR) \tag{a}$$

where these are the actual lengths of the lines on the drawing. Note that line EA represents to some scale the reaction R_1 and MR represents to some scale the distance from R_1 to force F_1, so that $(EA)(MR)$ represents, to some scale, the bending moment at F_1. Then the distance NP on the funicular polygon multiplied by OS, or the pole distance x, represents, to some scale, the bending moment at F_1. The true moment at F_1 is given by

$$M_{F_1} = \frac{EA}{e_f} \cdot \frac{MR}{e_s}$$

Then from Eq. (a)

$$\frac{(NP)(x)}{e_f e_s} = \frac{EA}{e_f} \cdot \frac{MR}{e_s} = M_{F_1}$$

and the scale to which the distance NP on the funicular polygon represents the bending moment is

$$e_m = \frac{e_f e_s}{x}$$

or one inch measured vertically between the two lines of the funicular polygon represents

$$1 \text{ in.} = \frac{x}{e_f e_s} = abx \quad \text{in.-lb}$$

In order to show that the vertical distance on the funicular polygon represents the bending moment at any point along the beam consider the section at point m on the beam. By reasoning as in the previous example we see that the moment caused by R_1 at m is $(P'N')(OS)$ to the same scale, and the moment caused by F_1 is $(AB)(PT)$. By similar triangles

$$(AB)(PT) = (P'U)(OS)$$

and the bending moment at m is represented by the line

$$(P'N')(x) - (P'U)(x) = (N'U)(x)$$

Since the distance x remains constant, the vertical distance across the polygon represents the bending moment at any point along the beam to the same scale.

For beams having uniform loads or loads varying along the beam as shown in Fig. 17.12 we divide the loading into increments and represent

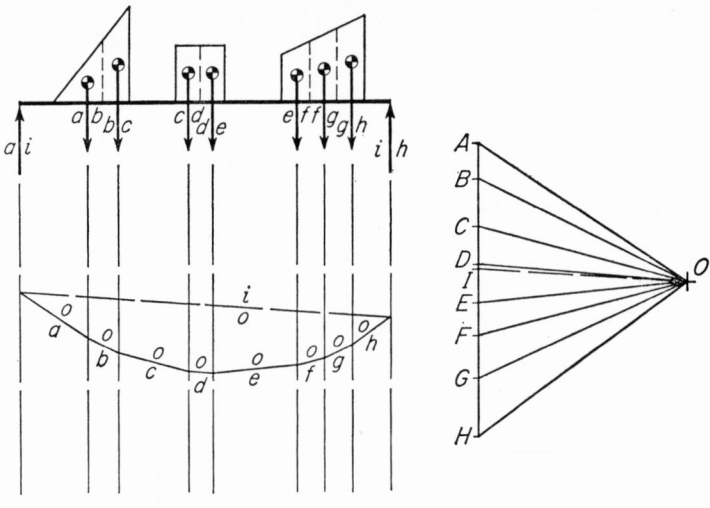

FIGURE 17.12

each increment as a concentrated load of magnitude equal to the load of the increment and acting along the line of action of the resultant of the increment. The concentrated load would then be equal to the area of the increment on the load-distance diagram and pass through its centroid. Figure 17.12 shows the force diagram and funicular polygon for a beam loaded in this manner. As will be noted the greater the number of increments taken, the more closely the concentrated loads will represent the true loading, and therefore the greater the accuracy of the bending moment diagram.

In this process, which is a double integration, the force diagram represents an integration of Eq. (17.23) giving us a shear diagram and the funicular polygon is the integration of Eq. (17.24) resulting in the bending moment diagram.

Comparing Eqs. (17.27) and (17.25) we see that if the moment of inertia of the cross section were constant along the beam, we could repeat this process in order to get a double integral of the bending moment diagram and thereby obtain a deflection curve to some scale. In doing this we would divide the bending moment diagram into increments or sections and draw vectors representing the area of the sections through their centroids. These vectors would then be the quantities we would be integrating.

If, however, the moment of inertia varies along the beam, we see from Eq. (17.25) that the moment of inertia must remain under the integral sign and we must integrate the quantity M/EI. In order to do this we must construct an M/EI diagram from the moment diagram and then integrate this diagram or curve. Such a diagram is constructed in Fig. 17.13 for a

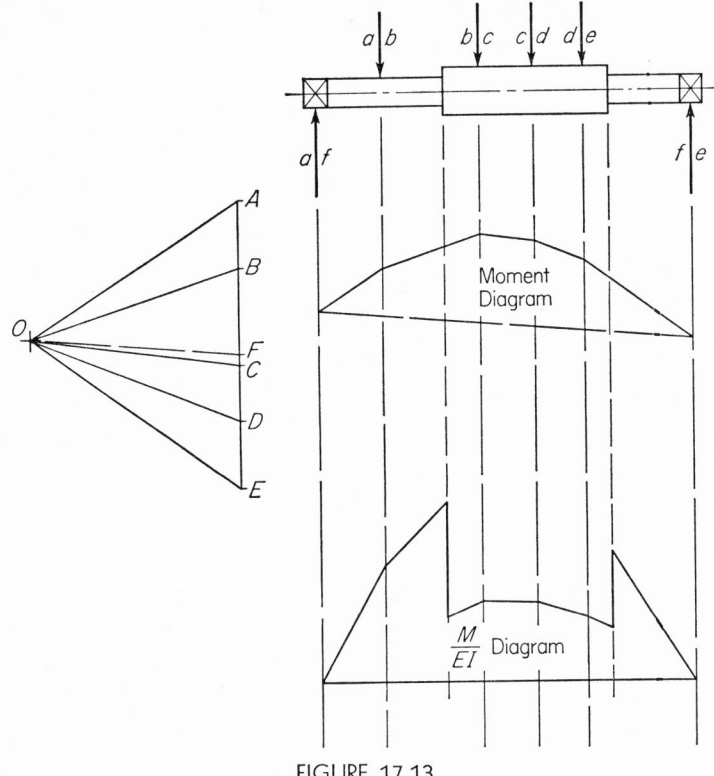

FIGURE 17.13

shaft or varying cross section. The M/EI diagram curve is laid off on a horizontal axis with the ordinates plotted to some appropriate scale. Note that where there is a sudden change in diameter of the shaft the diagram has a discontinuity since the moment of inertia changes suddenly at these points. The diagram is then composed of straight lines between points of change of cross section and load points.

If we were to repeat the process as described to get a bending moment diagram we would have to break up the diagram into increments along the beam, determine the area of each increment and then determine its centroid in order to get the vectors which we would integrate. The deflection curve can be gotten in a much simpler manner by resorting to two single graphical intregations which require no calculations of areas or locations of centroids.

Using the M/EI diagram as developed in Fig. 17.13 we divide it into sections or areas as shown in Fig. 17.14(a). The upper line of each incremental area is divided into two equal parts and the midpoint is projected onto a vertical line at the left as shown. These midpoints are the average vertical height of the individual areas. The midpoints and the projection of them on the vertical line should be numbered as shown so that they can

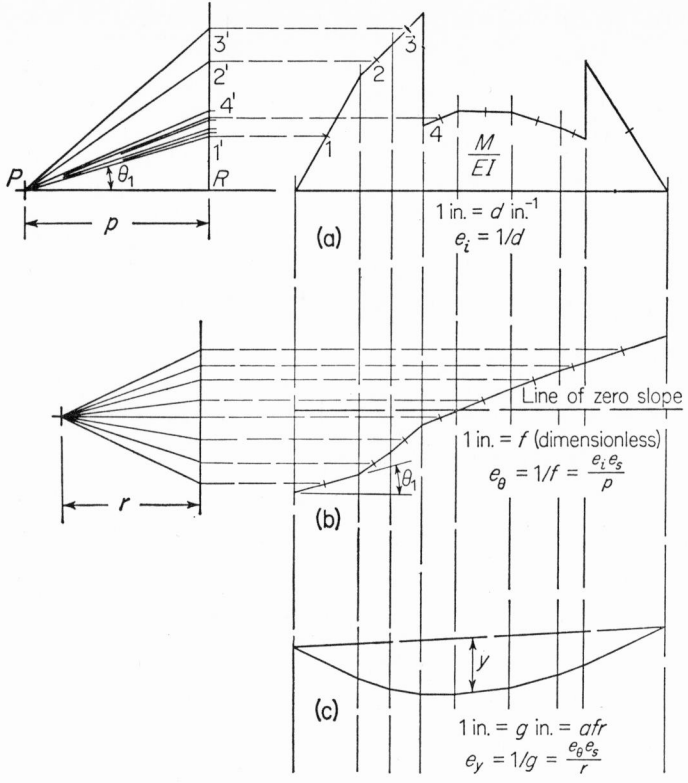

$$\frac{M}{EI}$$

$$1 \text{ in.} = d \text{ in.}^{-1}$$
$$e_i = 1/d$$

(a)

Line of zero slope

$$1 \text{ in.} = f \text{ (dimensionless)}$$
$$e_\theta = 1/f = \frac{e_i e_s}{p}$$

(b)

(c)

$$1 \text{ in.} = g \text{ in.} = afr$$
$$e_y = 1/g = \frac{e_\theta e_s}{r}$$

FIGURE 17.14

be kept in order. We now select a pole, P, some distance p from the vertical line and draw rays from the pole to each of the numbered points. The slopes of these rays are then proportional to the average heights of the individual areas. Lines are now drawn parallel to these rays across the vertical sections corresponding to the increments as shown in Fig. 17.14(b). For example, the line parallel to ray $1'-P$ is drawn between the vertical lines defining area 1. This first line can be started at any point on the left boundary line and each succeeding line is started at the end of the line to its left. This curve is an approximation of the integral curve of the M/EI curve. The true integral curve will be a curve tangent to the straight line sections at their mid-points.

Let us now examine this curve and show that it is an integral curve of the M/EI curve. The ordinate of the integral curve at any point must represent the area under the M/EI curve up to that point. Since the slope of any line of curve (b) represents to some scale the average height of the corresponding area, if this line is drawn across the width of the area, the increase in ordinate across each section represents the area of that section to some scale. Since each line starts at the end of the preceding line, these ordinates are added and at any point the ordinate represents the accumulated area under the M/EI diagram. From Eqs. (17.25) and (17.26) we see that this integral curve is the slope of the beam.

The scale for the slope curve can be found as follows. The tangent of the angle made by any ray with the horizontal, say for ray $1'-P$, is equal to the vertical distance to $1'$ divided by the distance p, *if* the scale of the M/EI diagram were one. If we let e_i be the scale to which the M/EI diagram is drawn, e_s be the space scale and e_θ be the slope scale, the actual angle θ_1 on the drawing is defined as

$$\tan \theta_1 = \frac{(M/EI)(e_i)}{p}$$

Also from the slope curve, the same angle θ_1 is defined by its tangent as

$$\tan \theta_1 = \frac{e_\theta}{e_s} \frac{d \text{ (slope)}}{dx}$$

Setting these equal and remembering that

$$\frac{d \text{ (slope)}}{dx} = \frac{M}{EI}$$

We can solve for the slope scale which is

$$e_\theta = \frac{e_i e_s}{p}$$

where p is the actual distance to the pole position.

This slope curve gives us the relative value of the slope at any point. The zero axis of this curve could readily be found if we knew the slope at some point along the curve; however, generally we do not know the slope at any point. This presents no difficulty since the integral of this curve gives us the relative deflections. The approximate position of the zero axis can be determined if we note that the integral of the area between the curve and the zero axis is equal to the deflection. Then, since the deflection at the right support of the beam is zero, the area below the zero axis must be equal to the area above the zero axis and we can draw the zero axis in its approximate position by judging the areas. An error in this axis will only affect the slope of the reference line for the deflections as will be explained below. If the zero axis is accurate, the reference line will be horizontal.

Graphically integrating the slope curve in the same manner as above will result in the deflection curve. This is shown in Fig. 17.14(c). The bottom curve is obtained from the integration and the top reference line can then be drawn since we know that the deflection is zero at the supports, and the deflection at any point is the vertical distance between the two curves as shown. Note that the reference line is not horizontal since we did not take the pole position along the line of zero slope. If we had done so the reference line on the deflection curve would have been horizontal. The scale for the deflection curve is found in the same manner as for the slope scale and its equation is

$$e_y = \frac{e_\theta e_s}{r}$$

where e_y is the scale of the deflection curve and r is the pole distance.

In the illustration the M/EI curve was divided into only a few areas for clarity but it should be pointed out that a more accurate deflection curve would have been obtained if the number of areas had been increased considerably Also to improve the accuracy the scales should be as large as possible and the drawing done on a large sheet of paper so that large scales could be used.

In determining the critical speed of shafting the deflections can be determined at the load points from the deflection curve and then substituted into Eq. (17.21). In cases of overhung shafts or those where the shaft extends beyond the bearings or supports, loads on the overhung portion should be reversed in direction in determining the deflection curve. The reason for this becomes obvious if we note the shape of the deflection curve for the first order critical speed. If the true direction of the overhung load were taken the deflection curve would correspond to a higher order critical speed.

In contrast to graphical differentiation, which we found to be only a good approximation, graphical integration is quite accurate if small increments are taken. With accurate drafting graphical integration should always give sufficient accuracy for engineering work. The single integration, as demonstrated in Fig. 17.14, as a method of finding the area under a curve compares favorably with the results of using a planimeter and has the advantage that the integral curve is obtained so that the area up to any given point on the abscissae can be determined. With the use of the drafting machine graphical integration is one of the quickest methods of obtaining an integral curve.

PROBLEMS

17.1 Determine the critical speed of a 60 lb rotor on a $1\frac{1}{2}$ in. dia. steel shaft if the rotor is midway between the bearings which are 22 in. apart. Calculate the static deflection analytically and check the deflection by graphical integration. Neglect the weight of the shaft.

17.2 Determine the critical speed of the shaft and rotor in Prob. 17.1 if the rotor is located 6 in. from one bearing.

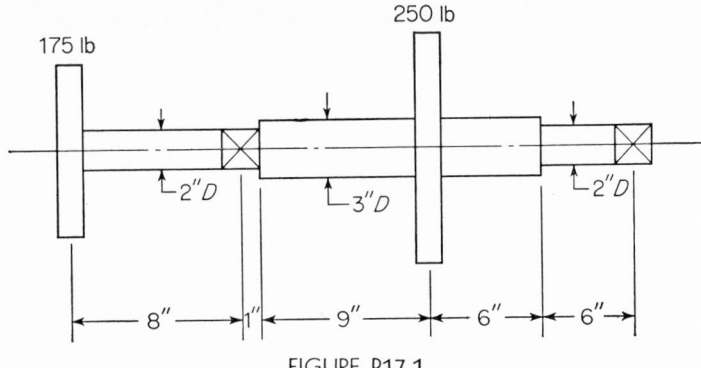

FIGURE P17.1

17.3 A $1\frac{1}{4}$ in. uniform diameter steel shaft supports two discs between bearings 25 in. apart. One disc, weighing 40 lbs, is 6 in. from the left bearing and the other disc, weighing 60 lbs, is 15 in. from the left bearing. Determine the critical speed of the shaft, neglecting the weight of the shaft.

17.4 Determine the critical speed of the shaft shown in Fig. P17.1. The shaft is steel and is assumed simply supported at the bearings. Neglect the weight of the shaft.

17.5 Determine the critical speed of the steel shaft shown in Fig. P17.2 neglecting the weight of the shaft. The loads indicated represent the weights of discs on the shaft.

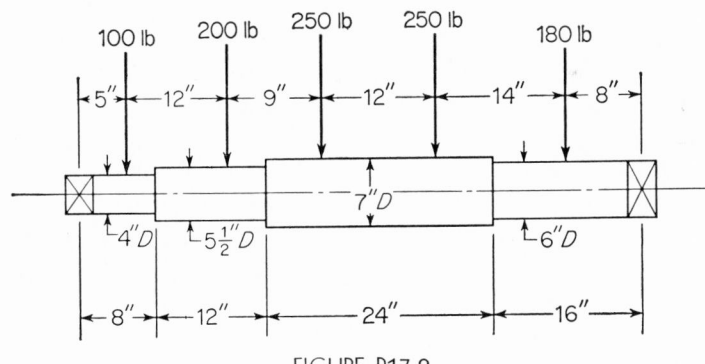

FIGURE P17.2

17.6 Determine the critical speed of the steel shaft shown in Fig. P17.2 considering only the weight of the shaft.

17.7 Determine the critical speed of the steel shaft shown in Fig. P17.2 considering both the weights of the discs and the weight of the shaft. The loads on the shaft represent the weights of discs.

Chapter 18

Balancing Machines

18.1 Introduction

Theoretically, any unbalance of a rotating body could be corrected by methods discussed in the previous chapter. However, careful design on the drawing board cannot be depended on to give satisfactory balance for members rotating at high speeds. In the actual manufacture of the rotating part, the casting or forging of the material leaves small unbalances which cannot be accounted for in the design, and machining also leaves small unbalances. For these reasons rotating members with high angular speeds must be accurately balanced after all machining processes have been completed. For low speed machinery this is usually not necessary but with modern machinery tending to run at higher speeds accurate balancing becomes necessary.

To emphasize the effect of a small unbalance at higher speeds, the curve in Fig. 18.1 shows the dynamic force caused by an inch-ounce of unbalance as a function of angular velocity. The inch-ounce is the unit of unbalance used in accurate balancing and is defined as the unbalance caused by one ounce of weight at a distance of one inch from the axis of rotation. That this is a small amount of unbalance is demonstrated by considering the unbalance of a large steam turbine weighing 5000 lb with the center of gravity 0.001 inch away from the axis of rotation. This corresponds to 80 inch-ounces of unbalance. If the turbine were rotating at 3600 rpm this unbalance would cause a centrifugal force of 1845 lb. Such a force could wreck a machine and would certainly cause bearing failure. As another example consider an aircraft gas turbine weighing only 300 lb and rotating at 16,000 rpm, with the center of gravity 0.001 inch from the axis of rotation. The 4.8 inch-ounce of unbalance would cause a centrifugal force of 2190 lb.

Since it is virtually impossible to hold tolerances close enough in the

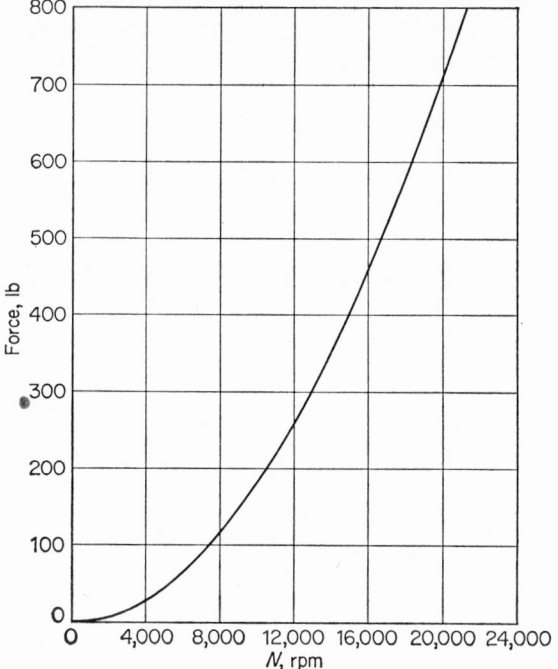

FIGURE 18.1

manufacture of such parts so that the center of gravity will not be offset by 0.001 inch or more, it becomes imperative that the parts be balanced after manufacture. In such a case the amount and position of unbalance is unknown and must be determined experimentally. Balancing machines have been developed for this purpose, and we will discuss several types in this chapter. The balancing machine is not actually used to determine the position and amount of the unbalance in a rotor but is used to determine the position and magnitude of the counterbalances in two planes necessary for balance.

18.2 Trial Method of Balancing

The simplest type of balancing machine is composed of a lightweight cradle or framework with bearings supporting the rotor, as shown in Fig. 18.2. The cradle is supported by pin joints or knife-edges in one of the balancing planes, say plane I, and by springs at the other end. Thus, if the cradle is displaced and released, it will oscillate about the support in plane I with a low frequency. The amplitude of the oscillation can then be determined by a pointer moving along a fixed scale as shown.

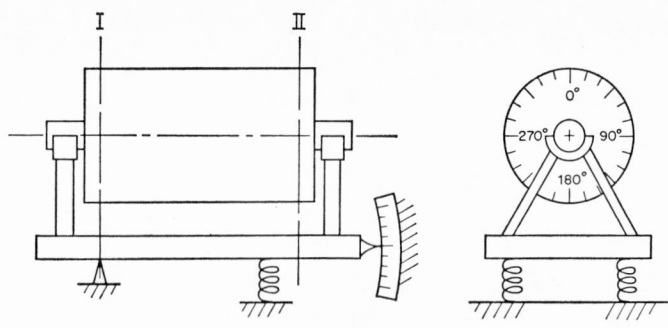

FIGURE 18.2

If the rotor is rotated by means of a light belt driven by a motor (which is usually independent of the frame in order to keep the weight of the frame as small as possible), any unbalance in the rotor will cause the frame to oscillate at the same frequency as the rotation of the rotor. The centrifugal force caused by the unbalance in the rotor will rotate with the rotor but since the frame is constrained to rotation about the horizontal axis in plane I, only the vertical component of this force can cause vibration of the cradle, and this component corresponds to a simple harmonic force with a circular frequency equal to the angular velocity of the rotor.

Setting up the equation of motion of the system we find

$$I \frac{d^2\theta}{dt^2} + k_t\theta = mr\omega^2 l \cos \omega t \qquad (18.1)$$

where I = moment of inertia of the cradle and rotor taken about the pivot point

$\quad\theta$ = angular displacement of system about the equilibrium position

$\quad k_t$ = torsional spring constant of system

$\qquad$ = k of spring multiplied by distance from spring to pivot point

$\quad m$ = mass of rotor

$\quad r$ = radius of center of gravity of rotor from center of rotation

$\quad l$ = distance from pivot point to center of gravity of rotor

$\quad\omega$ = angular velocity of rotor

From our previous observations we would guess that the system would oscillate with simple harmonic motion. Then we can assume that the motion of the system can be represented by the equation

$$\theta = \theta_0 \cos \omega t$$

where θ_0 is the amplitude of the motion. Substituting this into Eq. (18.1) and solving the resulting equation for the amplitude, we find after simplifying

$$\theta_0 = \frac{\dfrac{mrl}{I}\left(\dfrac{\omega}{\omega_n}\right)^2}{I - \left(\dfrac{\omega}{\omega_n}\right)^2} \qquad (18.2)$$

where
$$\omega_n = \sqrt{k_t/I}$$

and is the natural frequency of oscillation of the system. This equation is of the same form as Eq. (17.4) and we could plot a curve of amplitude as a function of ω/ω_n as in Fig. 17.2. If friction or damping were considered we would get equations similar to Eqs. (17.10) and (17.11) and could plot curves as in Figs. 17.6 and 17.7. We see from these curves that the amplitude would be a maximum at some angular velocity of the rotor.

These equations are not sufficient however to determine the amount or position of the unbalance in the rotor. This can be shown by reference to Eq. (18.2). If the rotor were rotated at some given speed and the amplitude of the vibration determined by means of the pointer attached to the frame, all the terms in the equation could be determined excepting the terms r and l. The product of these terms could be calculated from the equation, but we would have no way to separate the terms so that we would know neither the radius of the unbalance nor its position along the axis.

The simplest method of determining the counterweights necessary in each plane for balance is based on the phase angle curve for the system as represented in Fig. 17.6, where the angle would correspond to the angle between the position of the unbalance and the position of maximum amplitude of vibration. From this curve we see that for low rotational speeds, the unbalance would be at the so-called high spot corresponding to a phase angle of $0°$ indicating the heavy side flies out; above the critical speed the unbalance would be at a phase angle of $180°$ relative to the high spot, or the light side would fly out; at the critical speed, the phase angle would be $90°$. Then, if a pencil or marker were held above the end of the rotor over the spring and gradually moved towards the rotor until it just touched the rotor, it would scribe a mark on the rotor at the high spot of the vibration. Knowing the speed of the rotor relative to the critical speed we could then locate the position of the unbalance. A few trials of placing various weights at the position opposite the unbalance would then determine the magnitude of counterweight needed to balance the rotor in the plane. This method is not very accurate, however, since at low speeds and high speeds (relative to the critical) the amplitude of vibration would be so small that a large arc would be scribed on the rotor and the exact high spot would be difficult to determine. At the critical speed where the amplitude of the vibration is a maximum, we see from the curve that the phase angle changes rapidly with small change in speed and again the accuracy of the high spot would be questionable. In spite of these drawbacks this method is used quite often for rough balancing of rotors after installation. If such a procedure is used it is usually best to run the rotor at a speed considerably below the critical for most accurate results.

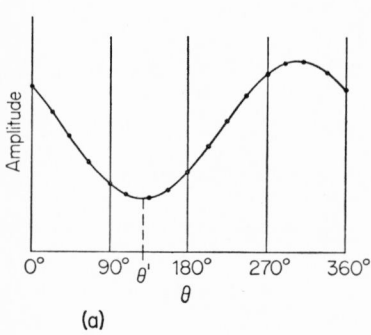

(a)

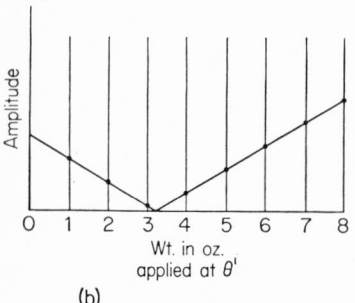

(b)

FIGURE 18.3

A more accurate trial method of determining the necessary counterweights in the two planes is as follows. The end of the rotor is marked with reference angles as shown in Fig. 18.2. Now if some given weight is attached to the rotor along its outside surface in plane II at the zero degree position and the rotor is brought up to speed above the critical speed and allowed to coast through this critical speed, the amplitude of vibration would be a maximum at the critical speed and it could be noted on the pointer. The mass could now be attached to some other angular position on the rotor and the process repeated. By determining the vibration amplitude for a large number of positions of the weight, a curve could be plotted as shown in Fig. 18.3(a). This curve is a plot of amplitude, as indicated by the pointer, as a function of the angular position of the weight. Since the amplitude of vibration is directly proportional to the unbalance in the system, there will be some position of the weight at which it will cause the unbalance to be a minimum and this position can be determined from the curve. Then from the curve we can determine the position in plane II at which the counterweight should be placed in order to balance the system about plane I. In Fig. 18.3(a) this position corresponds to θ'. Now knowing the position for the counterweight, we can place various weights at this position, measure the vibration amplitude for each different weight and plot a curve of amplitude as a function of magnitude of counterweight, as shown in Fig. 18.3(b). This curve will always be composed of two straight lines intersecting at some point on the zero amplitude ordinate *if* the angle θ' is accurate. Then, assuming θ' has been determined accurately, some counterweight will exactly balance the system, giving a zero amplitude; and it can be determined from the curve. In practice the procedure may have to be repeated in order to determine θ and the correct counterweight to the required accuracy. This would be done after an approximate counterweight was added according to the first runs.

Having the position and magnitude of the counterweight in plane II, the rotor can be reversed in the cradle so that the pivot is in plane II and the process repeated in order to determine the position and magnitude of the counterweight in plane I. Note that a counterweight in plane I will not affect the balance in plane II. Balancing the rotor in two planes then completely balances the rotor.

This is one of the first balancing machines developed and this basic method is still in use for heavy rotors in some instances. However, as presented, it is a slow process requiring many runs in order to achieve accurate balance, and many improvements have been made on the original method of plotting curves for a large number of runs.

In order to eliminate the need to attach weights to the rotor at various positions where a large number of rotors must be balanced a balancing head has been developed as part of the machine. Such a balancing head is shown in Fig. 18.4. The balancing head consists of two discs pinned at the center

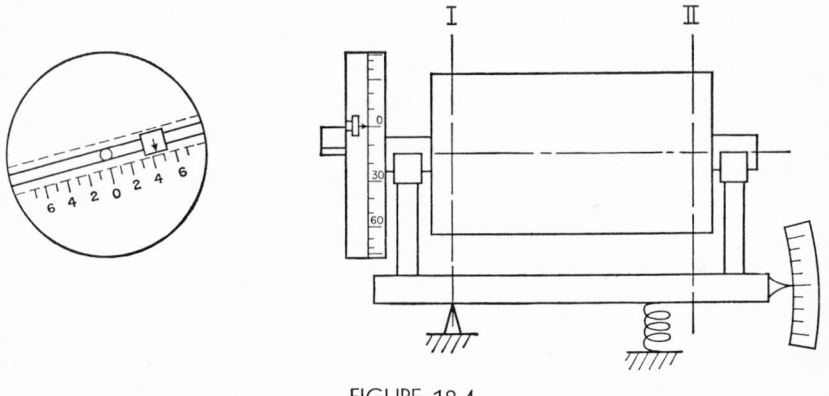

FIGURE 18.4

so that they can be rotated relative to each other. One disc is rigidly attached to the rotor as shown and this disc has the angular positions marked on it. The outer disc has a radial slot cut across its outer face in which a weight slides which can be fixed at any position along the slot. The balancing head is perfectly balanced when the weight is at the center of the disc, and therefore by sliding the weight along the slot, a given unbalance can be added to the system. By rotating the outer disc relative to the inner disc (which is attached to the rotor) the position of the unbalance can be changed at will and locked in any position. By a simple calculation the unbalance in the head can be converted to an equivalent weight attached to the planes of balance. In this way the balancing of a rotor can be greatly simplified.

A graphical method developed by Den Hartog for determining the correct balancing weights in each plane, and their positions, requires only four runs be made for each balancing plane. This method will be explained since it will be helpful in our discussion of balancing of rotors in the field after installation to be covered later.

The four runs required are as follows: (1) no counterweight is used so that the only unbalance in the system is that in the rotor; (2) a known unbalance is applied to the system at some given angular position, say at 0°; (3) the same unbalance at a position diametrically opposite the position in run (2), or at 180°; (4) the same unbalance at some position other than for runs (2) and (3). The maximum amplitude of the four runs as the rotor coasts through the critical speed is recorded and these four amplitudes can then be used to determine the magnitude and position of the required counterbalance for the given plane. An example will be used to demonstrate the method.

Assume that the maximum amplitudes recorded for the four runs are as follows:

(1) 0.050 in. with the only unbalance that in the rotor
(2) 0.035 in. with an unbalance of 4 in.-oz at the 0° position
(3) 0.075 in. with an unbalance of 4 in.-oz at the 180° position
(4) 0.070 in. with an unbalance of 4 in.-oz at the 75° position

The vector diagram is laid out as shown in Fig. 18.5(a) where the length of the vectors represent to some given scale the amplitudes recorded for the

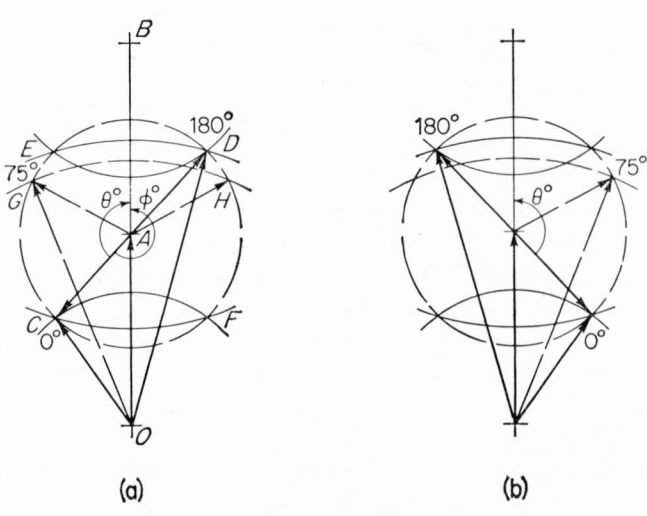

(a)   (b)

FIGURE 18.5

four runs. Since the amplitude is proportional to the unbalance, these vectors also represent to a different scale, unknown at present, the magnitude of the unbalance for each run. Line $O–B$ is laid off with $O–A = A–B = 0.050/e_s$ corresponding to the amplitude of the run with the only unbalance that in the rotor, where e_s is some convenient scale. With points O and B as centers, arcs are drawn with radius of $0.035/e_s$ and $0.075/e_s$ until they intersect at C, D, E, and F as shown, the arc radii being equal to the amplitude with the unbalance weight at $0°$ and $180°$, respectively, divided by the scale. Next a circle is drawn with center at A and radius $A–C$. This circle will pass through the points D, E, and F, as well as C. Now an arc of radius $0.070/e_s$ corresponding to the amplitude with the weight at $75°$ is drawn with center at O until it intersects the circle at points G and H.

The vector $\overline{O–A}$ represents to some scale the unbalance in the rotor, the vector $\overline{O–C}$ represents to the same scale the unbalance in the rotor and an added unbalance of 4 in.-oz at $0°$, and $\overline{O–D}$ represents the unbalance in the rotor together with an unbalance of 4 in.-oz at $180°$. Then the vector $\overline{A–C}$ must represent to the same scale the 4 in.-oz of unbalance at $0°$ and $\overline{A–D}$ must represent the 4 in.-oz of unbalance at $180°$. Note that these two vectors have opposite sense, being $180°$ apart. Then by dividing the length of these vectors by 4 we can determine the scale to which the vector $\overline{O–A}$ represents the unbalance in the rotor. The magnitude of the unbalance in the rotor can then be determined and there remains only the direction to be determined. Since $\overline{A–C}$ is in the $0°$ direction and $\overline{A–D}$ is in the $180°$ direction, the unbalance in the rotor must be in the direction of $\overline{O–A}$ which is either θ degrees of ϕ degrees depending on whether we measure the angle clockwise or counterclockwise. The fourth run is used to determine the direction in which the angle should be measured. The vector $\overline{A–G}$ or the vector $\overline{A–H}$, corresponding to the unbalance at $75°$, must make an angle of $75°$ with the zero degree vector $\overline{A–C}$ and we see that the vector $\overline{A–G}$ satisfies this condition indicating that the angle must be measured clockwise so that the angle θ is the angular position of the unbalance in the rotor, measured from $0°$.

There are two possibilities for drawing the vector diagram. The other possibility is shown in Fig. 18.5(b) and we see that either diagram gives us the same result and in the latter diagram the angle is measured in a counterclockwise direction. Then by scaling the figure we find that the unbalance in the rotor is 6.67 in.-oz at $137°$. Balance could then be achieved by adding a counterbalance of that amount at the diametrically opposite position or at $317°$.

In modern machines, the amplitude of the vibration of the cradle is measured electronically and since large amplification is possible in this manner, it is not necessary that the rotor be run at the critical speed. Other balancing heads have been also devised for use in special machines

where a large number of similar rotors must be balanced. We will discuss
one other type of balancing machine which is based on a somewhat different
principle.

18.3 Simultaneous Balancing in Two Planes

The last type of balancing machine which we will consider is shown in
Fig. 18.6(a). The machine consists of two half-bearings supported on thin

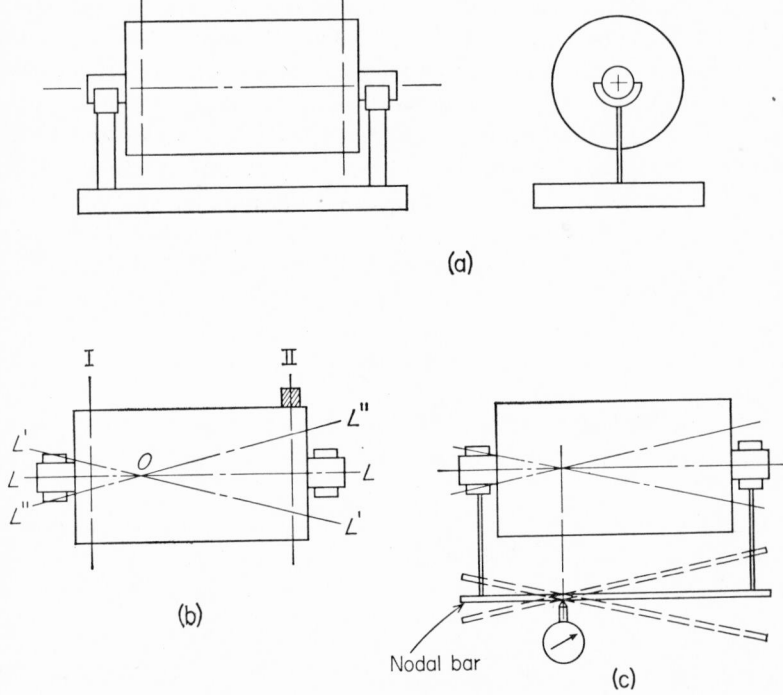

FIGURE 18.6

flexible springs so that the bearings can vibrate only in a horizontal plane.
Note that the parasitic mass of the machine, which must vibrate with the
rotor, consists only of the two bearings, giving a much higher amplitude
of vibration for any given unbalance in the rotor. Consider now a perfectly
balanced rotor in the bearings. Under rotation there will be no vibration
of the bearings, but if an unbalancing weight is placed in plane II, it will
cause the centerline of the rotor to move in a horizontal plane as shown in
Fig. 18.6(b), which is a top view of the rotor. The centerline will rotate
about a vertical axis through some point O to the extreme positions $L'-L'$

and $L''-L''$. This center of rotation will be the center of percussion relative to the plane II as discussed in Article 14.6. Regardless of the magnitude of the unbalance in plane II, there will be no motion of the center of percussion. Now if the weight is removed from plane II and placed in plane I, the centerline will rotate about the center of percussion relative to plane I and it will be a different position from point O, the center of percussion relative to plane II. If now a bar is attached to the bearings as shown in Fig. 18.6(c), it will oscillate in the same manner as the centerline of the rotor, and by moving a dial indicator along the bar, with weights alternately in planes I and II, the center of percussion relative to the two balancing planes can be located. Such a bar is called a nodal bar, and the positions of zero motion are called nodes. If the indicator is placed at the node corresponding to the center of percussion relative to plane II, any motion of the indicator will be caused by an unbalance in plane I, and by placing a known unbalance in plane I the magnitude of the vibration corresponding to that unbalance can be determined. In this manner the correct balance weights for the two planes can be determined for an unbalanced rotor similar to the balanced rotor used to determine the node points. The Gisholt Dynetric Balancing Machine is based on this principle.

Instead of the nodal bar, the Gisholt machine makes use of a small speaker coil moving in the field of a permanent magnet to indicate the motion of the two bearings, and uses electronic amplification in order to make the machine extremely sensitive. Therefore only a small magnitude of vibration is necessary for accurate balancing. A schematic sketch of the machine is shown in Fig. 18.7.

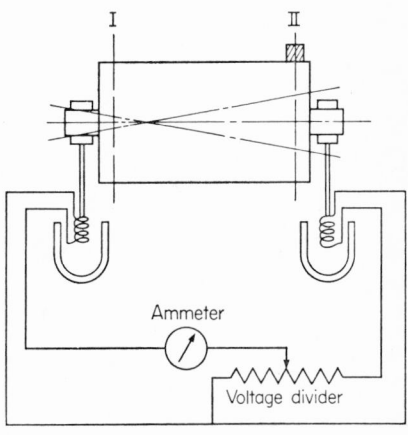

FIGURE 18.7

An electrical circuit as shown in the figure is used instead of the nodal bar to determine the centers of percussion relative to the two balancing planes. Assuming a perfectly balanced rotor with an unbalancing weight in plane II as shown, the oscillation of the axis will generate a voltage in each of the coils proportional to the amplitude of the vibration of the bearings. These voltages will be sinusoidal and 180° out of phase. By means of the voltage divider the two voltages can be exactly balanced so that the ammeter shows zero current. Then for any unbalance in plane II the ammeter will read zero and if, without changing the position of the voltage divider, the unbalance weight were removed from plane II and placed in plane I the ammeter reading would be proportional to the unbalance in plane I. Another similar circuit is used to eliminate the effects of an unbalance in plane I so that the unbalance in plane II could be determined. With the machine set so that it indicates only the unbalance in one of the planes a unit unbalance is placed in that plane in order to calibrate the ammeter readings. This is repeated for the other plane. Now if a similar *unbalanced* rotor is placed in the machine with the circuits set for the two planes, the magnitude of the unbalance in each of the planes could be determined just by turning a switch to the plane desired. The machine is now set and any number of similar rotors could be balanced without having to adjust the network for each piece.

The position of the unbalance in the two planes is determined in the Gisholt machine by means of a stroboscopic lamp and a pointer fixed to the frame. A numbered band is attached around the periphery of the rotor and the stroboscopic lamp flashes once each revolution of the rotor thereby causing the rotor to appear to stand still, with the pointer pointing to a position on the numbered band. The lamp is triggered to flash exactly when the voltage in the coils changes from positive to negative which corresponds to the maximum amplitude of vibration of the bearing. The natural frequency of the system is made very low by making the spring supports quite flexible and the rotor is run well above the natural frequency so that the phase angle is 180° for all practical purposes. Then the strobo-scopic light can be made to show the pointer at the position for adding the balance weight. This is done once for each plane. At low speeds of the rotor, say under 800 rpm, the flashing of the stroboscopic light is so slow that the flashing does not stop the motion satisfactorily and another means of locating the position of the unbalance is used. Heavy rotors would probably not be run at high speeds and a wattmeter is used to determine the position for low speeds. The wattmeter measures the average value of the product of the instantaneous voltage (supplied by the pickup coils) and an instantaneous current (supplied by an alternating-current generator coupled to the end of the rotating member). The stator of the generator can be shifted so that the phase of the current can be shifted relative to the voltage. When the two are 90° out of phase, the wattmeter indicates zero average power and by noting the position of the stator relative to the rotor the position of the unbalance can be determined.

This machine is well suited to the balancing of a large number of similar rotors on a mass-production basis since once it has been adjusted the necessary balance weight and position can be determined for each rotor very quickly. However it must be remembered that a perfectly balanced rotor is necessary for setting up the machine. This obstacle is eliminated by use of two alternating-current generators coupled to the rotor to be

balanced. These generators produce a current of the same frequency as the
pickup coils and their voltage and phase can be regulated. If the output
of the generators are fed into the circuit, while an unbalanced rotor is being
run, one at each coil, their output can be adjusted so that they exactly
balance the voltage in the coil and the rest of the circuit receives no current
and as far as the circuit is concerned the rotor is a balanced rotor. The
balancing procedure can then be carried out as previously explained, using
a balanced rotor.

18.4 Automatic Balancing

A very interesting method of balancing is based on the fact, previously
noted, that in a rotor operating above the critical speed the heavy side
of the rotor is on the concave side of the bent centerline. Consider an
unbalanced disc on a shaft with two arms containing weights at the ends
pinned to the shaft next to the disc, as shown in Fig. 18.8(a). The arms can

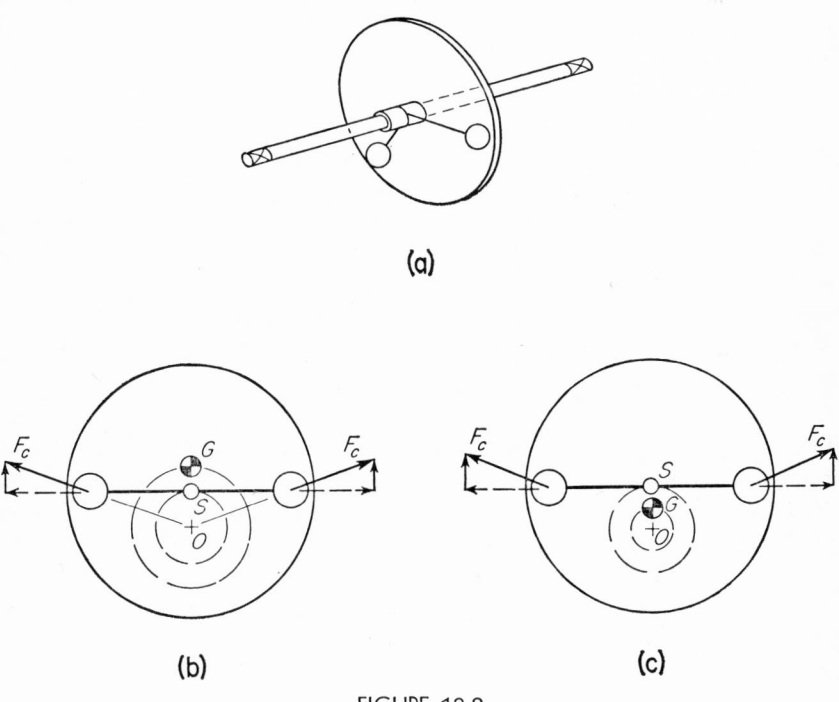

FIGURE 18.8

be clamped to the shaft at any position by means of a clutching arrangement but when released are free to rotate relative to the shaft. If the two
arms are clamped 180° apart and the shaft is rotating below the critical

speed, the center of gravity and the center of the shaft will whirl in a circle about the centerline of the bearings as shown in Fig. 18.8(b), where S is the center of the shaft (and disc), G is the center of gravity and O is the centerline of the bearings. The whole system is then rotating about O and the centrifugal force on the weights is acting radially outward from O as shown. This inertia force has a component normal to the arms and if they are released the arms will move upward so as to increase the unbalance. However, if the shaft is rotating above the critical speed the center of gravity is between S and O and if the arms are released at this speed they will still move upward but in this case they are moving toward the light side of the disc and shift the center of gravity towards S. They will continue to rotate about S until the center of gravity is at S, at which time the center of rotation has also moved to S (see discussion in Article 17.2), at which time there is no tangential force on the arms and the system is perfectly balanced. If the arms are now clamped in this position the center of gravity is at the center of the shaft and there is no unbalance in the system.

This method of balancing serves well for some systems which need rebalancing quite often. Such a system has been used for balancing grinding wheels which tend to wear unevenly and therefore need rebalancing periodically. Instead of the two arms, three balls, which can roll in concentric circular grooves, are used in practice. This system has also been used for automatically balancing domestic washing machines at the high spinning speeds used for drying the wet clothes. In this case two loose rings are attached to the tub holding the clothes. They are released above the critical speed and assume a position to counteract the large unbalance caused by the wet clothes, which varies with each load.

18.5 Complex Numbers and Vector Algebra

In the following Article on field balancing we shall make use of the multiplication and division of vectors; therefore, a brief review of complex numbers and vector algebra will be presented. It should be pointed out that this is a special way of handling *plane* vectors only and cannot be used for three dimensional vectors in general.

Consider a complex number z written as

$$z = a + ib$$

where a and b are real numbers and $i = \sqrt{-1}$. This complex number represents the coordinates of a point in the complex plane auch as P as shown in Fig. 18.9 where the real part of z is plotted as the abscissa and the imaginary part is plotted as the ordinate. The point P completely defines the vector $\overline{O\text{--}P}$ extending from the origin to P (the sense of the vector is always from the origin). Therefore the complex number z gives the

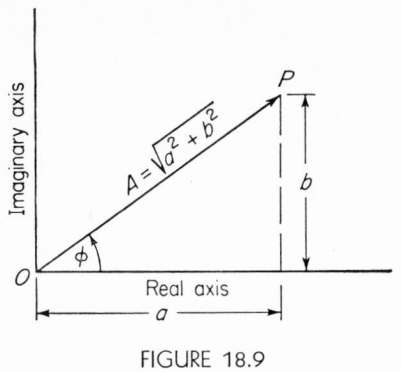

FIGURE 18.9

coordinates of the vector, and we refer to z as that vector. From the figure we see that we can represent the vector z as

$$z = A(\cos \phi + i \sin \phi) \quad (18.3)$$

where A = amplitude of the vector
$$= \sqrt{a^2 + b^2}$$

ϕ = phase or argument of the vector = $\tan^{-1}(b/a)$

$$a = A \cos \phi$$

$$b = A \sin \phi.$$

From this we see that the unit 1 is a unit vector in the direction of the positive real axis and i is the unit vector in the direction of the positive imaginary axis.

Making use of Euler's formula

$$e^{i\phi} = \cos \phi + i \sin \phi$$

which can be derived by expansion of the terms in series, and is given in most calculus texts, Eq. (18.3) can be written as

$$z = Ae^{i\phi} \qquad (18.4)$$

which is known as the polar form of z. Noting that A is the amplitude of the vector and ϕ is the angle the vector makes with the positive real axis, measured counterclockwise, we can use the polar form as a means of multiplying and dividing vectors. If we consider the two vectors

$$z_1 = A_1 e^{i\phi_1}, \qquad z_2 = A_2 e^{i\phi_2}$$

the product of the two vectors is

$$z_1 z_2 = A_1 e^{i\phi_1} A_2 e^{i\phi_2} = A_1 A_2 e^{i(\phi_1 + \phi_2)} \qquad (18.5)$$

and we see that the resultant vector is

$$z_3 = z_1 z_2 = A_3 e^{i\phi_3} \qquad (18.6)$$

where $A_3 = A_1 A_2$

$\phi_3 = \phi_1 + \phi_2$

We see that to multiply vectors, we multiply the amplitudes and add the phase angles. In a similar manner the division of the vectors can be accomplished as

$$\frac{z_1}{z_2} = \frac{A_1 e^{i\phi_1}}{A_2 e^{i\phi_2}} = \frac{A_1}{A_2} e^{i(\phi_1 - \phi_2)} \qquad (18.7)$$

or the resultant vector is

$$z_4 = \frac{z_1}{z_2} = A_4 e^{i\phi_4} \qquad (18.8)$$

where $A_4 = A_1/A_2$

$\phi_4 = \phi_1 - \phi_2$

and the division of vectors is accomplished by dividing the amplitudes and subtracting the phase angles.

The addition and subtraction of vectors can be handled analytically also by representing the vectors as complex numbers but ordinarily this is more readily accomplished graphically.

18.6 Field Balancing of Rotors

In many cases a rotor cannot be balanced satisfactorily in the shop on a balancing machine but must be balanced after it is installed in the field. In the case of steam turbines the balance of the rotor can change when the turbine is operating at temperature because of uneven expansion. Also a rotor often becomes unbalanced due to various causes after it has been in operation for a while and it is inconvenient to dismantle the machine and balance the rotor on a balancing machine. For these reasons and the one discussed below it is necessary in many cases to balance a rotor in its permanent bearings and at operating conditions.

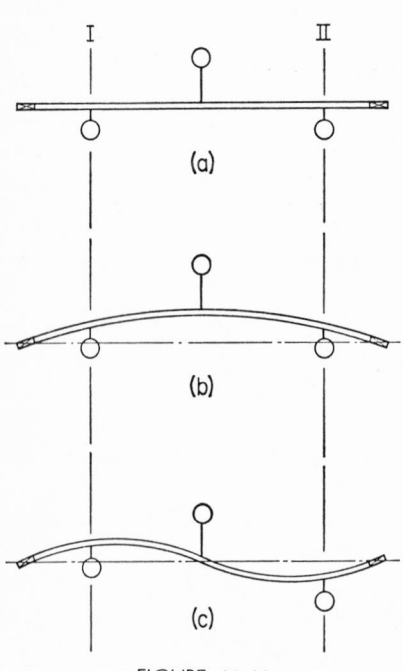

FIGURE 18.10

In all our previous discussion of balancing we have assumed that the rotor was rigid and did not deflect appreciably while rotating. This assumption is usually good as long as the rotor operates at low speeds, but for speeds higher than about half of the critical speed the deflection cannot be ignored in the balancing operations if the shaft or rotor is flexible. This can be demonstrated by reference to Fig. 18.10, where Fig. 18.10(a) shows a flexible rotor in the unflexed condition with an unbalance in the middle plane and correction weights in planes I and II. This rotor is then balanced if it remains rigid. However at a speed approaching the critical speed the rotor will deflect in a sinusoidal curve as shown in Fig. 18.10(b) and we see that the original unbalance has deflected

more than the corrective balances and while increasing the original unbalance the deflection has decreased the corrective balances, so that the
rotor is not balanced at this speed. At speeds in the neighborhood of the
second critical speed, the shaft will deflect in a manner as shown in Fig.
18.10(c), and the original unbalance is unaffected while the corrective
balances are changed. From this we draw the conclusion that a flexible
rotor balanced at one speed is not necessarily balanced at any other speed.
Variations in the rigidity of the bearings can have the same effect on
balancing as flexibility in the shaft. For these reasons many shafts are
balanced on machines in the shop at low speeds and then rebalanced after
installation in the field.

Balancing in the field is a bit more involved than balancing on a machine
in that we cannot rigidly fix the rotor at one of the balancing planes, thereby
eliminating the effects of an unbalance in that plane. Therefore we must
simultaneously balance in both planes. Portable balancing instruments
are available from several manufacturers for this purpose. These usually
consist of a vibration pickup which is used to measure the amplitude of the
vibration at the bearings and a phase indicating device which is run at the
speed of the rotor. The vibration pickup and phase measuring instrument
are similar to those described in Article 18.3.

The amplitude of the vibration and the angular position of the high spot
on the rotor, corresponding to the maximum amplitude, or the phase angle,
is determined at each bearing for the following three runs:

1. With no correction weights and the only unbalance that in the rotor.
2. With a trial weight in plane I.
3. With a trial weight in plane II.

The angular position of the trial weights is immaterial except the position
must be noted so that weights necessary for balancing can be located
relative to the trial weights.

Let us assume that the necessary data for balancing the rotor shown
in Fig. 18.11(a) has been obtained as in Table 18.1 where N represents the
amplitude at the near end balancing plane and F the amplitude at the far
balancing plane.

The amplitudes are plotted as vectors at their corresponding phase
angles in Fig. 18.11. The amplitude and phase of the vibrations in the
bearings for run 1 with no trial weights is shown in Fig. 18.11(b). In
Fig. 18.11(c) N_2 and F_2 represent the vibrations caused by the original
unbalance and the trial weight in the near plane. Note that since both
bearings are flexible a trial weight in the near end will have an effect on the
vibration at the far end. We can write the vector equations at the two ends
as

$$N \mathbin{+\mkern-8mu+} A = N_2 \qquad\qquad (18.9)$$

$$F \mathbin{+\mkern-8mu+} \alpha A = F_2 \qquad\qquad (18.10)$$

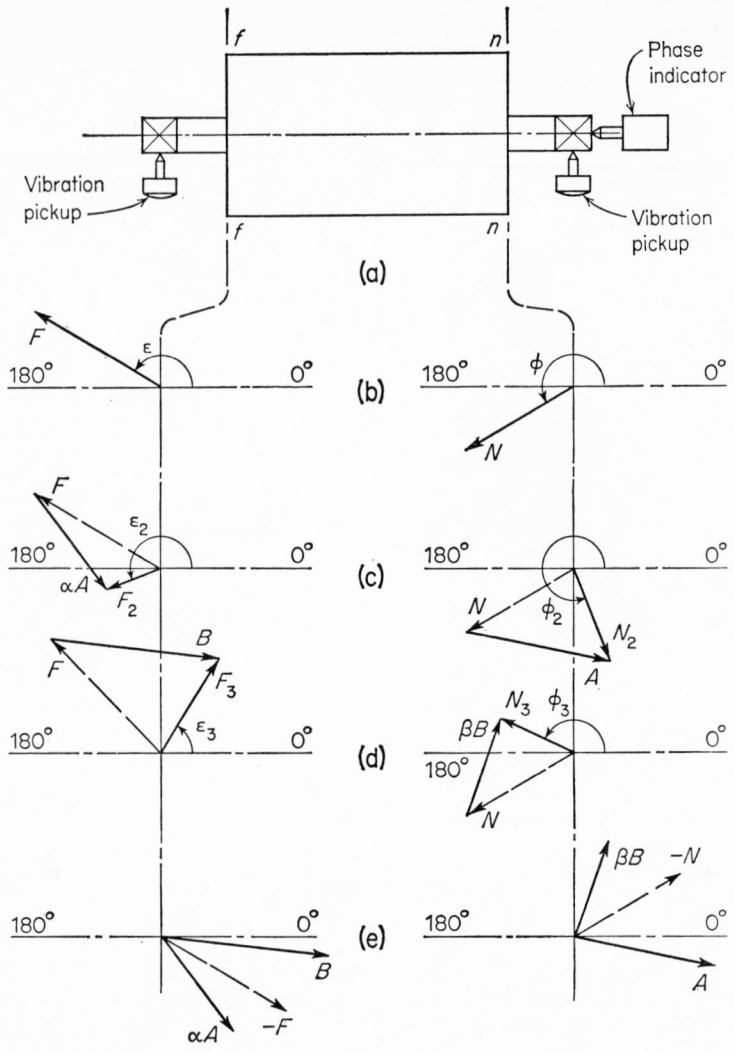

FIGURE 18.11

where A is the effect of the trial weight in the near end on the near end vibration and αA is the effect of the same weight on the far end vibration. If we have a linear system, which is usually assumed, a change in the magnitude of the trial weight will cause a proportionate change in the magnitude of A and αA and if we change the angular position of the trial weight, it will change the phase angle of the two vectors by the same amount so that the angle between them will always be the same. Therefore the vector αA is always proportional to the near end trial weight and is affected by the characteristics of the installation and α is called a vector

Table 18.1

Run	Trial weight	Near End Amplitude	Near End Phase angle	Far End Amplitude	Far End Phase angle
1	0	N	ϕ	F	ϵ
2	W_n at near end at position θ_n	N_2	ϕ_2	F_2	ϵ_2
3	W_f at far end at position θ_f	N_3	ϕ_3	F_3	ϵ_3

operator (having both magnitude and phase) dependent on the characteristics of the machine and its mounting.

The results of the third run with the trial weight at the far end are represented by Fig. 18.11(d) where B represents the effect on the vibration at the far end and βB the effect on the near end, where β is also a vector operator multiplying the vector B.

As a result of these three runs we have the information shown in Fig. 18.11(e) which shows the effect on each end of trial weights placed at each end. For balance of the rotor the effects of the correction weights must balance the vibrations of the original unbalance, or we must change the magnitude and position of the trial weights so that

$$A \;+\!\!\!\to\; \beta B = -N \tag{18.11}$$

$$B \;+\!\!\!\to\; \alpha A = -F \tag{18.12}$$

We do not yet know what we must do to the trial weights, but we do know what the effect of the trial weights is and that any change in the weights will cause a proportionate change in the vectors. Therefore we can write the equations

$$\text{Near end correction weight} = W_{nc} = \sigma W_n \tag{18.13}$$

$$\text{Far end correction weight} = W_{fc} = \gamma W_f \tag{18.14}$$

where σ and γ are vector operators having both magnitude and sense so that when the weights are multiplied by them the position and magnitude of the trial weights are changed. Since the vectors corresponding to the correction weights must balance the original unbalance and the vectors are proportional to the trial weights we can rewrite Eqs. (18.11) and (18.12) as

$$-N = \sigma A \;+\!\!\!\to\; \gamma \beta B \tag{18.15}$$

$$-F = \gamma B \;+\!\!\!\to\; \sigma \alpha A \tag{18.16}$$

These two equations can be solved for the vector operators σ and γ as

$$\sigma = \frac{\beta F \to N}{A(1 \to \alpha\beta)} \tag{18.17}$$

$$\gamma = \frac{\alpha N \to F}{B(1 \to \alpha\beta)} \tag{18.18}$$

and substituting the value of these operators into Eqs. (18.13) and (18.14) we can determine the magnitudes and positions of the correction weights necessary to balance the rotor. It should be emphasized that these are all vector equations and the operations in solving the equations must make use of vector algebra as presented in Artic e 18.5.

Quite often in practice the required degree of balance is not obtained on the first balancing run and subsequent runs must be made to improve the balance. Also it should be pointed out that the assumption of a linear system was made in the analysis and since some machines are nonlinear, the solution obtained by the above analysis may need further trial balancing to achieve the required accuracy.

An example of the balancing of a rotor in the field will be given to demonstrate the application of the process. Assume that the data in Table 18.2 were obtained for purposes of balancing a flexible rotor in the field. We must now determine the vector operators σ and γ by means of Eqs. (18.17) and (18.18). We will use graphical methods for the addition and subtraction of vectors and the complex notation for the multiplication and division of vectors. The graphical part of the solution is shown in Fig. 18.12. The steps in the calculation are

1. Determine graphically [Fig. 18.12(a)]

$$A = 26.5\underline{/350°}$$

$$\alpha A = 21.4\underline{/184°}$$

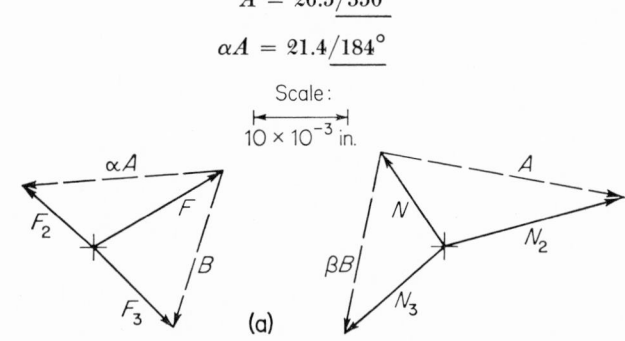

(a)

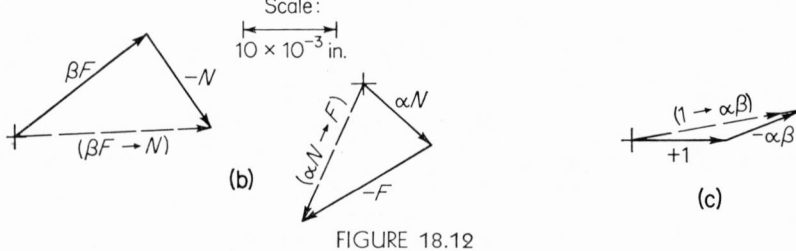

FIGURE 18.12

$$B = 17.2\underline{/252^\circ}$$

$$\beta B = 19.2\underline{/258.7^\circ}$$

2. Remembering that to divide vectors we divide the magnitudes and subtract the angles and to multiply vectors we multiply the magnitudes and add the angles, we find

$$\alpha = \frac{\alpha A}{A} = \frac{21.4}{26.5}\underline{/184^\circ - 350^\circ} = 0.808\underline{/194^\circ}$$

$$\beta = \frac{\beta B}{B} = \frac{19.2}{17.2}\underline{/258.7^\circ - 252^\circ} = 1.115\underline{/6.7^\circ}$$

$$\alpha N = (0.808 \times 12)\underline{/194^\circ + 125^\circ} = 9.69\underline{/319^\circ}$$

$$\beta F = (1.115 \times 16)\underline{/6.7^\circ + 30^\circ} = 17.85\underline{/36.7^\circ}$$

$$\alpha\beta = (0.808 \times 1.115)\underline{/194^\circ + 6.7^\circ} = 0.901\underline{/200.7^\circ}$$

Table 18.2

Run	Trial weight	Near End		Far End	
		Amplitude (in. $\times 10^3$)	Phase angle (deg.)	Amplitude (in. $\times 10^3$)	Phase angle (deg.)
1	0	$N = 12$	$\phi = 125^\circ$	$F = 16$	$\epsilon = 30^\circ$
2	$W_n = 10$ in. - oz at 0°	$N_2 = 20$	$\phi_2 = 15^\circ$	$F_2 = 10$	$\epsilon_2 = 140^\circ$
3	$W_f = 10$ in. - oz at 0°	$N_3 = 14$	$\phi_3 = 220^\circ$	$F_3 = 12$	$\epsilon_3 = 315^\circ$

3. Determine graphically, as shown in Fig. 18.12(b).

$$\beta F \rightarrow N = 21.3\underline{/2.5^\circ}$$

$$\alpha N \rightarrow F = 15.7\underline{/245.4^\circ}$$

and from Fig. 18.12(c), remembering that the unit 1 is a unit vector along the positive real axis,

$$1 \rightarrow \alpha\beta = 1.9\underline{/10^\circ}$$

4. Determine analytically

$$A(1 \rightarrow \alpha\beta) = (26.5 \times 1.9)\underline{/350^\circ + 10^\circ} = 50.4\underline{/0^\circ}$$

$$B(1 \rightarrow \alpha\beta) = (17.2 \times 1.9)\underline{/252^\circ + 10^\circ} = 33.5\underline{/262^\circ}$$

$$\sigma = \frac{\beta F \rightarrow N}{A(1 \rightarrow \alpha\beta)} = \frac{21.3}{50.4}\underline{/2.5^\circ - 0^\circ} = 0.423\underline{/2.5^\circ}$$

$$\gamma = \frac{\alpha N \rightarrow F}{B(1 \rightarrow \alpha\beta)} = \frac{15.7}{33.5}\underline{/245.4^\circ - 262^\circ} = 0.469\underline{/343.4^\circ}$$

5. Substituting these values into Eqs. (18.13) and (18.14) we find the near end and far end corrections to be

$$W_{nc} = \sigma W_n = (0.423 \times 10)\underline{/2.5^\circ + 0^\circ} = 4.23 \text{ in.-oz at } 2.5^\circ$$

$$W_{fc} = \gamma W_f = (0.469 \times 10)\underline{/343.4^\circ + 0^\circ} = 4.69 \text{ in.-oz at } 343.4^\circ$$

PROBLEMS

18.1 An unbalanced rotor has been placed in a cradle type balancing machine of the type shown in Fig. 18.4 and the maximum amplitudes were recorded as the rotor coasted through the critical speed. The following amplitudes were obtained for one balancing plane:
  (1) 0.030 in. with the only unbalance that in the rotor
  (2) 0.025 in. with an unbalance of 10 in.-oz at the 0° position
  (3) 0.045 in. with an unbalance of 10 in.-oz at the 180° position
  (4) 0.048 in. with an unbalance of 10 in.-oz at the 60° position
Determine the magnitude and position of the balance weight necessary to balance the rotor in the given plane at a radius of 8 in.

18.2 Same as Prob. 18.1 with following amplitudes:
  (1) 0.040 in. with the only unbalance that in the rotor
  (2) 0.065 in. with an unbalance of 20 in.-oz at the 0° position
  (3) 0.020 in. with an unbalance of 20 in.-oz at the 180° position
  (4) 0.057 in. with an unbalance of 20 in.-oz at the 90° position

18.3 The following data on an unbalanced turbine rotor have been obtained with portable balancing equipment while it was running at operating speed:

Run	Trial weight	Near End Amplitude (in. × 10³)	Near End Phase angle (deg.)	Far End Amplitude (in. × 10³)	Far End Phase angle (deg.)
1	0	$N = 10$	$\phi = 10°$	$F = 15$	$\epsilon = 100°$
2	$W_n = 20$ in.-oz at 0°	$N_2 = 15$	$\phi_2 = 95°$	$F_2 = 20$	$\epsilon_2 = 175°$
3	$W_f = 20$ in.-oz at 0°	$N_3 = 20$	$\phi_3 = 150°$	$F_3 = 8$	$\epsilon_3 = 315°$

Determine the magnitude and position of the counterbalances necessary to bring the rotor to balance with the counterbalance weights placed in the same planes as the trial weights.

18.4 Repeat Prob. 18.3 with the following data:

Run	Trial weight	Near End Amplitude (in. × 10³)	Near End Phase angle (deg.)	Far End Amplitude (in. × 10³)	Far End Phase angle (deg.)
1	0	$N = 12$	$\phi = 25°$	$F = 17$	$\epsilon = 315°$
2	$W_n = 24$ in.-oz at 0°	$N_2 = 18$	$\phi_2 = 105°$	$F_2 = 13$	$\epsilon_2 = 215°$
3	$W_f = 24$ in.-oz at 0°	$N_3 = 25$	$\phi_3 = 285°$	$F_3 = 7$	$\epsilon_3 = 10°$

Chapter 19

Gyroscopic Effects

19.1 Introduction

The forces imposed on a machine by gyroscopic effects are often of such magnitude that they must be taken into account in the design of the machine. Such forces are encountered in bearings of marine turbines as the ship pitches in the sea, in automobile engine bearings when a car turns a corner, and in the bearings of an aircraft engine as the airplane changes direction. In recent years gyroscopes have found wide use in the control of mechanisms and as compasses. Our analysis will be general and will make use of the concept of angular momentum as discussed in Chapter 12, and although our study of angular momentum was confined to plane motion, the study of gyroscopic action will involve three dimensional motion.

19.2 The Gyroscope

Consider a disc lying in plane x–z and rotating about the y-axis, which passes through its centroid, with a large angular velocity ω_s as shown in Fig. 19.1(a). The disc will have an angular momentum or moment of momentum of $H = I\omega_s$ where I is the moment of inertia about the y-axis. Since the angular momentum is a vector quantity we can represent it with an arrow using the right-hand rule as explained in Article 16.5 for moments. This vector H is shown in Fig. 19.1(a) extending in the positive direction along the y-axis. If now, while spinning at the constant angular velocity ω_s, which we will call the spin velocity, the disc is given a slow angular rotation, ω_p, about the z-axis as shown in the figure, there will be a change in the direction of the moment of momentum vector since it will rotate with the disc. From Eq. (12.8) we see that the change in angular momentum corresponds to an external moment which must be applied to cause the motion as described.

357

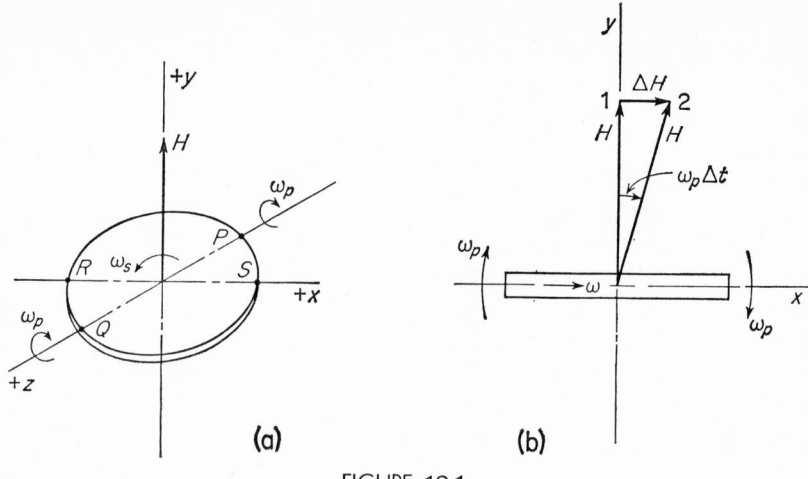

FIGURE 19.1

In order to determine the value of this moment, let the momentum vector H be in position 1 at some instant of time and in position 2 a short instant of time, Δt, later, as shown in Fig. 19.1(b). From the figure the angle through which the vector has rotated is $\omega_p \Delta t$ and the change in the momentum vector is

$$\Delta H = H \omega_p \Delta t$$

or
$$\frac{\Delta H}{\Delta t} = H \omega_p$$

and in the limit, as Δt approaches zero

$$\frac{d}{dt}(H) = H\omega_p = I\omega_s\omega_p \tag{19.1}$$

The length of the vector $I\omega_s\omega_p$ representing the change in angular momentum with respect to time is equal to the value of the moment which must be applied to the disc to cause the motion. From Fig. 19.1(b) and (a) we see that this moment vector in the limit is normal to H and therefore the moment acts about the x-axis and its direction, from the right-hand rule, must be so as to push up on P and down on Q if R moves up and S moves down.

It should be noted that the direction of the torque must be considered at some particular time since the spin axis is continually changing its direction. However at any instant the torque or moment vector is always normal to the spin axis. We see then that a moment equal in magnitude to $I\omega_s\omega_p$ must be applied in order to cause the spin axis to rotate with a velocity ω_p. This rotation of the spin axis is called precession, and the axis

about which the disc precesses is the
z-axis. The direction of precession is
always such as to rotate the momentum vector or the spin vector
towards the moment vector. In
order to simplify the determination
of the directions of the precession
and moment relative to the spin
vector, it is convenient to draw three
perpendicular axes corresponding to
the spin axis, the precession axis,
and the torque axis as shown in Fig.
19.2 and draw the vectors corresponding to the spin vector and the
precession vector or torque vector,
whichever is known, and then the

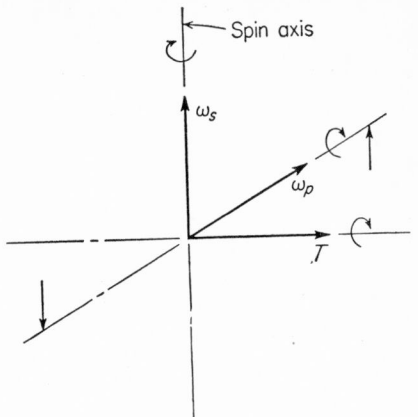

FIGURE 19.2

other vector can be drawn as shown in the figure, remembering that always
the precession tends to turn the spin vector towards the torque vector. In
the figure two forces corresponding to the direction of the external torque
are shown acting on the precession axis. As an example consider an automobile making a left-hand turn. The crankshaft and flywheel form a
gyroscope and the direction of rotation of the engine is, by American
convention, usually clockwise when facing the front of the engine so that
the spin vector is horizontal and pointing towards the rear of the car. For
a right-hand turn the precession axis will be vertical with the precession
vector pointing downwards. Therefore the torque vector will be horizontal
and pointing to the left-hand side of the car. The torque which must be
applied to the crankshaft of the car in order to cause this motion will be
such as to lift up on the rear end and push down on the front end. The
torque will be felt as forces on the bearings and therefore will push up on the
front bearings and down on the rear bearings tending to lift the front end
of the car and lower the rear end.

The previous discussion explains why a toy gyroscopic top, placed
horizontal on a pedestal while revolving rapidly, will not fall but will precess
around the pedestal. The weight of the top applies the external torque and
this moment causes the top to precess. If the top were prevented from
precessing by some means, such as holding a pencil in its path, it would
immediately fall. The friction of the pedestal dissipates some of the energy
and the top gradually drops lower. Also from Eq. (19.1) we see why the
precession velocity increases as the friction on the spindle slows down the
spin velocity.

It should be pointed out that we have confined our discussion to a high
spin velocity and a low velocity of precession so that for all practical

purposes the total moment of momentum is associated with the spinning of the disc. If the moment of momentum caused by the precession is of appreciable magnitude, analysis becomes quite complicated.

In the example of the automobile engine the gyroscopic moment is usually small and is neglected in the design of the bearings of the engine; however, in many cases, such as the jet engine or the propeller of an airplane, the gyroscopic forces are of appreciable magnitude and must be considered in the bearing design. Their effect on the plane's stability during maneuvers must also be taken into account. If the plane is making a horizontal turn, the gyroscopic couple tends to make the plane climb or dive. The gyroscopic couple is also of considerable magnitude in the turbines of ships when the ship pitches in a rough sea.

PROBLEMS

19.1 (a) The compressor-turbine unit of a jet propulsion airplane weighs 600 lbs and has a radius of gyration of 10 in. The unit rotates at 18,000 rpm and is supported by two bearings 60 in. apart. What is the direction and magnitude of the gyroscopic forces on the bearings if the airplane is making a clockwise turn of one mile radius in a horizontal plane at a speed of 500 mph?

(b) Compare the gyroscopic forces to the centrifugal forces on the bearings caused by the turn.

19.2 Determine the gyroscopic torque applied to the bearings of an automobile wheel if the car is making a turn of 150 ft radius while traveling at 60 mph. Assume the effective outside radius of the wheel is 13 in., weight of 30 lbs with a radius of gyration of 9 in.

Chapter **20**

Cams

20.1 *Introduction*

In all the preceding work we have dealt primarily with analysis of existing mechanisms, the mechanisms being represented by kinematic sketches. The dimensions of the mechanism were known and from these we determined the displacements, velocities, accelerations and forces, assuming the motion of some member was known. Usually this known motion was a constant angular velocity of some link. Our problem in the design of machines is quite often the synthesis of a mechanism which will take a given input motion and deliver a certain output motion. This output motion may be the positioning of some link of the mechanism and the forces involved may limit the allowable accelerations.

In most of the mechanisms discussed so far this synthesis is necessarily composed of a trial and error approach in which we design some given mechanism which we think may give us the desired motion and then analyze the mechanism to see if it gives us the output we wish as regards position, velocity, and acceleration. If it does not satisfy our given conditions we try changing the dimensions of the links until we get a satisfactory mechanism. In general this is a long, tedious, process and we seldom get a mechanism which gives the exact motion we desire. In this chapter we will find that cams lend themselves to synthesis in that we can take any output motion and design directly a cam that will give us this motion. However there are limitations in cam mechanisms as we will find in our discussion.

Cams are one of the most versatile types of mechanisms and are found in such mechanisms as internal combustion engines, sewing machines, computing mechanisms and nearly all automatic machinery.

20.2 *Classification of Cams*

In its simplest form a cam mechanism is composed of three links:

(1) the cam, the contact surface of which may be either curved or straight; (2) the cam follower, which is driven by the cam and the motion of which is produced by contact with the cam surface; and (3) the frame which guides and supports the cam and follower. The follower has a prescribed output motion and the cam, which drives the follower, usually rotates with a constant angular velocity, although some cams move in rectilinear translation. Cams are usually divided into six general classes as

(1) Translation cams
(2) Disc cams
(3) Cylindrical cams
(4) Conical cams
(5) Spherical cams
(6) Three-dimensional cams

Examples of these types of cams are shown in Fig. 20.1. These could all be thought of as modifications of the translation cam. The disc cam could be made by wrapping the translation cam around a circular disc whose axis is normal to the paper, and the cylindrical cam could be made by wrapping the translation cam around the end of a cylinder whose axis is parallel to the paper. The conical and spherical cam would represent the translation cam laid on the surface of a cone or sphere, and the three-dimensional cam would represent a translation cam composed of a varying surface with motion in two normal directions wrapped around a cylinder which could rotate and translate along its axis. However, we will find that the follower motion caused by a translation cam and one of the other types made from the same translation cam will have different follower characteristics. From another view point we can see that a translation cam is a disc cam with an infinite radius.

All the followers in Fig. 20.1 are of the roller follower type, but two types of follower motion are represented. The translation, disc, conical and three-dimensional cams have followers moving in translation while the cylindrical and spherical cams have rotating followers. Other types of followers will be shown later.

20.3 Displacement Diagrams

Since a majority of cams are designed to give a specified motion to the follower, we will start our discussion with the types of follower motion most used in practice. The follower motion is usually given as a function of the position of the cam and a curve with the follower motion as the ordinate and the cam position as the abscissae is called a displacement diagram. If the cam translates or rotates with constant velocity, such a curve would be a displacement-time curve since equal displacements of the cam correspond

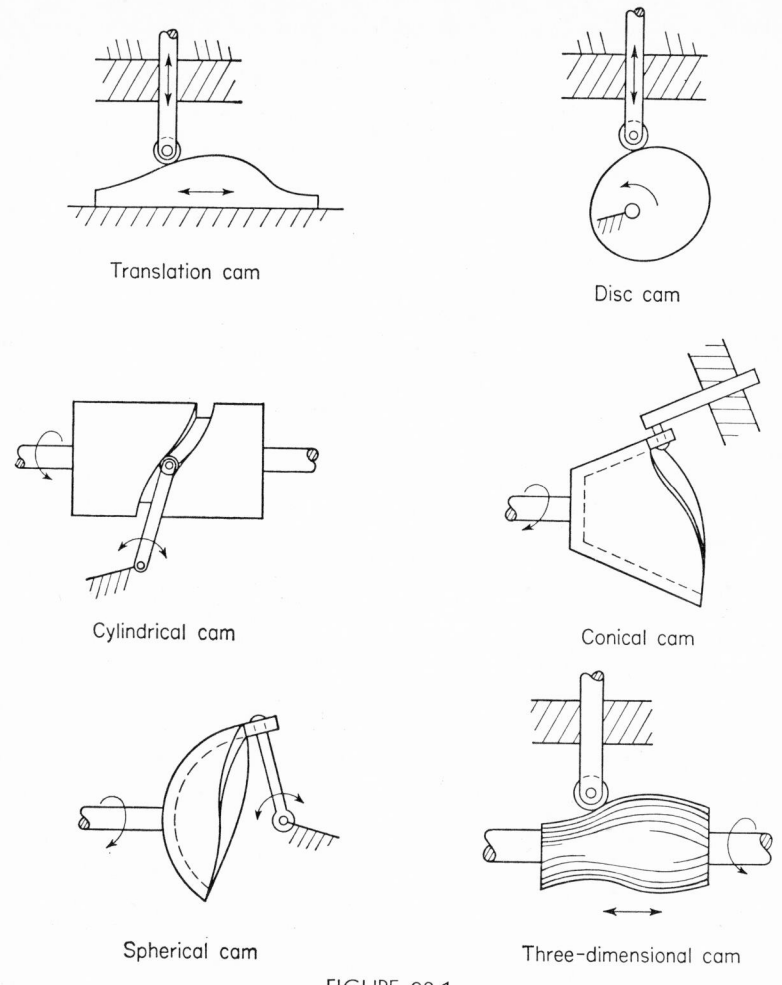

Translation cam

Disc cam

Cylindrical cam

Conical cam

Spherical cam

Three-dimensional cam

FIGURE 20.1

to equal time increments. Displacement diagrams usually cover one cycle of cam operation.

A typical displacement diagram for a disc cam with roller follower moving in translation is shown in Fig. 20.2. The follower stays at its lowest position during the first 30° of cam motion, this being called a dwell period, then rises to its highest position in 150° of cam motion at which position it dwells again for 60° of cam motion and then returns to its lowest position in 120° of cam motion. The dwell, rise, and return periods can be varied and in many cases one or both of the dwell periods are left out.

While the types of motions a follower can have are unlimited theoretically, they are limited from a practical viewpoint by the dynamics of the

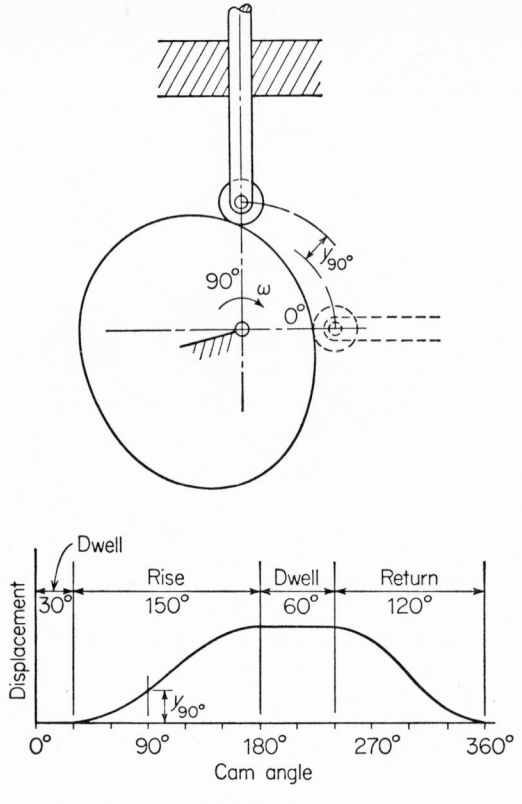

FIGURE 20.2

system and the methods available for forming the cam profile. Motions which are satisfactory for slow speed cams cause large forces and vibration if the cams are run at high speeds, thereby giving unsatisfactory operation. The motions which will be discussed in detail are (1) straight line or constant velocity, and modified straight line, (2) simple harmonic motion, (3) parabolic or constant acceleration, and (4) cycloidal. Although other motions are used in practice today, these are the simplest and probably the most-used in practice. The circular arc cam will also be discussed but, as we shall see, the design of the cam is a trial and error procedure and is not based on a known displacement diagram.

Any of these motions could be used for the rise or return period of the cycle, with dwell periods either preceding or following the period of motion, and in any combination. We will deal only with the rise period since the characteristics are the same for the return motion. However, dwell periods will affect the characteristics and their effect will be pointed out for each case.

The displacement curves will be discussed in relation to a disc cam rotating at constant velocity since this is the most common type of cam. We will be interested in the velocity and acceleration of the follower, and also the rate of change of acceleration with respect to time, which is commonly called jerk or pulse. The acceleration of the follower determines the dynamic characteristics and is important in medium and high speed cams. Shock, noise, vibration, and wear, which are all associated with the dynamic forces, are determined by the acceleration of the follower. Jerk, being the rate of change of acceleration, is an indication of the impact characteristics of the dynamic loading and its value should be as low as possible for high speed cams. It has been demonstrated experimentally that infinite values of jerk initiate vibrations in the follower system and affect the life of the cam. The acceleration and jerk should be considered together in determining the dynamic characteristics of the cam.

20.4 Straight Line or Constant Velocity Motion

The displacement diagram for constant velocity motion is shown in Fig. 20.3(a) and the velocity and acceleration curves for this motion are shown in Figs. 20.3(b) and (c) respectively. This motion is the simplest and has the shortest path for a given rise. The acceleration and jerk are infinite at the beginning and end of the motion causing an extreme shock at these points. For these reasons this curve is not practical but a modification of this curve can be used at low speeds.

A common modification is the use of circular arcs at the beginning and end of the motion tangent to the straight line portion as shown in Fig. 20.4, where the circular arc has a radius equal to the total rise. The accelerations in this case are finite, but the jerk is infinite at the beginning and end of the motion as well as at the transition points. Since this displacement curve is only satisfactory for very slow cam speeds, with corresponding low accelerations and forces, resulting in negligible dynamic effects, the equations of the motion are not given. Other modifications of the straight line motion will be discussed in relation to the other displacement curves later.

20.5 Simple Harmonic Motion Curve

The simple harmonic motion curve and its corresponding velocity and acceleration curves are shown in Fig. 20.5. The construction of the displacement diagram is as follows (see figure):

1. Draw a semicircle at one end of the diagram with diameter equal to the total rise. This semicircle represents the path of the end of the rotating vector defining the harmonic motion.

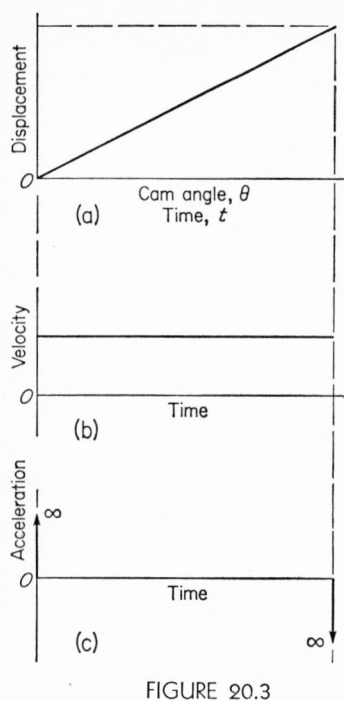

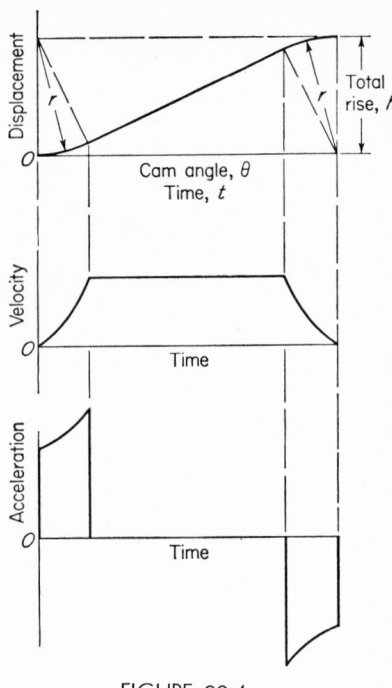

FIGURE 20.3   FIGURE 20.4

2. Divide the semicircle into some number of equal arcs.
3. Divide the total motion of the cam during the rise (the abscissae) into the same number of equal parts.
4. Project the intercepts of the circle horizontally until they intersect verticals through the abscissae at the division points.

In the figure the harmonic vector is rotating clockwise and the first division, where the vector is at 30°, is projected to the vertical through the 20° cam angle and the rest of the divisions are projected in consecutive order to the next vertical until the horizontal at the total rise intersects the vertical through the cam angle corresponding to the end of the rise. The displacement curve then is drawn as a smooth curve through the intersection points.

The equation of motion can be developed from the figure. Letting ϕ be the angle of rotation of the harmonic vector at any time and taking h as the total rise, the displacement, y, at any time is

$$y = \frac{h}{2}(1 - \cos\phi) \qquad (20.1)$$

We will find it desirable to define the displacement as a function of the cam position or cam angle θ and we can relate the position of the harmonic vector to the cam angle by noting that the harmonic vector turns through 180° or

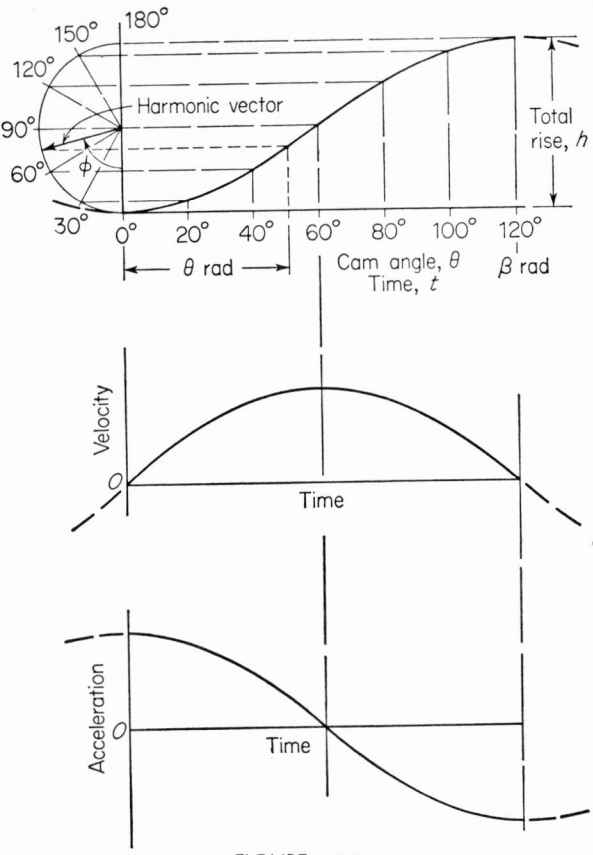

FIGURE 20.5

π radians while the cam turns through β rad, where β is the angular position of the cam in radians at the end of the rise period. Then

$$\frac{\phi}{\pi} = \frac{\theta}{\beta}$$

so that

$$\phi = \frac{\pi\theta}{\beta} \tag{20.2}$$

The displacement equation in terms of cam angle then becomes

$$y = \frac{h}{2}\left(1 - \cos\frac{\pi\theta}{\beta}\right) \tag{20.3}$$

The velocity is found by differentiating the displacement with respect to time, or

$$v = \frac{dy}{dt} = \frac{h\pi\omega}{2\beta}\sin\frac{\pi\theta}{\beta} \tag{20.4}$$

and differentiating again the acceleration is

$$a = \frac{dv}{dt} = \frac{h}{2}\left(\frac{\pi\omega}{\beta}\right)^2 \cos\frac{\pi\theta}{\beta} \qquad (20.5)$$

where ω is the angular velocity of the cam. These equations can be written in terms of time by noting that $\theta = \omega t$.

From the curves we see that the acceleration is finite at all times and that the velocity and acceleration curves are smooth and continuous, giving good dynamic characteristics. If there are dwell periods at either the beginning or end of the rise, however, the acceleration curve will be discontinuous at these points resulting in an infinite value of jerk and noise, vibration, and wear of the cam surface would result for high speed cams. If the cam were a rise-return cam with no dwell periods, the velocity and acceleration curves are continuous for the complete cycle, as shown by dashed lines in the figure and no shock would be present.

The modified straight line curve using a quarter cycle of harmonic motion at the beginning and end of the rise would be an improvement over the use of the circular arcs. As seen from Fig. 20.5 the acceleration curve passes through the zero point when the rotating vector has turned through 90° and therefore the velocity could be brought up to its maximum value with the acceleration decreasing to zero at the transition point where the constant velocity part of the curve is reached. This will give a continuous acceleration curve with finite jerk at the transition points. However the jerk would be infinite if there were dwell periods.

20.6 Parabolic or Constant Acceleration Curve

The constant acceleration curve is used quite often because of the ease with which the dynamic forces can be calculated and because no other curve will produce a given rise between two dwell positions with as small a maximum acceleration. For the latter reason this curve is often considered the best possible curve but we will find later that other curves are better for high speed cams because of factors other than maximum acceleration. This motion was discussed in Article 1.9.

The displacement, velocity, and acceleration curves are shown in Fig. 20.6 for a symmetrical curve of equal accelerations. The displacement curve is composed of two parabolas having the same slope at the midpoint where they join.

The simplest method of constructing a parabola is shown in Fig. 20.7. Letting the ordinate be the displacement and the abscissae the time we wish to construct a parabola that passes through the origin and some point P, at t_P and y_P. The distances y_P and t_P are both divided into any equal number of equal spaces or intervals as shown in the figure. Then lines drawn

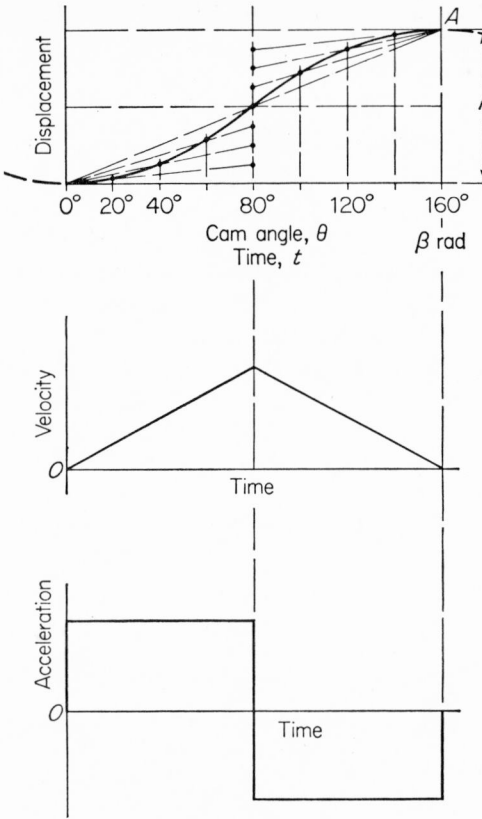

FIGURE 20.6

through the origin connecting the points on y_P will intersect verticals through the points on the abscissae and these intersections will define a parabola. We can show that these intersections lie on the given parabola by

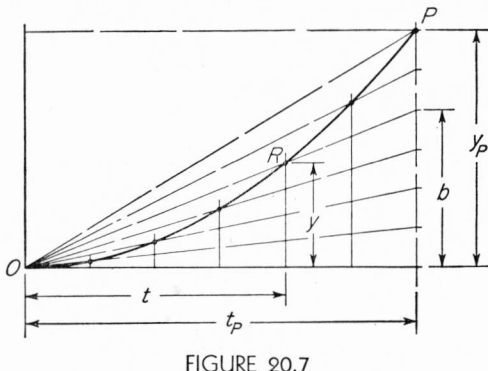

FIGURE 20.7

considering the point R with coordinates y and t. From similar triangles

$$\frac{y}{t} = \frac{b}{t_P}$$

and because of the equal intervals

$$\frac{b}{t} = \frac{y_P}{t_P}$$

Eliminating b from these equations and solving for y

$$y = \frac{y_P}{(t_P)^2}\, t^2 = ct^2$$

which is the equation for a parabola passing through the origin. We can also see that the parabola defined by this equation passes through P by substituting t_P for t.

The equation of motion for the curve in Fig. 20.6 must be written as two equations, one from zero to the transition point and the other for the motion from the transition point to the total rise. The equation for the first half, from 0 to $\beta/2$, in terms of time or the angular position of the cam is

$$y = \frac{1}{2}at^2 = \frac{1}{2}a\left(\frac{\theta}{\omega}\right)^2 \tag{20.6}$$

where a is the constant acceleration in in./sec², t is the time, θ is the cam angle in radians measured from the zero position, and ω is the angular velocity of the cam. Differentiating this equation

$$v = at = a\,\frac{\theta}{\omega} \tag{20.7}$$

For the curve shown in Fig. 20.6 where the positive and negative accelerations have equal time increments and therefore are of equal magnitude, the value of the acceleration, a, can be determined from the relationship

$$\frac{h}{2} = \frac{1}{2}\,a\left(\frac{\beta}{2\omega}\right)^2$$

giving

$$a = 4h\left(\frac{\omega}{\beta}\right)^2$$

Substituting this value for the acceleration in Eq. (20.6) the equation can be written in terms of the total rise, h, and the angle β as

$$y = 2h\left(\frac{\theta}{\beta}\right)^2 \tag{20.8}$$

and

$$v = \frac{4h\theta}{\beta^2}\,\omega \tag{20.9}$$

$$a = \frac{4h}{\beta^2}\omega^2 \qquad\qquad (20.10)$$

If the displacement diagram is rotated 180° in the plane of the paper we see that the second half of the curve has the same equation if the origin is placed at point A so that the displacement, y, now is measured from the total rise position and θ is measured from β taken as 0°.

As seen from Fig. 20.6 the acceleration curve is discontinuous at the transition point, and also at the beginning and end of the motion if there are dwell periods, indicating infinite values of jerk at these points. If there were no dwell periods and the displacement curve were continuous, as shown by the dashed lines in the figure, giving a rise-return cam the infinite jerk would be eliminated at the beginning and end of the rise period, although this would not affect the jerk at the transition point. Therefore this curve is not satisfactory for high speed operation since the infinite jerk would result in high impact and resulting vibration. However because of the low accelerations the curve can be used for low and intermediate speed cams.

In many cases it is desirable to use unequal magnitudes of acceleration in the constant acceleration curve as shown in Fig. 20.8. In this manner the dynamic forces would be smaller over the first part of the rise and higher over the latter part of the rise. In such a case the cam angles β_1 and β_2 would be given and the values of the accelerations a_1 and a_2 and the rises h_1 and h_2 can readily be determined by the use of Eqs. (20.8), (20.9), and (20.10). The equations are simplified by two sets of equations for the two parts of the motion, one set from O to A and the other from B to A, and setting slopes of the displacement curve, or the velocities, at point A equal.

The constant velocity curve could also be modified by using constant acceleration at the beginning and end of the motion as was done in the previous section on harmonic motion.

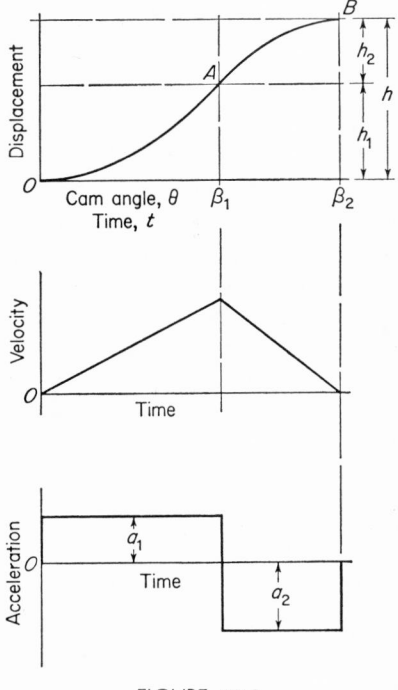

FIGURE 20.8

The resulting modified straight line curve would give infinite jerk at the transition points and would probably be no improvement over the modified curve using harmonic motion.

20.7 Cycloidal Curve

The cycloidal displacement curve has been recently shown to give better dynamic characteristics for high speed cams than any of the curves considered. The reason for its better performance at high speeds is that there is no sudden change in acceleration at the intersection of the dwell periods and the rise and return curves.

As the name implies, the displacement curve is generated from a cycloid which is the locus of a point on a circle as the circle rolls along a straight line. The displacement diagram is shown in Fig. 20.9 with the cycloid,

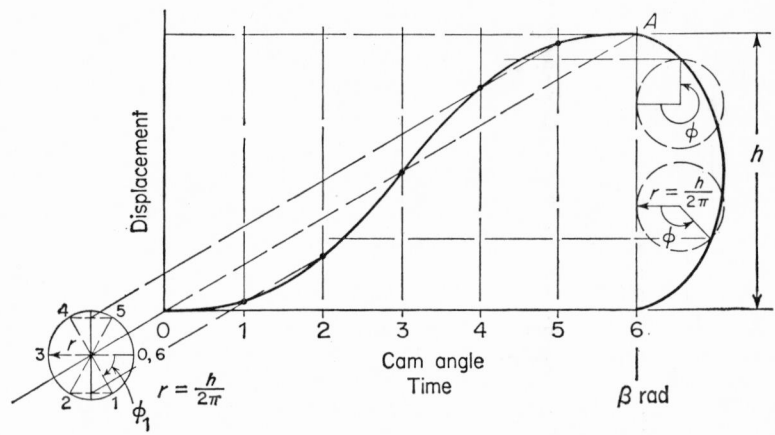

FIGURE 20.9

which generates the motion, shown to the right of the diagram. The cycloid was discussed in Article 8.2 and the equation for the rise as given there is

$$y = r(\phi - \sin \phi) \qquad (20.11)$$

where r is the radius of the generating circle and ϕ is the angle through which the circle has rotated at any given time. Since the total height is equal to the circumference of the circle

$$r = \frac{h}{2\pi}$$

and since

$$\frac{\phi}{\theta} = \frac{2\pi}{\beta}$$

Equation (20.11) can be written in terms of total rise, h, cam position, θ, and β as

$$y = \frac{h}{2\pi}\left(\frac{2\pi\theta}{\beta} - \sin\frac{2\pi\theta}{\beta}\right) \tag{20.12}$$

The curve can readily be laid out as shown in the figure. The diagonal line *O–A* represents the first term in Eqs. (20.11) and (20.12). In order to get the distance to be subtracted at the various ordinates from this term, as given by the second term, the diagonal is extended down to the left and a circle of radius $h/2\pi$ is drawn with its center on this extension. The circle is divided into sectors, the number of sectors being the same as the number of divisions of the abscissae and these sectors are numbered to correspond to the divisions of the abscissae as shown, starting with zero on the horizontal radius to the right. The points on the circle are projected to the vertical diameter of the circle and the distance from the center to the intersection of these projections represents the second term in the equations. Therefore lines drawn from these intersections parallel to the diagonal *O–A* will intersect the corresponding vertical lines through the divisions of the abscissae at the correct distance from the diagonal and the curve will pass through these points. Although only six points are shown in the illustration, more points should be determined in order to draw an accurate curve.

The displacement curve is redrawn in Fig. 20.10 with the velocity and acceleration curves. By differentiating the displacement equation the velocity and acceleration equations are found to be

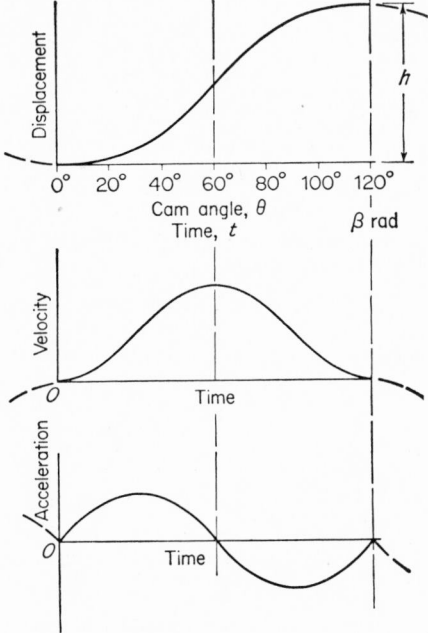

FIGURE 20.10

$$v = \frac{h}{\beta}\, \omega \left(1 - \cos \frac{2\pi\theta}{\beta} \right) \tag{20.13}$$

$$a = \frac{2\pi h}{\beta^2}\, \omega^2 \sin \frac{2\pi\theta}{\beta} \tag{20.14}$$

From the curves it is seen that the velocity and acceleration curves are smooth continuous curves. If there are dwell periods at either the beginning or end of the rise, the jerk is finite, being a maximum at the beginning and end of the rise motion. Therefore this curve gives the best dynamic characteristics of the curves presented if dwell periods are used, and is especially recommended for high speed cams of this type motion. If there are no dwell periods, however, and the motion is a rise-return motion, other motions might be better in that the acceleration for the cycloidal motion returns to zero unnecessarily at the beginning and end of the rise motion as shown by the dashed lines in the figure.

20.8 Combinations of the Basic Curves

The basic cam motions or portions of the basic cam motions can be combined in many cases to give better general characteristics than can be obtained with any one basic motion.

This combining of motions has already been used in relation to the straight line motion. Advantages and disadvantages of the various motions have been discussed and no one motion is preferable for all cams, but by combining some of the various motions into one displacement time curve we can get the advantages of the various motions in many cases and eliminate the disadvantages.

As a further example cycloidal motion could be used at the beginning and end of constant acceleration motion in order to make the jerk finite if dwell periods occur at the beginning and end of the motion. This is accomplished by matching the accelerations of the two motions at the points where the motion changes from one to the other. The equation of the basic curves can be used in setting the acceleration values equal at the points where the curves meet.

Other basic curves are used in the design of cams, but the ones discussed are the most common. These other curves can also be matched in combination with the basic curves presented. One other curve which should be mentioned is the eighth-power polynomial curve which has proved useful for high speed cams. Rothbart[1] has written an excellent book on cams, recommended for further study of cam motions and cams in general.

It should be pointed out that the displacement diagram characteristics are not the sole basis for the design of cams but other factors such as the

---

[1]Harold A. Rothbart, *Cams* (New York: John Wiley & Sons, Inc., 1956).

ease and accuracy of manufacture are also important as will be pointed out in following Articles. However, although good dynamic characteristics are not sufficient to guarantee satisfactory cam design, they are necessary for high speed cams.

20.9 Cam Layout

After the displacement diagram has been selected for a cam the next step is the layout of the cam profile to cause the follower to move with the desired motion. In most cases the cam layout is done graphically, although for accurate cams to be operated at high speeds an analytical layout is often used. A graphical layout is usually desired in any case since it will give much information to the designer and in many cases will determine whether the cam design is satisfactory. The graphical method will be covered in detail for the disc cam and the analytical method will be brought into the discussion but not covered in detail.

For a specified motion of the follower the cam profile will be dependent on the type of follower to be used. Cam followers are classified as to (1) the type of motion, as already mentioned, (2) the shape of the contact surface, and (3) the path of motion of the follower relative to the center of rotation of the cam. The types of motion are the translating and oscillating or rotating followers as shown in Fig. 20.1.

The types of follower contact surfaces are shown in Fig. 20.11. The simplest type is the knife-edge follower shown in Fig. 20.11(a) where the contact between the cam and follower is a line. The stresses at the line of contact are excessive and cause rapid wear on the follower and cam surface. For this reason this type follower is seldom used in practice but will be discussed in presenting the fundamentals of cam layout. The roller follower shown in Fig. 20.11(b) and Fig. 20.1 consists of a cylindrical roller pinned to the follower rolling along the cam surface. At low cam speeds true rolling contact is achieved but at higher speeds there will be sliding, as the roller speed changes, because of inertia effects. However there is less sliding action between the cam and follower for this type follower than for any other and the surface in contact with the cam is continually changing. For these reasons, and because these rollers are commercially available, this type follower is probably used more than any other type. The flat-faced follower shown in Fig. 20.11(c) consists of a circular flat surface in contact with the cam. This follower is simpler and less expensive than the roller follower but tends to wear faster. In order to decrease the wear on the flat surface the follower is often offset axially from the cam as shown in Fig. 20.11(d) so that the follower tends to rotate as the cam slides along the surface thereby spreading the wear over a greater surface. A spherical faced

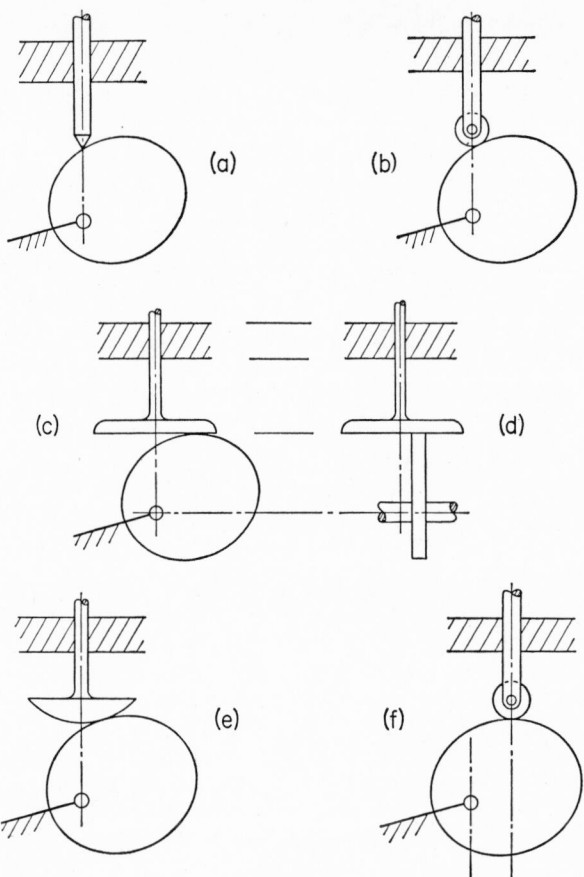

FIGURE 20.11

follower as shown in Fig. 20.11(e) is sometimes used instead of the flat-faced follower, where the circular flat face is replaced by a spherical surface.

If the line of action of the follower passes through the center of rotation of the cam, such as in Figs. 20.11(a), (b), (c), and (e), the follower is said to be a radial or in-line follower. For reasons which will be discussed later the line of action of the follower is sometimes displaced from the center of rotation of the cam as shown in Fig. 20.11(f). Such a follower is called an offset follower.

Since the layout of the cam profile depends on the type of follower to be used, the cam profile determination will be discussed in relation to the follower types. Advantages and disadvantages of the various follower types will be pointed out in the examples.

In all cam layouts the work is greatly simplified by using an inversion of the mechanism in which the cam is held fixed and the follower is rotated around the cam to its respective relative positions. Many techniques are available for the determination of the cam profile and the ones presented are not necessarily the only ones which will give the correct profile. The development of the cam profile is fairly simple and consists of drawing the follower contact surface in its position relative to the cam for a large number of phase positions and then drawing in the cam profile inside the envelope of the follower surfaces. Any method which will correctly position the follower relative to the cam at the various phase positions can be used to develop the profile.

20.10 Disc Cam with Translating Knife-Edge Follower

The knife-edge follower, although seldom used in practice, will be used in our first example since it forms a basis for all cam profiles and the cam profile for the knife-edge follower is the simplest to develop.

The cam shown in Fig. 20.12(a) is designed to cause a motion of the follower as given by the displacement diagram in Fig. 20.12(b). A base circle of radius r_b is first drawn establishing the lowest position of the follower and the profile is developed with this base circle as a reference. This circle is often called the minimum circle since it is the smallest circle

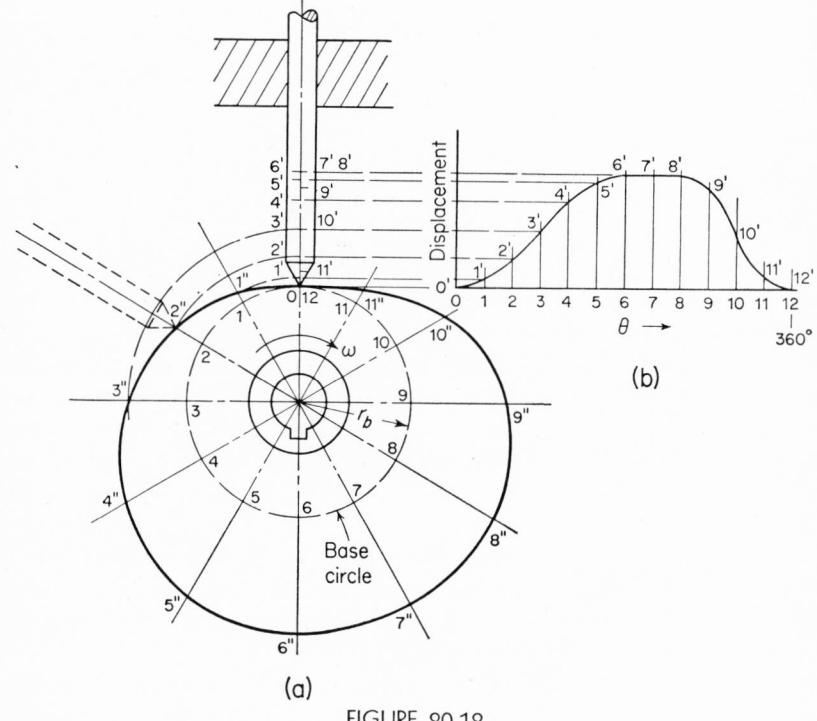

(b)

(a)

FIGURE 20.12

that can be drawn tangent to the cam profile. In the figure the base circle is divided into twelve equal parts and radii are drawn through these division points which are numbered from 0 to 12. The abscissae of the displacement diagram is also divided into twelve equal divisions and numbered to correspond to the numbers of the base circle, and ordinates are drawn through these points. The displacements of the follower for each numbered position are laid out on the follower center-line as $1'$, $2'$, $3'$, etc. Since the cam is rotating clockwise with uniform speed and we are going to hold it fixed and rotate the follower, the follower will move counterclockwise relative to the cam. Therefore when the cam has rotated two spaces the follower will be in the position shown by the dashed lines and will have moved radially a distance $0'-2'$. The point $2''$ indicates the position of the knife-edge relative to the cam at this time. This point is found by drawing an arc through $2'$ until it intersects the radial line through point 2. The other points on the cam profile such as $1''$, $3''$, etc. are found in the same manner as shown in the figure. A smooth curve drawn through these points determines the cam profile.

Only twelve points on the cam profile were determined in the example so that the construction could be easily followed. These are not enough points to determine an accurate cam profile and more points should be used. The more points used, the more accurate the profile will be.

20.11 Disc Cam with Translating Roller Follower

The layout of a cam for a translating roller follower is quite similar to the layout of a knife-edge follower. The base circle is first laid out and numbered in the same manner as for the knife-edge follower, as shown in Fig. 20.13. The roller follower is drawn in contact with the base circle at point O which corresponds to its lowest position. We cannot use the point of contact between the roller and the cam as the reference point because the point of contact will not lie on the radial line forming the line of motion of the follower except at dwell points as we shall see. The center of the roller, however, will always lie on a radial line and this point will be used as the reference point. The curve formed by the reference point as the cam rotates is called the pitch curve. For the knife-edge cam the pitch curve and the cam profile or working surface of the cam are the same. The various heights of the roller centers are laid off on the centerline of the follower and numbered as shown. Circular arcs are then drawn through these points until they intersect the corresponding radii at points $1''$, $2''$, $3''$, etc. Using these points as centers circles are drawn equal in diameter to the follower roller and the envelope of these circles form the cam profile. A curve drawn tangent to these circles then forms the cam profile, and we see that as the cam rotates the follower is forced to move with its prescribed motion.

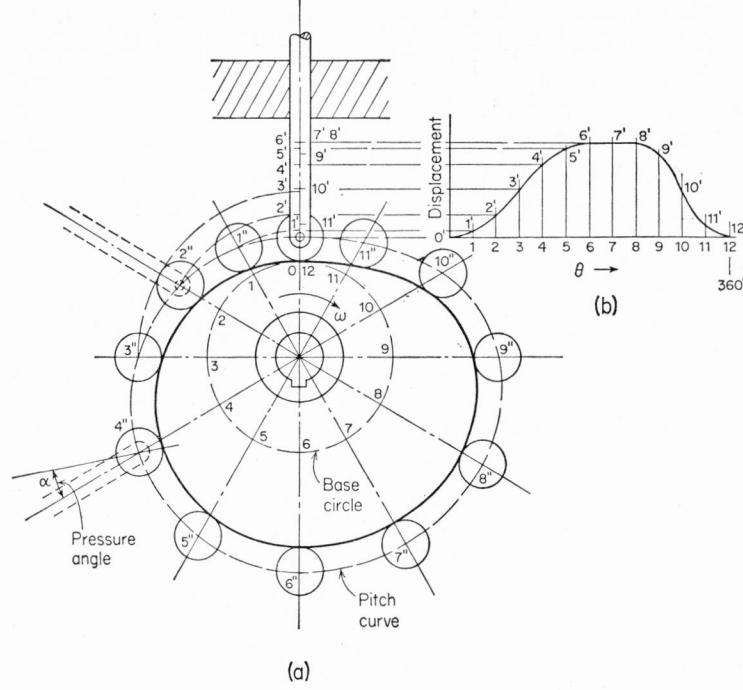

(b)

(a)

FIGURE 20.13

20.12 Pressure Angle

From Fig. 20.13 it is seen that the point of contact of the roller on the cam does not lie on the line of motion of the follower, as previously noted, except at certain points. Since the force between the cam and follower must be normal to the surfaces at the point of contact, the line of action of the force will not be along the line of motion of the follower, and the component of the force normal to the follower stem will tend to cause binding between the stem and its guide. Also the normal force between the cam and the follower must be greater than the force necessary to move the follower. The angle between the normal force and the centerline of the follower is called the pressure angle and should be as small as possible. The pressure angle is shown at follower position 4 in Fig. 20.13. An arbitrary angle of 30° has been set as the maximum pressure angle allowable for good cam performance, although in some special cases where forces are small and accurate bearings are used this angle can be exceeded.

For a translating cam as shown in Fig. 20.14 it is seen that the pressure angle at any point along the cam is equal to the angle that the tangent to the cam profile at that point makes with the horizontal axis. If we take this translation cam as the displacement diagram for a disc cam, the pressure

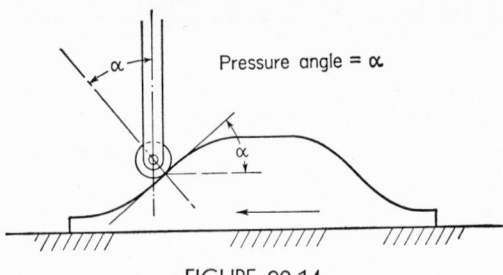

Pressure angle = α

FIGURE 20.14

angles on the disc cam will not be the same as those for the equivalent translation cam. This can be shown by reference to Fig. 20.15 where Fig. 20.15(a) shows a constant velocity or straight line displacement diagram and Fig. 20.15(b) shows a section of the pitch curve of a disc cam for a radial follower laid out for the same motion. The pressure angle on the displacement diagram is a constant angle α, and the pitch curve of the cam is drawn so that the pressure angle at point A is the same angle α.

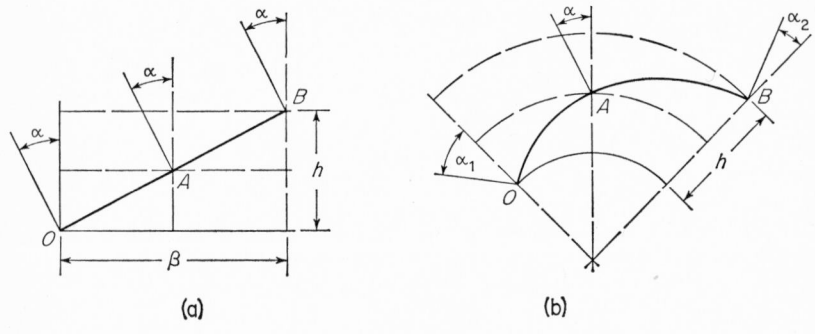

(a)   (b)

FIGURE 20.15

At point O the pressure angle is α_1, and we see that it is greater than α while at point B the pressure angle α_2 is smaller than α. The pressure angle is distorted when laid out on a radial cam and will be larger than α for points with smaller radii than point A and smaller than α for points having greater radii than A. The pressure angle is distorted for any pitch curve of a disc cam in this manner, and we see that the pressure angle depends on the radius of the cam. Therefore the pressure angle can be reduced by using a larger base circle, and thereby a larger cam. However space limitations usually limit the size of the cam and the pressure angle cannot always be held to a low value by this method.

An approximate method of cam layout is available which will give us the minimum cam size for a given pressure angle in the case of a disc cam with a radial roller follower. We will define a pitch point as the point on the

pitch curve of a cam at which the pressure angle is a maximum, and the
pitch circle of a disc cam as the circle with center at the center of rotation
and passing through the pitch point. These are shown in the cam in
Fig. 20.16(a). The displacement diagram for the cam is shown in Fig.
20.16(b) where the line A–B is equal in length to the circumference of the

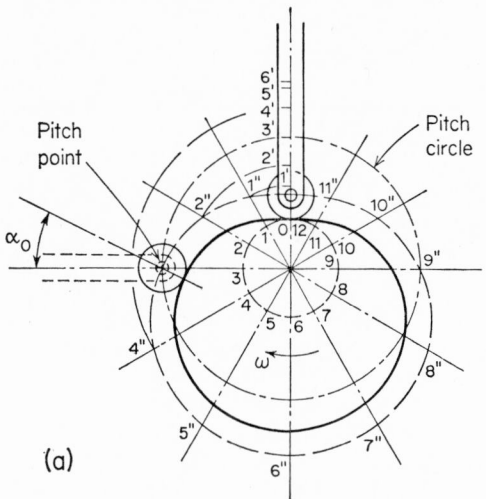

(a)

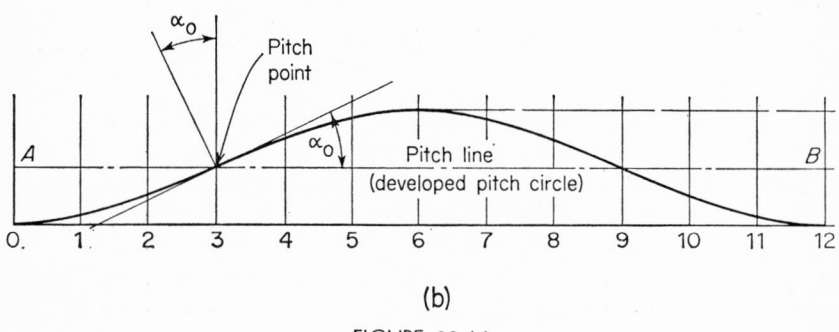

(b)

FIGURE 20.16

pitch circle, so that the pitch curve is rectified on the developed pitch circle
(called the pitch line) and the radial lines on the cam appear as parallel
vertical lines on the displacement diagram. If the displacement diagram
represented a translation cam, moving at a uniform velocity equal to the
linear velocity of the pitch circle, and driving a knife-edge follower, it would
cause a motion of the follower that would be identical to the motion of the

roller follower driven by the disc cam. Also, the pressure angle for the knife-edge follower would be the same as for the roller follower at positions 0, 3, 6, 9, and 12. Between the positions 0 and 3 the pressure angle for the roller follower would be greater than for the knife-edge follower and between positions 3 and 6 the roller follower would have a smaller pressure angle because of the distortion as previously explained.

Therefore the design of a minimum size disc cam for a given pressure angle is reduced to the layout of a displacement diagram to scale in which the maximum slope of the diagram is equal to the tangent of the given pressure angle. The pitch line on this diagram, passing through the point of maximum slope, is equal in length to the pitch circle of the cam having the given pressure angle. The cam profile can then be developed by starting the pitch curve at the pitch point at which point the pressure angle is a maximum. Because of the fact that the pressure angle on the cam is greater than the pressure angle on the displacement diagram at points inside the pitch circle (because of distortion), the maximum pressure angle of the cam might be slightly higher than the given angle for some cams but in cases where there is a difference, this error is so small that it is negligible and the approximation is usually satisfactory. However in cams where there is a constant velocity period, the pitch point on the displacement diagram should be taken at the lowest point on the velocity portion of the curve. In this manner the pressure angle will decrease along the constant velocity portion of the cam since those points beyond the pitch point will be at a larger radius from the center of the cam.

In laying out a minimum cam as described above, it is not necessary that the length of the displacement diagram be equal to the circumference of the pitch circle because the pitch circle radius can be determined analytically. Consider Fig. 20.17 which shows a displacement diagram drawn to

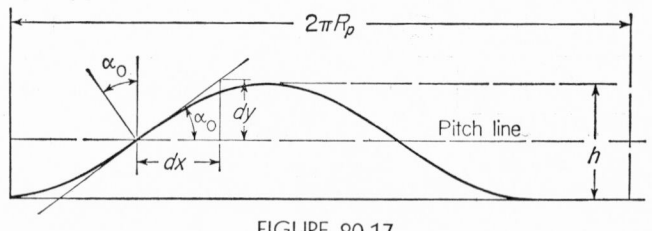

FIGURE 20.17

scale for a minimum size cam with a maximum pressure angle of α_0. The length of the diagram is $2\pi R_p$, the circumference of the pitch circle, where R_p is the pitch circle radius. If the displacement diagram were a translation cam moving with the same linear velocity as the pitch circle of the disc cam, it would have a velocity of $R_p\omega$. The slope of the diagram, or translation cam, at any point is

$$\frac{dy}{dx} = \tan \alpha$$

where α is the pressure angle. At the pitch point, where the pressure angle is a maximum, α_0, the slope of the diagram is a maximum and is the same as the slope of the cam surface relative to the pitch circle. From the figure

$$\tan \alpha_0 = \frac{dy}{dx} = \frac{dy}{R_p d\theta}$$

Dividing through by dt

$$\tan \alpha_0 = \frac{\dfrac{dy}{dt}}{R_p \dfrac{d\theta}{dt}} = \frac{v_m}{R_p \omega}$$

where v_m is the maximum velocity of the follower and ω is the angular velocity of the cam. Then solving for R_p we find

$$R_p = \frac{v_m}{\omega \tan \alpha_0} \qquad (20.15)$$

This gives us the pitch circle radius as a function of the maximum velocity of the follower, the angular velocity of the cam and the maximum pressure angle. The maximum velocity of the follower can be obtained from the equation of motion of the follower.

Using a simple harmonic motion cam as an example we find from Eq. (20.4) that the velocity at any time is

$$v = \frac{h\pi\omega}{2\beta} \sin \frac{\pi\theta}{\beta}$$

where θ = cam angle at any time

β = cam angle at completion of rise h

From Fig 20.5 we see that the velocity is a maximum for $\theta = \beta/2$ so that the maximum velocity becomes

$$v_m = \frac{h\pi\omega}{2\beta} \sin \frac{\pi}{2} = \frac{h\pi\omega}{2\beta}$$

Substituting this value into Eq. (20.15)

$$R_p = \frac{h\pi}{2\beta} \cot \alpha_0 \qquad (20.16)$$

In the same manner we could determine the minimum pitch circle radius for a given pressure angle for any follower motion. Then knowing the pitch circle radius the minimum cam could be developed starting at the pitch point on the pitch curve.

By reference to the equations of motion for the various follower motions we can show that for a given rise, occurring for the same cam displacement, the maximum velocity of the various motions differs. Therefore from Eq. (20.15) we see that some of the basic motions require larger cams for the same maximum pressure angle. The size of the cam is smallest for a constant velocity curve and must get progressively larger as we go to the simple harmonic motion, the constant acceleration motion and is largest for the cycloidal motion. Or, for the same size cam, the pressure angle increases as we change from one motion to the other in the same order.

20.13 Disc Cam with Translating Offset Roller Follower

The centerline of the follower stem is offset in some cam arrangements as shown in Fig. 20.18 so that the centerline of the follower is not a radial line. This might be done in order to eliminate interference with other parts of the machine. It also can be used to decrease the pressure angle on the rise portion of the motion, although it will increase the pressure angle on

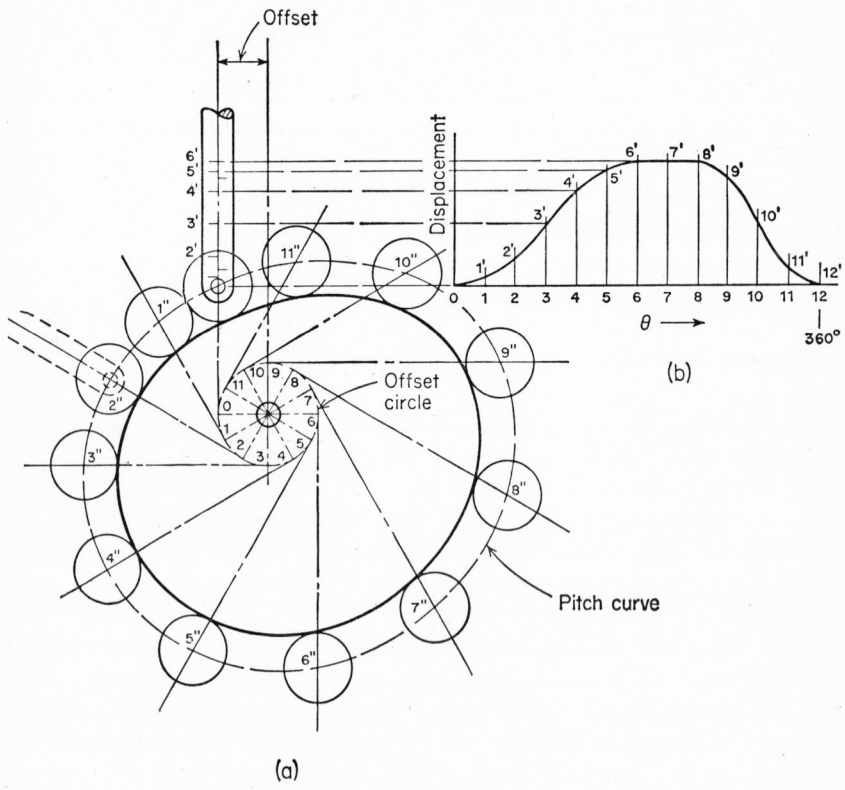

FIGURE 20.18

the return portion of the motion. In most cases the pressure angle is not too important on the return stroke since the forces are usually considerably less on the return stroke as will be seen when the force analysis is considered later.

The reference point is again the center of the follower roller and the follower displacements are laid out on the centerline of the follower as shown in the figure. A circle called the offset circle is drawn with radius equal to the offset and center at the center of rotation of the cam. This circle will then be tangent to the centerline of the follower. This circle is divided into increments corresponding to increments of the displacement diagram and numbered accordingly, starting with 0 at the point where the follower centerline is tangent to the circle. Tangents are then drawn at each numbered radii as shown in the figure. These tangent lines represent the centerline of the follower at the various phase positions. The points on the pitch curve are found by laying off the distance from the offset circle to the follower position along the various tangents. For point 3″ the distance 0–3′ is laid off along the tangent at point 3 so that the distance 3–3″ is equal to 0–3′. Using these points as centers the roller circles are drawn and the cam profile drawn tangent to these circles, in the same manner as the profile for the radial follower.

The determination of the maximum pressure angle and the cam angle at which it occurs, in this case, requires a complicated trial and error analytical solution and is best accomplished by graphical determination on accurate layouts. If a minimum size cam is to be laid out for a given pressure angle, this can be done by trial and error layouts.

20.14 Limitations of Cams with Roller Followers

Two limitations in the cam contour should be pointed out in relation to the size of the follower roller. These limitations are shown in Fig. 20.19. If the radius of curvature of the pitch curve at any point is less than the radius of the roller, the cam profile would have a loop in it as shown in Fig. 20.19(a). Obviously this profile could not be used and in order to eliminate the difficulty either a smaller roller must be used or the cam size must be increased. The limiting case is where the radius of curvature of the pitch circle is equal to the radius of the roller in which case the cam profile would come to a point.

The other limitation is shown in Fig. 20.19(b) where the concave portion of the cam profile has a smaller radius of curvature than the radius of the roller in which case the roller cannot follow the cam profile. This condition can also be eliminated by the use of a smaller roller or a larger cam size.

The use of a smaller roller in eliminating the conditions described has the disadvantage of causing higher stresses since the contact stresses

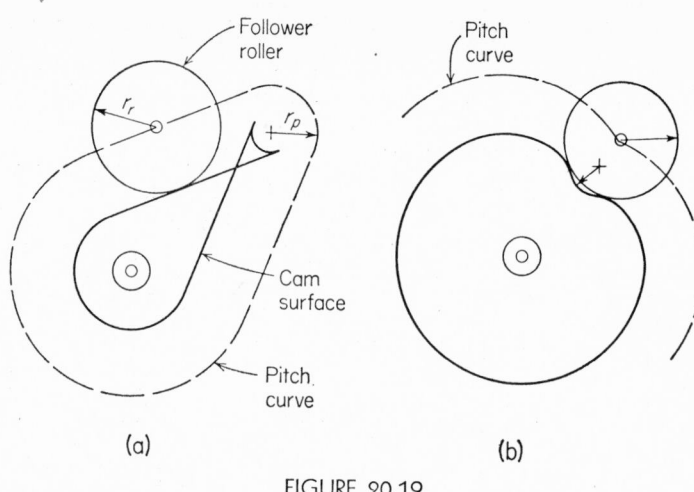

FIGURE 20.19

become greater as the radius of the roller gets smaller. Also if the rollers are too small, proper bearings cannot be housed in them. High stresses will also be encountered if the radius of curvature of the cam surfaces becomes small and therefore care should be exercised in the design of the cam so that the curvature of the cam does not become excessive. In particular a cam profile that comes to a point is in general not satisfactory except for very low speed cams.

20.15 Disc Cam with Translating Flat-Faced Follower

The layout of the cam profile for a flat-faced translating follower is shown in Fig. 20.20. The reference point in this case is taken as the intersection of the centerline of the follower stem and the face of the follower. Displacements are transferred to the cam centerline as shown at points $0'$, $1'$, $2'$, etc. These are then rotated about the center of the cam to points $1''$, $2''$, $3''$, etc. on the corresponding radial lines. Through these points, which locate the center of the follower face relative to the cam, a line is drawn perpendicular to the radial lines and these lines correspond to the face of the follower in their respective relative positions. A smooth curve tangent to these straight lines then gives us the correct cam profile to cause the follower to move with the prescribed motion.

Since the point of contact between the follower face and the cam varies with the relative positions, the radius of the circular flat face must be large enough so that the point of contact always lies on the face of the follower. The minimum radius of the face is indicated in the figure as r_m and is equal to the maximum distance from the point of contact to the radial line passing through the center of the follower. Ordinarily this minimum radius is

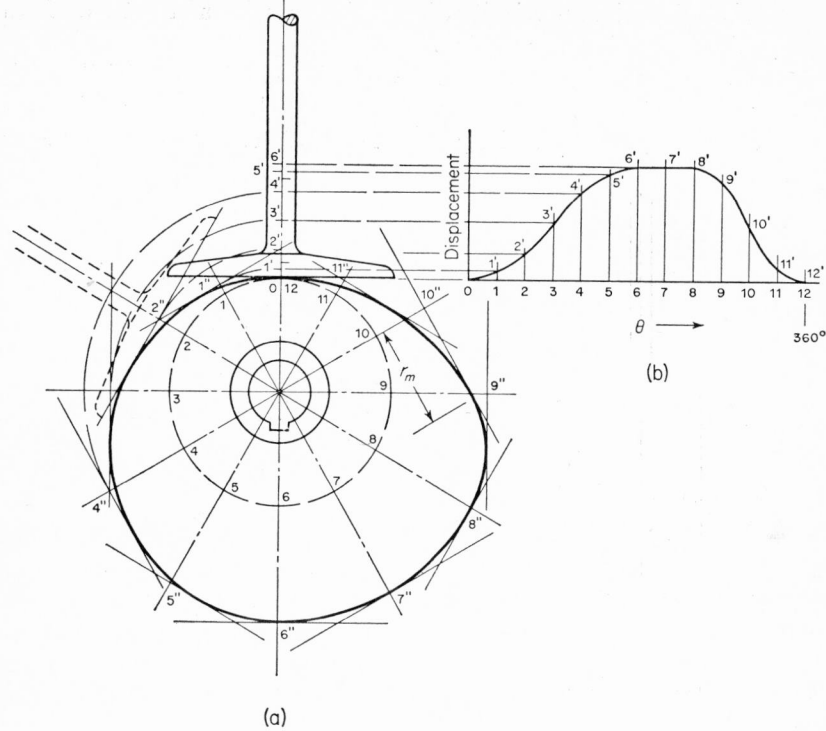

(b)

(a)

FIGURE 20.20

determined by inspection of the layout and the radius of the face is made somewhat larger to insure proper functioning of the mechanism. However it can be determined analytically by making use of the instant center common to the cam and follower.

Consider the cam and follower shown in Fig. 20.21 which shows a cam and follower in contact at point P. The common instant center will be at point Q and remembering that the instant center is a point on the cam which has the same velocity as the coincident point on the follower, we can write the equation for the velocity of the follower as

$$v_f = r\omega$$

where r is the distance from the centerline of the follower to the contact point and ω is the angular velocity of the cam. Since ω is a constant the distance r will vary directly with the velocity of the follower and the minimum radius of the face of the follower is

$$r_m = \frac{v_m}{\omega} \tag{20.17}$$

where v_m is the maximum velocity of the follower and can be obtained from the equation of the follower motion.

As seen from the figures the pressure angle for a flat-faced follower is always zero and the only cause of jamming of the follower in its guide is the moment caused by the eccentricity of the normal force and the friction force

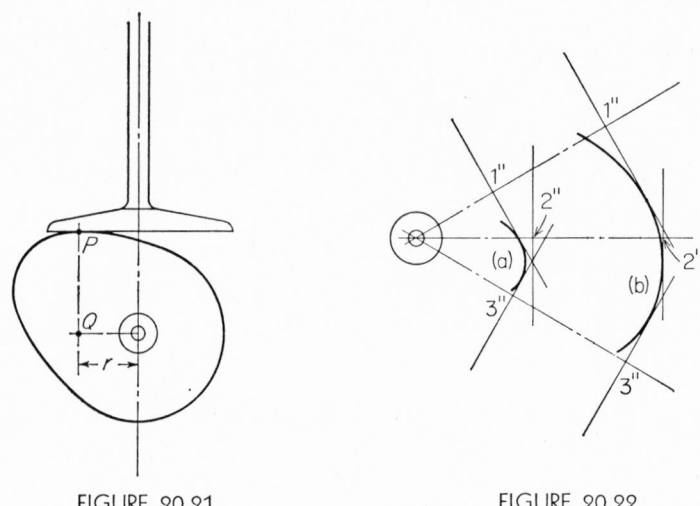

FIGURE 20.21   FIGURE 20.22

between the cam and follower. These effects are opposite during the rise portion of the motion and tend to balance each other. Therefore there is no limitation to the size of cam for a flat-faced follower because of pressure angle and small cam size is one of the advantages of the flat-faced follower. The contact stresses are generally smaller for a flat-faced follower since the radius of curvature of the follower face is infinite and this gives us another advantage.

There is one limitation on the size of cam that can be used with a flat-faced follower. This is shown in Fig. 20.22(a) which shows the face of the follower in its relative positions with reference points 1″, 2″, and 3″, and the cam drawn tangent to these lines. The cam profile cannot be drawn tangent to the face at position 2″. In order to draw a profile that will give the required motion the size of the cam must be increased as shown in Fig. 20.22(b)

20.16 Disc Cam with Oscillating Roller Follower

The layout of a cam for an oscillating roller follower is shown in Fig. 20.23. The base circle is drawn and the follower pivot point is located relative to the center of the cam with the roller in contact with the base

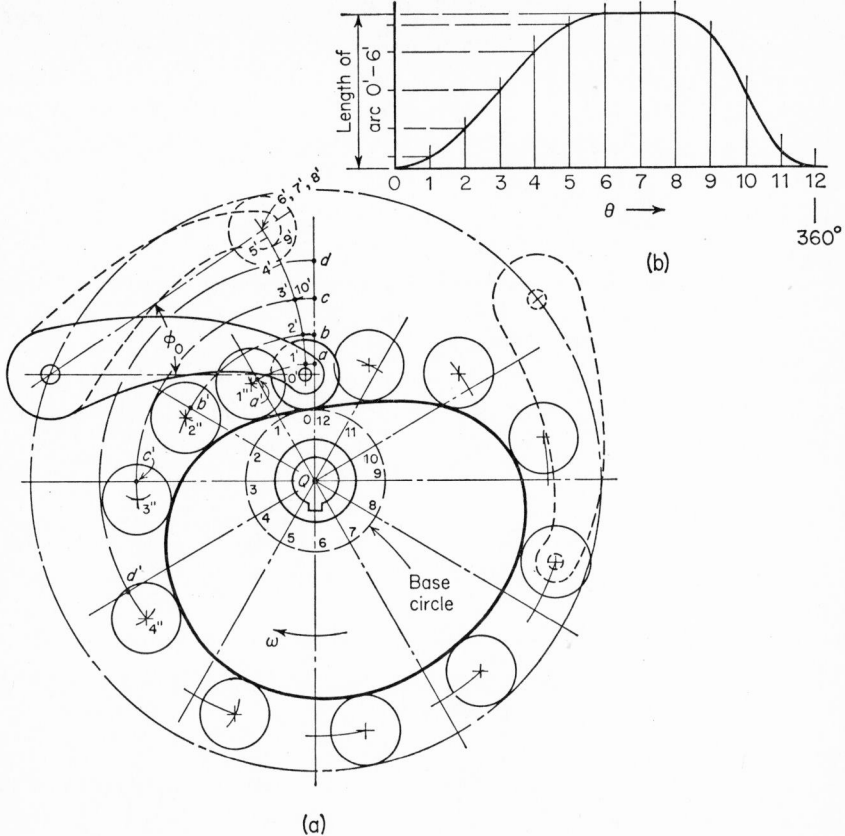

(b)

(a)

FIGURE 20.23

circle, locating the lowest position of the roller center at $0'$. The path of the roller will be the arc $0'$, $3'$, $6'$ as shown where the angle ϕ_0 is the maximum displacement of the follower. The ordinates of the displacement diagram will represent distance along the arc of motion so that the maximum ordinate is the rectified arc $0'$, $3'$, $6'$. The ordinates of the diagram are laid off along the arc of motion as $0'$–$1'$, $0'$–$2'$, etc. Draw arcs with center at Q and radii Q–$1'$, Q–$2'$, Q–$3'$, etc. to intersect radial line 0 at a, b, c, etc. and the corresponding radial lines at a', b', c', etc. Now with a radius equal to chord $1'$–a strike an arc from a' to locate $1''$, the position of the roller center corresponding to the displacement $0'$–$1'$. Chord $2'$–b is used to locate point $2''$ swinging arc from b'. This construction is repeated for the other points. The rollers are then drawn and the cam profile drawn tangent to the rollers.

Note that the centers of the follower roller do not lie on the radial lines Q–1, Q–2, etc. but are shifted by distances a'–$1''$, b'–$2''$, etc.

The pressure angle for the rotating follower can be considerably larger than in the case of the reciprocating follower without detrimental effects and therefore the pressure angle is of very little importance in rotating followers.

20.17 Disc Cam with Rotating Flat-Faced Follower

The layout of the cam for a rotating flat-faced follower follows the layout for the translating flat-faced follower in that the cam profile is drawn tangent to the faces of the follower when drawn in their relative positions. However for the rotating follower the angular position of the face is changing at all times.

The follower and the base circle are drawn in their relative positions with the follower in its lowest position as shown in Fig. 20.24. An arc of some arbitrary radius r_1 is drawn from the pivot point intersecting the face of the follower. Labeling the point of intersection with the face at its lowest position as $0'$, the displacements are laid out on this arc as $1'$, $2'$, $3'$, etc. in the same manner as for rotating roller follower. A radial line is drawn through the pivot point Q_0 as the 0 radial line and the divisions of the base circle are referenced from this line instead of the vertical line as in previous layouts. A circle of radius O–Q_0 is drawn with center at O and the intersections of this circle with the radial lines O–1, O–2, O–3, etc. locate points Q_1, Q_2, Q_3, etc. which are the relative positions of the pivot point.

A circle of radius r_t is drawn about Q_0 tangent to the face of the follower (extended as shown) and circles of this radius are then drawn about all the pivot points Q_1, Q_2, Q_3, etc. The face of the follower is always tangent to these circles at its relative positions. Arcs of radius r_1 are now drawn from the various pivot points and arcs are drawn through points $1'$, $2'$, $3'$, etc. with center at 0 to intersect the corresponding arcs about the pivot points at $1''$, $2''$, $3''$, etc. Lines drawn through these points and tangent to the circles of radius r_t at the corresponding pivot points represent the faces of the cam at their relative positions. The cam profile is then drawn tangent to these lines as shown in the figure.

The required length, and position relative to the pivot point, of the flat face is found by noting the maximum distance of the contact point to either side of the arcs of radius r_1, or, if all points of contact are on the same side of the arc, the minimum and maximum distance will determine the necessary follower face. The face should be extended a small amount in each direction to assure that the cam contacts a flat surface at all times.

20.18 The Circular Arc Disc Cam

In some cases cams are designed such that the contour is composed of tangent circular arcs or circular arcs and straight lines as shown in Fig.

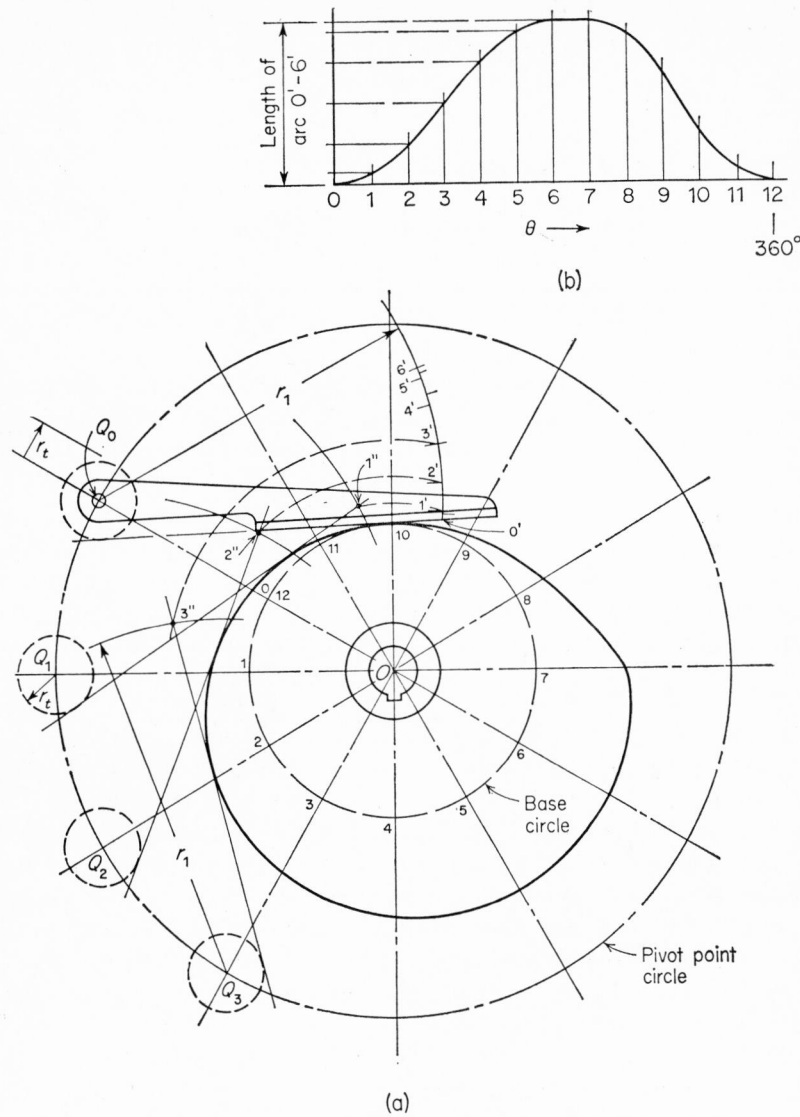

FIGURE 20.24

20.25. In these cases the cams are not based on a given follower motion and the motion of the follower is determined from the cam profile. The primary advantages of this type cam is the simplicity of the profile, the low cost of manufacture and the ease with which the dimensional accuracy can be checked. Most automotive cams are of this type.

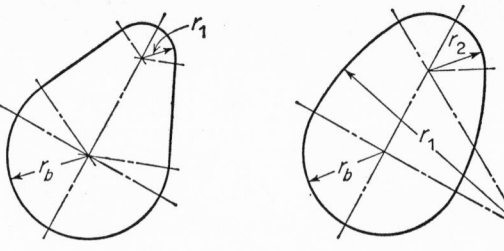

FIGURE 20.25

Means of determining the velocities and accelerations of the follower for this type cam have been covered in the chapters on kinematic analysis. In most cases an equivalent mechanism should be used in the analysis.

It should be pointed out that at the tangent points of the various radii there is an abrupt change in acceleration giving an infinite jerk at these points and in general these cams should not be operated at high speed.

20.19 Cam Manufacture

Various methods are used to fabricate cams, depending on speed of operation of the cam, accuracy needed and the number to be produced. Some cams are produced in quantity by mass production methods but in such cases highly accurate master cams or dies must be made. Usually, accurate cams are produced by milling or grinding. For highly accurate cams the method of increment cutting is used in which the contour is formed by intermittent cuts with a series of scallops or flats being cut tangent to the desired profile; in some cases the ridges are then removed by hand filing. Such a procedure requires accurate calculation of the cutter position for the various cuts and these calculations are generally made on a computer. Methods of making the calculations are found in the literature. Master cam templates for the mass production of cams on contour machines are usually made in this manner.

In the design of the cam profile the method of manufacture should be taken into consideration. Some of the more complicated high speed designs require accurate fabrication in order to gain the advantage of the particular profile.

The graphical layout of cam profiles should be used only for low speed cams since a master template made by this method cannot give high accuracy. Analytical methods must be used to take advantage of accurate machining methods.

20.20 *Force Analysis*

The forces encountered in cam mechanisms are external or output forces, gravity forces, inertia forces, friction forces, spring forces (when a spring is used to return the follower), and vibratory or shock forces. The analysis of vibratory forces is of considerable importance in high speed cams but is beyond the scope of this text and a detailed analysis will not be given. However, it has already been pointed out that an infinite jerk causes high shock loads and resulting vibrations which are detrimental to cam performance. In order to reduce vibratory effects the cam system should be made rigid and the jerk should be held to a minimum value. The vibratory forces are of a transient nature and their frequency is high in relation to the frequency of the cam cycle. Therefore they are usually considered independently of the other forces acting on the cam.

Follower systems which are highly flexible tend to aggravate vibration effects since in such systems the follower output motion varies considerably from the cam input motion because of the elasticity of the follower system. A method of cam design for high speed, flexible, systems has been developed in which the cam design takes into consideration the flexibility of the system. Such cams are known as polydyne cams.

In all the cams illustrated so far the cam profile causes the follower to move with the prescribed motion as long as the acceleration is positive, and a spring or some external force is required to hold the follower in contact with the cam at other times and to cause the follower to return to its lowest position. In some cases a positive return cam is used for this purpose

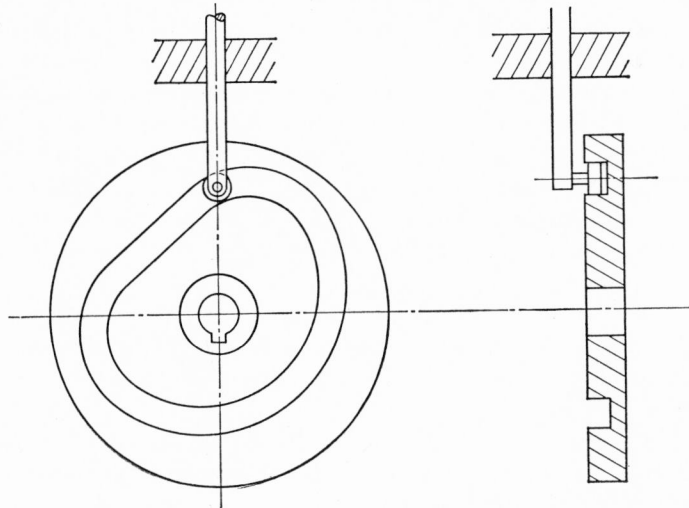

FIGURE 20.26

instead of a spring. Such a cam is shown in Fig. 20.26 where the follower roller moves in a groove in the cam. In all such cams, because of clearance between the roller and the groove, a phenomenon known as crossover shock occurs as the roller changes contact from one surface to the other. This crossover shock causes high impact loads and tends to set up vibrations in the follower. Also the roller must change directions of angular motion at such times and considerable sliding occurs between the roller and the cam because of the angular momentum of the roller.

A typical cam and follower arrangement for a radial roller follower is shown in Fig. 20.27 with the various forces where:

F_0 = Total external forces acting on the follower together with the weight and inertia force of follower

F_s = Spring force

F_1 and F_2 = Forces normal to follower stem

N = Normal force between cam and follower

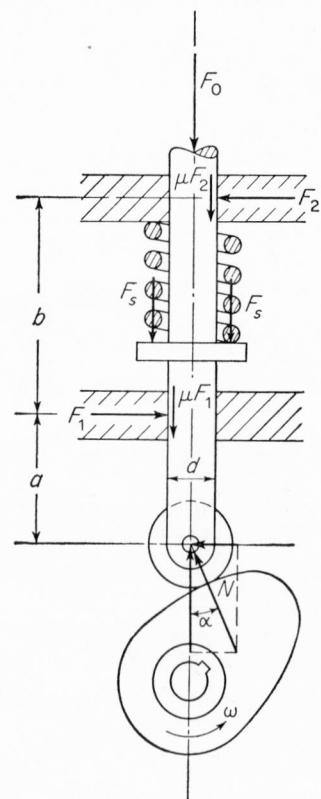

FIGURE 20.27

a = Follower overhang

b = Distance between bearing surfaces (for a single bearing, b is the length of the bearing)

d = Diameter of follower stem

α = Pressure angle

μ = Coefficient of friction between follower stem and its guide

Since the spring force, F_s, and the force F_0 are acting along the center-line of the follower they will be taken as a single force F with no subscript, so that

$$F = F_0 + F_s = F_e + F_s + F_i + W \qquad (20.18)$$

where F_e = External forces

F_i = Inertia forces

W = Weight of follower

The individual forces will be considered in detail later. Summing forces in a vertical direction

$$N \cos \alpha = F + \mu(F_1 + F_2) \qquad (20.19)$$

And in the horizontal direction

$$F_2 = F_1 - N \sin \alpha \qquad (20.20)$$

Summing moments about the point of application of F_1

$$F_2(b - \mu d) = Na \sin \alpha + \frac{d}{2}(F - N \cos \alpha) \qquad (20.21)$$

Eliminating F_1 and F_2 from the above equations the force normal to the cam can be found as a function of F, α, μ, and the cam dimensions as

$$N = \frac{Fb}{b \cos \alpha - (2\mu a + \mu b - \mu^2 d) \sin \alpha} \qquad (20.22)$$

This equation can be used to determine the normal force at any cam position, but it should be noted that both F and α vary with cam position. The friction forces have considerable effect on the normal force when the pressure angle becomes fairly large. The limiting pressure angle at which the follower will jam in its guide is the angle which makes N infinite. This occurs when the denominator in Eq. (20.22) equals zero and the limiting pressure angle can be determined from the relation

$$b \cos \alpha_m - (2\mu a + \mu b - \mu^2 d) \sin \alpha_m = 0$$

or

$$\tan \alpha_m = \frac{b}{\mu(2a + b - \mu d)} \qquad (20.23)$$

The inertia forces are determined from the mass and acceleration of the follower and since they reverse direction when the acceleration becomes negative, the spring force must be sufficient, together with the external forces, to keep the follower in contact with the cam. This separation of the cam and follower is called jump and occurs in high speed cams when the spring force is insufficient to balance the other forces. Care should be taken so that the spring force is sufficient to eliminate jump since returning contact between cam and follower causes shock loads and initiates vibrations.

The spring also serves to return the follower to its lowest position and should have some initial preload to insure contact at the lowest position. Helical compression springs as usually used have a constant spring rate and therefore the spring force will vary directly with the displacement. In designing the spring a curve of inertia force and external force should be plotted as a function of cam displacement and then the spring force at the critical points can be determined and a spring rate selected to give the desired force. The spring force can then be plotted as a function of cam displacement.

The torque required to drive the cam is usually desired so that the load on the cam-shaft, and the power required to drive the cam, can be determined. Fig. 20.28(a) shows a cam with a radial roller follower. Let F be the total force along the centerline of the follower, N the force normal to the cam, and r the distance from the center of the roller to the center of the cam. The torque is

$$T = N(O{-}R) = Nr \sin \alpha$$

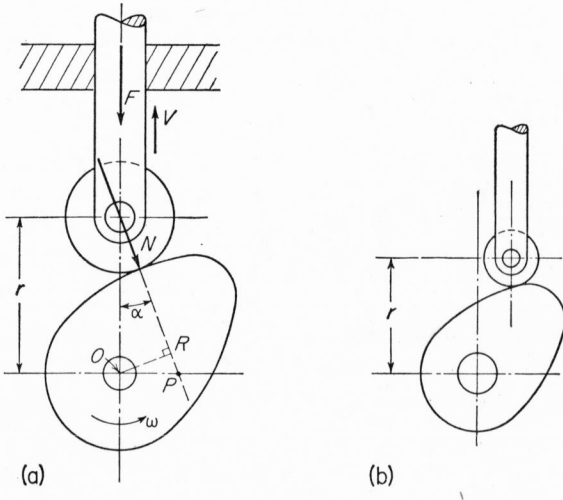

(a)   (b)

FIGURE 20.28

Substituting the equation for normal force

$$N = \frac{F}{\cos \alpha}$$

we find $T = Fr \tan \alpha$ (20.24)

Noting that point P is the instant center common to the follower stem and the cam we can write the equation for the velocity of the follower as

$$v = \omega(O–P)$$

and from the figure

$$\tan \alpha = \frac{(O–P)}{r}$$

so that $v = \omega r \tan \alpha$ (20.25)

Substituting Eq. (20.25) into Eq. (20.24)

$$T = \frac{Fv}{\omega}$$ (20.26)

The force F can be determined as previously explained and the velocity of the follower can be found from the motion equations for the various motions. In using Eq. (20.26) the sign of the velocity is important since the torque is reversed for the return portion of the motion. Although Eq. (20.26) was developed for a radial follower it can be shown that the same equation holds for an offset roller follower if the distance r is taken as shown in Fig. 20.28(b).

It can also be seen from Fig. 20.21 and Eq. (20.17) that the Eq. (20.26) holds for a flat-faced translating follower if friction between cam and follower is neglected.

The force analysis for the flat-faced follower will not be covered, since it is quite similar to that for the roller follower. It is a simpler analysis since only friction forces occur in the horizontal direction.

PROBLEMS

20.1 A radial cam follower for a disc cam is to have the following motion: rise $1\frac{1}{2}$ in. in 180° of cam motion with constant acceleration first 60°, constant velocity second 60°, and constant acceleration last 60°, dwell for 30°, return with simple harmonic motion in 150° cam motion.

Plot the displacement diagram for the above follower motion and determine analytically the maximum acceleration and velocity for the rise and return motions in terms of the constant angular velocity of the cam.

20.2 A radial cam follower for a disc cam is to have the following motion: rise 1 in. in 150° of cam motion with constant acceleration, the ratio of the acceleration in the first part of the rise motion to that in the second part to be 3:5, dwell for 30°, return in 120° with cycloidal motion, dwell for 60°.

Plot the displacement diagram for the above follower motion and determine analytically the maximum acceleration and maximum velocity for the rise and return motions in terms of the constant angular velocity of the cam.

20.3 A radial cam follower for a disc cam is to have the following motion: rise $1\frac{1}{4}$ in. in 150° of cam motion with cycloidal motion, dwell for 20°, return in 150° with simple harmonic motion, dwell for 40°.

Plot the displacement diagram for the above follower motion and determine analytically the maximum acceleration and velocity for the rise and return motion in terms of the constant angular velocity of the cam.

20.4 **(a)** Lay out the cam profile for the motion in Prob. 20.1 for a radial roller follower with roller diameter of $1\frac{1}{2}$ in. Use a base circle of $2\frac{3}{4}$ in. and assume cam is rotating counterclockwise.

(b) Determine the maximum pressure angle graphically from the layout and check the angle analytically.

20.5 Lay out the cam profile for the minimum size cam having a maximum pressure angle of 25° for a radial follower cam with motion as given in Prob. 20.1. Follower roller diameter is $1\frac{1}{2}$ in. and cam is rotating counterclockwise.

20.6 **(a)** Lay out the cam profile for the motion in Prob. 20.1 for an offset roller follower with roller diameter of $1\frac{1}{2}$ in. and offset to the right of the cam centerline of 1 in. Use a base circle of $2\frac{3}{4}$ in. and assume cam is rotating counterclockwise.

(b) Determine the maximum pressure angle graphically.

20.7 **(a)** Lay out the cam profile for the motion in Prob. 20.1 for a flat-faced radial follower. Use a base circle of $2\frac{3}{4}$ in. and assume cam is rotating counterclockwise.

(b) Determine the minimum radius of the circular follower face graphically from the cam layout and check analytically.

20.8 Lay out the cam profile for an oscillating or rotating roller follower with motion as given in Prob. 20.1 replacing the $1\frac{1}{2}$ in. rise with 30° rise. The pivot point of the follower lies on the horizontal centerline of the cam a distance of $5\frac{1}{8}$ in. from cam center. The center of follower roller, of $1\frac{1}{2}$ in. dia., is 5 in. from pivot point. Use a base circle of $2\frac{3}{4}$ in.

20.9 **(a)** Repeat Prob. 20.8 for an oscillating flat-faced follower. Pivot point is at same position and flat face is tangent to a $2\frac{3}{8}$ in. circle with center at pivot point.

(b) Determine the required length of the flat face and its position relative to the pivot point.

20.10 **(a)** For the cam and follower as given in Prob. 20.4 the weight of the follower and its associated mechanism, which has the same motion as the follower, is 10 lbs. The centerline of the follower is vertical so that the cam supports its weight. What is the minimum spring rate that a compression spring must have to assure contact between the cam and follower at all times if the spring exerts a force of 50 lbs on the follower when it is at its lowest position?

(b) What must the spring rate be if the spring force on the follower must at all times be 50 lbs greater than the minimum required to maintain contact?

(c) Using the spring as determined in part (b) determine the maximum normal force between cam and follower. Letting the cam and follower system be represented by Fig. 20.27, $a = 3$ in., $b = 4$ in., and $\mu = 0.1$.

(d) Determine the maximum torque required to drive the cam.

Chapter 21

Gearing

21.1 Introduction

Gearing is used to transmit motion from a rotating body to another body which may be rotating or translating. Our discussion will be limited to positive driving gears transmitting motion from one rotating shaft to another rotating shaft or from a shaft to a member in translation which can be considered as rotating about an axis at infinity. We will also consider only those gears having a constant velocity ratio.

The gears, with the exception of worm gears, discussed in this chapter are equivalent to rolling bodies with the exception that motion transmitted by rolling bodies depends on friction and the bodies are not positive driving members. We will make use of the equivalent rolling members in our discussion. As an example a pair of circular gears connecting two parallel shafts could be made to give the same motion to the shafts as a pair of equivalent rolling cylinders.

21.2 Fundamental Law of Gearing

Satisfactory gear operation can be obtained only if the angular velocity ratio of the gears remains constant at all times regardless of which portion of the tooth profile is in contact. Otherwise, if the driving gear had a constant angular velocity, the driven gear would alternately be increasing and decreasing its speed with corresponding high accelerations which would cause early failure of the gears.

Consider the links "a" and "b," shown in Fig. 21.1, pinned to rotate about points O and Q and in higher sliding at point R. These could represent the contacting teeth of a pair of mating gears. A normal to the profiles at the point of contact will cut the line of centers, O–Q, at point P. Point P is the instant center "ab" common to the rotating links and we found in Chapter 4 that the angular velocity ratio of the two rotating links is

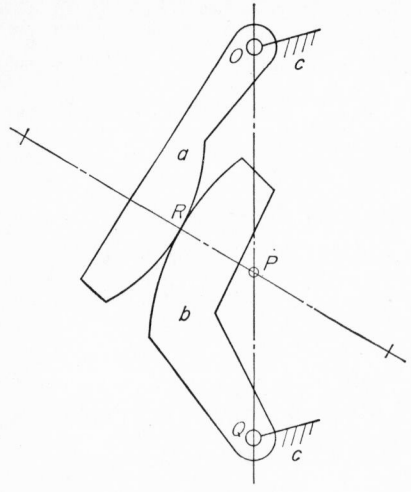

FIGURE 21.1

$$\frac{\omega_a}{\omega_b} = \frac{Q-P}{O-P} \qquad (21.1)$$

Then, for a constant angular velocity ratio, the common normal at any point of contact must pass through the same point on the line of centers. This is known as the fundamental law of gearing. Curves which make contact so as to satisfy this law are said to be conjugate to each other.

Point P in Fig. 21.1 is called the pitch point and is the point of contact between two rolling circles pinned at O and Q which would have the same velocity ratio as the sliding links. The rolling circles are called pitch circles and are kinematically equivalent to toothed gears having the same velocity ratio.

Within certain limits a conjugate tooth can be developed to mate with any given convex profile by making use of the fundamental law. However most gears at present have teeth whose profile is an involute because of the many advantages such a profile has over other curves. The cycloidal profile has been used in the past and is still used to a very limited extent.

21.3 Types of Gears

Gears whose axes are parallel or connect parallel shafts are called spur gears. The pitch surfaces of spur gears are rolling cylinders having the same velocity ratio as the gears. A pair of spur gears is shown in Fig. 21.2(a) and the equivalent rolling cylinders corresponding to the pitch surfaces whose diameters are equal to the pitch circle diameters are shown in Fig. 21.2(b). Ordinarily the term spur gears is applied only to gears whose teeth have elements parallel to the axis of rotation. In many cases the elements of the teeth form a helix around the axis of rotation and such gears are called helical gears. Helical gears usually have parallel axes but in some cases have non-parallel, non-intersecting axes. The pitch surfaces of helical gears are also cylinders.

Bevel gears are used to connect non-parallel, intersecting, shafts as shown in Fig. 21.3(a). The pitch surfaces of bevel gears are cones as shown in Fig. 21.3(b). Straight bevel gears have teeth whose elements are straight lines passing through the apex of the pitch cone and the teeth of spiral bevel

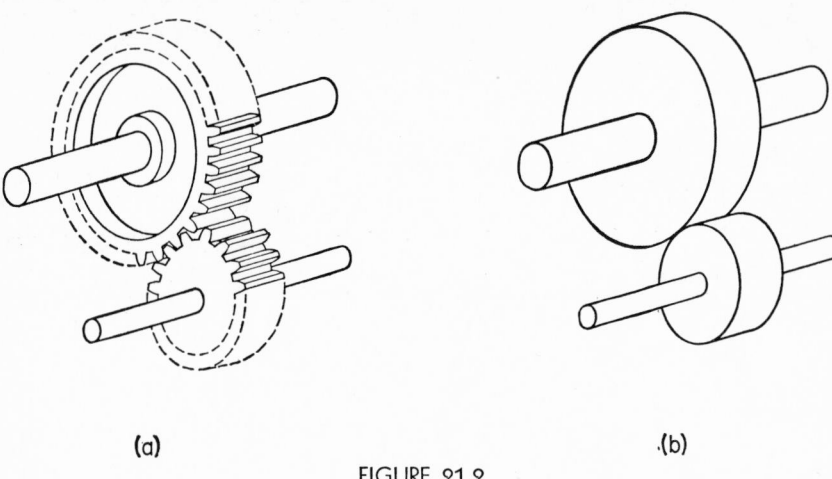

(a)   .(b)

FIGURE 21.2

gears are curved and are at an angle relative to the elements of the pitch cone. Spiral bevel gears bear a similar relation to straight bevel gears that helical gears bear to spur gears.

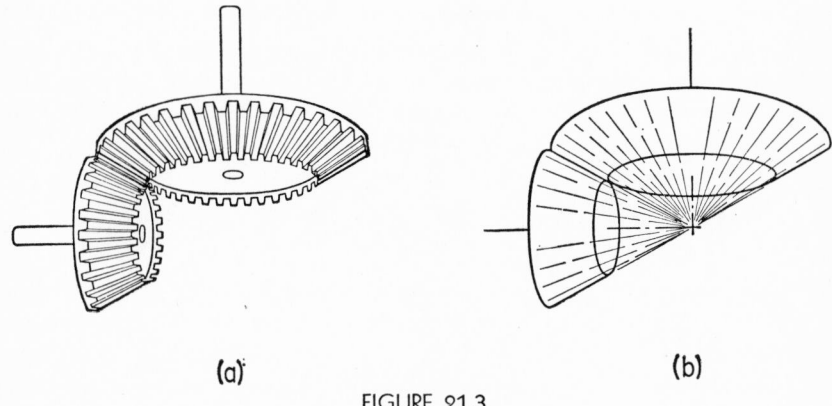

(a)   (b)

FIGURE 21.3

Gears that connect non-intersecting, non-parallel, shafts are of three types: (1) helical gears, already mentioned, (2) worm and worm gears, and (3) hypoid gears. For reasons which will be discussed later helical gears are seldom used for this type of service. The pitch surface of a worm is a cylinder while its mating worm gear can have a cylindrical pitch surface but usually does not as will be shown. The pitch surface of hypoid gears are hyperboloids from which their name is derived. It can be shown that two hyperboloids can have rolling contact in a direction normal to the surface elements but there will be relative sliding along the elements when two hyperboloids roll together.

There are other types of gears but our discussion will cover only those mentioned above. Other types are special purpose gears and an understanding of the basic types will give a sufficient background for further study if the need arises.

21.4 Terminology

As with most scientific subjects certain terms have been developed in the study of gearing and these terms should be defined before continuing our discussion. Most of the terms are indicated in Fig. 21.4.

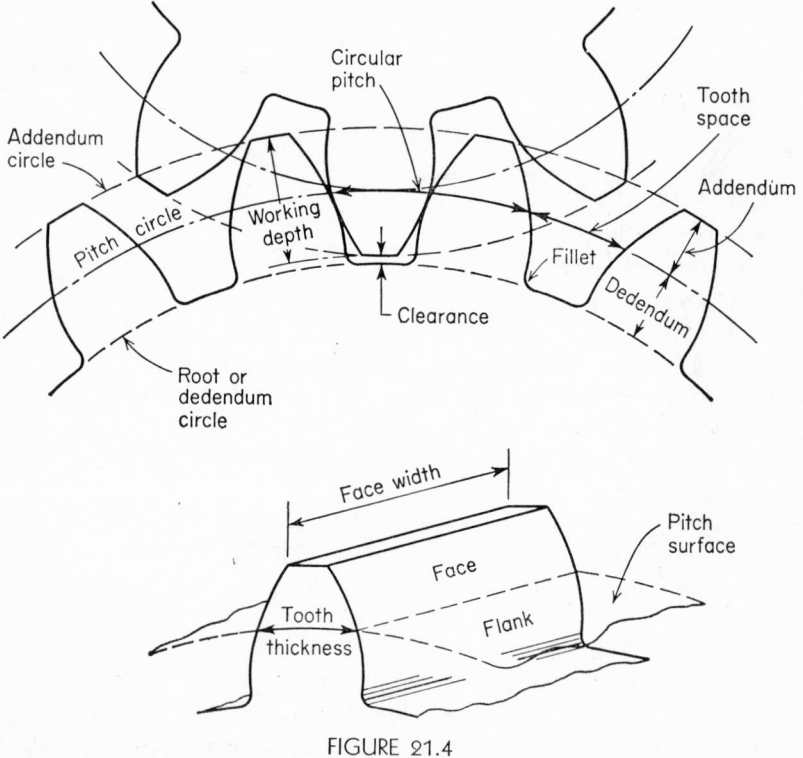

FIGURE 21.4

The *circular pitch*, p_c, is the distance along the pitch circle from a point on one tooth to the corresponding point on the next adjacent tooth. It is measured in inches and is equal to the circumference of the pitch circle divided by the number of teeth, or

$$p_c = \frac{\pi D}{N} \tag{21.2}$$

where D is the diameter of the pitch circle and N is the number of teeth on the gear

The *diametral pitch*, P_d, is the ratio of the number of teeth to the pitch diameter expressed in inches, or

$$P_d = \frac{N}{D} \tag{21.3}$$

There is a definite relation between the circular pitch and the diametral pitch which can be seen by the product of Eqs. (21.2) and (21.3)

$$p_c P_d = \pi \tag{21.4}$$

This equation can be used to determine either pitch if the other is known. The diametral pitch is usually used as a measure of the tooth size and ordinarily the diametral pitch is given in whole numbers or decimal fractions for the smaller pitches; i.e., the larger teeth.

Tooth thickness is the thickness of a tooth measured along the pitch circle.

Tooth space is the distance between adjacent teeth measured along the pitch circle.

Backlash is the difference in length between the tooth thickness of one gear and the tooth space of the mating gear.

The *addendum*, a, is the radial distance between the pitch circle and the tip of a tooth. The circle through the tips or ends of the teeth is called the addendum circle.

The *dedendum*, d, is the radial distance from the pitch circle to the bottom of the tooth spaces; also the radial distance between the pitch circle and the root or dedendum circle.

The *clearance*, c, is the radial distance that the dedendum of one gear exceeds the addendum of its mating gear.

The *working depth* is the sum of the addenda of mating gears. It is also equal to the depth of engagement of the tooth of a gear in the space of its mating gear.

The *whole depth*, h, or height of the tooth is the sum of the addendum and the dedendum. It is also equal to the working depth plus the clearance.

The *face width* or width of teeth is the length of the teeth in the axial direction.

The *face* of a tooth is that part of the tooth surface extending outside the pitch surface.

The *flank* of a tooth is that portion of the tooth surface extending from the pitch surface to the dedendum circle.

The smaller of a pair of mating gears is called a *pinion*. The larger of the pair is termed simply the gear.

The *gear ratio* is the ratio of the number of teeth on the gear to the number of teeth on the pinion.

A *rack* is a segment of a spur gear whose pitch circle has an infinite radius. The pitch surface is therefore a plane.

404   GEARING | Art. 21.5

21.5 Involute Gear Teeth

The involute tooth profile is used for most gears in use today. Therefore our study will deal primarily with involute gearing. Cycloidal gears will be discussed only to the extent of giving their advantages and to serve as a comparison to involute gears. An exhaustive discussion of involute gearing will not be attempted but the fundamental theory will be covered so that the student should be able to deal with the elementary problems of gearing usually encountered in design of machinery. Also sufficient background will be given to enable further study in the more advanced works on gearing.

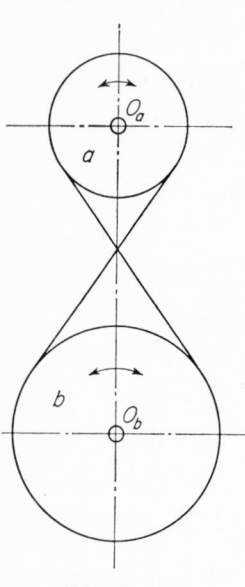

FIGURE 21.5

Consider two pulleys as shown in Fig. 21.5 with a crossed wire serving as a belt connecting the two pulleys. If there is no slipping of the wire the pulleys will rotate in opposite directions and with an angular velocity ratio inversely as the diameter of the pulleys. Now consider the path of a point Q, on one of the wires, traced on a plate attached to pulley "b" as shown in Fig. 21.6(a). This path will be an involute formed as the wire wraps around the pulley "b." In the same manner the same point Q will describe another involute on a plate attached to pulley "a" as shown in Fig. 21.6(b).

If the two plates attached to the pulleys are cut along the involute profile and a portion removed, leaving the convex portion, the two profiles will always be in contact while the two pulleys are turning with the wire serving as a belt. Also the wire will always be normal to the two surfaces at the point of contact. This is shown in Fig. 21.7. Since the wire always passes through the same point on the line of centers, these two surfaces satisfy the fundamental law of gearing. The wire could be dispensed with and the surface on pulley "a" would drive pulley "b" and its surface at a constant velocity ratio. Such profiles are the basis of involute gearing.

An important advantage of involute gearing should be pointed out at this time. If the center distance of the two pulleys is changed, the wire will still keep the velocity ratio a constant and still form the same two profiles; therefore the center distance of involute gears can be varied without affecting the velocity ratio. This will be discussed in more detail later.

From our previous discussion we recognize the point P in Fig. 21.7 as the pitch point and it can be readily seen that two rolling circles with the

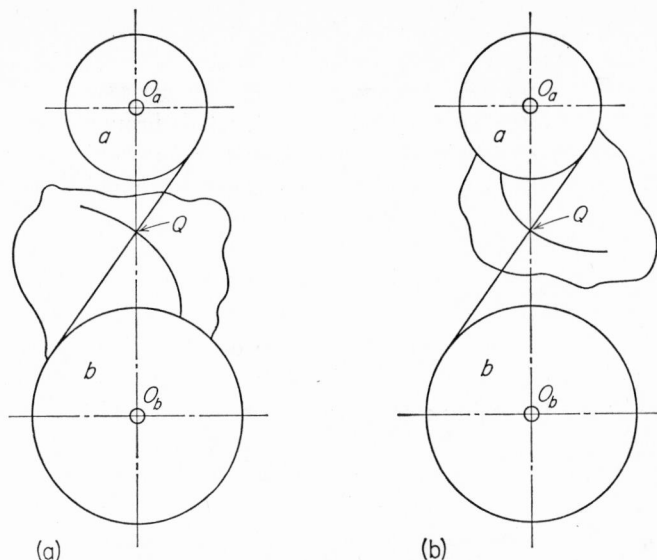

FIGURE 21.6

same centers as the two pulleys would have the same velocity ratio since the triangles formed by the wire, the line of centers and the normals to the wire from the centers are similar. Therefore the radii of the pulleys are proportional to the distance from the centers to the pitch point.

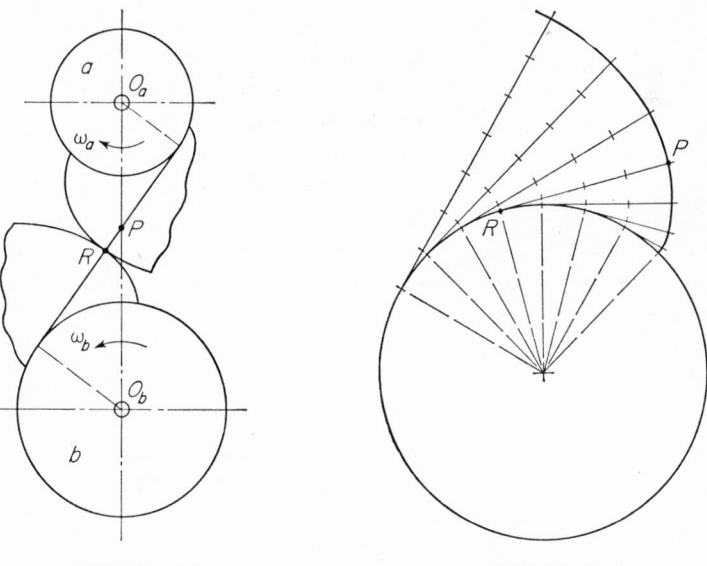

FIGURE 21.7   FIGURE 21.8

The two pulleys or circles on which the involute profile is based are called the base circles and are the controlling factors for any set of involute gears.

The involute profile can be readily constructed through a given point as shown in Fig. 21.8. Having the base circle and assuming we wish to construct an involute through point P, draw a line through P tangent to the circle at R and break this line P–R into some number of equal divisions. From R lay off distances along the circle equal to the divisions of the line and from each point along the circle draw tangents as shown. These tangents are also divided into the same length divisions thus locating points along the involute as shown. The involute can then be drawn through these points. An approximation to the involute can be drawn by using fewer tangents and drawing connecting arcs of radii equal to the distance from the point of tangency to the adjacent arc.

21.6 Involute Terminology

A portion of two involute gears in mesh is shown in Fig. 21.9. Gear "a," the top gear or pinion is turning clockwise and driving the bottom gear "b" counterclockwise. The line tangent to the two base circles, corresponding to a wire wrapped around the base circles, is called the line of action since the point of contact between any two teeth is always along this line. The angle that the line of action makes with a line normal to the line of centers, angle ϕ in the figure, is called the angle of obliquity or, more commonly, the pressure angle. In the absence of friction the force between two mating teeth is along the line of action and therefore makes the same angle relative to the normal line. Friction tends to increase or decrease the true pressure angle depending on its direction. The angle ϕ will be called the pressure angle, as is common practice, but it should be remembered that the true pressure angle deviates from this angle somewhat because of the friction force. The pressure angle is constant for involute gears and from the figure we see that the angle between the line of centers and a radius to the point of tangency of the line of action and the base circle is equal to the pressure angle for both gears. From this we see that the radius of the base circle is given by the equation

$$r_b = r_p \cos \phi \qquad (21.5)$$

where r_b and r_p are the radii of the base circle and pitch circle respectively.

We can define a base pitch, p_b, as the distance along the base circle from a point on one tooth to the corresponding point on the next adjacent tooth. It is also the normal distance between the corresponding sides of two adjacent teeth as shown on the line of action at the center of the figure. The base pitch can be determined by dividing the length of the base circle

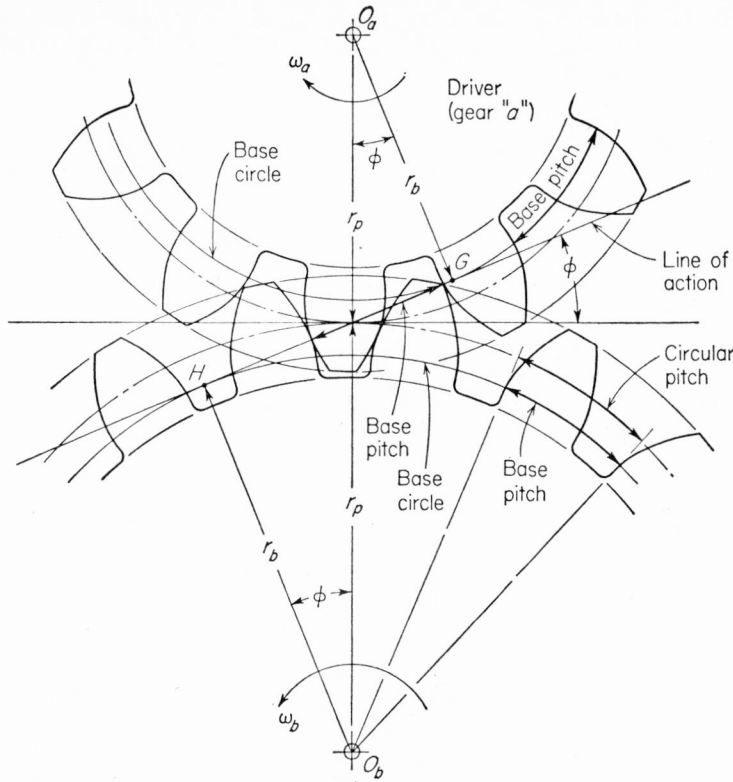

FIGURE 21.9

by the number of teeth. From Eq. (21.5) we can then determine the relation of the base pitch and the circular pitch as

$$p_b = p_c \cos \phi \qquad (21.6)$$

The base circle and base pitch are properties of a single involute gear and they are fixed once the gear has been made while the pitch circle and the circular pitch is determined by the center distance of two gears in mesh. As can be seen from the figure the pressure angle is also determined by the center distance of the two gears in mesh. The base pitch is a very important property of involute gears and must be the same for two gears if they are to mesh correctly.

Since the involute profile of a gear tooth cannot extend inside the base circle, that portion of the gear inside the base circle is usually made as a radial line from the base circle to the dedendum circle with a fillet at the dedendum circle in order to relieve the stress concentration at that point.

21.7 *Involute Gear Tooth Action*

A portion of two gears in mesh is shown in Fig. 21.10, with only a portion of the profiles of two mating teeth shown at three phase positions. The teeth first come into contact at point A, which is the intersection of the line of action and the addendum circle of the driven gear. The contact point follows the line of action through the pitch point P and contact between the teeth is broken at point B, the intersection of the line of action and the addendum circle of the driving gear. The line A–B is called the path of contact and its length is the length of the path of contact. Point C is the intersection of the tooth profile of a tooth on gear "a" and its pitch circle at the beginning of contact and point E is the same point on the profile when

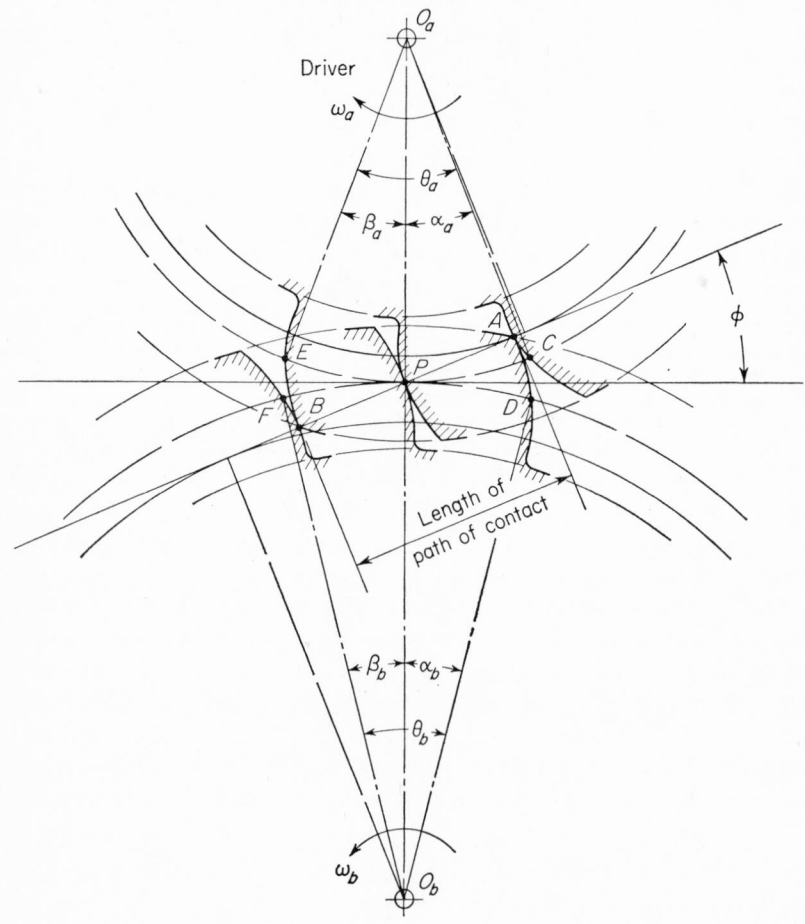

FIGURE 21.10

contact is broken. Points D and F are the corresponding points for gear "b." The arcs CPE and DPF are the arcs on the pitch circle through which a tooth profile moves from the beginning to the end of contact with a mating profile. Because of rolling contact between the pitch circles these arcs are equal. These arcs are called the arcs of action. The angles subtended by the arcs, θ_a and θ_b, are the angles of action of the respective gears. It should be noted that although the arcs of action are the same for a pair of gears in mesh, the angles of action are not the same except for gears of equal diameter. The arcs of action are usually divided into two parts called the arc of approach and the arc of recess. The corresponding angles of approach and angles of recess are shown in the figures as α and β where α is the angle of approach and β is the angle of recess with the subscripts denoting the particular gear. The angle of approach can be defined as the angle through which a gear turns from the time a pair of teeth come into contact until the teeth are in contact at the pitch point. The angle of recess is the angle through which a gear turns from the instant the pair of teeth are in contact at the pitch point until contact is broken. In general the angle of approach is not equal to the angle of recess.

The torque transmitted by a pair of gears is dependent only on the component of the normal force that is perpendicular to the line of centers. Therefore the greater the pressure angle, the greater will be the normal force between teeth for the same torque. This normal force is transmitted to the bearings and therefore the pressure angle should be kept to a minimum so as to keep the normal forces small. The pressure angle is dependent on other considerations however, as will be shown later, and a compromise must be made as to the most desirable pressure angle.

During approach the friction force tends to increase the pressure angle and during recess the friction force is such as to reduce the pressure angle. This accounts to some extent for the fact that gear tooth action is smoother during recess than during approach, and it is desirable that the angle of recess be large relative to the angle of approach.

The determination of the angles of approach and recess for a pair of gears requires the layout of the tooth profile if they are determined as shown in Fig. 21.10. These angles can be determined without drawing tooth profiles if we make use of the path of contact and the base circle. In the figure it will be noted that during approach the contact proceeds from point A to point P along the path of contact and since this represents a distance along the base circle the angle of approach can be found by the equation

$$\alpha = \frac{A\text{--}P}{r_b} \qquad (21.7)$$

Also in the same manner

$$\beta = \frac{P\text{--}B}{r_b} \qquad (21.8)$$

and
$$\theta = \frac{A-B}{r_b} = \alpha + \beta \qquad (21.9)$$

Pure rolling contact between a pair of mating teeth occurs at the pitch point, point P in Fig. 21.10. At all other points along the path of contact there is a combination of rolling and sliding. The sliding component represents the relative velocity of the two points in contact and can readily be determined by a velocity analysis. The sliding component is high at the point where contact begins, decreases to zero at the pitch point and then again increases until contact is broken. Since there is no relative sliding when teeth are in contact at the pitch point, there will be no friction force and the true pressure angle is the same as the angle of obliquity at this point.

21.8 Contact Ratio

In order for continuous action to take place between a pair of gears a pair of teeth must come into contact before the preceding pair of teeth break contact. For this to happen, the arc of action must be equal to or greater than the circular pitch. The ratio of the arc of action to the circular pitch is called the contact ratio. Then a contact ratio of one indicates that one tooth comes into action just as the preceding tooth breaks contact. Theoretically this is sufficient to insure continuous action of a pair of gears; however, from a practical viewpoint, a contact ratio of one should never be used. Because of the normal force between mating gears transmitting a load, there is some deflection of the teeth and this deflection is greater if the contact point is at the end of one of the teeth. This deflection together with slight inaccuracies in the profile caused by the cutting of the teeth causes the distance between two corresponding profiles along the line of action to differ somewhat from the base pitch so that the teeth do not mesh smoothly. Therefore it is desirable to have an adjacent tooth come into contact before the preceding tooth breaks contact. The contact ratio is an indication of the percentage of time that two pairs of teeth are in contact. A contact ratio of 1.4 has been found desirable for smooth action and this ratio should be taken as a minimum for good gear design. A contact ratio of 1.4 indicates that two pairs of teeth are in contact 40 per cent of the time; or, it means that when a pair of teeth have been in contact along the path of action for 60 per cent of its length another pair of teeth come into contact. The higher the contact ratio the smoother the action and therefore a high contact ratio is desirable.

The definition does not readily lend itself to the determination of the contact ratio and it is usually determined by dividing the length of the path of contact by the base pitch. In order to show that this gives us the contact ratio as defined we note from Fig. 21.10 that the path of contact, when rolled on the base circle, subtends the angle of action. Also from Fig. 21.9 we see that the base pitch subtends the same angle as the diametral pitch. Therefore the contact ratio is given by the equation

$$\text{Contact ratio} = \frac{\text{length of path of contact}}{p_b} \qquad (21.10)$$

The length of the path of contact can be determined graphically by drawing the addendum circles of two meshing gears at their correct center-to-center distance and drawing the line of action, as shown in Fig. 21.11, and meas-

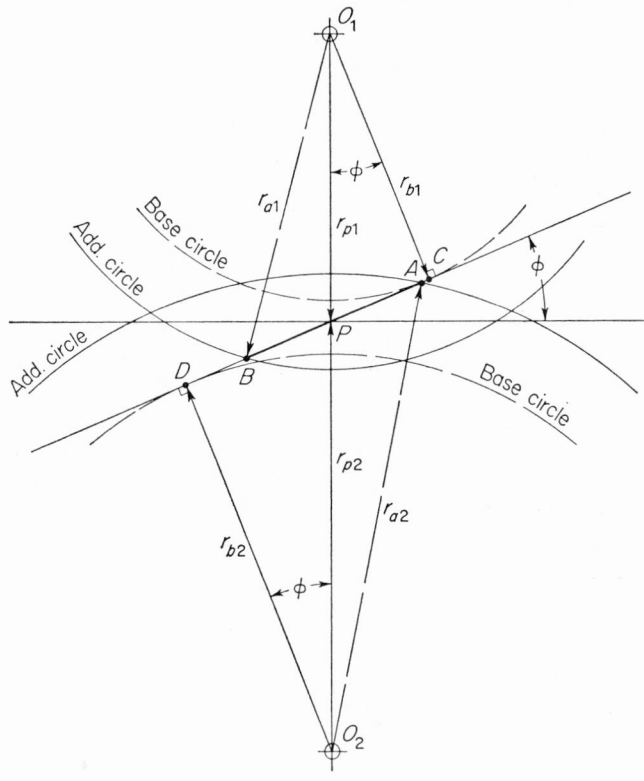

FIGURE 21.11

uring the length of the path of contact, line A–B. The length of the path of contact can also be determined analytically by noting in the figure that

$$AB = BC + DA - DC$$

Also from the figure

$$BC = \sqrt{r_{a1}^2 - r_{b1}^2}$$

$$DA = \sqrt{r_{a2}^2 - r_{b2}^2}$$
$$DC = (r_{p1} + r_{p2}) \sin \phi$$

so that

Contact ratio $= \dfrac{\sqrt{r_{a1}^2 - r_{b1}^2} + \sqrt{r_{a2}^2 - r_{b2}^2} - (r_{p1} + r_{p2}) \sin \phi}{p_b}$ (21.11)

where r_a = radius of addendum circle

       r_b = radius of base circle

       r_p = radius of pitch circle

From the figure it can be seen that the contact ratio can be increased by increasing the addenda of the gears. However there are limitations to the amount the addenda can be increased as will be discussed in the next Article.

21.9 Involute Interference and Undercutting

If we again refer to Fig. 21.9 we see that the involute profile cannot extend inside the base circle. Since the line of action is tangent to the base circle at points G and H, these two points are the limits of the path of action. If the addendum circle of gear "a" incloses point H or if the addendum of gear "b" incloses point G, the ends of these teeth extending beyond these points would be in contact with a portion of the mating tooth which is not an involute. Such a condition is called interference and involute action would not be maintained. Points G and H are called interference points and represent the limit of the addendum circles for which involute action can be maintained. The contact ratio could be increased however by extending the addendum of the gears to these points. In many cases the ends of the teeth would become pointed before the addenda could be increased to the interference point and this would limit the addendum for such a gear.

Now consider a gear meshing with a rack as shown in Fig. 21.12. The rack is a gear with an infinite pitch diameter and the pitch circle becomes a straight line called the pitch line. As the pitch circle diameter goes to infinity the base circle diameter also goes to infinity and the line of action is tangent to the base circle at infinity so that the profile of the rack teeth is a straight line normal to the line of action as shown in the figure.

If the rack has an addendum as shown in the figure the ends of the rack teeth would dig into the flank of the gear teeth, or there would be interference, as shown at point R, because the end of the tooth extends beyond the interference point C. Under these conditions the gear and rack would not mesh and would lock. The possibility of interference is one of the main disadvantages of involute gears. In order to eliminate interference or

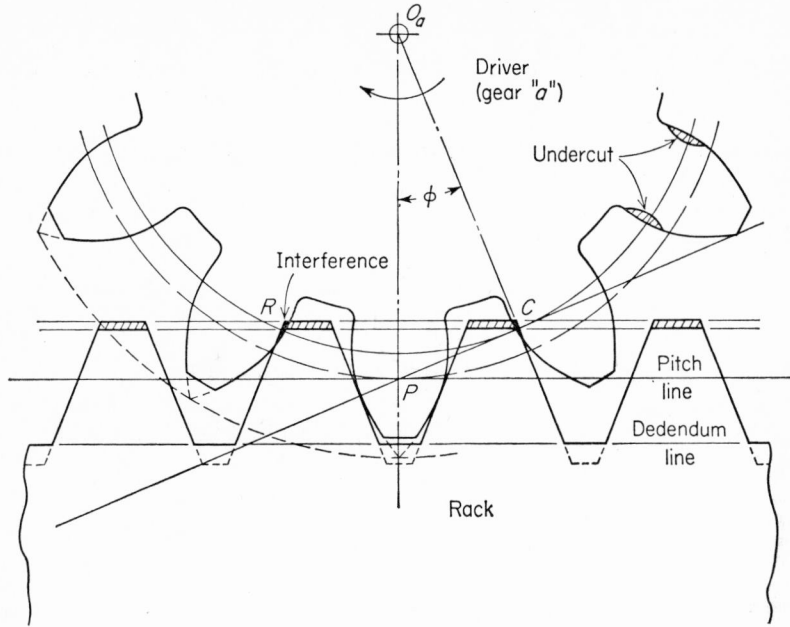

FIGURE 21.12

locking of the gears, a portion of the flank of the tooth of the gear would have to be removed, as shown in the tooth at the right, or the addendum of the rack would have to be decreased by removal of the crosshatched portion of the ends of the rack teeth. Removal of part of the flank of the gear is called undercutting and it is undesirable since it weakens the tooth and also removes part of the involute profile, thereby decreasing the contact ratio. Increasing the pitch radius of the gear by moving the center away from the rack will also eliminate interference, although this has the same effect as removing the ends of the rack teeth and has the disadvantage that it increases the backlash. Increasing the pressure angle will also remove the interference. This will require changing the angle that the surface of the rack teeth make with the pitch line.

There can be no interference between the ends of the gear teeth and the rack since the involute profile of the rack teeth can be continued until the flanks meet at a point. The contact ratio can be increased for the gear and rack shown by increasing the gear teeth to a point and increasing the dedendum of the rack as shown dotted at the left of the figure.

If a gear will mesh with a rack without interference, then it will mesh with any external gear of equal or greater diameter, having the same addendum as the rack, without interference. This can be seen from Fig. 21.12 by noting that the addendum circle will curve downward from the addendum line and intersect the line of action to the left of point C. The problem of interference will be considered in more detail in the discussion of standard gears.

21.10 Interchangeable and Standard Tooth Forms

In our discussion so far we have been concerned only with a single pair of gears and have not considered a set of gears which would be interchangeable. A set of interchangeable gears is one in which any gear of the set will mesh with any other gear of the set with involute action. For interchangeability all gears of the set must have the same pitch, the same pressure angle, the same addendum and same dedendum, and the tooth thickness must equal one-half the circular pitch.

Standard tooth forms have been adapted so that interchangeable gears are readily available. Non-standard gears are used in a number of instances, primarily in the automobile and aircraft industries. The proportions of the three systems of standard interchangeable involute gears are given in Table 21.1, where two pressure angles, $14\frac{1}{2}°$ and $20°$ are used. Note that in all systems the addenda and dedenda are the same for all gears and are given as a function of the diametral pitch. The most commonly used pitches are 1, $1\frac{1}{4}$, $1\frac{1}{2}$, $1\frac{3}{4}$, 2, $2\frac{1}{4}$, $2\frac{1}{2}$, $2\frac{3}{4}$, 3, $3\frac{1}{2}$, 4, 5, 6, 7, 8, 9, 10, 12, 14, and up to 200 by even increments. Before discussing the advantages and disadvantages of the various systems let us consider the problem of interference in standard gears.

Consider a pinion and gear, represented in Fig. 21.13, having equal addenda. The interference point C, corresponding to the point of tangency of the line of action and the base circle of the pinion or smaller gear, will always be closer to the normal to the line of centers passing through the pitch point than the interference point D. The distances $C-E$ and $D-F$ are

$$C\text{-}E = r_{pp} \sin^2 \phi \qquad (21.12)$$

$$D\text{-}F = r_{pg} \sin^2 \phi \qquad (21.13)$$

Table 21.1

	$14\frac{1}{2}°$ Full depth	$20°$ Full depth	$20°$ Stub
Addendum	$1/P_d$	$1/P_d$	$0.8/P_d$
Dedendum	$1.157/P_d$	$1.157/P_d$	$1/P_d$
Fillet radius	$0.209/P_d$	$0.239/P_d$	$0.304/P_d$

where r_{pp} is the pitch radius of the pinion and r_{pg} is the pitch radius of the gear. Therefore if interference is present in a pair of standard gears the tip of the gear teeth will always interfere with the root of the pinion since the radius of the addendum circle of the gear is greater than that of the pinion.

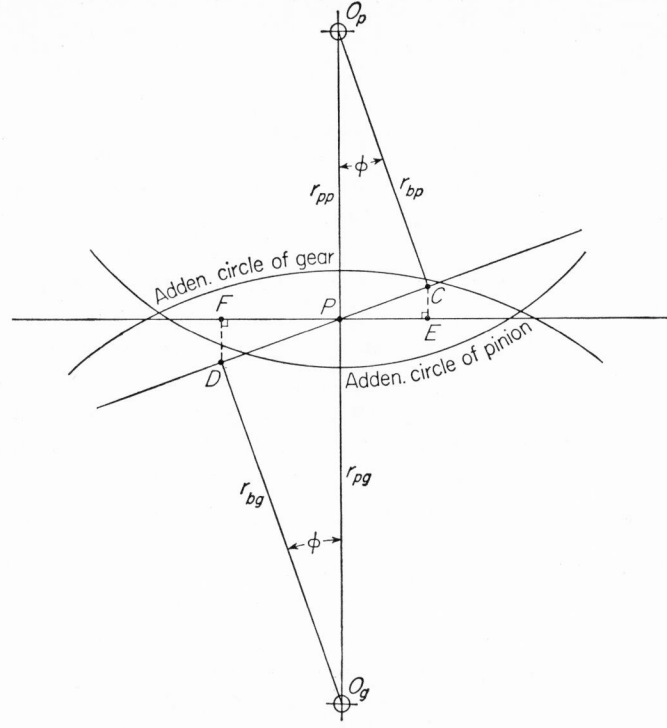

FIGURE 21.13

Noting that in Fig. 21.13 for a rack to mesh with the pinion without interference the addendum of the rack must be equal to or less than the distance C–E, we can determine the smallest gear that will mesh with a rack without interference from Eq. (21.12). Letting C–E be the addendum of the rack, a, and solving for the pitch radius of the pinion

$$r_{pp} = \frac{a}{\sin^2 \phi} \qquad (21.14)$$

Using k/P_d as the addendum for a standard gear, where $k = 1.00$ for the full depth systems and $k = 0.8$ for the stub systems, and making use of the relation

$$2r_{pp} = D_p = \frac{N}{P_d}$$

we find by substituting in Eq. (21.14) that the number of teeth on the smallest gear that will mesh with a rack without interference is

$$N = \frac{2k}{\sin^2 \phi} \qquad (21.15)$$

In case this number of teeth is not a whole number, the next largest whole
number must be used, since a gear cannot have a fraction of a tooth. Note
that the number of teeth on the smallest pinion that will mesh with a rack

Table 21.2

	$14\frac{1}{2}°$ Full depth	$20°$ Full depth	$20°$ Stub
N	32	18	14

is independent of the pitch and depends only on the addendum constant, k,
and the pressure angle. Using this equation we find that the number of
teeth for the smallest pinion that will mesh with a rack without interference
are as given in Table 21.2 for the three common systems.

Since gears other than a rack will mesh with the minimum gears given
in Table 21.2 without interference it is often desirable to know the largest
gear that will mesh with a given gear without interference. This can be
determined graphically as shown in Fig. 21.14 by letting the addendum

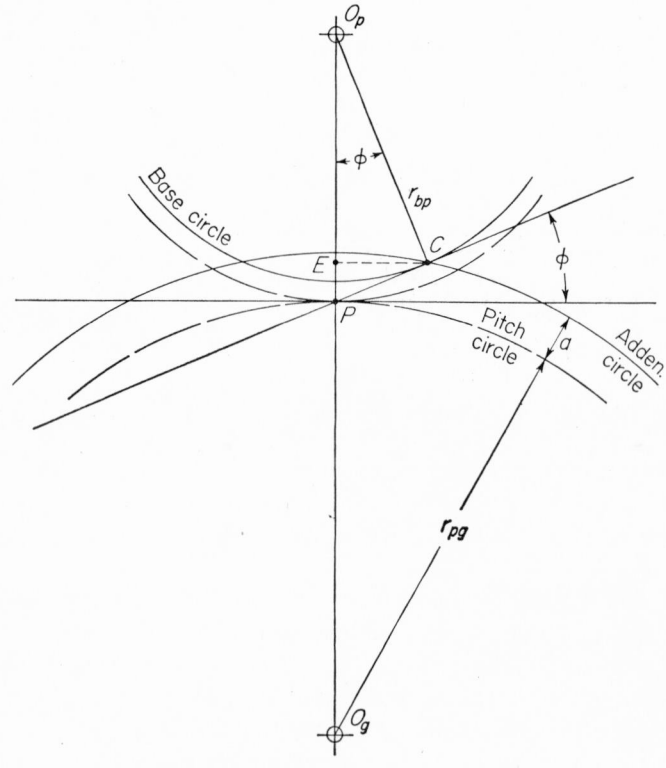

FIGURE 21.14

circle of the unknown gear pass through the interference point C, locating the center of the gear, point O, by trial and error. The pitch radius can then be measured and the number of teeth determined, knowing the pitch. The pitch radius can also be determined analytically. With reference to Fig. 21.14

$$O_g O_p = O_g E + O_p E = r_{pp} + r_{pg} \qquad \text{(a)}$$

Also from the figure

$$O_g E = \sqrt{(r_{pg} + a)^2 - (CE)^2} \qquad \text{(b)}$$

$$CE = r_{bp} \sin \phi = r_{pp} \cos \phi \sin \phi$$

so that

$$O_g E = \sqrt{(r_{pg} + a)^2 - r_{pp}^2 \cos^2 \phi \sin^2 \phi} \qquad \text{(c)}$$

Also

$$O_p E = r_{bp} \cos \phi = r_{pp} \cos^2 \phi \qquad \text{(d)}$$

Substituting (c) and (d) into (a) and rearranging

$$r_{pp} + r_{pg} - r_{pp} \cos^2 \phi = \sqrt{(r_{pg} + a)^2 - r_{pp}^2 \cos^2 \phi \sin^2 \phi} \qquad \text{(e)}$$

or

$$r_{pp}(1 - \cos^2 \phi) + r_{pg} = \sqrt{(r_{pg} + a)^2 - r_{pp}^2 \cos^2 \phi \sin^2 \phi}$$

$$r_{pp} \sin^2 \phi + r_{pg} = \sqrt{(r_{pg} + a)^2 - r_{pp}^2 \cos^2 \phi \sin^2 \phi} \qquad \text{(f)}$$

Squaring Eq. (f) and solving for r_{pg}

$$r_{pg} = \frac{a^2 - r_{pp}^2 \sin^2 \phi}{2(r_{pp} \sin^2 \phi - a)} \qquad (21.16)$$

Making use of the relations

$$a = \frac{k}{P_d}, \quad r_p = \frac{N}{2P_d}$$

Eq. (21.16) can be reduced to

$$N_g = \frac{4k^2 - N_p^2 \sin^2 \phi}{2N_p \sin^2 \phi - 4k} \qquad (21.17)$$

where N_g and N_p are the numbers of teeth on the gear and pinion respectively. Note that Eq. (21.17) is independent of the pitch which would be expected since the pitch is actually a scale factor and determines only the size of the gear for a given number of teeth.

In general Eq. (21.17) will give a fractional number of teeth and the next smallest whole number is the correct number of teeth on the gear that will mesh with the given pinion without interference.

To find the smallest pinion that will mesh with a given gear without interference, Eqs. (21.16) and (21.17) could also be used, although a trial and error solution must be used since the equations do not lend themselves to the direct solution of r_{pp} or N_p. A better method would be to determine the pitch radius graphically as in Fig. 21.14, using a convenient pitch, and use the equations to check the results.

A limiting condition is the smallest pair of equal gears that will mesh without interference. These are tabulated in Table 21.3 for the three systems.

The equation for the contact ratio for a pair of standard gears can be obtained in terms of the number of teeth by substituting the relations

$$r_p = \frac{N}{2P_d}, \quad a = \frac{k}{P_d}$$

into Eq. (21.11). The resulting equation after simplification is

$$\text{Contact ratio} = \frac{A_p + A_g - \left(\dfrac{N_1 + N_2}{2}\right)\sin\phi}{\pi\cos\phi} \tag{21.18}$$

where:

$$A_p = \sqrt{\frac{N_p^2}{4}\sin^2\phi + kN_p + k^2}$$

$$A_g = \sqrt{\frac{N_g^2}{4}\sin^2\phi + kN_g + k^2}$$

The contact ratios for the smallest pair of equal gears that will mesh without interference is also tabulated in Table 21.3 for the standard systems. Note that for the 20° stub system the contact ratio is less than 1:4 and therefore if these gears are used they must be accurately cut in order to have smooth action.

Because of the interference problems with small gears the $14\frac{1}{2}°$ full depth system is used primarily for gears having a large number of teeth. The lower pressure angle gives smaller normal forces between mating teeth for a given torque and thereby lower forces on the bearings. The main disadvantage of the $14\frac{1}{2}°$ system is that it gives a weaker tooth in relation to beam strength than the other systems.

The 20° full depth system was developed in order to increase the strength of the teeth and provide gears with smaller numbers of teeth without interference. The higher pressure angle gives a smaller contact ratio than the $14\frac{1}{2}°$ system for a given pitch.

The 20° stub system, because of the shorter tooth, is the strongest of the three. However some of this advantage is lost because of the smaller contact ratio, indicating that fewer pairs of teeth are in contact at a given instant. This system is usually used where space limitations require small gear diameters. Another advantage of the stub tooth system is the lower sliding velocities at the beginning and ending of contact, thereby causing less wear on the teeth.

Table 21.3

	$14\frac{1}{2}°$ Full depth	$20°$ Full depth	$20°$ Stub
N	23	13	10
$C.R.$	1.84	1.44	1.15

21.11 Internal Involute Gears

An internal or annular gear is a gear whose center is on the same side of the pitch line as the pinion meshing with it. An internal gear with a pinion in mesh is shown in Fig. 21.15. The addendum circle for internal gears is inside the pitch circle and the profiles of the teeth are concave rather than convex as in external gears.

The primary advantage of an internal gear meshing with a pinion is the compactness of the drive. Other advantages are the lower contact stresses

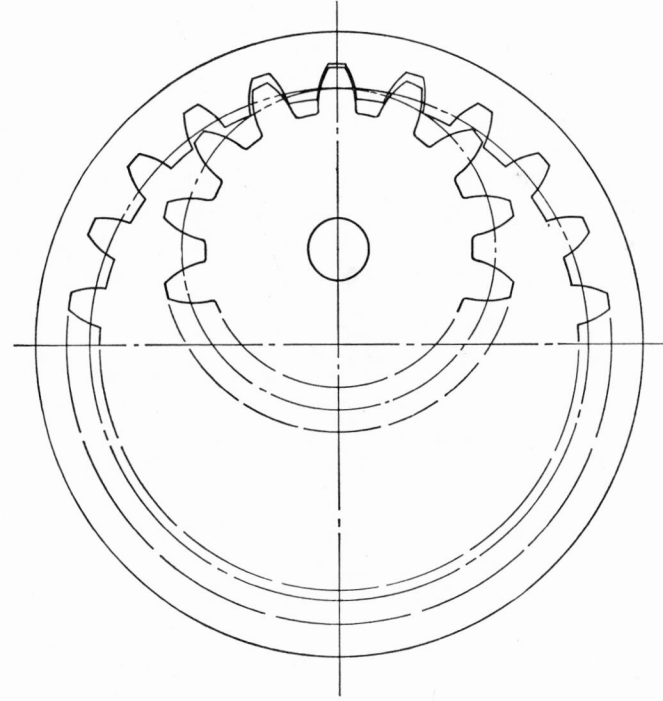

FIGURE 21.15

in the convex-concave contact, lower relative sliding between teeth, and greater length of contact possible between mating teeth since there is no limit to the involute profile on the flank of the annular tooth. The beam strength of an angular gear is much greater than that of a corresponding external gear but since the pinion is always the weakest of a pair of gears the added strength of annular gears is of little consequence unless different materials are used for the gear and pinion.

There is only one interference point for an internal gear and pinion as can be seen in Fig. 21.16. Point B is the point of tangency between the line

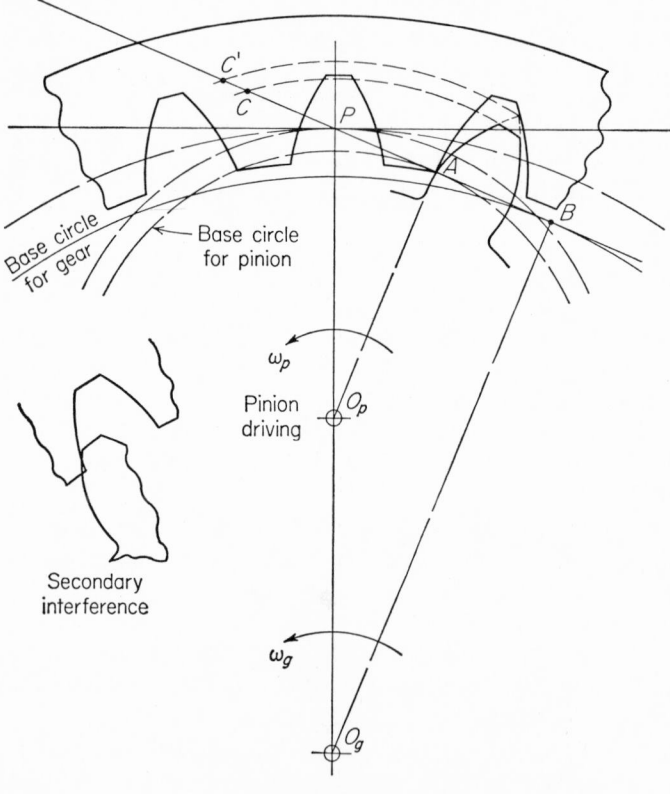

FIGURE 21.16

of action and the base circle of the gear and point A is the tangent point with the pinion base circle. Point A is the first point of contact along the involute profile of the pinion and therefore the addendum of the gear is limited to the distance shown. Since the involute profile of the internal gear can continue indefinitely outside the pitch circle the path of contact is limited only by the condition of pointed teeth on the pinion as shown at C'.

A secondary interference occurs for internal gears in cases where the number of teeth on the pinion is close to the number of teeth on the gear. As an exaggerated example of this interference consider an internal gear having only one tooth more than the meshing pinion. A tooth on the pinion will never completely withdraw from the tooth space in the internal gear, yet the tooth must move back one space for each revolution. This type of interference, which is called fouling, is shown in Fig. 21.16 at the left of the figure where we see an inactive tooth on the pinion interfering as it tries to withdraw from the tooth space of the annular gear.

Standard tooth proportions are not used for annular gears since the addendum of the gear must be shorter than those given in Table 21.1 in order to eliminate interference. The contact ratio and angles of action can be determined for annular gears in the same manner as for external gears.

21.12 Cycloidal Gears

Cycloidal gears are seldom used today because of their disadvantages in relation to involute gears; however they have some distinct advantages and since this tooth form is still used to some extent for special purposes a brief discussion will be included.

The cycloidal profile is formed by the path of a point on a circle as the circle rolls on the pitch circle. The rolling circle is called the generating circle and if the circle is rolled inside the pitch circle it forms the flank of the tooth. The face of the tooth is formed when the rolling circle is outside the pitch circle. Profiles of cycloidal teeth are shown in Fig. 21.17 for a pair of meshing gears with the generating circles in contact with the pitch circles at the pitch point. The path of action is along the arcs of the generating circles indicated by the curved line APB. The pressure angle varies along the path of contact, always being the angle made by a line from the point of contact to the pitch point and a line normal to the line of centers such as ϕ in the figure where the point of contact is at A. The pressure angle varies from a maximum at the beginning of action to zero for contact at the pitch point and then increases until contact is broken.

Interference is not encountered in cycloidal gears and this is their primary advantage over involute gears. Because of this fact cycloidal gears with very small numbers of teeth can be used. Other advantages of cycloidal teeth are that they are in general stronger than involute teeth and they have less sliding, thereby less wear. The important disadvantages of cycloidal teeth are that to satisfy the fundamental law of gearing a pair of gears can have only one theoretically correct center distance. They are also difficult to manufacture. If the center distance is not held exactly, the velocity ratio varies during the time a pair of teeth are in action resulting in high inertia loads, and noisy operation.

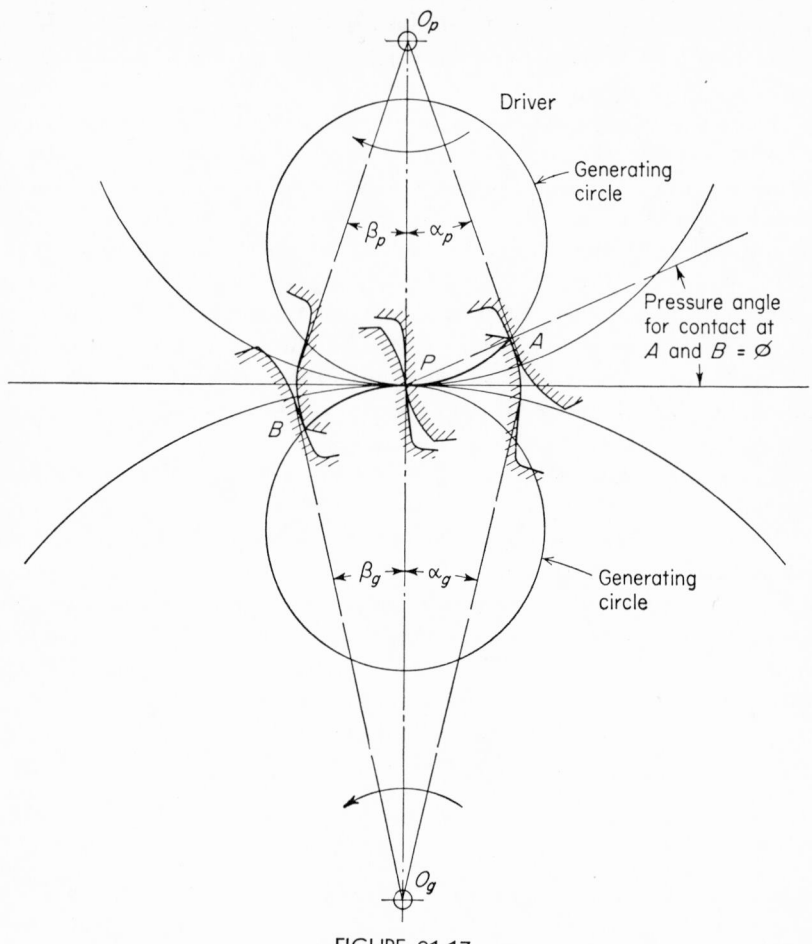

FIGURE 21.17

Cycloidal gears are used extensively in watches and clocks since they lend themselves to high reduction ratios, without the problem of interference, by the use of pinions with a small number of teeth resulting in a compact drive. Because of the slow speed in this case, the inertia forces are negligible.

21.13 Gear Manufacturing Methods

Gears can be cut on a milling machine with a milling cutter profile the same as that of the tooth space being cut. For accurate gears a single cutter can be used successfully only for a gear with a given number of teeth. In practice, a set of cutters is used in which a single cutter is used to cut gears having different numbers of teeth over a certain range. Such gears are satisfactory for low speeds and are used extensively where more accurate gears are not required.

Accurate involute gears are usually produced by the generating process. If a soft plastic gear blank were rolled along an accurately cut steel rack at the proper meshing depth so that the pitch circle of the blank rolled along the pitch line of the rack, the rack would form accurate conjugate teeth in the soft plastic blank. This is the basis of the generating principle. If the steel rack were relieved to form a shaping cutter and the rack then given a reciprocating motion parallel to the axis of the blank it could be used to cut teeth on a steel blank. Such a cutter is known as a rack-shaped cutter and can be used in special shaper machines for the cutting of accurate gears. An outstanding advantage of the generating process is that one cutter can be used for all gears of the same pitch and pressure angle. The clearance is cut in the gears by extending the addendum of the cutter the correct distance.

The most common methods of generating gears are the hobbing method and the Fellows gear-shaping method. The hobbing method is illustrated in Fig. 21.18 and makes use of a worm or screw with gashes cut in the threads to form a cutter. The shape of the threads in the plane of the gear blank is that of a rack so that hobbing corresponds to the use of a rack cutter. Hobbing is the fastest method of producing gears.

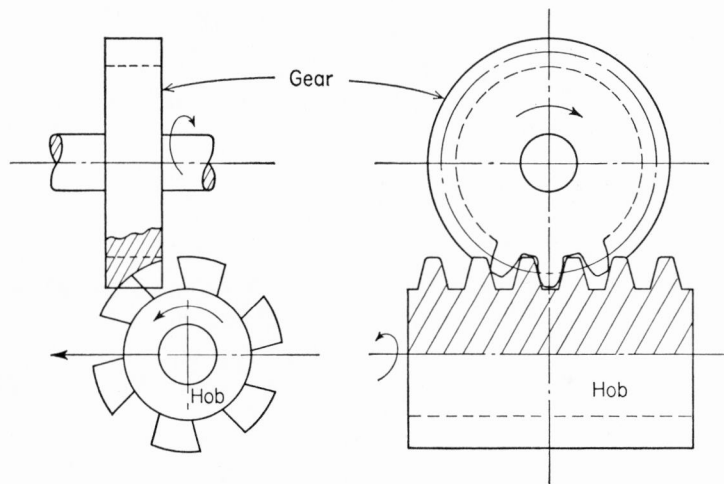

FIGURE 21.18

The Fellows gear-shaper uses a cutter in the form of a pinion which has an axial reciprocating motion as shown in Fig. 21.19. The cutter and gear blank are forced to rotate so that their pitch circles are in rolling contact.

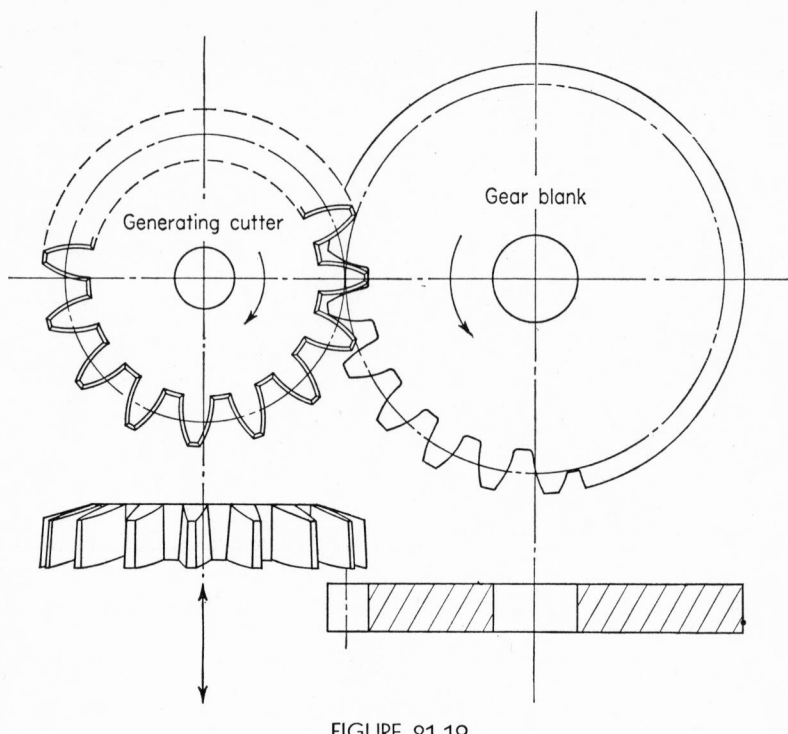

FIGURE 21.19

The cutter is fed into the blank in the plane of the blank to the proper distance and then the two are rotated and the teeth are formed in one complete revolution of the blank.

21.14 Unequal-Addendum Gears

In order to eliminate interference when small pinions and large gears are mated, a non-standard system of gears has been developed making use of unequal addendums for the pinion and gear. Such gears are not interchangeable but have the advantage of stronger teeth on the pinion, and an increased contact ratio is possible. Unequal addendum gears can be cut with standard generating cutters. These advantages can be demonstrated by considering a 20° full depth pinion of 12 teeth as cut with a rack cutter or hob. Fig. 21.20(a) shows the shape of the teeth as cut with the rack and it is seen that the cutter deeply undercuts the pinion when set at the correct meshing depth. If the pinion blank is increased in diameter so that its radius is increased by an amount "e," the distance that the rack interferes with the pinion, and the rack is moved away from the pinion by this same distance, as shown in Fig. 21.20(b), there will be no undercutting and the

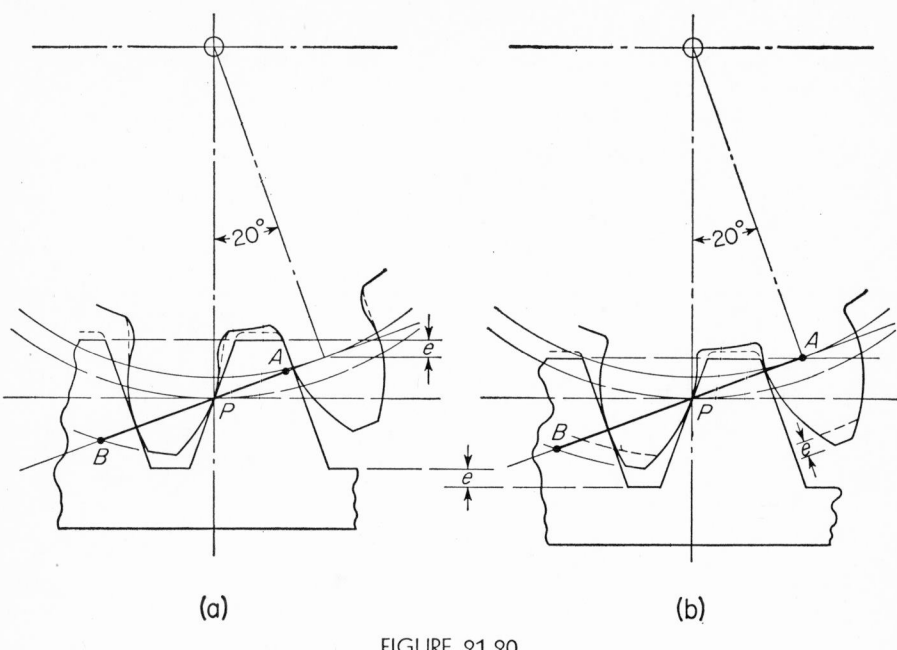

FIGURE 21.20

path of contact is increased. The pitch circle remains the same but the addendum has been increased while the dedendum has been decreased by the same amount. If in cutting the gear to mesh with the pinion its diameter were decreased by the same amount that the pinion blank were increased and the cutter were moved in towards the gear by the same amount, "e," a pair of gears with unequal addendums, and the same pressure angle and pitch circles as a pair of standard gears of the same number of teeth would result. The interference would be eliminated, the contact ratio would be increased and the angle of recess would be increased over that of a pair of standard gears. The tooth thickness of the pinion has been increased while that of the gear has been decreased. The beam strength of the pinion teeth has been increased while the gear teeth have been weakened somewhat. However since the pinion teeth for a standard gear are always weaker than the gear teeth, this is also an advantage.

21.15 *Variable Center Distance*

One of the advantages of the involute gears is the possibility of varying the center distance for a pair of gears without affecting their ability to mesh satisfactorily and still satisfy the fundamental law of gearing. Increasing the center distance of a pair of gears that interfere offers another means of eliminating the interference. The effect of increasing the center distance of a pair of gears which interfere is shown in Fig. 21.21. The broken lines show the gears at their correct center distance. Note that there will be interference at point A'. The solid lines show the same gears after the center distance has been increased by an amount "e" by moving the gear

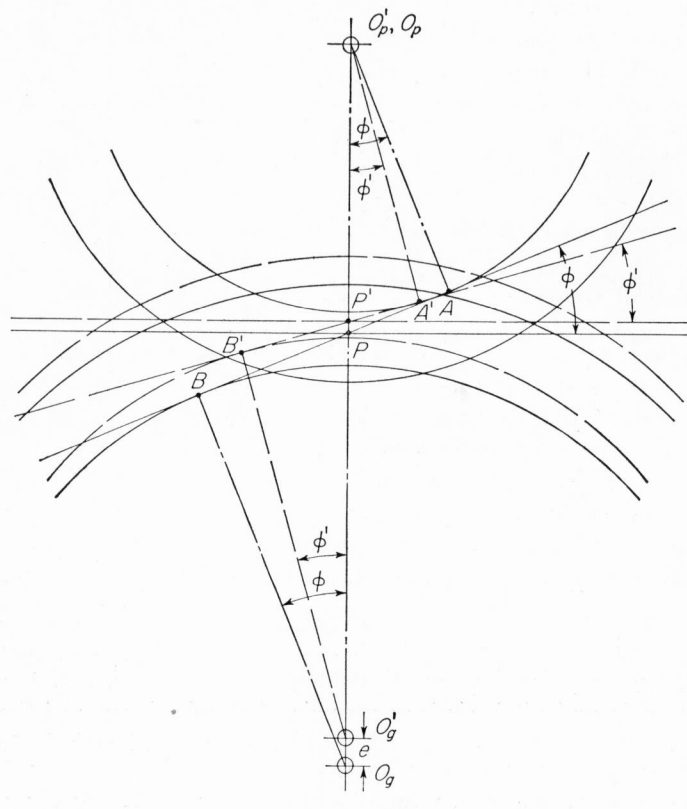

FIGURE 21.21

away from the pinion. Separating the gears changes the pressure angle from ϕ' to ϕ and changes the interference point from A' and B' to A and B. The pitch point has been shifted from P' to P. The interference has been eliminated as shown in the figure.

Remembering that the base circles are fixed in the generation of the gears, these base circles remain the same; separation of the gears changes the pressure angle and the diameter of the pitch circles. The diameters of the pitch circles are always proportional to the base circles and the cosine of the pressure angles, therefore the new pitch point P, after separation of the gears, will always be in such position that the following ratio holds

$$\frac{O_p - P}{O_g - P} = \frac{O'_p - P'}{O'_g - P'}$$

From the figure we can see that separation of the gears in order to eliminate interference causes a slight decrease in the length of the path of contact and increases the pressure angle, thereby decreasing the contact ratio. The diameters of the pitch circles are increased in proportion to the increase in center distance. The effect on the contact ratio can also be seen from Eq. (21.11), where only the last term in the numerator is changed when the center distance is increased. Also, separation of the gears increases the backlash.

This method of eliminating interference is used in practice when a pair of standard gears have slight interference, making it possible to use standard gears for drives where otherwise non-standard gears would be necessary.

21.16 Helical Gears

Consider a spur gear cut into a large number of slices by planes normal to its axis. If each of the slices is rotated a small amount relative to the preceding slice, as shown in Fig. 21.22 and the slices fixed in this position we have what is called a stepped gear. If the number of slices were made infinite we would have a helical gear in which the teeth wind around the gear in the form of a helix. In the discussion of the helical gears it is helpful to keep in mind their relation to stepped gears. Stepped gears are seldom used in practice but helical gears are used extensively because of their decided advantages over straight spur gears.

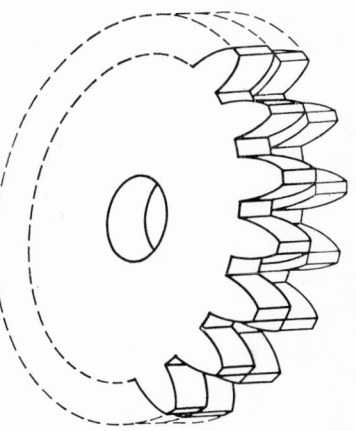

FIGURE 21.22

If a thin sheet of paper is unrolled from the base cylinder of a spur gear a line on the paper parallel to the axis of the gear will generate the surface of an involute gear tooth, as shown in Fig. 21.23(a). If the line on the paper is inclined relative to the axis it will form a helix on the surface of the cylinder and this line will generate the surface of a helical gear tooth as the paper is unrolled, as shown in Fig. 21.23(b). If the paper is rolled off one base cylinder onto the base cylinder of another gear the line will generate conjugate teeth on the two cylinders, and the line of contact across the face of the teeth will be the generating line.

The helix angle is the angle that a tangent to the helix at any point makes with an element of the cylinder on which the helix is formed. The

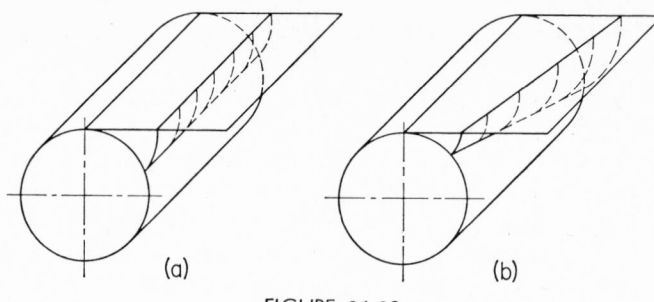

FIGURE 21.23

pitch helix is the helix formed by the intersection of a helical gear tooth and the pitch cylinder. The helix angle, ψ, for helical gears and worms refers to the helix angle on the pitch surface. The lead, L, is the axial distance along the cylinder that a helix advances for one turn around the cylinder. Since the lead for a helical gear is the same on the base circle and the pitch circle, the helix angle on the base cylinder is less than the pitch helix. The relationship between the two angles is shown in Fig. 21.24 where the base

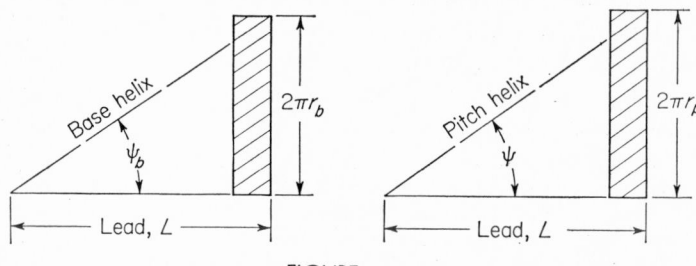

FIGURE 21.24

cylinder and the pitch cylinder have been rolled out flat. From the figure

$$\tan \psi_b = \frac{2\pi r_b}{L}$$

$$\tan \psi = \frac{2\pi r_p}{L}$$

Substituting the relation

$$r_b = r_p \cos \phi$$

we find

$$\tan \psi_b = \tan \psi \cos \phi \qquad (21.19)$$

Helical gears can be used to connect parallel or non-parallel, non-intersecting shafts. Helical gears connecting parallel shafts are called parallel helical gears or helical spur gears. Helical gears with non-parallel, non-intersecting axes are called crossed helical gears. So far our discussion has been concerned with parallel helical gears but the individual gears can also be used for crossed helical gears, which will be covered later.

Parallel helical gears correspond to regular spur gears but have advantages over regular spur gears which will be brought out in a comparison of the two. For regular spur gears the teeth come into contact along the entire face width and the contact is along the line parallel to the axes at all times. Parallel helical gears start contact at a point along one edge of the tooth and the contact progresses across the tooth width along a line as shown in Fig. 21.23(b), resulting in contact along a diagonal straight line. The teeth therefore assume the load gradually, resulting in less impact and smoother operation. The strength of helical gears is also greater than that of regular spur gears. As a result helical gears can be operated at higher speeds or greater loads than equivalent spur gears, and are quieter in operation with less vibration. The advantages are not all in one direction however. Since the force between teeth is always normal to the tooth surface, helical gears have a component of force along the axis of the gear causing end thrust which must be taken by the shaft bearings.

This end thrust can be eliminated by using herringbone gears which correspond to two helical gears of opposite hand (the hand of a gear being right-handed for a right-hand helix) as shown in Fig. 21.25. Herringbone gears in general are expensive and require accurate alignment along the shafts they connect.

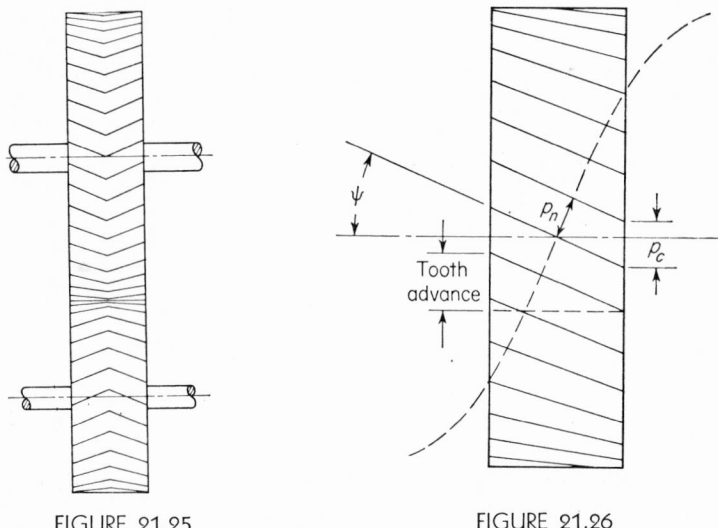

FIGURE 21.25   FIGURE 21.26

In order to gain the full advantage of parallel helical gears the tooth advance of a tooth along the pitch helix should be equal to or greater than the circular pitch. This is shown in Fig. 21.26. Under this condition at least one pair of teeth are always in contact at the pitch point and this has the effect of increasing the contact ratio since there is always a greater number of teeth in contact at any given time than for an equivalent pair of spur gears. In order to gain the full advantage of helical gears it is recommended that the tooth advance be at least 15 per cent greater than the circular pitch.

The normal pitch, p_n, of helical gears is the circular pitch measured along the normal helix as shown in Fig. 21.26. Its relation to the circular pitch is given by the equation

$$p_n = p_c \cos \psi \qquad\qquad (21.20)$$

The normal pitch is used in the manufacture of helical gears by the hobbing method and is also important in helical gears connecting non-parallel shafts.

21.17 Crossed Helical Gears

The meshing action of crossed helical gears is quite different from that of parallel helical gears. Consider two tangent cylinders whose axes makes an angle θ as shown in Fig. 21.27(a). The cylinders are in contact at point

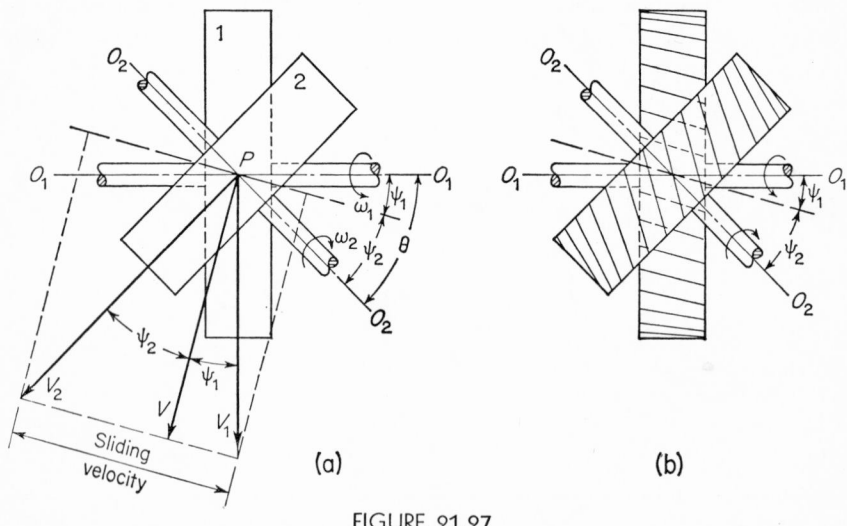

(a)   (b)

FIGURE 21.27

P. If the axes were parallel they would be in contact along a line corresponding to an element of each of the cylinders; but when the axes are at an angle the cylinders make contact at a point. When the two cylinders are rotating about their axes as shown the velocities of their contact points lie in the common tangent plane and are normal to their respective axes as shown where V_1 and V_2 are the velocities of the coincident points of cylinders one and two. The difference in their linear velocities, or their relative velocity, is represented by the dashed line joining the head of the vectors. A vector, V, normal to their relative velocity represents a common normal component which is the rolling velocity, and the difference in velocities is the velocity of sliding of the contact points. If the angular velocities of the cylinders are constant the direction of sliding will be tangent to a helix making an angle ψ_1, with the axis of cylinder one and an angle ψ_2 with the axis of cylinder two. Then the cylinders could be the pitch cylinders of two helical gears, as shown in Fig. 21.27(b), if the helix angles of the gears are ψ_1 and ψ_2 respectively. The normal pitch of these crossed helical gears would necessarily have to be the same if they are to mesh.

From the above discussion we can draw the following observations concerning crossed helical gears. They will have point contact and there will be relative sliding across the teeth. Since the normal pitches of the two gears must be equal, the circular pitches will be different unless the helix angles are the same. The sum or difference of the helix angles must be equal to the angle made by the shafts. Since the angular velocities were arbitrarily set, the angular velocity ratio is not directly proportional to the pitch diameters, but is a function of the pitch diameters and the helix angles. This relation will be developed in the next paragraph where it will also be shown that the angular velocity ratio is inversely proportional to the number of teeth on the gears.

Referring to Fig. 21.27

$$\frac{\omega_1}{\omega_2} = \frac{V_1/r_{p1}}{V_2/r_{p2}} = \frac{V_1 r_{p2}}{V_2 r_{p1}}$$

But

$$V = V_1 \cos \psi_1 = V_2 \cos \psi_2$$

$$\frac{V_1}{V_2} = \frac{\cos \psi_2}{\cos \psi_1}$$

so that

$$\frac{\omega_1}{\omega_2} = \frac{r_{p2} \cos \psi_2}{r_{p1} \cos \psi_1} \tag{21.21}$$

From the definition of circular pitch and Eq. (21.20)

$$N_1 = \frac{2\pi r_{p1}}{p_{c1}}$$

$$N_2 = \frac{2\pi r_{p2}}{p_{c2}}$$

$$\frac{N_1}{N_2} = \frac{p_{c2} r_{p1}}{p_{c1} r_{p2}} = \frac{r_{p1} \cos \psi_1}{r_{p2} \cos \psi_2} \tag{21.22}$$

and from Eqs. (21.21) and (21.22)

$$\frac{\omega_1}{\omega_2} = \frac{N_2}{N_1}$$

Because of the point contact, together with the high sliding across the teeth, crossed helical gears are limited to use where small amounts of power are to be transmitted.

21.18 Worm Gearing

A worm is a helical gear in which the number of teeth is small, usually one to four, and the teeth make a complete revolution around the pitch cylinder. Its mating gear is called a worm wheel which is not a true helical gear. A worm and worm wheel are used for high reduction ratios and usually connect non-intersecting shafts at right angles. The worm wheel is not a helical gear because its face is made concave to fit the curvature of the worm, resulting in line contact instead of point contact. A worm and worm wheel in mesh is shown in Fig. 21.28. Because of the line contact worm gearing can transmit high loads and is widely used in cases where high reduction ratios are desired. However worm gearing has the disadvantage of high sliding velocities across the teeth the same as crossed helical gears.

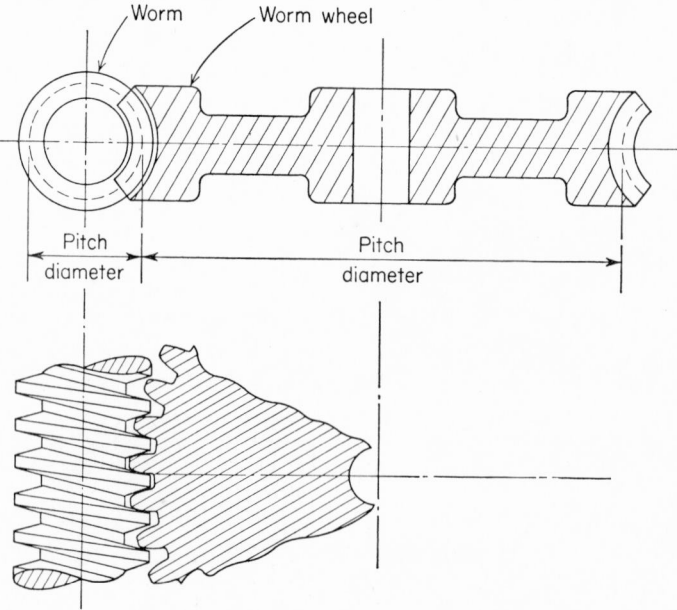

FIGURE 21.28

The worm gear is made with a hob but the hob is moved radially into the blank in cutting the wheel and does not move axially along the wheel as for spur and helical gears. In this way the worm wheel is made so that line contact is accomplished with the worm.

Since worm gears resemble screws the teeth are usually called threads. A single tooth worm gear is therefore called a single-threaded worm, a double tooth worm, a double-threaded worm, and so forth.

21.19 Bevel Gearing

The pitch surfaces of bevel gears are cones as shown in Fig. 21.3. Two cones rolling together and having a common apex have spherical motion, and therefore the path of contact of bevel gears is along the surface of a sphere. A cross section of a bevel gear is shown in Fig. 21.29 which shows the bevel gear terminology. Since the teeth get smaller as they approach the apex of the cone, the face width is usually limited to one-third of the cone distance. The smaller portion of the teeth which is left out would carry very little load and is difficult to cut.

The development of involute teeth on a base cone is demonstrated in Fig. 21.30. The cone is covered with a thin sheet which is slit along the line *OA*. If point *A* on the sheet is lifted from the surface, holding the sheet taught at all times, the element *OA* will develop the surface of an involute

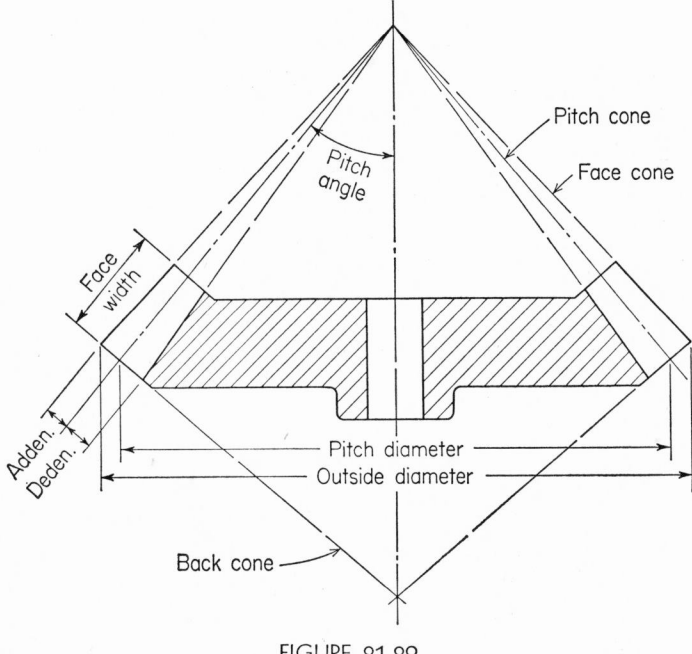

FIGURE 21.29

on the cone as shown in the figure. Considering point A as it moves to point B, it is seen that it always remains the same distance from the apex of the cone, O, and therefore remains on the surface of a sphere. For this reason this is called a spherical involute.

A crown gear is a bevel gear whose pitch angle is 90°; the pitch surface then becomes a plane and such a gear corresponds to a spur gear rack in the bevel system. However the base cone for a crown gear cannot be a plane as shown in Fig. 21.31. The base cone angle must be less than 90° and the

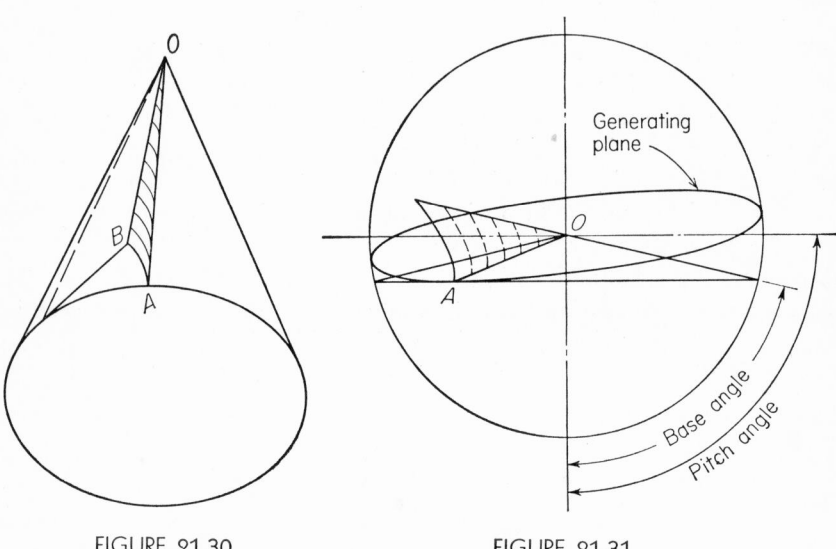

FIGURE 21.30   FIGURE 21.31

involute which is generated by rolling a plane on the base cone will have a curved surface instead of a plane surface such as is found on a spur gear rack. True spherical involute teeth are difficult to cut and are not used in practice. The bevel gear system in use is one in which the crown gear has teeth with plane surfaces as shown in Fig. 21.32, where the surfaces of the teeth lie in meridional planes, such as plane APB. The path of contact of such a gear with a conjugate surface (the teeth extending indefinitely in the plane) will be in the form of a figure eight on the surface of the sphere, as shown in the figure. For this reason gears conjugate to such a crown gear are called octoid gears. Only a portion of the path of contact is used such as CD or $C'D'$ in the figure corresponding to the height of the teeth.

In studying bevel gear tooth action it is difficult to work with the true profile since it lies on the surface of a sphere; therefore, an approximation in a plane is used. In Fig. 21.33 a pair of bevel gears in mesh is shown with the corresponding back cones. The back cones are cones whose elements are normal to the pitch cones as shown in the figure and it will be noted that a

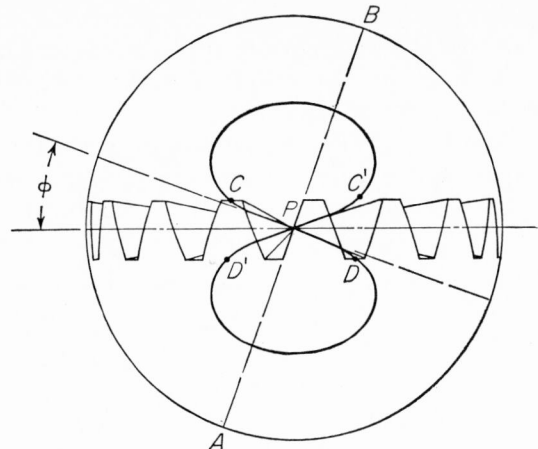

FIGURE 21.32

projection of the tooth profile, lying in the spherical surface, onto the back cone will be very nearly the true shape of the gear teeth at their outer ends.

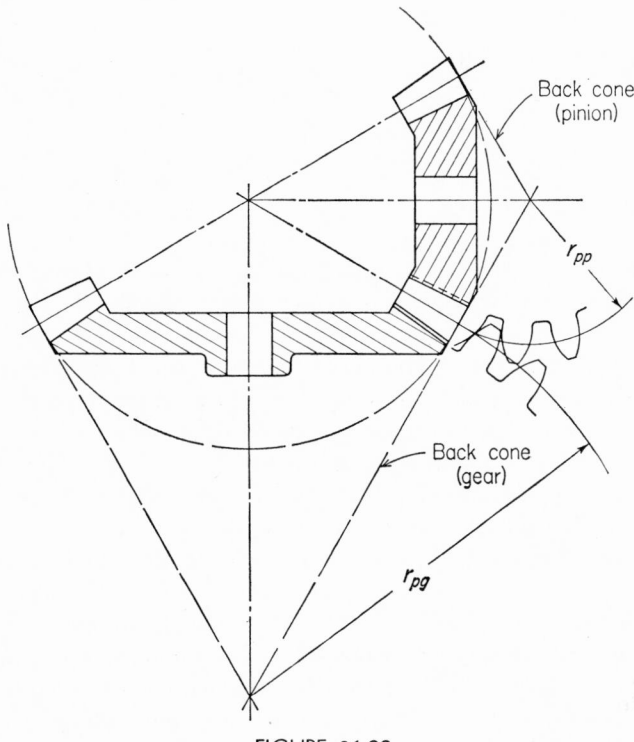

Back cone
(pinion)

r_{pp}

Back cone
(gear)

r_{pg}

FIGURE 21.33

Then if the back cone is spread out flat we can study the gear action of the bevel gears by using a pair of spur gears of radii equal to the length of the elements of the corresponding back cones. This is known as Tredgold's approximation. Note that for the equivalent spur gears the numbers of teeth on the spur gears differ from the number of actual teeth on the bevel gears. The number of teeth on the developed spur gears are known as the formative number of teeth since the profile or form of the teeth on the bevel gears corresponds to a spur gear with the back cone radius. While a bevel gear must have a whole number of teeth, the formative number of teeth is usually fractional.

Bevel gears are usually made with unequal addenda as discussed previously in order to eliminate undercutting and to increase the strength of the teeth. Because of this bevel gears are usually made in pairs and are not interchangeable.

Since the elements of bevel gear teeth are not parallel to the axis of the gears, bevel gears produce end thrust which must be taken by the bearings.

Spiral bevel gears differ from straight bevel gears in the same manner that helical spur gears differ from ordinary spur gears in that the elements of the teeth are curved. They have the same advantages of being stronger than straight bevel gears and having progressive contact. The elements of spiral bevel gears are not true spirals but are circular arcs. The circular arcs are used because of their ease of manufacture.

21.20 Hypoid Gears

Gears whose pitch surfaces are rolling hyperboloids are called hypoid gears and can be used to connect non-parallel, non-intersecting shafts. They are usually made for right angle drives, are made in pairs and are not interchangeable. There is sliding along the teeth in hypoid gears which is a disadvantage; however, since the pinions are larger for a given gear ratio than an equivalent bevel gear, they are stronger than equivalent bevel gears.

Hypoid gears resemble spiral gears in that the teeth are curved and in practice the pitch surface is really a cone instead of a hyperboloid but because of the short length of teeth the cones very nearly approximate sections of hyperboloids.

PROBLEMS

21.1 (a) A pair of involute gears are meshing at their correct center-to-center distance. Their diametral pitch is two and the numbers of teeth are 24 and 12. The teeth are standard full depth teeth with a pressure angle of $14\frac{1}{2}°$ and the pinion is driving in a clockwise direction. Make a layout of the gears and label the following on the drawing: pitch circles, base circles, addendum circles, root or dedendum circles, line of action and driver and driven gears.

(b) Indicate the interference and determine the length of the path of action after correction of the interference by cutting off the ends of the gear teeth.

(c) Indicate the angles of action, approach and recess for both gears as shown in Fig. 21.10 after interference has been eliminated.

(d) Determine the contact ratio for the gears graphically and check the result analytically.

21.2   Repeat Prob. 21.1 for gears having a pressure angle of $20°$.

21.3   For the gear pairs given below and meshing at their correct center-to-center distance determine if there is any interference present and determine the contact ratio for each case. Assume that the addendum is $1/P_d$ in each case and if there is any interference present assume the interference is removed by cutting off the ends of the gear teeth before determining the contact ratio.

(a) $14\frac{1}{2}°$ involute gears having 30 and 60 teeth.

(b) $18°$ involute pinion having 15 teeth meshing with a rack.

(c) $20°$ involute gears having 25 to 80 teeth.

21.4   (a) A $20°$ involute pinion having 20 teeth is meshing with a 60-tooth internal gear. The addendum of the pinion is $1.25/P_d$ and the addendum of the gear is $0.60/P_d$. Is there any interference?

(b) Determine the contact ratio. If there is interference assume that the interfering portion is removed by cutting off the ends of the teeth.

21.5   (a) What standard system must be used to avoid interference in a 15-tooth pinion meshing with a 60-tooth gear?

(b) What is the contact ratio?

21.6   What is the largest gear that will mesh with a $20°$ standard full depth gear of 20 teeth with no interference?

21.7   What is the smallest gear that will mesh with a $20°$ standard full depth gear of 20 teeth with no interference?

21.8   A pair of standard $14\frac{1}{2}°$ full depth spur gears of two pitch with 14 teeth on the pinion and 20 teeth on the gear are found to interfere when meshed at their correct center-to-center distance. In order to eliminate interference the center-to-center distance is increased 0.15 in.

(a) Would the increase in center-to-center distance eliminate interference?

(b) Determine the pitch diameters of both gears in the new position.

(c) Determine the new pressure angle.

(d) Determine the angle of action, angle of approach and angle of recess for both gears in the new position.

(e) What is the contact ratio for the new position?

(f) What is the maximum contact ratio that could be obtained in the new position by increasing the addendum of the pinion?

21.9   A pair of crossed helical gears connect shafts making an angle of $45°$. The right-hand pinion has a helix angle of $20°$ and contains 30 teeth. The right-hand gear contains 45 teeth and its diametral pitch in the plane of rotation is 5. Determine:

(a) The pitch diameters of the gears.

(b) The normal pitch of the gears.

(c) The lead of each of the gears.

(d) The tooth advance of each of the gears in terms of the circular pitch if the face width is $1\frac{1}{4}$ in.

21.10 Determine the velocity of sliding along the helix for the pair of gears in Prob. 21.9 when they are in contact at the pitch point if the pinion is rotating at 1000 rpm.

21.11 Does the tooth advance have any importance in crossed helical gears?

Chapter **22**

Gear Trains

22.1 Simple and Compound Gear Trains

A gear train is composed of two or more gears in mesh so as to transmit motion from one shaft to another. Ordinary gear trains are those in which the axes of all the gears are fixed relative to the frame and are of two types, simple gear trains and compound gear trains.

Simple gear trains are those in which there is only one gear on each shaft, such as is shown in Fig. 22.1 where the gears are represented by

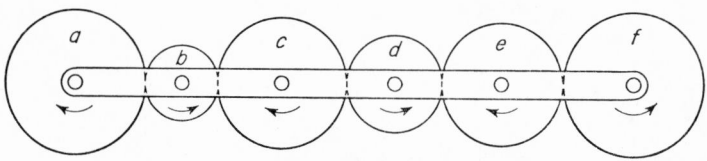

FIGURE 22.1

circles corresponding to the pitch circles. Let the number of teeth on the gears in Fig. 22.1 be given by N_a, N_b, etc. Then for the gears in the figure the angular velocity ratios for each meshing pair are given by the equations

$$\frac{\omega_b}{\omega_a} = \frac{N_a}{N_b} \qquad \frac{\omega_c}{\omega_b} = \frac{N_b}{N_c} \qquad \frac{\omega_d}{\omega_c} = \frac{N_c}{N_d}$$

$$\frac{\omega_e}{\omega_d} = \frac{N_d}{N_e} \qquad \frac{\omega_f}{\omega_e} = \frac{N_e}{N_f} \qquad (22.1)$$

The train value of a gear train is the ratio of the angular velocity of the last gear in the train to that of the first. The sign of the train value depends on the relative directions of rotation of the first and last gear. It is positive if they turn in the same direction and negative if they have opposite directions of rotation. For the train shown in Fig. 22.1

$$T.V. = \frac{\omega_f}{\omega_a} = \frac{\omega_f}{\omega_e} \times \frac{\omega_e}{\omega_d} \times \frac{\omega_d}{\omega_c} \times \frac{\omega_c}{\omega_b} \times \frac{\omega_b}{\omega_a}$$

439

and by substitution of Eqs. (22.1)

$$T.V. = \frac{\omega_f}{\omega_a} = \frac{N_e}{N_f} \times \frac{N_d}{N_e} \times \frac{N_c}{N_d} \times \frac{N_b}{N_c} \times \frac{N_a}{N_b} = \frac{N_a}{N_f} \qquad (22.2)$$

The sign of the train value can be determined by drawing directional arrows as shown in the figure, where we see that the train value is negative in this case. It will be found convenient later to use positive and negative signs to indicate the direction of the individual gears. The plus sign will indicate counterclockwise rotation and the minus sign clockwise rotation.

From Eq. (22.2) we see that the train value is independent of the number of teeth on those gears which serve both as driving and driven gears. This also becomes obvious by noting that the pitch line velocity of all the gears is the same because of the rolling contact between the pitch circles. These gears are called idler gears or idlers. Idlers are used to connect gears with large center distances where otherwise large gears would be necessary. Idler gears give a compact train and are usually less expensive than equivalent large gears. Idlers also are used to change the sign of the train value since each added idler changes the direction of the last gear in the train.

A compound gear train has one or more gears attached to the same shaft. Two examples of compound gear trains are shown in Fig. 22.2. Let us

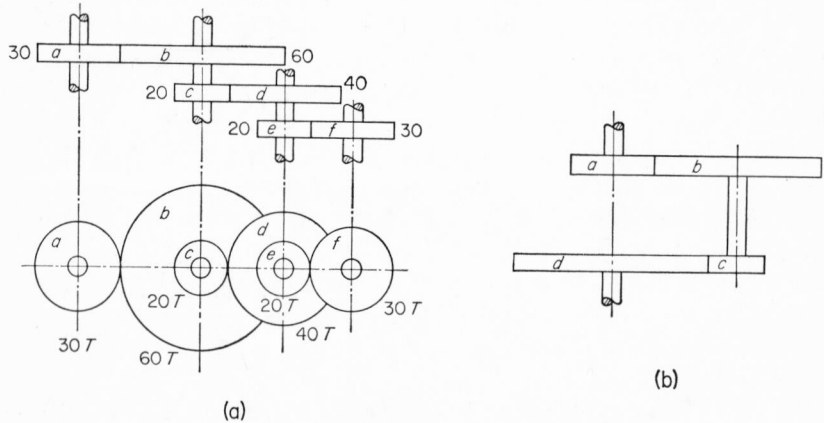

(a)   (b)

FIGURE 22.2

consider the six gear train shown in Fig. 22.2(a). If gear "a" is rotating at 1800 rpm counterclockwise the speeds of the various gears will be

$$\omega_a = + 1800 \text{ rpm}$$

$$\omega_b = \omega_c = \frac{30}{60} \times 1800 = -900 \text{ rpm}$$

$$\omega_d = \omega_e = \frac{20}{40} \times 900 = +450 \text{ rpm}$$

$$\omega_f = \frac{20}{30} \times 450 = -300 \text{ rpm}$$

The train value then is

$$T.V. = \frac{\omega_f}{\omega_a} = -\frac{300}{1800} = -\frac{1}{6}$$

The train value can also be obtained as follows

$$T.V. = \frac{\omega_f}{\omega_a} = \frac{\omega_f}{\omega_e} \times \frac{\omega_e}{\omega_d} \times \frac{\omega_d}{\omega_c} \times \frac{\omega_c}{\omega_b} \times \frac{\omega_b}{\omega_a}$$

$$= \frac{N_e}{N_f} \times 1 \times \frac{N_c}{N_d} \times 1 \times \frac{N_a}{N_b}$$

$$= \frac{30 \times 20 \times 20}{60 \times 40 \times 30} = -\frac{1}{6}$$

Then for a compound gear train the train value can be written as

$$T.V. = \frac{\text{product of teeth on driving gears}}{\text{product of teeth on driven gears}}$$

The compound train shown in Fig. 22.2(b) is known as a reverted gear train since the input and output shaft are coaxial. Reverted gear trains are used in the standard gear transmission of automobiles so that the input and output shafts can be directly connected for high gear. Any compound gear train can be reverted by the use of idlers, but in the special case shown in the figure, in which there are no idlers, the sum of the pitch radii of gears "a" and "b" must be equal to the sum of the pitch radii of gears "c" and "d."

Compound gear trains allow a much higher reduction ratio with small gears than is possible with simple gear trains. From Eq. (22.2) it can be seen that for a high reduction ratio with a simple gear train there must be a large difference in the numbers of teeth on the first and last gear, necessitating a large gear. This disadvantage can be overcome by the use of compound gearing. In general practice simple gear trains composed of spur gears are seldom used for reduction ratios greater than 7 to 1. For greater ratios compound gearing or worm gearing is ordinarily used.

22.2 Epicyclic Gear Trains

An epicyclic gear train is a gear train in which the axis of one or more of the gears is not fixed to the frame and rotates about one of the other axes. Two simple epicyclic gear trains are shown in Fig. 22.3. The train in Fig. 22.3(a) consists of a gear "a" fixed to the frame and a gear "b" whose axis rotates about the axis of gear "a," the two axes connected by an arm. Gear "b" is forced by the meshing teeth to rotate about its axis when the arm

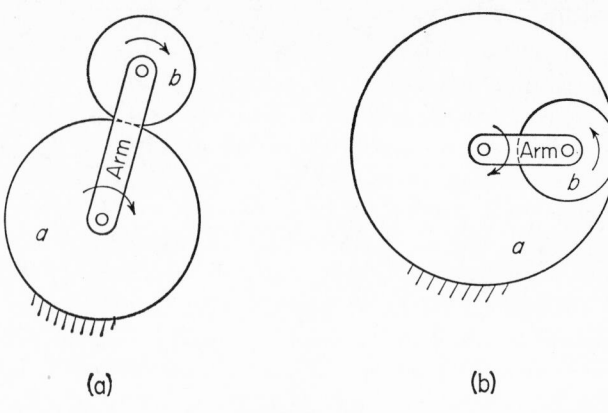

(a)   (b)

FIGURE 22.3

rotates about the axis of gear "*a*." An epicyclic of this type is often called a planetary gear system with gear "*b*" called the planet gear and the fixed gear "*b*" called the sun gear. The train in Fig. 22.3(b) is a similar system with the fixed gear in this case an internal gear.

For planetary systems such as shown in Fig. 22.3 the ratio of the angular velocity of the planet gear to that of the arm is usually required. We can readily visualize the relative motions of such a system by considering the planetary system shown in Fig. 22.4 where the two gears have the same

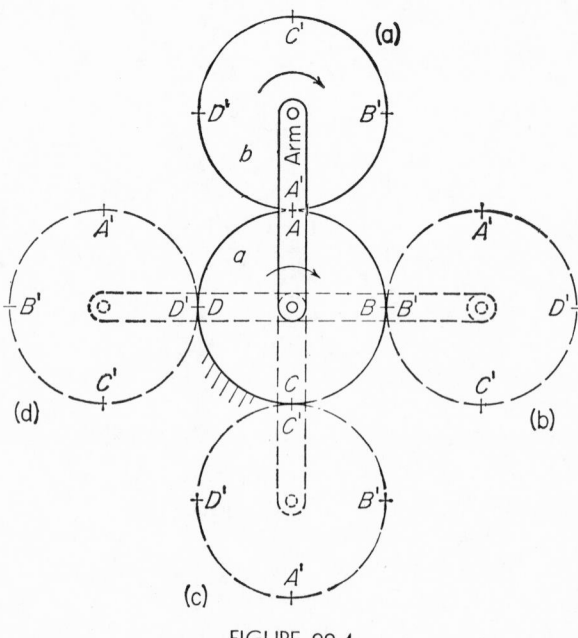

FIGURE 22.4

number of teeth. With the sun gear at position (*a*) and the arm vertical, point A' on the planet will be in contact with point A on the sun gear. If now the arm is rotated clockwise one-quarter turn, so that the planet is at position (*b*), point B' on the planet comes in contact with B on the sun gear. Comparing position (*b*) with position (*a*) we see that the planet has made one-half revolution clockwise. Turning the arm another one-quarter turn so that the planet is at position (*c*), C' is in contact with C and the planet has made one complete revolution clockwise. During the next half revolution of the arm, in returning to its initial position, the planet will make another complete revolution. Then for a complete revolution of the arm the planet will make two revolutions in the same direction.

A similar analysis can be made for a system with an internal gear such as shown in Fig. 22.5 where the planet, gear "*b*," has half the number of teeth

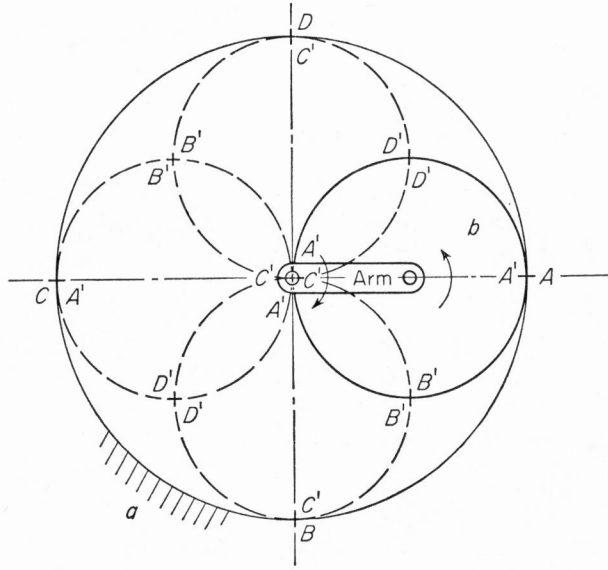

FIGURE 22.5

of the internal or sun gear, gear "*a*." For a quarter turn clockwise of the arm the planet will turn one-quarter revolution counterclockwise. Then for a complete revolution of the arm the planet will turn a complete revolution in the opposite direction.

For a complex epicyclic system such a method of analysis would become quite involved and it is almost impossible to make such an analysis without making errors. We will develop a tabular method of analysis which can be used for all epicyclic systems. The tabular method is straight forward and actually reduces to an analysis of an ordinary compound gear train. The

basis of the tabular method is the relative velocity equation which can be
stated as: the absolute velocity of the planet is equal to the algebraic sum
of the absolute velocity of the arm and the velocity of the planet relative to
the arm.

As an example of the tabular method consider the system shown in
Fig. 22.4 which has already been discussed. The tabulation is shown in
Table 22.1. In order to get the motion of the planet relative to the arm we

Table 22.1

	Arm	Gear "a"	Gear "b"
Arm fixed	0	+1	−1
Train locked	−1	−1	−1
Algebraic sum	−1	0	−2

make an inversion of the mechanism by locking the arm and allowing the
sun gear, gear "a," to rotate. Then, with the inverted train, gear "a" is
rotated one time counterclockwise, causing gear "b" to rotate one time
clockwise. These results are tabulated in the first line of Table 22.1, where
the positive and negative signs indicate counterclockwise and clockwise
motion. Next, in order to get the absolute motion of the arm, we lock the
train so that there cannot be any relative motion between the two gears and
the arm and rotate the locked train one time clockwise. This is the same
as if we put the train in a box and rotated the box one time clockwise.
Under these conditions both gears and the arm will rotate one time clockwise. These results are tabulated in line two of the table. These two lines
are then added algebraically to give the result in line three. From line three
we see that if the sun gear, gear "a," is held fixed and the arm is rotated one
time clockwise, then the planet, gear "b," will rotate two times clockwise,
the same result found in the previous analysis. Note that in the second step,
with the train locked, the train was turned the same number of times, but in
opposite direction, that gear "a" was turned in the first step so that the
total motion of the fixed gear is zero.

Table 22.2 shows the tabulation for the train shown in Fig. 22.5. Note
that with the arm locked the internal gear and meshing pinion turn in the
same direction.

Table 22.2

	Arm	Gear "a"	Gear "b"
Arm fixed	0	+1	+2
Train locked	−1	−1	−1
Algebraic sum	−1	0	+1

Let us now apply this method to a more complicated system such as the reverted epicyclic shown in Fig. 22.6. Gear "*d*" is fixed and gears "*b*" and "*c*" are attached to the same shaft which rotates relative to the arm. If the arm is rotating at 1200 rpm clockwise, we wish to determine the angular velocity of the gear "*a*." The tabulation is given in Table 22.3. As a first step we fix the arm and rotate the fixed gear one turn in either direction, in the tabulation it was turned counterclockwise, and tabulate the velocities

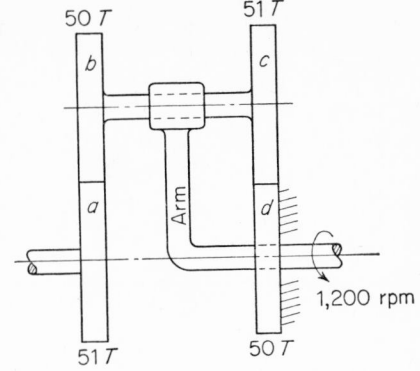

FIGURE 22.6

of the other gears. This is readily accomplished since in the inversion we have an ordinary compound reverted gear train. Then with the train locked the whole system is rotated one time in the opposite direction of gear "*d*" so that the algebraic sum for gear "*d*" is zero. The summation then gives us the motions of each of the gears if in the original system, with "*d*" fixed, the arm were turned one time. The last line of the tabulation then can be used to determine the ratio of velocities of any of the gears to the velocity of the arm. If the arm is turning at 1200 rpm clockwise, we see from the tabulation that gear "*a*" will turn $(101)/(2601)$ times the angular velocity of the arm and in the same direction, or

$$\omega_a = \frac{101}{2601} \times 1200 = 46.6 \text{ rpm clockwise}$$

It should be pointed out that the values in the tabulation should not be reduced to decimal fractions. They are exact numbers, depending on the numbers of teeth on the gears, and if reduced to decimal fractions accumulative errors could be introduced. Only the final results should be reduced to decimal fractions if the answer is desired in decimal form.

In many cases an epicyclic train drives, or is driven by, other gears which are not a part of the epicyclic. In such cases the epicyclic should be analyzed separately and then the results combined with the rest of the gear system for final analysis. The epicyclic part of the system is composed only of those gears whose axes are the same as the axis of rotation of the arm and those gears whose axes rotate about the axis of rotation of the arm. Consider the system shown in Fig. 22.7, containing gear "*g*" which is not a part of the epicyclic since its axis is fixed and not along the axis of the arm. Gear "*c*" is a fixed internal gear and gears "*e*" and "*f*" are on the same hollow shaft which rotates relative to the arm. We wish to determine the

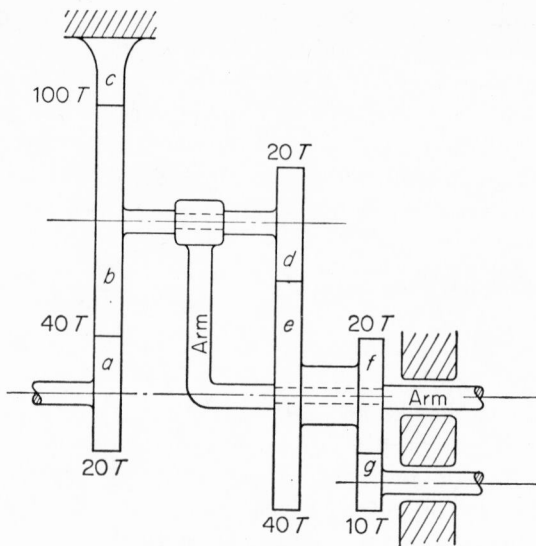

FIGURE 22.7

number of turns of gears "a" and "g" if the arm turns one time clockwise. Table 22.4 shows the tabulation of the epicyclic and for the present we will ignore the column for gear "g." From the tabulation we see that when the arm turns one time clockwise gear "a" turns six times clockwise and gears "e" and "f" turn 9/4 times clockwise. Then from the figure we see that gear "g" turns twice the number of turns of gear "f" and in opposite directions so that gear "g" actually turns 9/2 turns counterclockwise.

Table 22.3

	a	b and c	d	Arm
Arm fixed	$+\dfrac{50 \times 50}{51 \times 51}$	$-\dfrac{50}{51}$	$+1$	0
Train locked	-1	-1	-1	-1
Algebraic sum	$-\dfrac{101}{2601}$	$-\dfrac{101}{51}$	0	-1

In order to show that gear "g" cannot be considered as part of the epicyclic and its motion determined in the tabulation, it has been placed in a column at the right of the tabulation. If it were considered a part of the epicyclic the result would show it to turn 3/2 times counterclockwise. This is in error however because when the train was locked and turned clockwise one time, the axis of gear "g" made one revolution clockwise about the axis of the arm and the summation shows the number of turns of gear "g" under these conditions. Since gear "g" cannot rotate about the arm we must rotate its axis one time counterclockwise about the arm in order to get its correct relative motion. If the other gears are held fixed and the axis of gear "g" rotated one time about the axis of the arm, gear "g" will rotate three times counterclockwise. Adding this to the result from the tabulation we find that gear "g" actually turns 9/2 turns as previously determined. From this we can see that it is much simpler to isolate the epicyclic and analyze it separately.

22.3 Epicyclics with Two Inputs

Note that in all epicyclic trains discussed so far, one of the gears has been fixed. If the fixed gear in the train shown in Fig. 22.6 is released and given a definite motion at the same time that the arm is rotating, the angular motion of gear "a" will be a function of the motions of both the arm and gear "d." If the arm turns at a constant speed, the motion of gear "a" can be controlled by the motion given to gear "d." In this case then we have an epicyclic train with two input motions and such a system is called a controlled differential, or more commonly a differential. In general both input motions are variable in a differential. The most common use of differential gear trains is in the rear axle transmissions of automobiles. These will be considered in detail when we discuss epicyclic trains containing bevel gears. Differentials are also widely used in computing mechanisms and control mechanisms of various types.

Table 22.4

	a	b,d	c	e,f	Arm	g
Arm fixed	-5	$+\dfrac{5}{2}$	$+1$	$-\dfrac{5}{4}$	0	$+\dfrac{5}{2}$
Train locked	-1	-1	-1	-1	-1	-1
Sum	-6	$+\dfrac{3}{2}$	0	$-\dfrac{9}{4}$	-1	$+\dfrac{3}{2}$

The tabular method lends itself to the analysis of epicyclics with two input motions, although the method of attack is somewhat different since there is no fixed gear. As an example of such a system consider the epicyclic train in Fig. 22.8 in which the gears "h" and "j," turning at 100 rpm, drive the gears "f" and "g," the gear "g" being attached to the arm. Gears "h" and "j" are not a part of the epicyclic train and therefore are not entered in the tabulation. Assuming gears "h" and "j" are turning counterclockwise the motions of gears "f" and "g" can be determined directly as

$$\omega_f = -100\,\frac{50}{20} = -250 \text{ rpm}$$

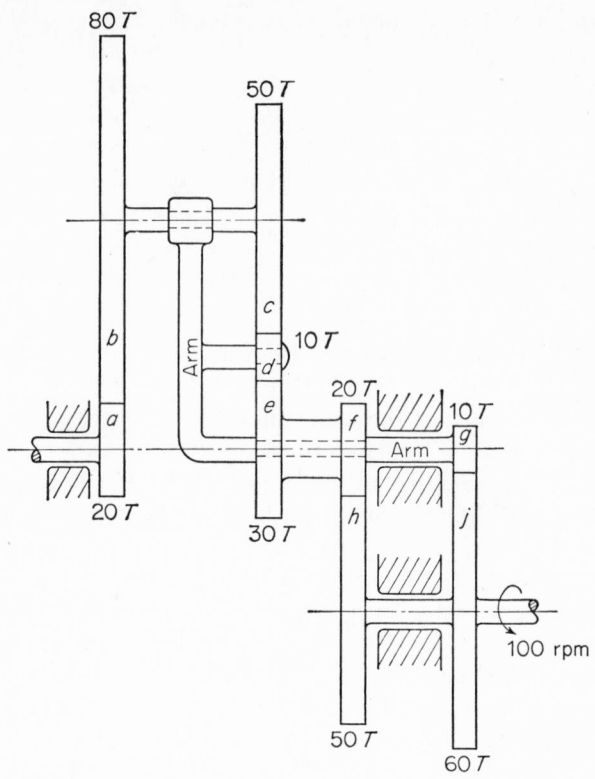

FIGURE 22.8

$$\omega_g = -100 \frac{60}{10} = -600 \text{ rpm}$$

The tabulation is shown in Table 22.5. Since we know the absolute motions of gears "f" and "g" these values are placed in the line of sums as shown circled in the table. As in the previous cases we now fix the arm, giving it

Table 22.5

	a	b,c	d	e,f	g, Arm
Arm fixed	-840	$+210$	-1050	$+350$	0
Train locked	-600	-600	-600	-600	-600
Sum	-1440	-390	-1650	$\boxed{-250}$	$\boxed{-600}$

zero turns in the first line, but since we have no fixed gear we cannot complete line one. However we know that the sum of the motions of the arm must be -600, therefore the second line, representing the motion of the train with the train locked, must have a value of -600 in the arm column.

Then we enter this value, -600, in all the columns of that line representing the rotation of the whole train 600 times clockwise. The sum of the column for gears "e" and "f" must be -250, therefore a value of $+350$ must be entered in the first line of that column, representing the motion of the gears "e" and "f" with the arm fixed. Then the other values in line one can be determined since with the arm fixed the train becomes an ordinary compound train. The summation for gear "a" then becomes -1440 and we see that if the gears "h" and "j" are turning counterclockwise at 100 rpm, gear "a" will turn at 1440 rpm clockwise.

22.4 Epicyclic Trains Containing Bevel Gears

Bevel gears are quite often used in epicyclic trains and examples of such systems will be discussed since the analysis of bevel gear epicyclics differs somewhat from the analysis of spur gear epicyclics. Bevel gears can be used to make a more compact epicyclic system and allow very high reduction ratios with few gears.

Consider the compound reverted epicyclic system shown in Fig. 22.9. Gear "f," attached to the arm which holds the bevel gears "b" and "c," and

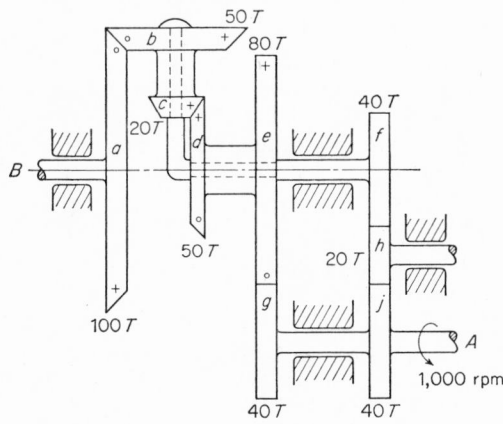

FIGURE 22.9

gear "e," are driven by gears on shaft A which turns at 1000 rpm counterclockwise. We wish to determine the speed and direction of gear "a." The tabulation of the epicyclic part of the system is shown in Table 22.6. The absolute velocities of gears "e" and "f" are determined and entered in the last line. These values are found by the equations

$$\omega_e = \omega_d = -\frac{40}{80} \times 1000 = -500 \text{ rpm}$$

$$\omega_f = +\frac{40}{40} \times 1000 = +1000 \text{ rpm}$$

Note that gear "h" is an idler serving only to reverse the direction of gear "f." The rest of the tabulation is then completed as in the previous example. However in completing the first line, where the epicyclic is treated as an ordinary compound train with the arm fixed, it will be noted that the sign of the gears "b" and "c" has been left out. This is because these gears do not rotate in the same plane as the other gears of the system. In determining the direction of rotation of gear "a" it is often convenient to indicate the directions by placing crosses on the part of the gear that is moving into the paper and circles in that part moving away from the paper as shown in the figure. With these symbols in the figure it is obvious that gear "a" turns in opposite direction to gear "d" and therefore its sign is positive in the tabulation.

Also since the two motions of gears "b" and "c" in the first and second line are not in the same plane the sum of that column is not entered in the sum line. Actually gears "b" and "c" could have been left out of the tabulation since their sum has no meaning; however, the values of their relative motions in the first and second lines of the tabulation are important in the mechanical design of the gear train. The value 3750 in the first line gives the angular speed of the gears relative to the arm and this speed is needed in the design of the bearing for the gears. The value 1000 in the second line indicates the angular speed of the arm and this speed is used in determining the centrifugal force that the two gears exert on the arm. Therefore these values should be tabulated as shown.

Table 22.6

	a	b,c	d,e	f, Arm
Arm fixed	+1875	3750	−1500	0
Train locked	+1000	+1000	+1000	+1000
Sum	+2875		−500	+1000

In many cases of epicyclic trains with two inputs the driven gears are not attached to the arm and the arm serves as the output member. In determining the motion of the arm in such cases the tabular method results in two simultaneous algebraic equations which must be solved in order to determine the motion of the output member or arm. A gear train of this type is shown in Fig. 22.10 where gears "b" and "f" are driven at some given speed and the direction and speed of the arm is to be determined. The tabulation is given in Table 22.7. The absolute motions of the gears "b" and "f" are determined from the given information, see figure, and tabulated as shown with both turning clockwise. The absolute value for the

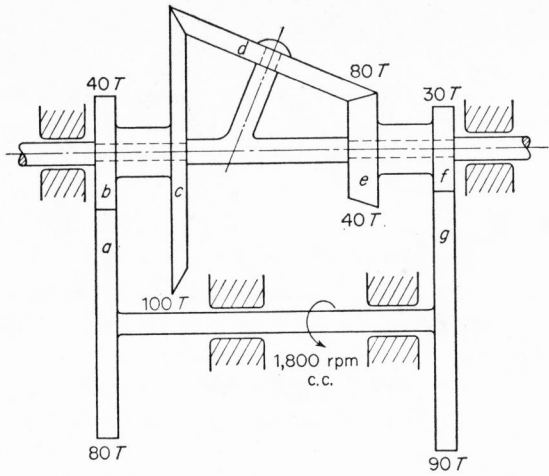

FIGURE 22.10

arm is given as $+x$ and then the column for the arm can be completed since the first line must be zero with the arm fixed. Therefore with the train

Table 22.7

	b,c	d	e,f	Arm
Arm fixed	$+y$	$\dfrac{5y}{4}$	$-\dfrac{10y}{4}$	0
Train locked	$+x$	$+x$	$+x$	$+x$
Sum	-3600		-5400	$+x$

locked the whole system must be rotated $+x$ times. Now any other gear of the system can be given an unknown number of turns, say $+y$ turns, for the inverted system with the arm fixed. In the table we let gears "b" and "c" turn $+y$ times and then determine the other values in that line as a function of y, as shown. The two columns having a known sum now form a set of simultaneous equations in x and y from which the values of x and y can be determined. These equations are

$$+x + y = -3600$$

$$+x - \frac{5}{2}y = -5400$$

solving these equations we find

$$x = -\frac{28{,}800}{7}$$

$$y = +\frac{3600}{7}$$

and we see that the arm turns 28,800/7 rpm clockwise. It is immaterial which gear is given the $+y$ turns in the first column since the same results would have been obtained regardless of which gear was given this motion.

As a last example let us consider the differential shown in Fig. 22.11 which is typical of the differential used in the rear axles of automobiles. The gear "f" is attached to the driveshaft and drives gear "e" which serves as an arm carrying gears "c" and "d," the planet gears. Gears "a" and "b"

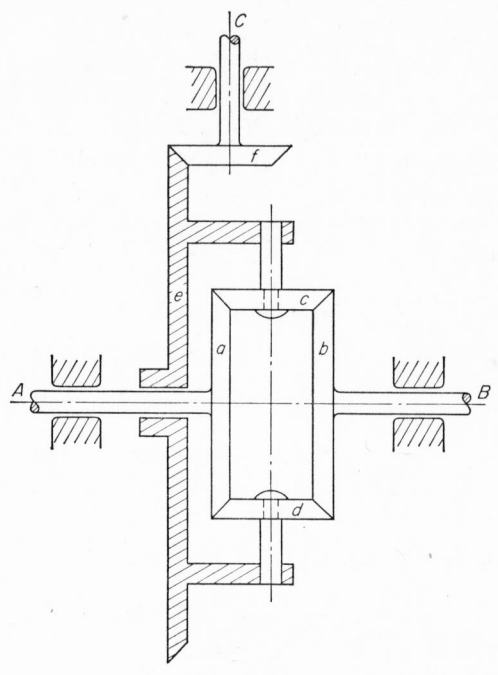

FIGURE 22.11

are attached to the axles A and B to which the rear wheels are attached. Note that gear "d" is a redundant gear and is unnecessary so far as the kinematic motion is concerned. However, in many cases more than one planet gear such as this is used in order to distribute the load and thereby allow smaller gears to be used.

If the car is going in a straight line shafts A and B are rotating with the same velocity, gears "a," "b," "c," "d," and "e" have no relative motion and the wheels turn at the same speed as gear "e." When the car is going around a curve, the outside wheel must rotate faster than the inside wheel and shafts A and B will be rotating at different speeds setting the epicyclic train in action. If the system is analyzed it will be found that the speed of gear "e" is always the algebraic sum of the speeds of gears "a" and "b."

Therefore if one of the wheels is held fixed, the other wheel will rotate at twice the speed of gear "*e*" and in the same direction. This is what occurs when one of the wheels is in mud or on ice. That wheel will have a small resistance to turning and will therefore spin at twice the speed of the gear "*e*" while the other wheel will stand still and the car will not move.

In order to explain this better consider the gear "*c*" as a lever between gears "*a*" and "*b*" with a fulcrum at the center, its attachment to gear "*e*." If gear "*e*" pushes on gear "*c*," gear "*c*" will exert equal forces on gears "*a*" and "*b*." This will always be true regardless of the motion of the gears, therefore the same torque is always applied to the gears "*a*" and "*b*." Then if one wheel offers no resistance to motion, there is no torque applied to either gear. This disadvantage of the automobile differential can be overcome if a brake is applied to each of the shafts *A* and *B*. Then if one of the wheels started to slip, the brake on that shaft would be applied, giving resistance to the motion and equal torque would then be applied to the wheel which has traction.

PROBLEMS

22.1 Determine the speed and direction of shafts *B* and *C* in Fig. P22.1 if shaft *A* is turning 1000 rpm clockwise.

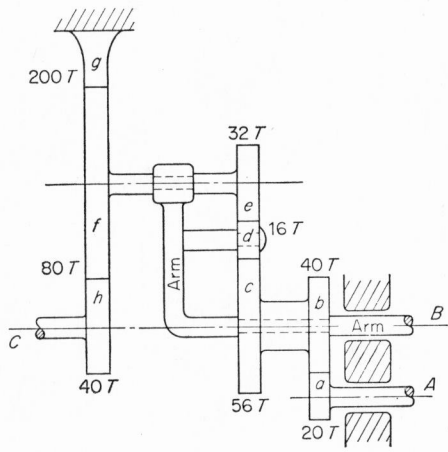

FIGURE P22.1

22.2 If gear "*g*" were removed from the gear train shown in Figs. P22.1 and shaft *C* is rotating 500 rpm counterclockwise at the same time that shaft *A* is rotating 1000 rpm clockwise, what would be the speed and direction of shaft *B*?

22.3 Determine the speed and direction of shaft *B* in Fig. P22.2 if shaft *A* is turning 250 rpm clockwise.

22.4   Determine the speed and direction of shaft B in Fig. P22.2 if shaft A is turning 250 rpm clockwise and the gear which is indicated as fixed is turning 200 rpm counterclockwise.

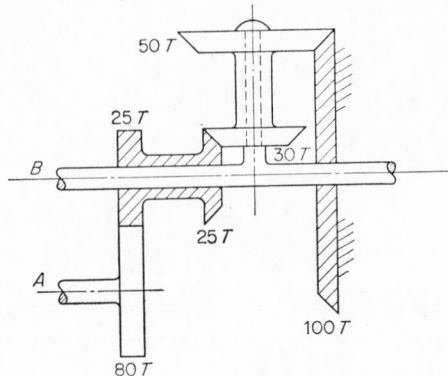

FIGURE P22.2

22.5 Determine the centrifugal force and gyroscopic couple exerted by the planet gears in Prob. 22.3 if their total weight is 2.5 lb and their radius of gyration about their axis of rotation (which is also rotating) is 4 in. and their center of gravity is 5 in. from the center of shaft B.

22.6   In the gear train shown in Fig. P22.3 gear "d" has both internal and external teeth. Determine the angular velocity of shaft C in magnitude and direction if shaft A is turning at 1500 rpm clockwise.

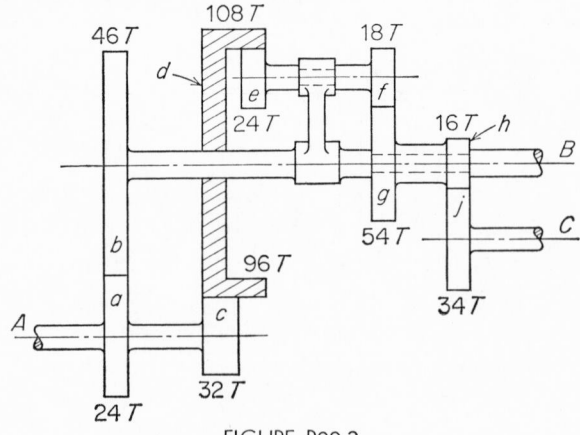

FIGURE P22.3

22.7   If gears "a" and "b" are removed from the gear train shown in Fig. P22.3 determine the angular velocity of the shaft B in magnitude and direction if shaft A is rotating at 1500 rpm clockwise at the same time that shaft C is rotating 1000 rpm clockwise.

22.8   In Fig. P22.4, M and N represent band brakes which can be used to stop the rotation of the arm and gear "c" one at a time. Determine the speed and direction of shaft B if shaft A is rotating at 1000 rpm clockwise if: (a) brake M holds the arm fixed, (b) brake N holds gear "c" fixed.

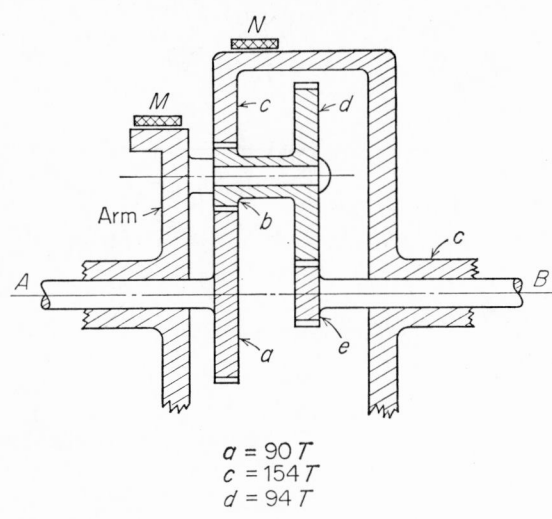

$a = 90\ T$
$c = 154\ T$
$d = 94\ T$

FIGURE P22.4

22.9   In Fig. P22.5, M and N represent band brakes which can be used to stop the rotation of gears "e" and "d" one at a time. Shaft A is rotating at 500 rpm counterclockwise.

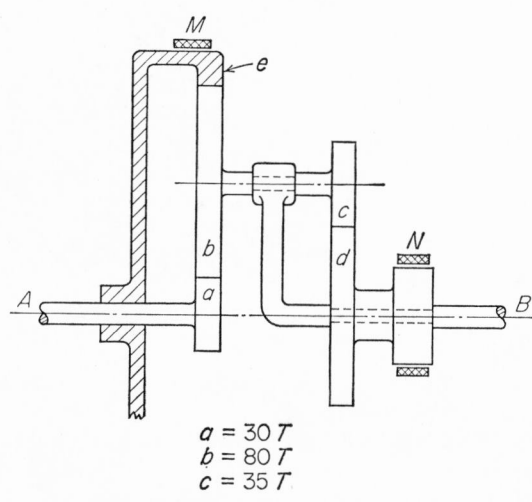

$a = 30\ T$
$b = 80\ T$
$c = 35\ T$

FIGURE P22.5

(a) Determine the speed and direction of shaft B and gear "d" if brake M is applied.

(b) Determine the speed and direction of shaft B and gear "e" if brake N is applied.

22.10 Determine the speed and direction of shaft A in Fig. P22.6 if shaft B is rotating at 600 rpm clockwise at the same time that shaft C is rotating at 140 rpm counterclockwise.

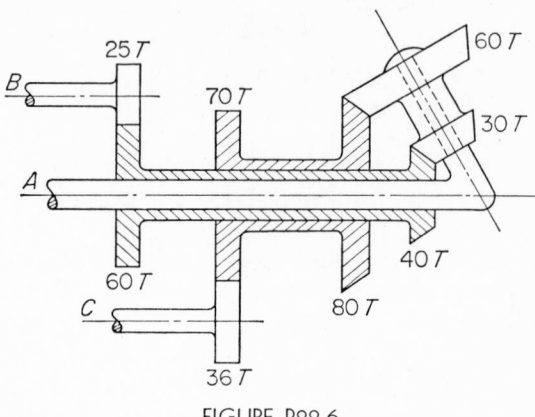

FIGURE P22.6

Chapter 23

Flywheels and Governors

23.1 Flywheels

In many machines the angular velocity of the crank varies considerably over a cycle because of the variations of external forces over the cycle. These variations may be caused by a variation in the driving torque during the cycle or a variation of the output forces of the machine. Consider an electric generator driven by a single cylinder, four-stroke cycle internal combustion engine. It is desirable that the generator rotate at a constant speed and in order to do so the generator must be driven with a constant torque. However the engine delivers torque to the generator in a very erratic manner since there is a power stroke only once every two revolutions; therefore, the speed of the generator varies considerably over the two cycles. Flywheels are used in such instances to assure a fairly uniform velocity and torque to the generator.

A flywheel is a rotating member, usually of large mass, conserving for later use excess kinetic energy. Ordinarily it is composed of a heavy rim with spokes, or a thin disc, connecting the rim to the hub. The heavy rim concentrates the mass at the outer radius in order to give it a large moment of inertia. In the example above the flywheel would absorb the excess work delivered by the engine during the power stroke, in the form of kinetic energy, and deliver it to the generator during the remainder of the two revolutions. In this manner the flywheel would smooth out the torque applied to the generator and decrease the speed variation during the cycle. However, since the only way that the kinetic energy of the flywheel can change is by changing its angular velocity, it would not remove all variations in speed during the two revolutions.

As another example consider a punch press driven by an electric motor. The electric motor delivers a fairly uniform torque but the punch press is doing work for only a portion of the cycle of operation and therefore it needs the energy delivered to it in spurts rather than continuously. A flywheel in this case would absorb the work of the motor during the part of the cycle when the punch is not doing work and then deliver this energy to the punch at the required time. By the use of the flywheel a much smaller motor would be required.

The analysis required to determine the necessary flywheel in both cases is essentially the same. In both cases the allowable variation in speed is used to determine the moment of inertia of the flywheel necessary to keep the speed within the prescribed limits. The total permissible variation of speed is usually given as the coefficient of fluctuation which is defined as

$$C_f = \frac{\omega_2 - \omega_1}{\omega}$$

where ω_2 = maximum angular speed of the flywheel

ω_1 = minimum angular speed of the flywheel

ω = average speed of the flywheel

$= \dfrac{\omega_2 + \omega_1}{2}$

Sometimes the reciprocal of the coefficient of fluctuation, called the coefficient of steadiness, is used. The values of these coefficients that have proven satisfactory for various applications can be found in engineering handbooks and machine design texts.

23.2 Flywheel for a Punch Press

As an example of flywheel analysis we will determine the required moment of inertia for a flywheel to be used on a punch press designed to punch forty holes per minute. The size motor needed to drive the press, with and without the flywheel, will also be determined. Figure 23.1(a) shows a typical force-displacement curve for the punching of a hole in a ductile material such as steel. The area under the curve represents the work required to punch the hole. We will assume that the punch is driven by a slider-crank mechanism, in which the punch serves as the slider, and that the punching operation occurs during a crank displacement of 60°, or one-sixth of a cycle.

The torque which must be applied to the crank is plotted as a function of crank angle or time in Fig. 23.1(b) and again the area under the curve represents the work required to punch the hole. Let us assume that 4800 ft-lb of work is required to punch the hole in the example. The time rate at which this work is done determines the power requirements. If there is no flywheel the driving motor must supply all the work necessary to punch the hole in the time required for the punching operation, or in 0.25 sec. Then the *average rate* of the work is 4800/0.25 or 19,200 ft-lb/sec, which

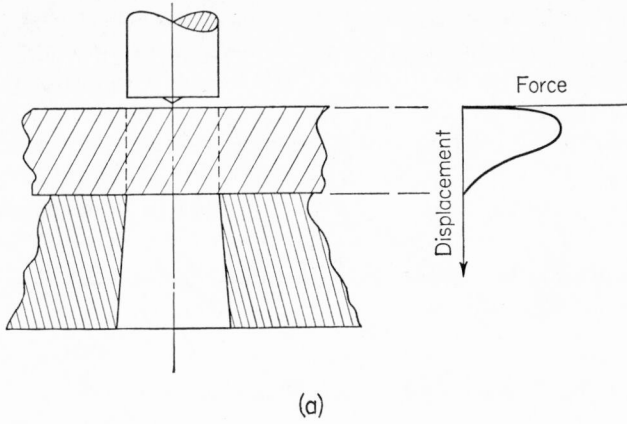

(a)

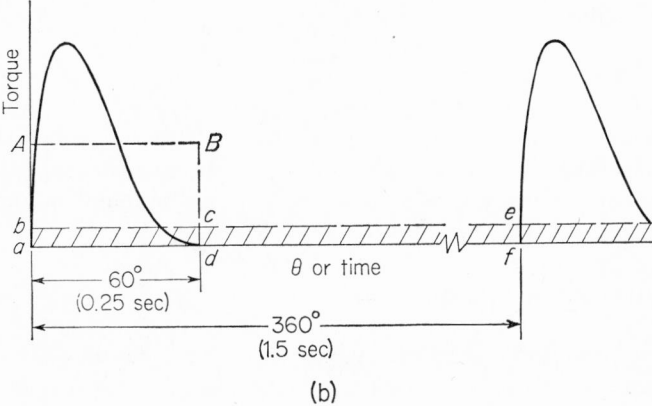

(b)

FIGURE 23.1

corresponds to 34.8 hp, and this is the approximate size motor necessary to drive the punch if no flywheel is used. The average rate corresponds to a uniform torque over the time of the punching cycle as shown by the dashed line $A–B$ in the figure. The maximum instantaneous rate, corresponding to the highest portion of the torque curve, would be considerably higher but since most electric motors can carry high overloads for short periods of time a 35 hp motor would probably be satisfactory.

If a flywheel is used on the punch, it could be storing the excess energy supplied by the motor during the time no work is done by the punch, in the form of kinetic energy, and then give up this energy to the punch during the punching operation. In this case the motor could supply the total work required at an average rate over the whole cycle as shown by the cross-hatched area in the figure and this rate would be 4800/1.5 or 3200 ft-lb/sec corresponding to 5.82 hp. Then, by the use of a flywheel, a motor of only 6 hp would be needed to drive the punch. A 6 hp motor and a flywheel is much less expensive than a 35 hp motor.

In order to determine the moment of inertia of the flywheel, or the size of the flywheel, we need to select a coefficient of fluctuation. We will assume that the maximum and minimum speed do not differ by more than 10 per cent from the mean speed, corresponding to a coefficient of fluctuation of

$$C_f = \frac{1.1\omega - 0.9\omega}{\omega} = 0.2$$

the value usually used for punch presses. We will also assume that the flywheel is geared to the crankshaft so that it turns at an average speed of 400 rpm. Then its maximum speed is 440 rpm and its minimum speed is 360 rpm. During the punching operation the motor would supply work corresponding to the shaded area $abcd$, or one-sixth of the total and the flywheel must supply energy corresponding to the area $dcef$, or five-sixths of the total or 4000 ft-lb. The kinetic energy of the flywheel is given by the equation

$$KE = \frac{1}{2}I\omega^2$$

Then if the maximum speed of the flywheel is ω_2 and the minimum is ω_1, the change in kinetic energy corresponding to a change in speeds is

$$\Delta KE = \frac{1}{2}I(\omega_2^2 - \omega_1^2) \tag{23.1}$$

If the speed increases the flywheel stores energy and if the speed decreases the flywheel gives up energy. Knowing the change in kinetic energy the moment of inertia required to store that amount of energy for a given change of speed can be determined from Eq. (23.1) as

$$I = \frac{2\Delta KE}{\omega_2^2 - \omega_1^2}$$

Ordinarily in the design of a flywheel a mean radius is selected and then the weight of the flywheel is determined as a function of the mean radius. The mean radius is usually taken as the radius of gyration. Using the above equation the weight of the flywheel is given by the equation

$$W = \frac{2g\Delta KE}{k_G^2(\omega_2^2 - \omega_1^2)}$$

where ω is in rad/sec. If the angular speed is given in terms of rpm the equation reduces to

$$W = 70,000 \frac{\Delta KE}{k_G^2(N_2^2 - N_1^2)} \tag{23.2}$$

Assuming a mean radius of fifteen inches for the flywheel under discussion
we find by the use of Eq. (23.2) that the flywheel weight must be

$$W = 70,000 \frac{4000 \times 12}{(15)^2[(440)^2 - (360)^2]}$$

$$= 234.0 \text{ lb}$$

It will be noted that in the problem discussed the flywheel turned at a
higher speed than the crank of the punch press. From Eq. (23.2) we can see
that the higher the average speed of the flywheel, for a given coefficient of
fluctuation, the smaller the flywheel need be. Therefore it is desirable that
the flywheel be attached to the shaft in the mechanism having the highest
speed in order to reduce the size of the flywheel. However there are limitations in the speed of the flywheel. Because of the high stresses developed
by centrifugal forces, these stresses must be considered in the selection of
the flywheel speed. Also the gears connecting the flywheel and crank would
have sudden loads imposed on them necessitating expensive gears. In most
punch presses the flywheel is attached to the crank in order to eliminate the
gears between the flywheel and crank.

23.3 Flywheel for an Internal Combustion Engine

As another example of flywheel analysis let us consider the requirements
of a flywheel for a single cylinder four-stroke cycle engine. Figure 23.2

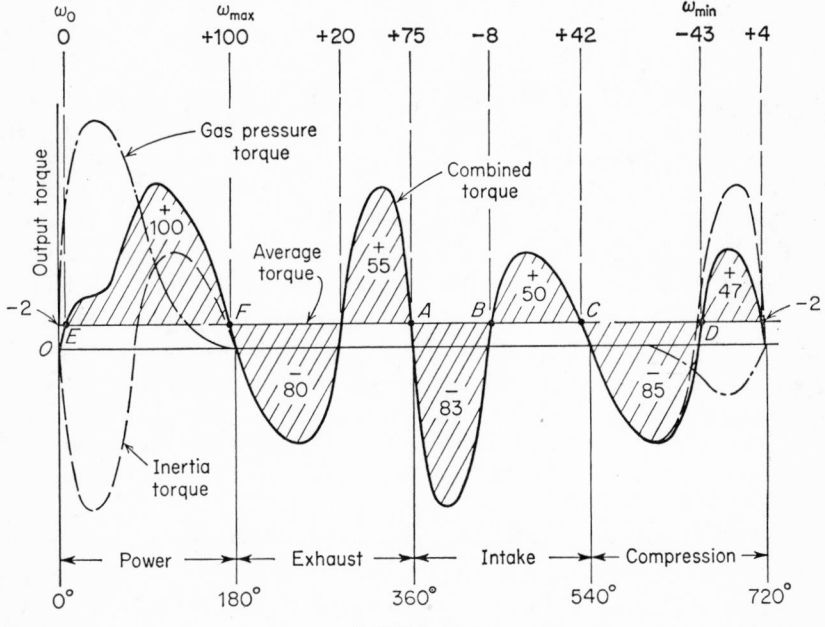

FIGURE 23.2

shows a typical curve of output torque or turning effort on the crank for two revolutions of the crankshaft. The total output torque is the sum of the torque caused by the gas pressure on the piston and the torque caused by the inertia forces. The gas pressure and inertia torques are shown in the figure as well as the combined torque. For the first 180°, which represents the power stroke, the gas pressure does positive work on the crank and for the latter part of the compression stroke work must be done on the gas in order to compress it and this work is negative. This gas pressure curve can be obtained by a static force analysis where the gas pressure on the piston is gotten from an indicator diagram which is a plot of gas pressure as a function of piston position. The indicator diagram can be approximated from thermodynamic considerations if the maximum gas pressure is known or assumed. The inertia torque is obtained from an inertia force analysis.

The areas between the combined curve and the zero torque line represent the work done by the engine, those above the zero line representing positive output work and those below the line represent negative work that must be done on the engine. The average output torque, which is shown in the figure, is the algebraic sum of these areas divided by the total displacement of 720°. If the machine driven by the motor opposes the motion of the crankshaft with a uniform torque equal to the average output torque, some means must be supplied to level out the output torque. The purpose of the flywheel is to give a uniform output. The crosshatched areas above and below the average torque line represent work which must be absorbed or given up by the flywheel in order to keep the output torque constant. The positive areas above the line represent excess energy which increases the speed of the flywheel and the negative areas represent a deficiency of energy which the flywheel supplies with a resulting decrease in speed. The relative magnitudes of the crosshatched areas are given in the figure by numbers in the crosshatched areas.

In order to determine the net change in energy of the flywheel we must know the points of maximum and minimum speed, and then the algebraic sum of the areas between these two points will be the change in kinetic energy which must be used in Eqs. (23.1) and (23.2). At first thought we would say that the maximum speed would occur at the end of the power stroke and that the minimum speed would occur at the beginning of the power stroke. Upon examination of the torque curve, however, we will see that these are not the correct positions. Starting at point A where the combined torque curve crosses the average torque line, the first area from A to B is negative indicating that the flywheel must give up energy and therefore its speed must decrease until point B is reached. From B to C, since the area is positive, the speed will increase. Then we see that the intersections of the two torque curves represent points of high or low speeds and the maximum and minimum speed must occur at some intersection point.

In order to find the points of maximum and minimum speed we will assume that the speed at point E, the first intersection, is some value, ω_0, with a total kinetic energy of KE_0. At the next intersection the energy has increased by a value of 100 because of the positive work done on it; and at the third intersection, because of the negative work, the energy level is down to a value of $(KE_0 + 20)$. The relative energy level is indicated on the figure at each intersection, and we see that the maximum energy corresponding to the maximum speed occurs at point F and the minimum energy level corresponding to minimum speed occurs at point D. Then we find that the maximum change in energy is given by the algebraic sum of the areas between these two points, and this is the value to be used in determining the flywheel size.

23.4 Governors

A governor is a device or mechanism used to control or regulate the output of a machine automatically. Since this same definition could be used in defining a flywheel, we must distinguish between the two. The flywheel controls the speed of a machine by means of a transfer of energy over a cycle of operation while a governor controls the speed by changing the input energy of the machine and holds the speed essentially constant over long periods of time when there are variations in output load. A governor can be used to control the average speed of a system while the flywheel only controls the deviation from this average speed. If the output torque of an internal combustion engine is decreased the speed of the engine will increase until a balance is achieved between the input and output energy. The flywheel will not affect this change in average speed but will continue to hold the speed fairly constant over a complete cycle at the new average speed. A governor, on the other hand, would sense this increase in speed and change the throttle setting of the engine until the speed returned to the value at which the governor is set.

A governor is an example of what is presently called a feedback control. In the above example the governor senses the change in speed and by means of an appropriate mechanism changes the throttle setting so as to hold the speed at a nearly constant value. In other words, it feeds back its information to the throttle. In a broad sense all automatic controls could be termed governors but the term as usually applied refers to a mechanism for control of the speeds of various prime movers. Our discussion will be limited to mechanical governors of the flyball and shaft types and will serve only as an introduction to the subject.

23.5 *Flyball Governors*

A flyball governor of the earliest type is shown in Fig. 23.3(a). It consists of two or more arms, links "*a*," pinned at one end, point *O*, to a rotating shaft, link "*d*," and having heavy weights or balls at the other end.

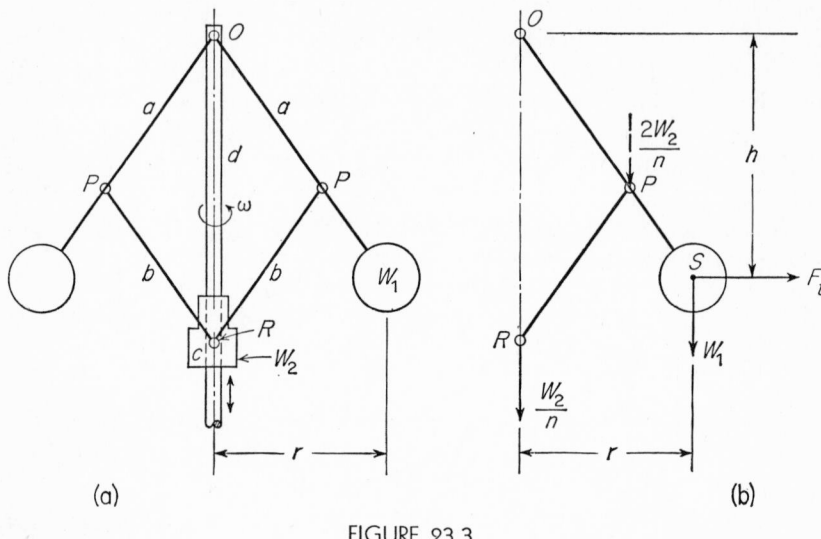

FIGURE 23.3

Link "*b*" is pinned to link "*a*" at *P* and to a slider, link "*c*," which slides vertically along the rotating shaft. For the present we will assume that the weight of the slider is negligible. For a given angular speed of the shaft, ω, centrifugal force will cause the balls to move away from the shaft until at some radius *r*, the torque about *O* caused by the centrifugal force will balance the torque caused by the weight of the balls. If the speed increases the balls will move to a greater radius and if the speed decreases the balls will assume a position at some smaller radius. As the balls change position the slider will move along the shaft, moving upward as the radius of the balls increases, corresponding to an increase in speed, and downward as the radius decreases. If the throttle of an engine were attached to the slider with an appropriate mechanism so that the throttle moved towards the closed position as the slider moves upward and toward the open position as the slider moves downwards, the governor could be used to control the speed of the engine. Assuming that the load on the engine is suddenly increased, the speed would decrease, and, if the speed of the governor is driven by the engine so that its speed is proportional to the speed of the engine, the centrifugal force would decrease. This would cause the radius to decrease, moving the slider downwards and opening the throttle so that more energy would be supplied to the engine.

For an analysis of the governor consider the forces acting on the balls as shown in Fig. 23.3(b). We will assume at present that the weights of the links and slider are negligible in relation to the weight of the balls. Taking moments about O, for equilibrium

$$F_i h = W_1 r$$

or
$$\frac{W_1}{g} r\omega^2 h = W_1 r \qquad\qquad (23.3)$$

Solving for h, which is called the *height* of the governor

$$h = \frac{g}{\omega^2} \qquad\qquad (23.4)$$

we see that the height of the governor is independent of the weight of the balls and the length of the arms. An inherent disadvantage of this type governor, where the weight of the slider is negligible, is shown if we plot a curve of height versus angular speed as in Fig. 23.4. The bottom curve,

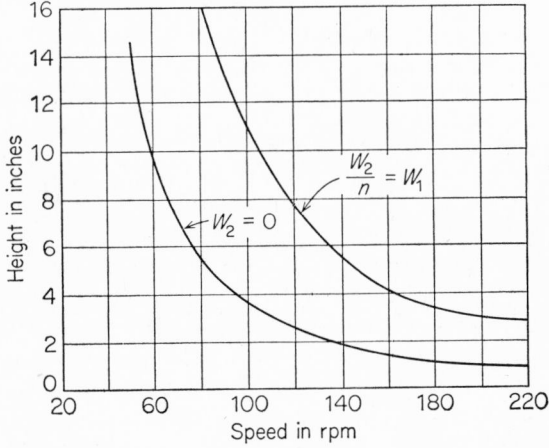

FIGURE 23.4

which corresponds to $W_2 = 0$, shows that such a governor is suitable only for very low speeds since at the higher speeds a large change in angular speed causes a very small change in height and a corresponding small change in sleeve position. Therefore the output would not be sufficient to achieve suitable control.

It is obvious that a heavy weight attached to the slider will improve the high speed characteristics of the governor since then a greater speed would be required to move the balls out to a given radius. An analysis of this system can be made by use of Fig. 23.3(b) with the slider weight equal to W_2/n, where n is the number of balls. The analysis can be simplified by using the principle of virtual work to replace the force due to W_2/n by an equivalent force acting at point P so that an equilibrium equation can be written for a single arm. If the distance $O–P$ is equal to the distance $P–R$ a change in radius of the balls will cause the point P to move a vertical distance equal to half the vertical distance that R moves. Therefore a weight at P equal to twice the weight at R would give us an equivalent system. In the same manner we could replace the force at P by an equivalent vertical force at the center of the ball S such that

$$W_S = \frac{2W_2(O–P)}{n(O–S)}$$

Now taking moments about O

$$\frac{W_1}{g} r\omega^2 h = \left[W_1 + \frac{2W_2}{n}\left(\frac{OP}{OS}\right) \right] r$$

so that

$$h = \frac{g}{\omega^2}\left[1 + \frac{2W_2}{nW_1}\left(\frac{OP}{OS}\right) \right] \tag{23.5}$$

The upper curve in Fig. 23.4 gives the height as a function of speed by use of this equation where W_2/n has been taken equal to W_1 and the balls are located at point P so that $O–P = O–S$.

Although the weighted slider is an improvement it is still limited to fairly low speeds and has the added disadvantage, since it depends on gravity for the controlling force, that its axis must be vertical. High speed governors usually use a spring to control the position of the balls and then the axis of rotation can be at any position. A typical example of a spring controlled governor is shown in Fig. 23.5. Such a system is quite versatile since the spring force can be varied so that the governor can be set for any

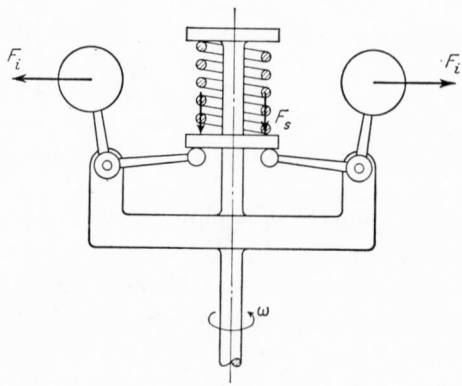

FIGURE 23.5

given speed. An analysis of a spring controlled governor is similar to that of the gravity controlled governors considered except that in the case of springs the controlling force is not constant and becomes greater as the spring is deflected.

For high speed governors where the controlling force is necessarily high the stability of the governor must be examined. Consider the governor shown in Fig. 23 5. If it is in equilibrium at some given speed, so that the moments of the inertia forces and spring force are in balance, and some disturbance moves the balls out to a greater radius the inertia moment will increase and the spring moment must increase more so that the spring tends to restore the system to its original position. If the inertia moment increased at a greater rate than the spring force, the system would be unstable and any slight disturbance would cause the governor to move to one or the other extreme positions.

23.6 Shaft Governors

In many high speed engines the governor is attached directly to the flywheel and rotates about the shaft axis. A governor of this type is shown in Fig. 23.6 where the arm carrying the mass of the governor is pinned to

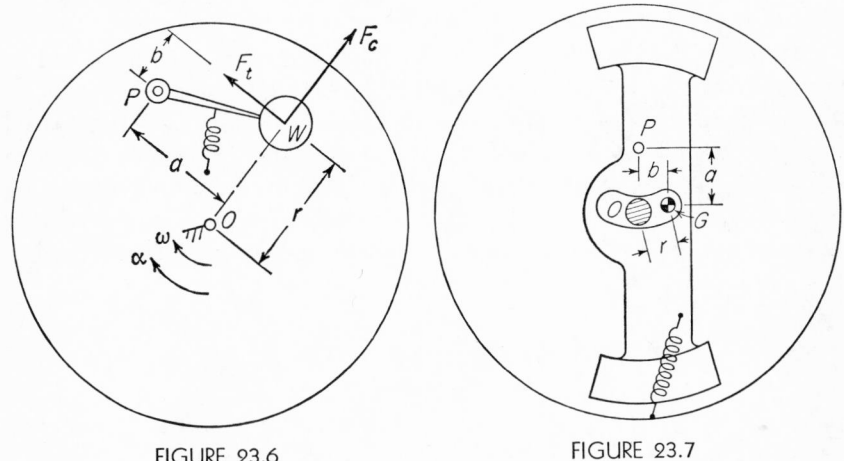

FIGURE 23.6   FIGURE 23.7

the flywheel at point P and held in equilibrium with a spring as shown. An increase in speed of the flywheel will cause a greater centrifugal force on the mass and the governor will rotate about P until a new equilibrium position is reached with the mass at a greater distance from the center of rotation.

The shaft governor has an important feature that is not present in the flyball type governor. The shaft governor is also sensitive to the angular acceleration of the engine. There are then two force components tending to change the position of the governor in Fig. 23.6. An increase in velocity from ω_1 to ω_2 will increase the centrifugal force on the weight causing a counterclockwise torque about the pin P of magnitude

$$T_c = \frac{W}{g} r(\omega_2^2 - \omega_1^2)a \qquad (23.6)$$

and the angular acceleration which must occur if the velocity changes will cause a tangential inertia force having a counterclockwise moment about P of

$$T_t = \frac{W}{g} r\alpha b \qquad (23.7)$$

if the total mass of the governor is assumed concentrated at the weight W. In cases where the torque caused by the angular acceleration is the predominant torque the shaft governor is called an inertia governor. A typical inertia governor is shown in Fig. 23.7. For this governor the mass is not concentrated at the center of gravity and the effect of the moment of inertia about the center of gravity must also be included in the equation for the tangential torque. A pure torque caused by the angular acceleration of the governor about its center of gravity must be added to the torque given by Eq. (23.7) so that the total torque about the pin P because of the angular acceleration is

$$T_t = \frac{W}{g} r\alpha b + I_G \alpha \qquad (23.8)$$

The inertia governor is more sensitive than the centrifugal governor since its action depends on the rate of change of velocity whereas the centrifugal governor will only act after a definite change in speed has occurred. However there must always be some centrifugal action in an inertia governor in order to hold the operating speed at some fixed value. If the center of gravity of the governor in Fig. 23.7 were located at the pin P, there would be no centrifugal component of torque about the pin and only the second term in Eq. (23.8) would have magnitude. Under these conditions the engine could be run at any speed and as long as the speed did not change the governor would not operate. If the speed were higher than the desirable operating speed it would continue to operate at that speed since there would be no force on the governor tending to change the throttle setting. If, however, the C.G. is located at the position shown in the figure the centrifugal component, being in equilibrium with the spring torque at the operating speed, would tend to return the speed to the operating speed.

PROBLEMS

23.1 A punch press is to punch 25 holes per minute. The flywheel is directly connected to the driving motor and the ratio of flywheel speed to crank speed is 10:1.

A force-displacement diagram of the work done in punching a hole has an area of 4 in.² where the scales are: 1 in. = 10,000 lb and 1 in. = 0.1 ft. The punching operation is completed during one-fourth cycle of the crank. If the radius of gyration of the flywheel is to be 30 in. and the coefficient of fluctuation is to be 0.25, determine:

(a) the size motor needed with and without the flywheel.

(b) the required weight of the flywheel.

23.2 A punch press is to punch 30 holes per minute. A maximum force of 105,000 lb and an energy of 55,000 in.-lb is required to punch each hole. The flywheel is directly connected to the driving motor and the ratio of flywheel speed to crank speed is 8:1. The punching operation takes place over 75° of crank travel, and the speed fluctuation is to be limited to 15 per cent of the average speed. The overall mechanical efficiency is 80 per cent. For a radius of gyration of 24 in., determine:

(a) the weight of the flywheel required.

(b) the motor hp required with and without the flywheel.

(c) the weight of the flywheel required if the flywheel is attached directly to the crank.

23.3 (a) A flyball governor similar to that shown in Fig. 23.3 has three balls weighing 1 lb each; the slider weight, W_2, is 6 lb. Distance $O–P = P–R = 3$ in. and distance $P–S$ is $1\frac{1}{2}$ in. If the distance h is 3 in. when the governor is rotating at operating speed what is the operating speed of the governor?

(b) What distance will the slider, W_2, move if the speed is increased to 10 per cent above operating speed?

(c) What distance will the slider move if the speed is decreased to 10 per cent below operating speed?

(d) What force is required to hold the slider at the position corresponding to operating speed if the speed is increased to 10 per cent above operating speed?

23.4 It is desired to have the governor given in Prob. 23.3 operate with the same distance h of 3 in. at an operating speed of 800 rpm. What spring force acting on the slider would be necessary?

Index